Instructor's Solutions Manual to accompany

# INTERMEDIATE ALGEBRA

## A TEXT/WORKBOOK

CHARLES P. McKEAGUE

FOURTH EDITION

PATRICIA K. BEZONA
Valdosta State College

SAUNDERS COLLEGE PUBLISHING

Fort Worth, Philadelphia, San Diego, New York, Orlando, San Antonio, Austin, Toronto, Montreal, London, Sydney, Tokyo

Printed in the United States of America.

Bezona: Instructor's Solutions Manual to accompany INTERMEDIATE ALGEBRA: A TEXT/WORKBOOK, 4/e, by Charles P. McKeague

ISBN 0-03-003378-0

456 017 987654321

# CONTENTS

# PREFACE

This Instructor's Solutions Manual accompanies *Intermediate Algebra, 4th Edition* by Charles P. McKeague. This supplement contains solutions and answers that are instructor-appropriate.

I would like to thank Charles P. McKeague for giving me this opportunity to work on his excellent textbooks once again and Laurie Golson and Kelly Andrews, editors, for their patience and understanding. Thanks to our keyboarders, David and Hope Ince for a wonderful job.

Patricia K. Bezona

# Chapter 1

## Section 1.1

2. $y + (-3)$

3. $6 - x$

4. $x - 6$

6. $5xy = z$

7. $\frac{3x}{2y} > 6$

8. $\frac{2y}{3x} < 7$

10. $2(a + b) = 15$

11. $3(x - 5) > y$

12. $xy \geq \frac{x}{y}$

14. $\frac{2x}{y} \leq 2x + y$

15. $2(t + 3) \ngtr t - 6$

16. $3(xy) = 2x + 3z$

18. $8^2 = 8 \cdot 8 = 64$

19. $10^2 = 10 \cdot 10 = 100$

20. $10^3 = 10 \cdot 10 \cdot 10 = 1000$

22. $5^3 = 5 \cdot 5$

23. $2^4 = 2 \cdot 2$

24. $1^4 = 1 \cdot 1$

26. $4^3 = 4 \cdot 4$

27. $11^2 = 11 \cdot 11 =$ ,

28. $10^5 = 10 \cdot 10 \cdot 10 \cdot 10 \cdot$
$= 100{,}000$

30. $3 \cdot 7 - 6 = 21 - 6 = 15$

31. $3(5 + 4) = 3(9) = 27$

32. $3(7 - 6) = 3(1) = 3$

34. $12 - 3 \cdot 3 = 12 - 9 = 3$

35. $(2 + 8)5 = (10)5 = 50$

36. $(12 - 3)3 = (9)3 = 27$

38. $8 + 2 \cdot 7 - 3 = 8 + 14 - 3$
$= 22 - 3$
$= 19$

39. $6 + 3(4 - 2) = 6 + 3(2)$
$= 6 + 6$
$= 12$

3) $= 8 + 2(4)$
$= 8 + 8$
$= 16$

2)(7 − 3) $= 10(4) = 40$

$\cdot 2^2 + 5 \cdot 2^3 = 4 \cdot 4 + 5 \cdot 8$
$= 16 + 40$
$= 56$

. $3 \cdot 4^2 + 2 \cdot 4^3 = 3 \cdot 16 + 2 \cdot 64$
$= 48 + 128$
$= 176$

46. $(3 \cdot 4)^2 + (2 \cdot 4)^3 = 12^2 + 8^3$
$= 144 + 512$
$= 656$

47. $(5 + 3)^2 = 8^2 = 64$

48. $(8 - 3)^2 = (5)^2 = 25$

50. $8^2 - 3^2 = 64 - 9 = 55$

51. $5^2 + 2(5)(3) + 3^2 = 25 + 30 + 9$
$= 64$

52. $8^2 - 2(8)(3) + 3^2 = 64 - 48 + 9$
$= 16 + 9$
$= 25$

54. $(8 - 5)(8 + 5) = 3(13) = 39$

55. $7^2 - 4^2 = 49 - 16 = 33$

56. $8^2 - 5^2 = 64 - 25 = 39$

58. $3 + 4 \cdot 4^2 + 5^2 = 3 + 4 \cdot 16 + 25$
$= 3 + 64 + 25$
$= 92$

59. $2 + 3(2^2 + 3^2) = 2 + 3(4 + 9)$
$= 2 + 3(13)$
$= 2 + 39$
$= 41$

60. $3 + 4(4^2 + 5^2) = 3 + 4(16 + 25)$
$= 3 + 4(41)$
$= 3 + 164$
$= 167$

62. $(3 + 4)(4^2 + 5^2) = (7)(16 + 25)$
$= (7)(41)$
$= 287$

63. $40 - 10 \div 5 + 1 = 40 - 2 + 1$
$= 38 + 1$
$= 39$

64. $20 - 10 \div 2 + 3 = 20 - 5 + 3$
$= 15 + 3$
$= 18$

66. $(20 - 10) \div 2 + 3 = 10 \div 2 + 3$
$= 5 + 3$
$= 8$

67. $(40 - 10) \div (5 + 1) = 30 \div 6 = 5$

68. $(20 - 10) \div (2 + 3) = 10 \div 5 = 2$

70. $36 \div 3 + 9 \div 3 = 12 + 3 = 15$

71. $24 \div (4 + 8) \div 2 = 24 \div 12 \div 2$
$= 2 \div 2$
$= 1$

72. $36 \div (3 + 9) \div 3 = 36 \div 12 \div 3$
$= 3 \div 3$
$= 1$

74. $6 \cdot 10^3 + 5 \cdot 10^2 + 4 \cdot 10 + 3$
$= 6 \cdot 1{,}000 + 5 \cdot 100 + 4 \cdot 10 + 3$
$= 6{,}000 + 500 + 40 + 3$
$= 6{,}543$

75. $2^3 + 3(8 + 12 \div 2) = 8 + 3(8 + 6)$
$= 8 + 3(14)$
$= 8 + 42$
$= 50$

76. $3^2 + 2(10 + 15 \div 5) = 9 + 2(10 + 3)$
$= 9 + 2(13)$
$= 9 + 26$
$= 35$

78. $18 - (3 \cdot 4^3 - 19 \cdot 10)$
$+ 18 - (3 \cdot 64 - 190)$
$= 18 - (192 - 190)$
$= 18 - 2$
$= 16$

79. $40 - [10 - (4 - 2)]$
$= 40 - [10 - 2]$
$= 40 - 8$
$= 32$

80. $50 - [17 - (8 - 3)]$
$= 50 - [17 - 5]$
$= 50 - 12$
$= 38$

82. $50 - 17 - 8 - 3 = 33 - 8 - 3$
$= 25 - 3$
$= 22$

83. $3 + 2(2 \cdot 3^2 + 1)$
$= 3 + 2(2 \cdot 9 + 1)$
$= 3 + 2(18 + 1)$
$= 3 + 2(19)$
$= 3 + 38$
$= 41$

84. $4 + 5(3 \cdot 2^2 - 5)$
$= 4 + 5(3 \cdot 4 - 5)$
$= 4 + 5(12 - 5)$
$= 4 + 5(7)$
$= 4 + 35$
$= 39$

86. $(4 + 5)(3 \cdot 2^2 - 5) = (9)(3 \cdot 4 - 5)$
$= (9)(12 - 5)$
$= (9)(7)$
$= 63$

87. $3[2 + 4(5 + 2 \cdot 3)] = 3[2 + 4(5 + 6)]$
$= 3[2 + 4(11)]$
$= 3[2 + 44]$
$= 3[46]$
$= 138$

88. $2[4 + 2(6 + 3 \cdot 5)] = 2[4 + 2(6 + 15)]$
$= 2[4 + 2(21)]$
$= 2[4 + 42]$
$= 2[46]$
$= 92$

90. $8[7 + 2(6 \cdot 9 - 14)]$
$= 8[7 + 2(54 - 14)]$
$= 8[7 + 2(40)]$
$= 8[7 + 80]$
$= 8[87]$
$= 696$

91. $5(7 \cdot 4 - 3 \cdot 4) + 8(5 \cdot 9 - 4 \cdot 9)$
$= 5(28 - 12) + 8(45 - 36)$
$= 5(16) + 8(9)$
$= 80 + 72$
$= 152$

92. $4(3 \cdot 9 - 2 \cdot 9) + 5(6 \cdot 8 - 5 \cdot 8)$
$= 4(27 - 18) + 5(48 - 40)$
$= 4(9) + 5(8)$
$= 36 + 40$
$= 76$

94. $6^3 + 2^6 \div 4^2 - 3^4$
$= 216 + 64 \div 16 - 81$
$= 216 + 4 - 81$
$= 220 - 81$
$= 139$

95. $(2 \cdot 8) + 5 = 16 + 5 = 21$

96. $\frac{12}{4} + 9 = 3 + 9 = 12$

98. $5 \cdot 9 - 4 = 45 - 4 = 41$

99. $9 - 4 + 2 = 5 + 2 = 7$

100. $10 - 7 + 8 = 3 + 8 = 11$

102. $A \cup C = \{0,1,2,3,4,5,6,7\}$

103. $A \cap B = \{2,4\}$

104. $A \cap C = \varnothing$

106. $B \cup C = \{1,2,3,4,5,7\}$

107. $A \cup (B \cap C) = A \cup \{1,3,5\}$
$= \{0,1,2,4,5,6\}$

108. $C \cup (A \cap B) = C \cup \{2,4\}$
$= \{1,2,3,4,5,7\}$

110. $\{x | x \in B \text{ and } x > 3\} = \{4,5\}$

111. $\{x | x \in A \text{ and } x \notin B\} = \{0,6\}$

112. $\{x | x \in B \text{ and } x \notin C\} = \{2,4\}$

114. $\{x | x \in A \text{ or } x \in B\} = \{0,1,2,3,4,5,6\}$

115. $\{x | x \in B \text{ and } x \neq 3\} = \{1,2,4,5\}$

116. $\{x | x \in C \text{ and } x \neq 5\} = \{1,3,7\}$

118. $n(A \cap B) = 0$

119. $n(A \cup B) = 7 + 8 - 2$
$= 15 - 2$
$= 13$

120. $n(A \cup B) = 4 + 10 - 3$
$= 14 - 3$
$= 11$

## Section 1.2

2.

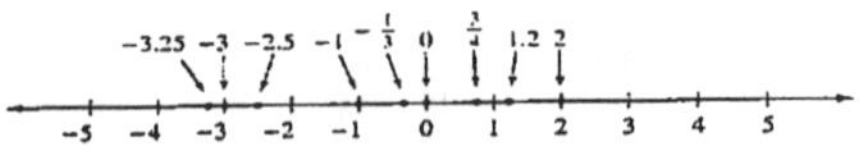


3. $-4, \frac{1}{4}$

4. $3, -\frac{1}{3}$

6. $-\frac{5}{6}, \frac{6}{5}$

7. $5, \frac{1}{5}$

8. $-7, -\frac{1}{7}$

10. $-\frac{1}{2}, -2$

11. $-\frac{1}{2}, -2$

12. $-\frac{1}{3}, \frac{1}{3}$

14. $-4, 4$

15. $-1, 1$

16. $0$

18. *True*

19. $|-2| = 2$

20. $|-7| = 7$

22. $\left|\frac{5}{6}\right| = \frac{5}{6}$

23. $|\pi| = \pi$

24. $|-\sqrt{2}| = \sqrt{2}$

26. $-|5| = -5$

27. $-|-2| = -2$

28. $-|-10| = -10$

30. $-\left|\frac{7}{8}\right| = -\frac{7}{8}$

31. $-(-2) = 2$

32. $-\left(-\frac{3}{4}\right) = \frac{3}{4}$

34. $-[-(-1)] = -1$

35. $|7 - 3| = 4$

36. $|8 - 5| = 3$

38. $|8| - |5| = 3$

39. $|-8| - |-3| = 5$

40. $|-6| - |-1| = 5$

42. $|7 - 4| + |5 - 2| = 5$

43. $|-2| + |-3| - |5| = 10$

44. $|-6| - |-2| + |-4| = 8$

46. $|10 - 6 - 2| = 2$

47. $|9 - 5| - 3 = 1$

48. $|10 - 6| - 2 = 2$

48. $|10 - 6| - 2 = 2$

50. $10 - |6 - 2| = 6$

51. $2|-3| + 3|-2| = 12$

52. $4|-5| + 2|-3| = 26$

54. $8|-4| - 2|-3| = 26$

55. 1,2

56. 0,1,2

58. -6,0,1,2

59. $-\sqrt{7}, -\pi, \sqrt{17}$

60. *All are real numbers.*

62. 1,2

63. *False*

64. *False*

66. *False*

67. *True*

68. *False*

70. *False*

71. $\frac{3}{5} \cdot \frac{7}{8} = \frac{21}{40}$

72. $\frac{6}{7} \cdot \frac{9}{5} = \frac{54}{35}$

74. $\frac{1}{4} \cdot 8 = 2$

75. $\left(\frac{2}{3}\right)^3 = \frac{8}{27}$

76. $\left(\frac{4}{5}\right)^2 = \frac{16}{25}$

78. $\left(\frac{1}{2}\right)^5 = \frac{1}{32}$

79. $\frac{3}{5} \cdot \frac{4}{7} \cdot \frac{6}{11} = \frac{72}{385}$

80. $\frac{4}{5} \cdot \frac{6}{7} \cdot \frac{3}{11} = \frac{72}{385}$

82. $\frac{5}{8} \cdot \frac{8}{5} = 1$

83. $\sqrt{2} \cdot \frac{1}{\sqrt{2}} = 1$

84. $\sqrt{3} \cdot \frac{1}{\sqrt{3}} = 1$

86. $25\left(\frac{1}{2}\right)^2 = 1$

87. $\pi \cdot \frac{1}{\pi} = 1$

88. $e \cdot \frac{1}{e} = 1$

90. $-9$ *and* $3$

91. 1

92. 0.777...

94. 0.123123123...

95. −$15

96. −$20

98. $-\frac{3}{4}, \frac{3}{4}$

99. $60 = 2^3 \cdot 3 \cdot 5$

100. $154 = 2 \cdot 7 \cdot 11$

102. $385 = 5 \cdot 7 \cdot 11$

103. $111 = 3 \cdot 37$

104. $735 = 3 \cdot 5 \cdot 7^2$

106. $1{,}155 = 3 \cdot 5 \cdot 7 \cdot 11$

107. $\frac{165}{385} = \frac{3}{7}$

108. $\frac{550}{735} = \frac{110}{147}$

110. $\frac{266}{285} = \frac{14}{15}$

111. $\frac{111}{185} = \frac{3}{5}$

112. $\frac{279}{310} = \frac{9}{10}$

114. $\frac{205}{369} = \frac{5}{9}$

115. $5! = 5 \cdot 4 \cdot 3 \cdot 2 \cdot 1 = 120$

116. $6! = 6 \cdot 5 \cdot 4 \cdot 3 \cdot 2 \cdot 1 = 720$

118.
$$\begin{aligned} (2+3)! &= 2! + 3! \\ 5! &= 2 \cdot 1 + 3 \cdot 2 \cdot 1 \\ 5 \cdot 4 \cdot 3 \cdot 2 \cdot 1 &= 2 + 6 \\ 120 &= 8 \qquad \textit{False} \end{aligned}$$

119. $\frac{5!}{8!} = \frac{1}{8 \cdot 7 \cdot 6} = \frac{1}{336}$

120. $\frac{4!}{6!} = \frac{1}{6 \cdot 5} = \frac{1}{30}$

122. $\frac{99!}{100!} = \frac{1}{100}$

## Section 1.3

2. 

3. 

4. 

6. 

7. 0 4

8. −3 0

10. 0

11. $-2 < x$ means $x > -2$

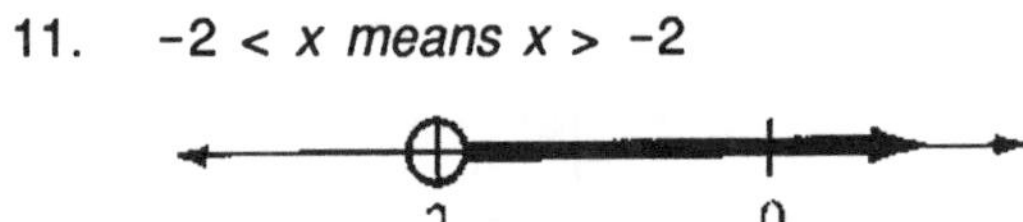

12. $3 \geq x$ means $x \leq 3$

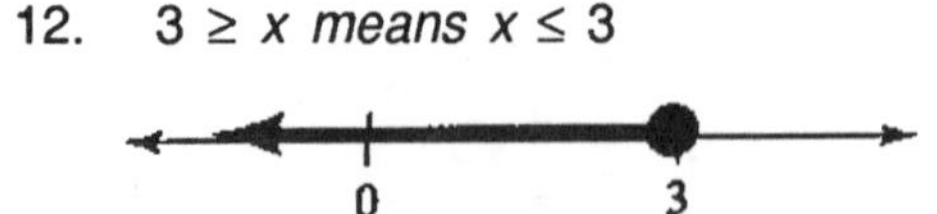

14. $2 > x$ means $x < 2$

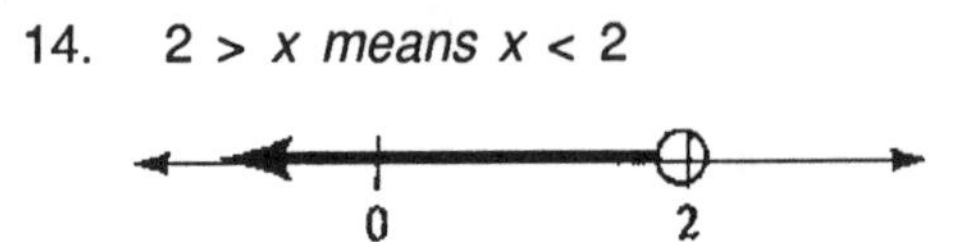

15. −3 1

16. 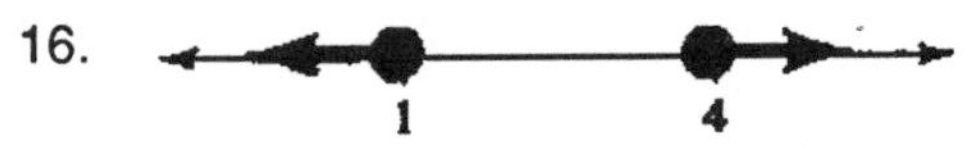

18. 

19. $-3 \leq x$ means $x \geq -3$

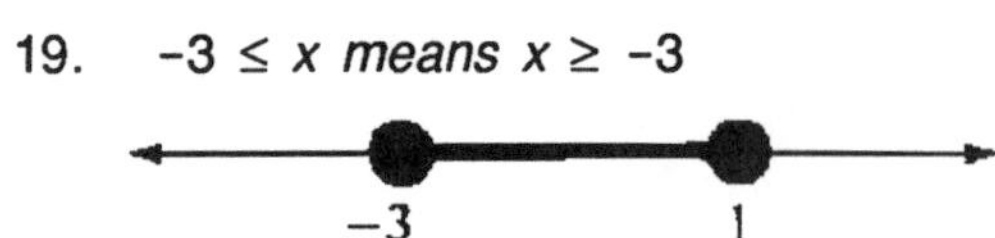

20. $1 < x$ means $x > 1$

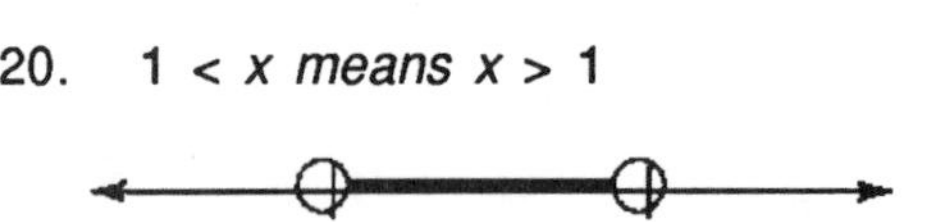

22. $1 \leq x$ means $x \geq 1$

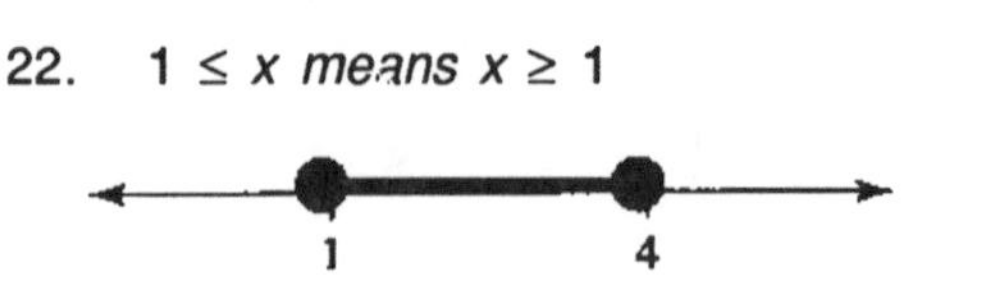

23. 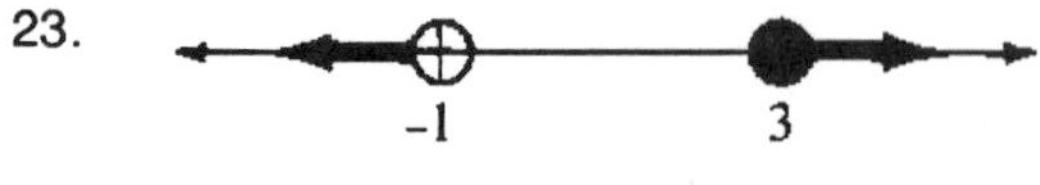

24. 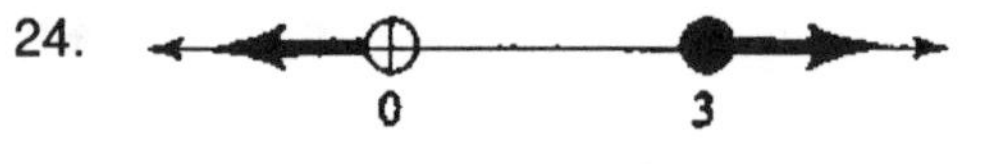

26. No solution; there are no real numbers that are less than or equal to 0 and also greater than or equal to 3.

27. 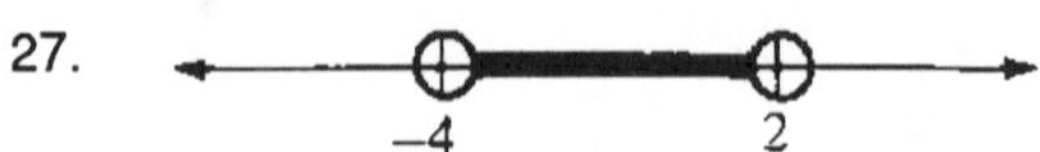

28. 

30. 

31. 1 2

32. 

34. 

35. 

36. 

38. −1 5

39. 3 2 4

40. −4 −2 3

42. −3 0 5

43. −5 −2 2 5

44. −3 −1 1 3

46. $x \geq -2$

47. $x \leq -3$

48. $x \leq 8$

50. $x \leq -5$

51. $x \geq -2$

52. $x \geq 3$

54. $-3 \leq x \leq 3$

55. $-4 \leq x \leq 4$

56. $-3 \leq x \leq 3$

58. $2 \leq t \leq 5$

59. $3 < x < 13$

60. $2 < x < 8$

62. $x < 2$ *or* $x > 8$

**Section 1.4**

2. $6 + (5 + 3x) = (6 + 5) + 3x$
$= 11 + 3x$

3. $(a + 3) + 5 = a + (3 + 5)$
$= a + 8$

4. $(4a + 5) + 7 = 4a + (5 + 7)$
$= 4a + 12$

6. $7(4y) = (7 \cdot 4)y = 28y$

7. $\frac{1}{3}(3x) = \left(\frac{1}{3} \cdot 3\right)x = 1x = x$

8. $\frac{1}{5}(5x) = \left(\frac{1}{5} \cdot 5\right)x = 1x = x$

10. $7\left(\frac{1}{7}a\right) = \left(7 \cdot \frac{1}{7}\right)a = 1a = a$

11. $\frac{2}{3}\left(\frac{3}{2}x\right) = \left(\frac{2}{3} \cdot \frac{3}{2}\right)x = 1x = x$

12. $\frac{4}{3}\left(\frac{3}{4}x\right) = \left(\frac{4}{3} \cdot \frac{3}{4}\right)x = 1x = x$

14. $5(x + 9) = 5x + 5(9) = 5x + 45$

15. $2(6x + 4) = 2(6x) + 2(4) = 12x + 8$

16. $3(7x + 8) = 3(7x) + 3(8) = 21x + 24$

18. $7(2a + 3b) = 7(2a) + 7(3b)$
$= 14a + 21b$

19. $4(7 + 3y) = 4(7) + 4(3y) = 28 + 12y$

20. $8(6 + 2y) = 8(6) + 8(2y) = 48 + 16y$

22. $\frac{1}{2}(3x + 8) = \frac{1}{2}(3x) + \frac{1}{2}(8)$

$= \left(\frac{1}{2} \cdot 3\right)x + 4$

$= \frac{3}{2}x + 4$

23. $\frac{1}{2}(2a + 4) = \frac{1}{2}(2a) + \frac{1}{2}(4)$
$= \left(\frac{1}{2} \cdot 2\right)a + 2$
$= 1a + 2$
$= a + 2$

24. $\frac{1}{2}(4a + 2) = \frac{1}{2}(4a) + \frac{1}{2}(2)$
$= \left(\frac{1}{2} \cdot 4\right)a + 1$
$= 2a + 1$

26. $\frac{1}{6}(12 + 6y) = \frac{1}{6}(12) + \frac{1}{6}(6y)$
$= 2 + \left(\frac{1}{6} \cdot 6\right)y$
$= 2 + 1y$
$= 2 + y$

27. $(5t + 1)8 = 5t(8) + 1(8)$
$= (5 \cdot 8)t + 8$
$= 40t + 8$

28. $(3t + 2)5 = 3t(5) + 2(5)$
$= (3 \cdot 5)t + 10$
$= 15t + 10$

30. $4(3x + 2) + 5 = 4(3x) + 4(2) + 5$
$= 12x + 8 + 5$
$= 12x + 13$

31. $4(2y + 6) + 8 = 4(2y) + 4(6) + 8$
$= 8y + 24 + 8$
$= 8y + 32$

32. $6(2y + 3) + 2 = 6(2y) + 6(3) + 2$
$= 12y + 18 + 2$
$= 12y + 20$

34. $2(1 + 5t) + 6 = 2(1) + 2(5t) + 6$
$= 2 + 10t + 6$
$= 10t + 8$

35. $3 + (2 + 7x)4 = 3 + 2(4) + 7x(4)$
$= 3 + 8 + 28x$
$= 28x + 11$

36. $4 + (1 + 3x)5 = 4 + 1(5) + 3x(5)$
$= 4 + 5 + 15x$
$= 15x + 9$

38. $7(2x + 4y + 6) + 10$
$= 7(2x) + 7(4y) + 7(6) + 10$
$= 14x + 28y + 42 + 10$
$= 14x + 28y + 52$

39. $\frac{3}{7} + \frac{1}{7} + \frac{2}{7} = (3 + 1 + 2)\frac{1}{7}$
$= (6)\frac{1}{7}$
$= \frac{6}{7}$

40. $\frac{3}{8} + \frac{1}{8} + \frac{1}{8} = (3 + 1 + 1)\frac{1}{8}$
$= 5\left(\frac{1}{8}\right)$
$= \frac{5}{8}$

42. $\frac{1}{\sqrt{5}} + \frac{8}{\sqrt{5}} = (1 + 8)\frac{1}{\sqrt{5}}$
$= (9)\frac{1}{\sqrt{5}}$
$= \frac{9}{\sqrt{5}}$

43. $\frac{4}{x} + \frac{7}{x} = (4 + 7)\frac{1}{x}$
$= 11(\frac{1}{x})$
$= \frac{11}{x}$

44. $\frac{5}{y} + \frac{9}{y} = (5 + 9)\frac{1}{y}$

$= (14)\frac{1}{y}$

$= \frac{14}{y}$

46. $\frac{5}{8} + \frac{1}{4} = \frac{5}{8} + \frac{2}{8}$ $\quad LCD = 8$

$= \frac{7}{8}$

47. $\frac{5}{6} + \frac{7}{8} = \frac{20}{24} + \frac{21}{24}$ $\quad LCD = 24$

$= \frac{41}{24}$

48. $\frac{3}{4} + \frac{2}{3} = \frac{9}{12} + \frac{8}{12}$ $\quad LCD = 12$

$= \frac{17}{12}$

50. $28 = 2^2 \cdot 7$
$42 = 2 \cdot 3 \cdot 7$
$LCD = 2^2 \cdot 3 \cdot 7 = 84$

$\frac{6}{28} + \frac{5}{42} = \frac{18}{84} + \frac{10}{84} = \frac{28}{84} = \frac{1}{3}$

51. $\frac{3}{4} + \frac{1}{8} + \frac{2}{3}$ $\quad LCD = 24$

$= \frac{18}{24} + \frac{3}{24} + \frac{16}{24}$

$= \frac{37}{24}$

52. $\frac{1}{3} + \frac{5}{6} + \frac{5}{12}$ $\quad LCD = 12$

$= \frac{4}{12} + \frac{10}{12} + \frac{5}{12}$

$= \frac{19}{12}$

54. $5x + 1 + 7x + 8$
$= (5x + 7x) + (1 + 8)$
$= (5 + 7)x + 9$
$= 12x + 9$

55. $x + 3 + 4x + 9$
$= (x + 4x) + (3 + 9)$
$= (1 + 4)x + 12$
$= 5x + 12$

56. $5x + 2 + x + 10$
$= (5x + x) + (2 + 10)$
$= (5 + 1)x + 12$
$= 6x + 12$

58. $6a + 4 + a + 4a$
$= (6a + a + 4a) + 4$
$= (6 + 1 + 4)a + 4$
$= 11a + 4$

59. $3y + y + 5 + 2y + 1$
$= (3y + y + 2y) + (5 + 1)$
$= (3 + 1 + 2)y + 6$
$= 6y + 6$

60. $4y + 2y + 3 + y + 7$
$= (4y + 2y + y) + (3 + 7)$
$= (4 + 2 + 1)y + 10$
$= 7y + 10$

62. $5 + x + 6 + x + 7 + x$
$= (x + x + x) + (5 + 6 + 7)$
$= (1 + 1 + 1)x + 18$
$= 3x + 18$

63. $2(5x + 1) + 2x$
$= 2(5x) + 2(1) + 2x$
$= 10x + 2 + 2x$
$= (10x + 2x) + 2$
$= 12x + 2$

64. $3(4x + 1) + 9x$
$= 3(4x) + 3(1) + 9x$
$= 12x + 3 + 9x$
$= (12x + 9x) + 3$
$= 21x + 3$

66. $6 + 3(5y + 2)$
$= 6 + 3(5y) + 3(2)$
$= 6 + 15y + 6$
$= 15y + 6 + 6$
$= 15y + 12$

67. $3 + 4(5a + 3) + 4a$
$= 3 + 4(5a) + 4(3) + 4a$
$= 3 + 20a + 12 + 4a$
$= (20a + 4a) + 3 + 12$
$= 24a + 15$

68. $8 + 2(4a + 2) + 5a$
$= 8 + 2(4a) + 2(2) + 5a$
$= (8a + 5a) + (8 + 4)$
$= 13a + 12$

70. $7x + 3(4x + 1) + 7$
$= 7x + 3(4x) + 3(1) + 7$
$= (7x + 12x) + (3 + 7)$
$= 19x + 10$

71. $2t + 3(1 + 6t) + 2$
$= 2t + 3(1) + 3(6t) + 2$
$= 2t + 3 + 18t + 2$
$= (2t + 18t) + (3 + 2)$
$= 20t + 5$

72. $3t + 2(4 + 2t) + 6$
$= 3t + 2(4) + 2(2t) + 6$
$= 3t + 8 + 4t + 6$
$= (3t + 4t) + (8 + 6)$
$= 7t + 14$

74. $7(x + 8)$
$= 7(x) + 7(8)$ (*Right-hand side*)
$= 7x + 56$

75. $3x + 4x = (3 + 4)x$
$= 7x$ (*Right-hand side*)

76. $3x + 4x = (3 + 4)x$
$= 7x$ (*Right-hand side*)

78. $\frac{5}{9} + \frac{2}{9} = (5 + 2)\frac{1}{9}$
$= (7)\frac{1}{9}$
$= \frac{7}{9}$

79. Commutative property of addition

80. Associative property of multiplication

82. Additive identity property

83. Additive inverse property

84. Multiplicative identity property

86. Associative property of addition

87. Associative and commutative properties of multiplication

88. Commutative property of multiplication

90. Associative and commutative properties of addition

91. Distributive property

92. Multiplicative inverse property

94. $8(5) - 5 = 8$
$35 \neq 8$

95. $15 - (8 - 2) = 15 - 6 = 9$
$(15 - 8) - 2 = 7 - 2 = 5$

96. $(48 \div 6) \div 2 = 8 \div 2 = 4$
$48 \div (6 \div 2) = 48 \div 3 = 16$

**Section 1.5**

2. $11 + (-5) = 6$

3. $-6 + 2 = -4$

4. $-11 + 5 = -6$

6. $-\frac{1}{2} + \left(-\frac{1}{4}\right) + \left(-\frac{1}{10}\right)$ $\quad LCD = 20$

$$= -\frac{10}{20} + \left(-\frac{5}{20}\right) + \left(-\frac{2}{20}\right)$$

$$= \frac{-10 + (-5) + (-2)}{20}$$

$$= -\frac{17}{20}$$

7. $-7 - 3 = -7 + (-3)$
$= -10$

8. $-6 - 9 = -6 + (-9)$
$= -15$

10. $-6 - (-9) = -6 + 9$
$= 3$

11. $\frac{3}{4} - \left(-\frac{5}{6}\right) = \frac{9}{12} + \frac{10}{12}$

$$= \frac{19}{12}$$

12. $\frac{2}{3} - \left(-\frac{7}{5}\right) = \frac{10}{15} + \frac{21}{15} = \frac{31}{15}$

14. $70 = 2 \cdot 5 \cdot 7$
$42 = 2 \cdot 3 \cdot 7$
$LCD = 2 \cdot 3 \cdot 5 \cdot 7 = 210$

$$\frac{13}{70} - \frac{19}{42} = \frac{39}{210} - \frac{95}{210}$$

$$= -\frac{56}{210}$$

$$= -\frac{4}{15}$$

15. $6 - (-2) + 11 = 6 + 2 + 11 = 19$

16. $8 - (-3) + 12 = 8 + 3 + 12 = 23$

18. $-\frac{1}{6} - \left(-\frac{1}{3}\right) - \frac{1}{2}$

$$= -\frac{1}{6} + \frac{2}{6} - \frac{3}{6}$$

$$= -\frac{2}{6}$$

$$= -\frac{1}{3}$$

19. $-5 - (2 - 6) - 3 = -5 - (-4) - 3$
$= -5 + 4 - 3$
$= -4$

20. $-4 - (5 - 9) - 2 = -4 - (-4) - 2$
$= -4 + 4 - 2$
$= -2$

22. $-(8 - 10) - (6 - 1) = -(-2) - (5)$
$= 2 - 5$
$= -3$

23. $-3 - 5 = -3 + (-5) = -8$

24. $5 - (-3) = 5 + 3 = 8$

26. $8 - (-4) = 8 + 4 = 12$

27. $-3x - 4x = -3x + (-4x) = -7x$

28. $7x - (-5x) = 7x + 5x = 12x$

30. $-3 - x = 9$
$x = -12$

31. $(2 - 9) + (-7) = -7 + (-7) = -14$

32. $(9 - 2) + (-3) = 7 + (-3) = 4$

34. $(3a + 5a) - (-3a) = 8a + 3a = 11a$

35. $3(-5) = -15$

36. $-3(5) = -15$

38. $4(-6) = -24$

39. $-8(3) = -24$

40. $-7(-6) = 42$

42. $-3(-2)(5) = 6(5) = 30$

43. $2(-3)(4) = -6(4) = -24$

44. $-2(3)(-4) = -6(-4) = 24$

46. $-5(4x) = -20x$

47. $-\frac{1}{3}(-3x) = \left[-\frac{1}{3}(-3)\right]x$
$= 1x$
$= x$

48. $-\frac{1}{6}(-6)x = x$

50. $-\frac{2}{5}(-\frac{5}{2}y) = y$

51. $-2(4x - 3) = -2(4x) + (-2)(-3)$
$= -8x + 6$

52. $-6(2x-1) = -6(2x) + (-6)(-1)$
$= -12x + 6$

54. $-2(-5t + 6) = -2(-5t) + (-2)(6)$
$= 10t - 12$

55. $-\frac{1}{2}(6a - 8) = -\frac{1}{2}(6a) - \left(-\frac{1}{2}\right)8$
$= -\frac{6a}{2} + \frac{8}{2}$
$= -3a + 4$

56. $-\frac{1}{3}(6a - 9) = -\frac{1}{3}(6a) + \left(-\frac{1}{3}\right)(-9)$
$= -2a + 3$

58. $-\frac{1}{2}(-5x - 8)$
$= \left(-\frac{1}{2}\right)(-5x) + \left(-\frac{1}{2}\right)(-8)$
$= \frac{5}{2}x + 4$

59. $3(-4) - 2 = -12 - 2 = -14$

60. $-3(-4) - 2 = 12 - 2 = 10$

62. $-6(-3) - 5(-7) = 18 + 35 = 53$

63. $2 - 5(-4) - 6 = 2 + 20 - 6$
$= 22 - 6$
$= 16$

64. $3 - 8(-1) - 7 = 3 + 8 - 7 = 4$

66. $3 - 8(-1 - 7)$
$= 3 - 8(-8)$
$= 3 + 64$
$= 67$

67. $(2-5)(-4 - 6) = (-3)(-10) = 30$

68. $(3 - 8)(-1 - 7) = (-5)(-8) = 40$

70. $8 - 5(6 - 3) - 7$
$= 8 - 5(3) - 7$
$= 8 - 15 - 7$
$= -14$

71. $2(-3)^2 - 4(-2)^3$
$= 2(9) - 4(-8)$
$= 18 + 32$
$= 50$

72. $5(-2)^2 - 2(-3)^3$
$= 5(4) - 2(-27)$
$= 20 + 54$
$= 74$

74. $(5 - 8)^2 - (4 - 8)^2$
$= (-3)^2 - (-4)^2$
$= 9 - 16$
$= -7$

75. $7(3 - 5)^3 - 2(4 - 7)^3$
$= 7(-2)^3 - 2(-3)^3$
$= 7(-8) - 2(-27)$
$= -56 + 54$
$= -2$

76. $3(-7 + 9)^3 - 5(-2 + 4)^3$
$= 3(2)^3 - 5(2)^3$
$= 3(8) - 5(8)$
$= 24 - 40$
$= -16$

78. $-5(5 - 6) - 7(2 - 8)$
$= -5(-1) - 7(-6)$
$= 5 + (42)$
$= 47$

79. $-5(-8 - 2) - 3(-2 - 8)$
$= -5(-10) - 3(-10)$
$= 50 + 30$
$= 80$

80. $-3(-5 - 15) - 4(-12 - 8)$
$= -3(-20) - 4(-20)$
$= 60 + 80$
$= 140$

82. $6 - 5[2 - 4(-8)]$
$= 6 - 5[2 + 32]$
$= 6 - 5[34]$
$= 6 + [-170]$
$= -164$

83. $(8 - 7)[4 - 7(-2)]$
$= (8 - 7)[4 + 14]$
$= (1)(18)$
$= 18$

84. $(6 - 9)[15 - 3(-4)]$
$= (6 - 9)[15 + 12]$
$= (-3)(27)$
$= -81$

86. $-2 + 7[2 - 6(-3 - 4)]$
$= -2 + 7[2 - 6(-7)]$
$= -2 + 7[2 + 42]$
$= -2 + 7[44]$
$= -2 + 308$
$= 306$

87. $5 - 6[-3(2 - 9) - 4(8 - 6)]$
$= 5 - 6[-3(-7) - 4(2)]$
$= 5 - 6[21 - 8]$
$= 5 - 6[13]$
$= 5 - 78$
$= -73$

88. $9 - 4[-2(4 - 8) - 5(3 - 1)]$
$= 9 - 4[-2(-4) - 5(2)]$
$= 9 - 4[8 - 10]$
$= 9 - 4(-2)$
$= 9 + 8$
$= 17$

90. $4(7x + 3) - x$
$= 4(7x) + 4(3) - x$
$= 28x + 12 - x$
$= 27x + 12$

91. $6 - 7(3 - m)$
$= 6 - 7(3) -(-7)m$
$= 6 - 21 + 7m$
$= 7m - 15$

92. $3 - 5(5 - m)$
$= 3 + (-5)(5) - (-5)m$
$= 3 - 25 + 5m$
$= 5m - 22$

94. $8 - 5(2x - 3) + 4x$
$= 8 - 5(2x) - 5(-3) + 4x$
$= 8 - 10x + 15 + 4x$
$= - 6x + 23$

95. $5(3y + 1) - (8y - 5)$
$= 5(3y) + 5(1) - 1(8y) - 1(-5)$
$= 15y + 5 - 8y + 5$
$= 7y + 10$

96. $4(6y + 3) - (6y - 6)$
$= 4(6y) + 4(3) - 1(6y) - 1(-6)$
$= 24y + 12 - 6y + 6$
$= 18y + 18$

98. $7(1 - 2x) - (4 - 10x)$
$= 7(1) -(7)(2x) - 1(4) - 1(-10x)$
$= 7 - 14x - 4 + 10x$
$= -4x + 3$

99. $10 - 4(2x + 1) - (3x - 4)$
$= 10 - 4(2x) - 4(1) - 1(3x) - 1(-4)$
$= 10 - 8x - 4 - 3x + 4$
$= -8x - 3x + 10 - 4 + 4$
$= -11x + 10$

100. $7 - 2(3x + 5) - (2x - 3)$
$= 7 - 2(3x) - 2(5) - 1(2x) - 1(-3)$
$= 7 - 6x - 10 - 2x + 3$
$= -8x$

102. $\frac{-8}{4} = -2$

103. $\frac{-8}{-4} = 2$

104. $\frac{-12}{-4} = 3$

106. $\frac{-7}{0} =$ *undefined*

107. $\frac{0}{-3} = 0$

108. $\frac{0}{5} = 0$

110. $-\frac{2}{3} \div \frac{4}{9} = -\frac{2}{3} \cdot \frac{9}{4}$
$= -\frac{18}{12}$
$= -\frac{3}{2}$

111. $-8 \div \left(-\frac{1}{4}\right) = -8 \cdot \left(-\frac{4}{1}\right)$
$= -8(-4)$
$= 32$

112. $-12 \div \left(-\frac{2}{3}\right) = -\frac{12}{1} \cdot \left(-\frac{3}{2}\right)$
$= \frac{36}{2}$
$= 18$

114. $-30 \div \left(-\frac{5}{6}\right) = -30 \cdot \left(-\frac{6}{5}\right)$
$= -\frac{30}{1} \cdot -\frac{6}{5}$
$= \frac{180}{5}$
$= 36$

115. $\frac{4}{9} \div (-8) = \frac{4}{9} \cdot \left(-\frac{1}{8}\right)$
$= -\frac{4}{72}$
$= -\frac{1}{18}$

116. $\frac{3}{7} \div (-6) = \frac{3}{7} \cdot \left(-\frac{1}{6}\right)$
$= -\frac{3}{42}$
$= -\frac{1}{14}$

118. $\frac{8(-3) - 6}{-7 - (-2)} = \frac{-24 + (-6)}{-7 + 2}$
$= \frac{-30}{-5}$
$= 6$

119. $\frac{3(-1) - 4(-2)}{8 - 5} = \frac{-3 + 8}{8 - 5} = \frac{5}{3}$

120. $\frac{6(-4) - 5(-2)}{7 - 6} = \frac{-24 + 10}{1} = -14$

122. $-9 - 5\left[\dfrac{11(-1) - 9}{4(-3) + 2(5)}\right]$

$= -9 - 5\left[\dfrac{-11 - 9}{-12 + 10}\right]$

$= -9 - 5\left[\dfrac{-20}{-2}\right]$

$= -9 - 5[10]$
$= -9 - 50$
$= -59$

123. $6 - (-3)\left[\dfrac{2 - 4(3 - 8)}{1 - 5(1 - 3)}\right]$

$= 6 - (-3)\left[\dfrac{2 - 4(-5)}{1 - 5(-2)}\right]$

$= 6 - (-3)\left[\dfrac{2 + 20}{1 + 10}\right]$

$= 6 - (-3)\left[\dfrac{22}{11}\right]$

$= 6 - (-3)(2)$
$= 6 - (-6)$
$= 6 + 6$
$= 12$

124. $8 - (-7)\left[\dfrac{6 - 1(6 - 10)}{4 - 3(5 - 7)}\right]$

$= 8 - (-7)\left[\dfrac{6 - 1(-4)}{4 - 3(-2)}\right]$

$= 8 - (-7)\left[\dfrac{6 + 4}{4 + 6}\right]$

$= 8 - (-7)[1]$

$= 8 + 7$
$= 15$

126. $-12\left(\dfrac{3}{4}\right) - (-3)$

$= -\dfrac{12}{1}\left(\dfrac{3}{4}\right) + 3$

$= -\dfrac{36}{4} + 3$
$= -9 + 3$
$= -6$

127. $\left[-3 \div \left(\dfrac{1}{2}\right)\right] + (-5)$

$= \left[-3 \cdot \left(\dfrac{2}{1}\right)\right] + (-5)$

$= (-6) + (-5)$
$= -11$

128. $6 \div \left(-\dfrac{1}{2}\right) + (-7)$

$= 6 \cdot \left(-\dfrac{2}{1}\right) + (-7)$

$= -12 + (-7)$
$= -19$

130. $-5(-2x) + 7x = 10x + 7x = 17x$

## Section 1.6

2. *If you think you can, then you can.*

   *Hypothesis*: *you think you can.*
   *Conclusion*: *you can.*

3. *If x is an even number, then x is divisible by 2.*

   *Hypothesis*: *x is an even number.*
   *Conclusion*: *x is divisible by 2.*

4. *If x is an odd number, then x is not divisible by 2.*

   *Hypothesis*: *x is an odd number.*
   *Conclusion*: *x is not divisible by 2.*

6. *If a triangle is isosceles, then two of its angles are equal.*

   *Hpothesis*: *a triangle is isosceles.*
   *Conclusion*: *two of its angles are equal.*

7. *If* $x + 5 = -2$, *then* $x = -7$.

   *Hypothesis*: $x + 5 = -2$
   *Conclusion*: $x = -7$

8. *If* $x - 5 = -2$, *then* $x = 3$.

   *Hypothesis*: $x - 5 = -2$
   *Conclusion*: $x = 3$

10. *If* $x = y$, *then* $x^2 = y^2$.

    *Converse*: *If* $x^2 = y^2$, *then* $x = y$
    *Inverse*: *If* $x \neq y$, *then* $x^2 \neq y^2$
    *Contrapositive*: *If* $x^2 \neq y^2$, *then* $x \neq y$

11. *If* $\frac{a}{b} = 1$, *then* $a = b$.

    *Converse*: *If* $a = b$, *then* $\frac{a}{b} = 1$

    *Inverse*: *If* $\frac{a}{b} \neq 1$, *then* $a \neq b$

    *Contrapositive*: *If* $a \neq b$, *then* $\frac{a}{b} \neq 1$

12. *If* $a + b = 0$, *then* $a = -b$.

    *Converse*: *If* $a = -b$, *then* $a + b = 0$
    *Inverse*: *If* $a + b \neq 0$, *then* $a \neq -b$
    *Contrapositive*: *If* $a \neq -b$, *then* $a + b \neq 0$

14. *If you live in a glass house, then you shouldn't throw stones.*

    *Converse*: *If you shouldn't throw stones, then you live in a glass house.*
    *Inverse*: *If you don't live in a glass house, then you should throw stones.*
    *Contrapositive*: *If you should throw stones, then you don't live in a glass house.*

15. *If better is possible, then good is not enough.*

*Converse: If good is not enough, then better is possible.*
*Inverse: If better is not possible, then good is enough.*
*Contrapositive: If good is enough, then better is not possible.*

16. *If a and b are positive, then ab is positive.*

*Converse: If ab is positive, then a and b are positive.*
*Inverse: If a and b are not both positive, then ab is not positive.*
*Contrapositive: If ab is not positive, then a and b are not both positive.*

18. $a^3 = b^3 \Rightarrow a = b$

*If* $a^3 = b^3$, *then* $a = b$

19. *Misery loves company.*

*If it is misery, then it loves company.*

20. *Rollerblading is not a crime.*

*If it is rollerblading, then it is not a crime.*

22. *The girl who can't dance says the band can't play.*

*If it is the girl who can't dance, then she says the band can't play.*

23. *c*

24. *b*

26. *b*

27. *c*

28. *a*

30. *a*

**Section 1.7**

2. 4

3. 10

4. 9

6. 125

7. 29

8. 4,096

10. 35

11. △

12. →

14. □
□□□

15. 17, 21

16. 34, 40

18. −12, −18

19. −4, −7

20. −4, −8

22. $-\frac{4}{5}, -\frac{6}{5}$

23. $\frac{5}{2}, 3$

24. $\frac{7}{3}, 3$

26. 343

27. −270

28. −80

30. $\frac{1}{27}$

31. $\frac{5}{2}$

32. 1

34. 256

35. $-\frac{1}{125}$

36. $-\frac{1}{8}$

38. (*a*) −9
(*b*) 16

39. 144

40. 233

42. 8, 34, 144 *among others*

43. 2, 8, 34

44. 1, 3, 5, 13, 21, 55

46. 2, 4, 8, 16. . . .

47. 32

48. 1,024

# Chapter 2

## Section 2.1

2. $$x + 2 = 7$$
$$x + 2 + (-2) = 7 + (-2)$$
$$x = 5$$

3. $$2x - 4 = 6$$
$$2x - 4 + 4 = 6 + 4$$
$$2x = 10$$
$$\frac{1}{2}(2x) = \frac{1}{2}(10)$$
$$x = 5$$

4.
$$\begin{aligned} 3x - 5 &= 4 \\ 3x - 5 + 5 &= 4 + 5 \\ 3x &= 9 \\ \frac{1}{3}(3x) &= \frac{1}{3}(9) \\ x &= 3 \end{aligned}$$

6.
$$\begin{aligned} 10 &= 3a - 5 \\ 10 + 5 &= 3a - 5 + 5 \\ 15 &= 3a \\ \frac{1}{3}(15) &= \frac{1}{3}(3a) \\ 5 &= a \end{aligned}$$

7.
$$\begin{aligned} 3 - y &= 10 \\ 3 + (-3) - y &= 10 + (-3) \\ (-1)(-y) &= (-1)7 \\ y &= -7 \end{aligned}$$

8.
$$\begin{aligned} 5 - 2y &= 11 \\ 5 + (-5) - 2y &= 11 + (-5) \\ \left(-\frac{1}{2}\right)(-2y) &= \left(-\frac{1}{2}\right)(6) \\ y &= -3 \end{aligned}$$

10.
$$\begin{aligned} -8 - 5x &= -6 \\ -8 + 8 - 5x &= -6 + 8 \\ \left(-\frac{1}{5}\right)(-5x) &= \left(-\frac{1}{5}\right)2 \\ x &= -\frac{2}{5} \end{aligned}$$

11.
$$\begin{aligned} -3 &= 5 + 2x \\ -3 + (-5) &= 5 + (-5) + 2x \\ \left(\frac{1}{2}\right)(-8) &= \left(\frac{1}{2}\right)2x \\ -4 &= x \end{aligned}$$

12.
$$\begin{aligned} -12 &= 6 + 9x \\ -12 + (-6) &= 6 + (-6) + 9x \\ \left(\frac{1}{9}\right)(-18) &= \left(\frac{1}{9}\right)(9x) \\ -2 &= x \end{aligned}$$

14.
$$\begin{aligned} -20y + 80 &= 30 \\ -20y + 80 + (-80) &= 30 + (-80) \\ \left(-\frac{1}{20}\right)(-20y) &= \left(-\frac{1}{20}\right)(-50) \\ y &= \frac{5}{2} \end{aligned}$$

15.
$$\begin{aligned} 160 &= -50x - 40 \\ 160 + 40 &= -50x - 40 + 40 \\ \left(-\frac{1}{50}\right)200 &= \left(-\frac{1}{50}\right)(-50x) \\ -4 &= x \end{aligned}$$

16.
$$\begin{aligned} 110 &= -60x - 50 \\ 110 + 50 &= -60x - 50 + 50 \\ \left(-\frac{1}{60}\right)(160) &= \left(-\frac{1}{60}\right)(-60x) \\ -\frac{8}{3} &= x \end{aligned}$$

18.
$$\begin{aligned} 8 - 2a &= -13 \\ 8 + (-8) - 2a &= -13 + (-8) \\ \left(-\frac{1}{2}\right)(-2a) &= \left(-\frac{1}{2}\right)(-21) \\ a &= \frac{21}{2} \end{aligned}$$

19.
$$\begin{aligned} 9 + 5a &= -2 \\ 9 + (-9) + 5a &= -2 + (-9) \\ (\frac{1}{5})5a &= (\frac{1}{5})(-11) \\ a &= -\frac{11}{5} \end{aligned}$$

20.
$$\begin{aligned} 3 + 7a &= -7 \\ 3 + (-3) + 7a &= -7 + (-3) \\ \left(\frac{1}{7}\right)7a &= \left(\frac{1}{7}\right)(-10) \\ a &= -\frac{10}{7} \end{aligned}$$

22. $-x = \frac{1}{2}$

$(-1)(-x) = (-1)\frac{1}{2}$

$x = -\frac{1}{2}$

23. $-a = -\frac{3}{4}$

$-1(-a) = -1\left(-\frac{3}{4}\right)$

$a = \frac{3}{4}$

24. $-a = -5$
$(-1)(-a) = (-1)(-5)$
$a = 5$

26. $\frac{3}{2}x = 9$

$\left(\frac{2}{3}\right)\frac{3}{2}x = \left(\frac{2}{3}\right)9$

$x = \frac{18}{3}$

$x = 6$

27. $-\frac{3}{5}a + 2 = 8$

$-\frac{3}{5}a + 2 + (-2) = 8 + (-2)$

$\left(-\frac{5}{3}\right)\left(-\frac{3}{5}a\right) = -\frac{5}{3}(6)$

$a = -\frac{30}{3}$

$a = -10$

28. $-\frac{5}{3}a + 3 = 23$

$-\frac{5}{3}a + 3 + (-3) = 23 + (-3)$

$\left(-\frac{3}{5}\right)\left(-\frac{5}{3}a\right) = \left(-\frac{3}{5}\right)(20)$

$a = -\frac{60}{5}$

$a = -12$

30. $1 = 4 + \frac{3}{7}y$

$1 + (-4) = 4 + (-4) + \frac{3}{7}y$

$\left(\frac{7}{3}\right)(-3) = \left(\frac{7}{3}\right)\left(\frac{3}{7}y\right)$

$-7 = y$

31. $9 - \frac{3}{4}t = 12$

$9 + (-9) - \frac{3}{4}t = 12 + (-9)$

$\left(-\frac{4}{3}\right)\left(-\frac{3}{4}t\right) = \left(-\frac{4}{3}\right)(3)$

$t = -4$

32. $3 - \frac{2}{3}t = 1$

$3 + (-3) - \frac{2}{3}t = 1 + (-3)$

$\left(-\frac{3}{2}\right)\left(-\frac{2}{3}t\right) = \left(-\frac{3}{2}\right)(-2)$

$t = 3$

34. $5x - 1 = 4x + 3$
$5x + (-4x) - 1 = 4x + (-4x) + 3$
$x - 1 = 3$
$x - 1 + 1 = 3 + 1$
$x = 4$

35.
$$\begin{aligned} -3a + 2 &= -2a + 1 \\ -3a + 3a + 2 &= -2a + 3a + 1 \\ 2 &= a + 1 \\ 2 + (-1) &= a + 1 + (-1) \\ 1 &= a \end{aligned}$$

36.
$$\begin{aligned} -4a - 8 &= -3a + 7 \\ -4a + 4a - 8 &= -3a + 4a + 7 \\ -8 &= a + 7 \\ -8 + (-7) &= a + 7 + (-7) \\ -15 &= a \end{aligned}$$

38.
$$\begin{aligned} 8y - 2 &= 6y - 10 \\ 8y + (-6y) - 2 &= 6y + (-6y) - 10 \\ 2y - 2 &= -10 \\ 2y - 2 + 2 &= -10 + 2 \\ \left(\frac{1}{2}\right)(2y) &= \left(\frac{1}{2}\right)(-8) \\ y &= -4 \end{aligned}$$

39.
$$\begin{aligned} 5 - 2x &= 3x + 1 \\ 5 - 2x + 2x &= 3x + 2x + 1 \\ 5 + (-1) &= 5x + 1 + (-1) \\ \frac{1}{5}(4) &= \frac{1}{5}(5x) \\ \frac{4}{5} &= x \end{aligned}$$

40.
$$\begin{aligned} 7 - 3x &= 8x - 4 \\ 7 - 3x + 3x &= 8x + 3x - 4 \\ 7 + 4 &= 11x - 4 + 4 \\ \left(\frac{1}{11}\right)(11) &= \left(\frac{1}{11}\right)(11x) \\ 1 &= x \end{aligned}$$

42.
$$\begin{aligned} 3x - 5 - 2x &= 2x - 3 \\ x + (-x) - 5 &= 2x + (-x) - 3 \\ -5 + 3 &= x - 3 + 3 \\ -2 &= x \end{aligned}$$

43.
$$\begin{aligned} 5y - 2 + 4y &= 2y + 12 \\ 9y - 2 &= 2y + 12 \\ 9y + (-2y) - 2 &= 2y + (-2y) + 12 \\ 7y - 2 + 2 &= 12 + 2 \\ 7y &= 14 \\ \frac{1}{7}(7y) &= \frac{1}{7}(14) \\ y &= 2 \end{aligned}$$

44.
$$\begin{aligned} 7y - 3 + 2y &= 7y - 9 \\ 9y - 3 &= 7y - 9 \\ 9y + (-7y) - 3 &= 7y + (-7y) - 9 \\ 2y - 3 &= -9 \\ 2y - 3 + 3 &= -9 + 3 \\ 2y &= -6 \\ \frac{1}{2}(2y) &= \frac{1}{2}(-6) \\ y &= -3 \end{aligned}$$

46.
$$\begin{aligned} 2x + 7 - 3x + 4 &= -2x \\ -1x + 11 &= -2x \\ -1x + 1x + 11 &= -2x + 1x \\ (-1)(11) &= (-1)(-1x) \\ -11 &= x \end{aligned}$$

47.
$$\begin{aligned} 8x - 1 + 3x + 5 &= 7x + 3 - 4x + 5 \\ 11x + (-3x) + 4 &= 3x + (-3x) + 8 \\ 8x + 4 + (-4) &= 8 + (-4) \\ 8x &= 4 \\ x &= \frac{1}{2} \end{aligned}$$

48.
$$\begin{aligned} 6x + 3 + 2x - 10 &= 3x - 4 + 2x - 4 \\ 8x + (-5x) - 7 &= 5x + (-5x) - 8 \\ 3x - 7 + 7 &= -8 + 7 \\ 3x &= -1 \\ x &= -\frac{1}{3} \end{aligned}$$

50.
$$\begin{aligned} 2 - 4x &= -x + 11 \\ 2 - 4(-3) &= -(-3) + 11 \\ 14 &= 14 \end{aligned}$$
*Yes*

51.
$$\begin{aligned} &3(2y - 1) + y \\ &6y - 3 + y \\ &7y - 3 \end{aligned}$$

52.
$$\begin{aligned} &2(4y - 3) + y \\ &8y - y + y \\ &9y - 6 \end{aligned}$$

54.
$$\begin{aligned} &6 - 2(3x + 1) \\ &6 - 6x - 2 \\ &-6x + 4 \end{aligned}$$

55. $24 \cdot \frac{2}{3} = 16$

56. $24\left(-\frac{3}{8}\right) = -9$

58. $\frac{3}{5}\left(-\frac{35}{18}\right) = -\frac{7}{6}$

59. $-\frac{3}{8} + \left(-\frac{1}{2}\right) = -\frac{7}{8}$

60. $-\frac{1}{3} + \left(-\frac{5}{6}\right) = -\frac{7}{6}$

62. $\frac{5}{12} + \frac{7}{18} = \frac{29}{36}$

**Section 2.2**

2. $$\begin{aligned} 4(x + 1) &= 12 \\ 4x + 4 &= 12 \\ 4x + 4 + (-4) &= 12 + (-4) \\ 4x &= 8 \\ x &= 2 \end{aligned}$$

3. $$\begin{aligned} k &= 2(3k - 5) \\ k &= 6k - 10 \\ k + (-6k) &= 6k + (-6k) - 10 \\ -5k &= -10 \end{aligned}$$

$$-\frac{1}{5}(-5k) = -\frac{1}{5}(-10)$$

$$k = 2$$

4. $$\begin{aligned} 9k &= 3(4k - 1) \\ 9k &= 12k - 3 \\ 9k + (-12k) &= 12k + (-12k) - 3 \end{aligned}$$

$$\left(-\frac{1}{3}\right)(-3k) = \left(-\frac{1}{3}\right)(-3)$$

$$k = 1$$

6. $$\begin{aligned} -3(5x + 7) - 4 &= -10x \\ -15x - 21 - 4 &= -10x \\ -15x - 25 &= -10x \\ -15x + 15x - 25 &= -10x + 15x \end{aligned}$$

$$\frac{1}{5}(-25) = \left(\frac{1}{5}\right)(5x)$$

$$-5 = x$$

7. $$\begin{aligned} 5(y + 2) - 4(y + 1) &= 3 \\ 5y + 10 - 4y - 4 &= 3 \\ y + 6 &= 3 \\ y + 6 + (-6) &= 3 + (-6) \\ y &= -3 \end{aligned}$$

8. $$\begin{aligned} 6(y - 3) - 5(y + 2) &= 8 \\ 6y - 18 - 5y - 10 &= 8 \\ y - 28 &= 8 \\ 6 - 28 + 28 &= 8 + 28 \\ y &= 36 \end{aligned}$$

10. $$\begin{aligned} 3 - 5(2m - 5) &= -2 \\ 3 - 10m + 25 &= -2 \\ -10m + 28 &= -2 \\ -10m + 28 + (-28) &= -2 + (-28) \\ -10m &= -30 \end{aligned}$$

$$\left(-\frac{1}{10}\right)(-10m) = \left(-\frac{1}{10}\right)(-30)$$

$$m = 3$$

11. $$\begin{aligned} 4(a - 3) + 5 &= 7(3a - 1) \\ 4a - 12 + 5 &= 21a - 7 \\ 4a - 7 &= 21a - 7 \\ 4a + (-4a) - 7 &= 21a + (-4a) - 7 \\ -7 &= 17a - 7 \\ -7 + 7 &= 17a - 7 + 7 \\ 0 &= 17a \end{aligned}$$

$$\frac{1}{17}(0) = \frac{1}{17}(17a)$$

$$0 = a$$

12. $$\begin{aligned} 6(a - 4) + 6 &= 2(5a + 2) \\ 6a - 24 + 6 &= 10a + 4 \\ 6a - 18 &= 10a + 4 \\ 6a + (-6a) - 18 &= 10a + (-6a) + 4 \\ -18 + (-4) &= 4a + 4 + (-4) \end{aligned}$$

$$-22\left(\frac{1}{4}\right) = 4a\left(\frac{1}{4}\right)$$

$$-\frac{22}{4} = a$$

$$-\frac{11}{2} = a$$

14.
$$\begin{aligned} 5 + 2(4x - 4) &= 3(2x - 1) \\ 5 + 8x - 8 &= 6x - 3 \\ 8x + (-6x) - 3 &= 6x + (-6x) - 3 \\ 2x - 3 + 3 &= -3 + 3 \end{aligned}$$

$$\left(\frac{1}{2}\right)2x = \left(\frac{1}{2}\right)$$

$$x = 0$$

15.
$$\begin{aligned} 5 &= 7 - 2(3x - 1) + 4x \\ 5 &= 7 - 6x + 2 + 4x \\ 5 &= -2x + 9 \\ 5 + (-9) &= -2x + 9 + (-9) \\ -4 &= -2x \end{aligned}$$

$$-\frac{1}{2}(-4) = -\frac{1}{2}(-2x)$$

$$2 = x$$

16.
$$\begin{aligned} 20 &= 8 - 5(2x - 3) + 4x \\ 20 &= 8 - 10x + 15 + 4x \\ 20 + (-23) &= -6x + 23 + (-23) \end{aligned}$$

$$-3\left(-\frac{1}{6}\right) = -6x\left(-\frac{1}{6}\right)$$

$$\frac{1}{2} = x$$

18.
$$\begin{aligned} 7 - 2(3x + 5) - (2x - 3) &= -5x + 3 - 2x \\ 7 - 6x - 10 - 2x + 3 &= -7x + 3 \\ -8x &= -7x + 3 \\ -8x + 7x &= -7x + 7x + 3 \\ (-1)(-x) &= -1(3) \\ x &= -3 \end{aligned}$$

19. Method I

$$\frac{1}{2}x + \frac{1}{4} = \frac{1}{3}x + \frac{5}{4}$$

$$\frac{1}{2}x + \left(-\frac{1}{3}x\right) + \frac{1}{4} = \frac{1}{3}x + \left(-\frac{1}{3}x\right) + \frac{5}{4}$$

$$\frac{1}{2}x + \left(-\frac{1}{3}x\right) + \frac{1}{4} = \frac{5}{4}$$

$$\frac{1}{6}x + \frac{1}{4} = \frac{5}{4}$$

$$\frac{1}{6}x + \frac{1}{4} + \left(-\frac{1}{4}\right) = \frac{5}{4} + \left(-\frac{1}{4}\right)$$

$$\frac{1}{6}x = \frac{4}{4}$$

$$\frac{6}{1}\left(\frac{1}{6}x\right) = \frac{6}{1}(1)$$

$$x = 6$$

Method II

$$\frac{1}{2}x + \frac{1}{4} = \frac{1}{3}x + \frac{5}{4} \qquad LCD = 12$$

$$12\left(\frac{1}{2}x\right) + 12\left(\frac{1}{4}\right) = 12\left(\frac{1}{3}x\right) + 12\left(\frac{5}{4}\right)$$

$$\begin{aligned} 6x + 3 &= 4x + 15 \\ 6x + (-4x) + 3 &= 4x + (-4x) + 15 \\ 2x + 3 &= 15 \\ 2x + 3 + (-3) &= 15 + (-3) \\ 2x &= 12 \end{aligned}$$

$$\frac{1}{2}(2x) = \frac{1}{2}(12)$$

$$x = 6$$

20. Method I

$$\frac{2}{3}x - \frac{3}{4} = \frac{1}{6}x + \frac{21}{4}$$

$$\frac{2}{3}x + \left(-\frac{1}{6}x\right) - \frac{3}{4} = \frac{1}{6}x + \left(-\frac{1}{6}x\right) + \frac{21}{4}$$

$$\frac{4}{6}x + \left(-\frac{1}{6}x\right) - \frac{3}{4} = \frac{21}{4}$$

$$\frac{3}{6}x - \frac{3}{4} + \frac{3}{4} = \frac{21}{4} + \frac{3}{4}$$

$$\frac{1}{2}x = \frac{24}{4}$$

$$(2)\left(\frac{1}{2}x\right) = 2(6)$$

$$x = 12$$

Method II

$$\frac{2}{3}x - \frac{3}{4} = \frac{1}{6}x + \frac{21}{4} \qquad LCD = 12$$

$$12\left(\frac{2}{3}x\right) - 12\left(\frac{3}{4}\right) = 12\left(\frac{1}{6}x\right) + 12\left(\frac{21}{4}\right)$$

$$8x - 9 = 2x + 63$$

$$8x + (-2x) - 9 = 2x + (-2x) + 63$$

$$6x - 9 + 9 = 63 + 9$$

$$\left(\frac{1}{6}\right)(6x) = \frac{1}{6}(72)$$

$$x = 12$$

22. Method I

$$-\frac{1}{6}x + \frac{2}{3} = \frac{1}{4}$$

$$-\frac{1}{6}x + \frac{2}{3} + \left(-\frac{2}{3}\right) = \frac{1}{4} + \left(-\frac{2}{3}\right)$$

$$-\frac{1}{6}x = \frac{3}{12} + \left(-\frac{8}{12}\right)$$

$$(-6)\left(-\frac{1}{6}x\right) = (-6)\left(-\frac{5}{12}\right)$$

$$x = \frac{5}{2}$$

Method II

$$-\frac{1}{6}x + \frac{2}{3} = \frac{1}{4} \qquad LCD = 12$$

$$12\left(-\frac{1}{6}x\right) + 12\left(\frac{2}{3}\right) = 12\left(\frac{1}{4}\right)$$

$$-2x + 8 = 3$$

$$-2x + 8 + (-8) = 3 + (-8)$$

$$\left(-\frac{1}{2}\right)(-2x) = \left(-\frac{1}{2}\right)(-5)$$

$$x = \frac{5}{2}$$

23. Method I

$$\frac{1}{2}y - \frac{2}{7} = \frac{1}{7}y + \frac{11}{14}$$

$$\frac{1}{2}y + \left(-\frac{1}{7}y\right) - \frac{2}{7} = \frac{1}{7}y + \left(-\frac{1}{7}y\right) + \frac{11}{14}$$

$$\frac{1}{2}y - \frac{1}{7}y - \frac{2}{7} = \frac{11}{14}$$

$$\frac{5}{14}y - \frac{2}{7} = \frac{11}{14}$$

$$\frac{5}{14}y - \frac{2}{7} + \frac{2}{7} = \frac{11}{14} + \frac{2}{7}$$

$$\frac{5}{14}y = \frac{15}{14}$$

$$\frac{14}{5}\left(\frac{5}{14}y\right) = \frac{14}{5}\left(\frac{15}{14}\right)$$

$$y = 3$$

Method II

$$\frac{1}{2}y - \frac{2}{7} = \frac{1}{7}y + \frac{11}{14} \qquad LCD = 14$$

$$14\left(\frac{1}{2}y\right) - 14\left(\frac{2}{7}\right) = 14\left(\frac{1}{7}y\right) + 14\left(\frac{11}{14}\right)$$

$$7y - 4 = 2y + 11$$
$$7y + (-2y) - 4 = 2y + (-2y) + 11$$
$$5y - 4 = 11$$
$$5y - 4 + 4 = 11 + 4$$
$$5y = 15$$

$$\frac{1}{5}(5y) = \frac{1}{5}(15)$$

$$y = 3$$

24. Method I

$$\frac{1}{2}y - \frac{1}{8} = \frac{3}{8}y - \frac{5}{8}$$

$$\frac{1}{2}y + \left(-\frac{3}{8}y\right) - \frac{1}{8} = \frac{3}{8}y + \left(-\frac{3}{8}\right) - \frac{5}{8}$$

$$\frac{4}{8}y + \left(-\frac{3}{8}y\right) - \frac{1}{8} = -\frac{5}{8}$$

$$\frac{1}{8}y - \frac{1}{8} + \frac{1}{8} = -\frac{5}{8} + \frac{1}{8}$$

$$(8)\frac{1}{8}y = (8)\left(-\frac{4}{8}\right)$$

$$y = -4$$

Method II

$$\frac{1}{2}y - \frac{1}{8} = \frac{3}{8}y - \frac{5}{8} \qquad LCD = 8$$

$$8\left(\frac{1}{2}y\right) - 8\left(\frac{1}{8}\right) = 8\left(\frac{3}{8}y\right) - 8\left(\frac{5}{8}\right)$$

$$4y - 1 = 3y - 5$$
$$4y + (-3y) - 1 = 3y + (-3y) - 5$$
$$y - 1 + 1 = -5 + 1$$
$$y = -4$$

26. Method I

$$\frac{3}{5}(5x + 10) = \frac{5}{6}(12x - 18)$$

$$\frac{3}{5}(5x) + \frac{3}{5}(10) = \frac{5}{6}(12x) - \frac{5}{6}(18)$$

$$\begin{aligned} 3x + 6 &= 10x - 15 \\ 6 &= 7x - 15 \\ 21 &= 7x \\ 3 &= x \end{aligned}$$

Method II

$$\frac{3}{5}(5x + 10) = \frac{5}{6}(12x - 18) \quad LCD = 30$$

$$30\left(\frac{3}{5}\right)(5x + 10) = 30\left(\frac{5}{6}\right)(12x - 18)$$

$$\begin{aligned} 18(5x + 10) &= 25(12x - 18) \\ 90x + 180 &= 300x - 450 \\ 180 &= 210x - 450 \\ 630 &= 210x \\ 3 &= x \end{aligned}$$

27. Method I

$$\frac{1}{4}(12a + 1) - \frac{1}{4} = 5 \quad LCD = 4$$

$$\frac{1}{4}(12a) + \frac{1}{4}(1) - \frac{1}{4} = 5$$

$$3a + \frac{1}{4} - \frac{1}{4} = 5$$

$$3a = 5$$

$$\frac{1}{3}(3a) = \frac{1}{3}(5)$$

$$a = \frac{5}{3}$$

Method II

$$\frac{1}{4}(12a+1) - \frac{1}{4} = 5$$

$$4 \cdot \frac{1}{4}(12a + 1) - 4 \cdot \frac{1}{4} = 4 \cdot 5$$

$$\begin{aligned} 1(12a + 1) - 1 &= 20 \\ 12a + 1 - 1 &= 20 \\ 12a &= 20 \end{aligned}$$

$$\frac{1}{12}(12a) = \frac{1}{12}(20)$$

$$a = \frac{20}{12}$$

$$a = \frac{5}{3}$$

28. Method I

$$\frac{2}{3}(6x-1) + \frac{2}{3} = 4$$

$$4x - \frac{2}{3} + \frac{2}{3} = 4$$

$$4x = 4$$
$$x = 1$$

Method II

$$\frac{2}{3}(6x-1) + \frac{2}{3} = 4 \quad LCD = 3$$

$$3\left(\frac{2}{3}\right)(6x - 1) + 3\left(\frac{2}{3}\right) = 3(4)$$

$$2(6x - 1) + 2 = 12$$
$$12x - 2 + 2 = 12$$
$$12x = 12$$
$$x = 1$$

30. Method I

$$\frac{1}{3}x + \frac{1}{4}x + \frac{1}{5}x = 47$$

$$\frac{20}{60}x + \frac{15}{60}x + \frac{12}{60}x = 47$$

$$\frac{47}{60}x = 47$$

$$x = 60$$

Method II

$$60\left(\frac{1}{3}x\right) + 60\left(\frac{1}{4}x\right) + 60\left(\frac{1}{5}x\right) = 60(47) \quad LCD{=}60$$

$$20x + 15x + 12x = 2{,}820$$
$$47x = 2{,}820$$
$$x = 60$$

31. Method I

$$.08x + .09(9000 - x) = 750$$
$$.08x + 810 - .09x = 750$$
$$810 - .01x = 750$$
$$-.01x = -60$$
$$x = 6{,}000$$

Method II

$$100(.08x) + 100(.09)(9000 - x) = 100(750)$$
$$8x + 9(9000 - x) = 75{,}000$$
$$8x + 81{,}000 - 9x = 75{,}000$$
$$-x = -6{,}000$$
$$x = 6{,}000$$

32. Method I

$$
\begin{aligned}
.08x + .09(9000 - x) &= 500 \\
.08x + 810 - .09x &= 500 \\
-.01x + 810 &= 500 \\
-.01x &= -310 \\
x &= 31{,}000
\end{aligned}
$$

Method II

$$
\begin{aligned}
100(.08x) + 100(.09)(9000 - x) &= 100(500) \\
8x + 9(9000 - x) &= 50{,}000 \\
8x + 81{,}000 - 9x &= 50{,}000 \\
-x &= -31{,}000 \\
x &= 31{,}000
\end{aligned}
$$

34. Method I

$$
\begin{aligned}
.09x + .11(11{,}000 - x) &= 1{,}150 \\
.09x + 1210 - .11x &= 1{,}150 \\
-.02x + 1210 &= 1{,}150 \\
-.02x &= -60 \\
x &= 3{,}000
\end{aligned}
$$

Method II

$$
\begin{aligned}
100(.09x) + 100(.11)(11{,}000 - x) &= 100(1150) \\
9x + 11(11{,}000 - x) &= 115{,}000 \\
9x + 121{,}000 - 11x &= 115{,}000 \\
-2x + 121{,}000 &= 115{,}000 \\
-2x &= -6{,}000 \\
x &= 3{,}000
\end{aligned}
$$

35. Method I

$$
\begin{aligned}
.35y - .2 &= .15x + .1 \\
.35y + (-.15x) - .2 &= .15x + (-.15x) + .1 \\
.20x - .2 &= .1 \\
.20x &= .3
\end{aligned}
$$

$$\frac{.20x}{.20} = \frac{.30}{.20}$$

$$x = \frac{30}{20}$$

$$x = \frac{3}{2}$$

Method II

$$
\begin{aligned}
.35x - 2 &= .15x + .1 \\
100(.35x) - 100(.2) &= 100(.15x) + 100(.1) \\
35x - 20 &= 15x + 10 \\
20x - 20 &= 10 \\
20x - 20 + 20 &= 10 + 20 \\
20x &= 30
\end{aligned}
$$

$$\frac{20x}{20} = \frac{30}{20}$$

$$x = \frac{3}{2}$$

36. Method I

$$
\begin{aligned}
.25x - .05 &= .2x + .15 \\
.05x - .05 &= .15 \\
.05x &= .20 \\
x &= 4
\end{aligned}
$$

Method II

$$
\begin{aligned}
100(.25x) - 100(.05) &= 100(.2x) + 100(.15) \\
25x - 5 &= 20x + 15 \\
5x - 5 &= 15 \\
5x &= 20 \\
x &= 4
\end{aligned}
$$

38. Method I

$$\begin{aligned} .3 - .12x &= .18x + .06 \\ .3 &= .30x + .06 \\ .24 &= .30x \\ \frac{4}{5} &= x \\ .8 &= x \end{aligned}$$

Method II

$$\begin{aligned} 100(.3) - 100(.12x) &= 100(.18x) + 100(.06) \\ 30 - 12x &= 18x + 6 \\ 30 &= 30x + 6 \\ 24 &= 30x \\ \frac{4}{5} &= x \end{aligned}$$

39. $$\begin{aligned} 6x - 2(x - 5) &= 4x + 3 \\ 6x - 2x + 10 &= 4x + 3 \\ 4x + 10 &= 4x + 3 \\ 10 &= 3 \quad \textit{False statement} \end{aligned}$$

40. $$\begin{aligned} 5(x - 2) - 2x &= 3x + 7 \\ 5x - 10 - 2x &= 3x + 7 \\ 3x - 10 &= 3x + 7 \\ -10 &= 7 \quad \textit{False statement} \end{aligned}$$

42. $$\begin{aligned} 7(x + 2) - 4x &= 3x + 14 \\ 7x + 14 - 4x &= 3x + 14 \\ 3x + 14 &= 3x + 14 \\ 14 &= 14 \quad \textit{True statement} \end{aligned}$$

43. $$\begin{aligned} 3x - 6 &= 3(x + 4) \\ 3x - 6 &= 3x + 12 \\ -6 &= 12 \end{aligned}$$

This equation has no solution.

44. $$\begin{aligned} 7x - 14 &= 7(x - 2) \\ 7x - 14 &= 7x - 14 \\ -14 &= -14 \end{aligned}$$

All real numbers are solutions.

46. $$\begin{aligned} 7y + 5 - 2y - 3 &= 6 + 5y - 4 \\ 5y + 2 &= 5y + 2 \\ 2 &= 2 \end{aligned}$$

All real numbers are solutions.

47. $$\begin{aligned} 2(4t - 1) + 3 &= 5t + 4 + 3t \\ 8t - 2 + 3 &= 5t + 4 + 3t \\ 8t + 1 &= 8t + 4 \\ 1 &= 4 \end{aligned}$$

This equation has no solution.

48. $$\begin{aligned} 5(2t - 1) + 1 &= 2t - 4 + 8t \\ 10t - 5 + 1 &= 10t - 4 \\ 10t - 4 &= 10t - 4 \\ -4 &= -4 \end{aligned}$$

All real numbers are solutions.

50. Multiplicative inverse property

51. Associative property of addition

52. Commutative property of addition

54. Distributive property

55. Multiplicative identity property

56. Additive identity property

58. Commutative and associative properties of multiplication

59. Additive identity of addition

60. Additive inverse property

62. $x = 1$ *because* $|1 - 3| = |-2| = 2$

**Section 2.3**

2. $$\begin{aligned} 3x - 4y &= 12 \\ 3(-2) - 4y &= 12 \\ -6 - 4y &= 12 \\ -4y &= 18 \\ y &= -\frac{18}{4} \\ y &= -\frac{9}{2} \end{aligned}$$

3.
$$\begin{aligned} 3x - 4y &= 12 \\ 3(4) - 4y &= 12 \\ 12 - 4y &= 12 \\ -4y &= 0 \\ y &= 0 \end{aligned}$$

4.
$$\begin{aligned} 3x - 4y &= 12 \\ 3(-4) - 4y &= 12 \\ -12 - 4y &= 12 \\ -4y &= 24 \\ y &= -6 \end{aligned}$$

6.
$$\begin{aligned} y &= 2x - 3 \\ -3 &= 2x - 3 \\ 0 &= 2x \\ 0 &= x \end{aligned}$$

7.
$$\begin{aligned} y &= 2x - 3 \\ 5 &= 2x - 3 \\ 8 &= 2x \\ 4 &= x \end{aligned}$$

8.
$$\begin{aligned} y &= 2x - 3 \\ -5 &= 2x - 3 \\ -2 &= 2x \\ -1 &= x \end{aligned}$$

10.
$$\begin{aligned} x &= 1300 - 100p \\ 400 &= 1300 - 100p \\ -900 &= -100p \\ 9 &= p \end{aligned}$$

The company should charge $9 per ribbon.

11.
$$\begin{aligned} x &= 1300 - 100p \\ 300 &= 1300 - 100p \\ -1000 &= -100p \\ 10 &= p \end{aligned}$$

The company should charge $10 per ribbon.

12.
$$\begin{aligned} x &= 1300 - 100p \\ 900 &= 1300 - 100p \\ -400 &= -100p \\ 4 &= p \end{aligned}$$

The company should charge $4 per ribbon.

14. $V = 308 \quad r = \frac{7}{2} \quad \textit{and} \quad \pi = \frac{22}{7}$
$$\begin{aligned} V &= \pi\, r^2 h \\ 308 &= \frac{22}{7}\left(\frac{7}{2}\right)^2 h \\ 308 &= \frac{77}{2} h \\ 8 &= h \end{aligned}$$

The height is 8 centimeters.

15. $V = 628 \quad r = 10 \quad \textit{and} \quad \pi = 3.14$
$$\begin{aligned} V &= \pi r^2 h \\ 628 &= 3.14(10)^2 h \\ 628 &= 314h \\ 2 &= h \end{aligned}$$

The height is 2 inches

16. $V = 12.56 \quad r = 5 \quad \textit{and} \quad \pi = 3.14$
$$\begin{aligned} V &= \pi r^2 h \\ 12.56 &= 3.14(5)^2 h \\ 12.56 &= 78.5h \\ .16 &= h \end{aligned}$$

The height is .16 inches.

18. $S = 471 \quad r = 5 \quad \textit{and} \quad \pi = 3.14$
$$\begin{aligned} S &= 2\pi r^2 + 2\pi rh \\ 471 &= 2(3.14)(5)^2 + 2(3.14)(5)h \\ 471 &= 157.00 + 31.4h \\ 314 &= 31.4h \\ 10 &= h \end{aligned}$$

The height is 10 feet.

19.
$$\begin{aligned} A &= lw \\ \frac{A}{w} &= l \end{aligned}$$

20. $A = \frac{1}{2}bh$

$2A = bh$

$\frac{2A}{h} = b$

22. $I = prt$

$\frac{I}{pt} = r$

23. $PV = nRT$

$\frac{PV}{nR} = T$

24. $PV = nRT$

$\frac{PV}{nT} = R$

26. $y = mx + b$

$y - b = mx$

$\frac{y - b}{m} = x$

27. $S = \frac{1}{2}(a + b + c)$

$2S = a + b + c$

$2S - a - b = c$

28. $S = \frac{1}{2}(a + b + c)$

$2S = a + b + c$

$2S - a - c = b$

30. $A = P + Prt$

$A - P = Prt$

$\frac{A - P}{Pr} = t$

31. $C = \frac{5}{9}(F - 32)$

$\frac{9}{5}C = F - 32$

$\frac{9}{5}C + 32 = F$

32. $F = \frac{9}{5}C + 32$

$F - 32 = \frac{9}{5}C$

$\frac{5}{9}(F - 32) = C$

34. $h = vt - 16t^2$

$h + 16t^2 = vt$

$\frac{h + 16t^2}{t} = v$

35. $A = a + (n - 1)d$

$A - a = (n - 1)d$

$\frac{A - a}{n - 1} = d$

36. $A = a + (n - 1)d$

$A - a = nd - d$

$A - a + d = nd$

$\frac{A - a + d}{d} = n$

38. $2x - 3y = 6$

$-3y = -2x+6$

$y=\frac{2}{3}x - 2$

39. $-3x + 5y = 15$

$5y = 3x + 15$

$y = \frac{3}{5}x + 3$

40. $-2x - 7y = 14$

$-7y = 2x + 14$

$y = -\frac{2}{7}x - 2$

42. $9x + 3y = 15$

$3y = -9x + 15$

$y = -3x + 5$

43. $2x - 6y + 12 = 0$

$-6y=-2x - 12$

$y = \frac{1}{3}x + 2$

44. $7x - 2y - 6 = 0$
$$-2y = -7x + 6$$
$$y = \frac{7}{2}x - 3$$

46. $6x - 3y + 12 = 0$
$$6x = 3y - 12$$
$$x = \frac{1}{2}y - 2$$

47. $$z = \frac{x - \mu}{s}$$
$$sz = x - \mu$$
$$sz + \mu = x$$

48. $$z = \frac{x - \mu}{s}$$
$$sz = x - \mu$$
$$sz - x = -\mu$$
$$-sz + x = \mu$$
$$x - sz = \mu$$

50. $ax - 5 = cx - 2$
$$ax - cx = 5 - 2$$
$$x(a - c) = 3$$
$$x = \frac{3}{a - c}$$

51. $A = P + Prt$
$$A = P(1 + rt)$$
$$\frac{A}{1 + rt} = P$$

52. $S = 2\pi r + \pi rh$
$$S = \pi(2r + rh)$$
$$\frac{S}{2r + rh} = \pi$$

54. $4x + 2y = 3x + 5y$
$$2y - 5y = 3x - 4x$$
$$-3y = -1x$$
$$y = \frac{1}{3}x$$

55. $$\frac{x}{8} + \frac{y}{2} = 1$$
$$16\left(\frac{x}{8}\right) + 16\left(\frac{y}{2}\right) = 16(1)$$
$$2x + 8y = 16$$
$$8y = -2x + 16$$
$$y = -\frac{1}{4}x + 2$$

56. $$\frac{x}{7} + \frac{y}{9} = 1$$
$$63\left(\frac{x}{7}\right) + 63\left(\frac{y}{9}\right) = 63(1)$$
$$9x + 7y = 63$$
$$7y = -9x + 63$$
$$y = -\frac{9}{7}x + 9$$

58. $$\frac{x}{16} + \frac{y}{-2} = 1$$
$$-16\left(\frac{x}{16}\right) + (-16)\left(\frac{y}{-2}\right) = -16(1)$$
$$-x + 8y = -16$$
$$8y = x - 16$$
$$y = \frac{1}{8}x - 2$$

59. What number is 54% of 38?

$N = .54 \cdot 38$
$N = 20.52$

60. What number is 11% of 67?

$N = .11 \cdot 67$
$N = 7.37$

62. What number is 6% of 6,000?

$N = .06 \cdot 6{,}000$
$N = 360$

63. What percent of 36 is 9?

$p \cdot 36 = 9$

$p = \frac{1}{4}$

$p = 25\%$

64. What percent of 50 is 5?

$p \cdot 50 = 5$

$p = \frac{1}{10}$

$p = 10\%$

66. 8 is 2% of what number?

$8 = .02 \cdot N$
$400 = N$

67. $a_n = 3n + 1$
$a_1 = 3(1) + 1 = 4$
$a_2 = 3(2) + 1 = 7$
$a_3 = 3(3) + 1 = 10$
$a_4 = 3(4) + 1 = 13$
$a_5 = 3(5) + 1 = 16$

68. $a_n = 4n - 1$
$a_1 = 4(1) - 1 = 3$
$a_2 = 4(2) - 1 = 7$
$a_3 = 4(3) - 1 = 11$
$a_4 = 4(4) - 1 = 15$
$a_5 = 4(5) - 1 = 19$

70. $a_n = n^3 + 1$
$a_1 = a^3 + 1 = 2$
$a_2 = 2^3 + 1 = 9$
$a_3 = 3^3 + 1 = 28$
$a_4 = 4^3 + 1 = 65$
$a_5 = 5^3 + 1 = 126$

71. $a_n = \frac{n}{n + 3}$

$a_1 = \frac{1}{1 + 3} = \frac{1}{4}$

$a_2 = \frac{2}{2 + 3} = \frac{2}{3}$

$a_3 = \frac{3}{3 + 3} = \frac{1}{2}$

$a_4 = \frac{4}{4 + 3} = \frac{4}{7}$

$a_5 = \frac{5}{5 + 3} = \frac{5}{8}$

72. $a_n = \frac{n}{n + 2}$

$a_1 = \frac{1}{1 + 2} = \frac{1}{3}$

$a_2 = \frac{2}{2 + 2} = \frac{1}{2}$

$a_3 = \frac{3}{3 + 2} = \frac{3}{5}$

$a_4 = \frac{4}{4 + 2} = \frac{2}{3}$

$a_5 = \frac{5}{5 + 2} = \frac{5}{7}$

74. $a_n = \frac{1}{n^3}$

$a_1 = \frac{1}{1^3} = 1$

$a_2 = \frac{1}{2^3} = \frac{1}{8}$

$a_3 = \frac{1}{3^3} = \frac{1}{27}$

$a_4 = \frac{1}{4^4} = \frac{1}{64}$

$a_5 = \frac{1}{5^3} = \frac{1}{125}$

75. $a_n = 2^N$

$a_1 = 2^1 = 2$
$a_2 = 2^2 = 4$
$a_3 = 2^3 = 8$
$a_4 = 2^4 = 16$
$a_5 = 2^5 = 32$

76. $a_n = 3^N$

$a_1 = 3^1 = 3$
$a_2 = 3^2 = 9$
$a^3 = 3^3 = 27$
$a_4 = 3^4 = 81$
$a_5 = 3^5 = 243$

78. $a_n = a - \frac{1}{N}$

$a_1 = 1 - \frac{1}{1} = 0$

$a_2 = a - \frac{1}{2} = \frac{1}{2}$

$a_3 = 1 - \frac{1}{3} = \frac{2}{3}$

$a_4 = a - \frac{1}{4} = \frac{3}{4}$

$a_5 = 1 - \frac{1}{5} = \frac{4}{5}$

79. $a_n = \frac{(-1)^N}{N^2}$

$a_7 = \frac{(-1)^7}{7^2} = -\frac{1}{49}$

80. $a_N = \frac{(-1)^N}{N^2}$

$a_{10} = \frac{(-1)^{10}}{10^2} = \frac{1}{100}$

82. $a_n = \frac{(-1)^{N+1}}{N^2 + 1}$

$a_7 = \frac{(-1)^{7+1}}{7^2 + 1} = \frac{1}{50}$

83. $a_N = \frac{(-1)^N}{N^3}$

$a_1 = \frac{(-1)^1}{1^3} = -1$

$a_2 = \frac{(-1)^2}{2^3} = \frac{1}{8}$

$a_3 = \frac{(-1)^3}{3^3} = -\frac{1}{27}$

$a_4 = \frac{(-1)^4}{4^3} = \frac{1}{64}$

84. $a_N = \frac{(-1)^{N+1}}{N^3}$

$a_1 = \frac{(-1)^{1+1}}{1^3} = 1$

$a_2 = \frac{(-1)^{2+1}}{2^3} = -\frac{1}{8}$

$a_3 = \frac{(-1)^{3+1}}{3^3} = \frac{1}{27}$

$a_4 = \frac{(-1)^{4+1}}{4^3} = -\frac{1}{64}$

86. $2x + 3$

87. $2(x + 3) = 16$

88. $2x + 3 = 16$

90. $5(x - 3) = 10$

91. $3x + 2 = x - 4$

92. $x + (x + 2) = x - (x + 2) + 12$

94. $\frac{x}{a} + \frac{y}{b} = 1$

$$ab\left(\frac{x}{a}\right) + ab\left(\frac{y}{b}\right) = ab(1)$$

$$bx + ay = ab$$
$$ay = ab - bx$$

$$y = \frac{ab - bx}{a}$$

$$y = -\frac{b}{1} + b$$

$$y = -\frac{b}{a}x + b$$

95.
$$\frac{1}{a} + \frac{1}{b} = \frac{1}{c}$$
$$abc\left(\frac{1}{a}\right) + abc\left(\frac{1}{b}\right) = abc\left(\frac{1}{c}\right)$$
$$bc + ac = ab$$
$$bc = ab - ac$$
$$bc = a(b - c)$$
$$\frac{bc}{b - c} = a$$

96.
$$\frac{1}{a} + \frac{1}{b} = \frac{1}{c}$$
$$abc\left(\frac{1}{a}\right) + abc\left(\frac{1}{b}\right) = abc\left(\frac{1}{c}\right)$$
$$bc + ac = ab$$
$$ac = ab - bc$$
$$ac = b(a - c)$$
$$\frac{ac}{a - c} = b$$

98.
$$\frac{1}{R} = \frac{1}{a} + \frac{1}{b} + \frac{1}{c}$$
$$Rabc\left(\frac{1}{R}\right) = Rabc\left(\frac{1}{a}\right) + Rabc\left(\frac{1}{b}\right) + Rabc\left(\frac{1}{c}\right)$$
$$abc = Rbc + Rac + Rab$$
$$abc - Rac - Rab = Rbc$$
$$a(bc - Rc - Rb) = Rbc$$
$$a = \frac{Rbc}{bc - Rc - Rb}$$

## Section 2.4

2.
$$5(x - 3) = 10$$
$$5x - 15 = 10$$
$$5x = 25$$
$$x = 5$$

3.
$$2(2x + 1) = 3(x - 5)$$
$$4x + 2 = 3x - 15$$
$$x + 2 = -15$$
$$x = -17$$

4.
$$3x + 2 = x - 4$$
$$2x + 2 = -4$$
$$2x = -6$$
$$x = -3$$

6.
$$6x - 5 = 4x - 5 + 7$$
$$6x - 5 = 4x + 2$$
$$2x - 5 = 2$$
$$2x = 7$$
$$x = \frac{7}{2}$$

7.
$$x + (x + 2) = 18$$
$$2x + 2 = 18$$
$$2x = 16$$
$$x = 8$$
$$x + 2 = 10$$

8.
$$x + (x + 2) = 16$$
$$2x + 2 = 16$$
$$2x = 14$$
$$x = 7$$
$$x + 2 = 9$$

10.
$$x + (x + 1) = 3(x + 1) - 5$$
$$2x + 1 = 3x + 3 - 5$$
$$2x + 1 = 3x - 2$$
$$1 = x - 2$$
$$3 = x$$
$$4 = x + 1$$

11.
$$2x + (x + 1) = 7$$
$$3x + 1 = 7$$
$$3x = 6$$
$$x = 2$$

12. $2(x + 1) + x = 23$
$2x + 2 + x = 23$
$3x + 2 = 23$
$3x = 21$
$x = 7$

14. $2(x + 2) - x = 12$
$2x + 4 - x = 12$
$x + 4 = 12$
$x = 8$
$x + 2 = 10$

15. *Width* $= x$, *length* $= 2x$
$P = 2L + 2W$
$60 = 2(2x) + 2x$
$60 = 4x + 2x$
$60 = 6x$
$10 = x$
$20 = 2x$
10 *ft by* 20 *ft*

16. *Width* $= x$, *length* $= 5x$
$P = 2L + 2W$
$48 = 2(5x) + 2x$
$48 = 10x + 2x$
$48 = 12x$
$4 = x$
$20 = 5x$
4 *in. by* 20 *in.*

18. $4S = 36$
$S = 9$

The side is 9 centimeters.

19. *Shortest side* $= x$
*Medium side* $= x + 3$
*Longest side* $= 2x$

$x + (x + 3) + (2x) = 23$
$4x + 3 = 23$
$4x = 20$
$x = 5$ *in.* (*Shortest*)

20. *Shortest side* $= x$
*Medium side* $= 2x$
*Longest side* $= 3x$

$x + 2x + 3x = 18$
$6x = 18$
$x = 3m$ (*Shortest*)
$2x = 6m$ (*Medium*)
$3x = 9m$ (*Longest*)

22. *Width* $= x$, *length* $= 2x + 1$
$P = 2L + 2W$
$20 = 2(2x + 1) + 2x$
$20 = 4x + 2 + 2x$
$20 = 6x + 2$
$18 = 6x$
$3 = x$
$7 = 2x + 1$
3 *ft. by* 7 *ft.*

23. *Width* $= x$, *length* $= 2x$

$P = 2L + 2W$
$48 = 2(2x) + 2x$
$48 = 6x$
$8 = x$
$16 = 2x$
$2(8)(2.25) + 2(16)(1.75) = \$92$

24. $42 = 4s$

$$10\frac{1}{2} = s$$

$$4\left(10\frac{1}{2} + 6\right) = 66$$

$42(1.28) + 66(1.28) = \$138.24$

26. 150% *of what number is* 300?

$1.50x = 300$
$x = \$200$

27. *Let* $x$ = *number of items sold*

$\$1x + .085x + 125.50 = 1{,}058.60$
$1.085x - 125.50 = 1{,}058.60$
$1.085x = 933.10$
$x = 860$ *items*

28. $100\% - 1.8\% = 98.2\%$
98.2%(5.4 *million*) = 5.3 *million viewers*

30. 133% *of what number is* 45?

$1.33x = 45$
$x = \$33.83$

31. 105.5% *of what number is* \$3,440?

$1.055x = 3{,}440$
$x = \$3{,}260.67$ *per month*

32. 104.5% *of what number is* \$26.80

$$1.045x = 26.80$$
$$x = 25.65$$
$$\$26.80 - 25.65 = \$1.15$$

34. $x + 5x = 90$
$6x = 90$
$x = 15°$
$5x = 75°$

35. *a.* $x + (4x - 12) = 90$
$5x - 12 = 90$
$5x = 102$
$x = 20.4°$
$4x - 12 = 69.6°$

*b.* $x + (4x - 12) = 180$
$5x - 12 = 180$
$5x = 192$
$x = 38.4°$
$4x - 12 = 141.6°$

36. *a.* $x + (3x + 4) = 90$
$4x + 4 = 90$
$4x = 86$
$x = 21.5°$
$3x + 4 = 68.5°$

*b.* $x + (3x + 4) = 180$
$4x + 4 = 180$
$4x = 176$
$x = 44°$
$3x + 4 = 136°$

38. $-\pi, \sqrt{5}$

39. $\frac{10}{12} = \frac{5}{6}$

40. $\frac{65}{39} = \frac{5}{3}$

42. $\frac{495}{975} = \frac{33}{65}$

**Section 2.5**

2. *a number* $= x$
*the other number* $= 16 - x$

$x = 3(16 - x)$
$x = 48 - 3x$
$4x = 48$
$x = 12$ *The two*
$16 - x = 4$ *numbers*

3. *a number* $= x$
*the other number* $= 16 - x$

$x = 2(16 - x) - 2$
$x = 32 - 2x - 2$
$x = 30 - 2x$
$3x = 30$
$x = 10$ *The two*
$16 - x = 6$ *numbers*

4. *a number* $= x$
*the other number* $= 21 - x$

$x = 2(21 - x) + 3$
$x = 42 - 2x + 3$
$x = 45 - 2x$
$3x = 45$
$x = 15$ *The two*
$21 - x = 6$ *numbers*

6. Let x = dimes and 14 - x = quarters

| | Dimes | Quarters | Total |
|---|---|---|---|
| Number of | x | 14 - x | 14 |
| Value of | 10x | 25(14 - x) | 200 |

$10x + 25(14 - x) = 200$
$10x + 350 - 25x = 200$
$350 - 15x = 200$
$-15x = -150$
$x = 10$ *Dimes*
$14 - x = 4$ *Quarters*

7. Let x = nickels and 26 - x = quarters

| | Nickels | Quarters | Total |
|---|---|---|---|
| Number of | x | 26 - x | 26 |
| Value of | 5x | 25(26 - x) | 250 |

$$\begin{aligned} 5x + 25(26 - x) &= 250 \\ 5x + 650 - 25x &= 250 \\ 650 - 20x &= 250 \\ -20x &= -400 \\ x &= 20 \textit{ Nickels} \\ 26 - x &= 6 \textit{ Quarters} \end{aligned}$$

8. Let nickels = x and quarters = 24 - x

| | Nickels | Quarters | Total |
|---|---|---|---|
| Number of | x | 24 - x | 24 |
| Value of | 5x | 25(24 - x) | 300 |

$$\begin{aligned} 5x + 25(24 - x) &= 300 \\ 5x + 600 - 25x &= 300 \\ 600 - 20x &= 300 \\ -20x &= -300 \\ x &= 15 \textit{ Nickels} \\ 24 - x &= 9 \textit{ Quarters} \end{aligned}$$

10. Let 10% = x and 7% = 12,000 - x

| | Dollars at 10% | Dollars at 7% | Total |
|---|---|---|---|
| Number of | x | 12,000 - x | 12,000 |
| Interest on | .10x | .07(12,000-x) | 960 |

$$\begin{aligned} .10x + .07(12{,}000 - x) &= 960 \\ .10x + 840 - .07x &= 960 \\ 840 + .03x &= 960 \\ .03x &= 120 \\ x &= \$4{,}000 \textit{ at } 10\% \\ 12{,}000 - x &= \$8{,}000 \textit{ at } 7\% \end{aligned}$$

11. Let 12% = x and 10% = 15,000 - x

| | Dollars at 12% | Dollars at 10% | Total |
|---|---|---|---|
| Number of | x | 15,000 - x | 15,000 |
| Interest on | .12x | .10(15,000-x) | 1,600 |

$$\begin{aligned} .12x + .10(15{,}000 - x) &= 1{,}600 \\ .12x + 1{,}500 - .10x &= 1{,}600 \\ 1{,}500 + .02x &= 1{,}600 \\ .02x &= 100 \\ x &= \$5{,}000 \textit{ at } 12\% \\ 15{,}000 - x &= \$10{,}000 \textit{ at } 10\% \end{aligned}$$

12. Let 9% = x and 11% = 11,000 - x

| | Dollars at 9% | Dollars at 11% | Total |
|---|---|---|---|
| Number of | x | 11,000 - x | 11,000 |
| Interest on | .09x | .11(11,000-x) | 1,150 |

$$\begin{aligned} .09x + .11(11{,}000 - x) &= 1{,}150 \\ .09x + 1{,}210 - .11x &= 1{,}150 \\ 1{,}210 - .02x &= 1{,}150 \\ -.02x &= -60 \\ x &= \$3{,}000 \textit{ at } 9\% \\ 11{,}000 - x &= \$8{,}000 \textit{ at } 11\% \end{aligned}$$

14.

| | Dollars at 6% | Dollars at 8% | Total |
|---|---|---|---|
| Number of | x | 6,000 - x | 6,000 |
| Interest on | .06x | .08(6,000-x) | 410 |

$$\begin{aligned} .06x + .08(6{,}000 - x) &= 410 \\ .06x + 480 - .08x &= 410 \\ 480 - .02x &= 410 \\ -.02x &= -70 \\ x &= \$3{,}500 \textit{ at } 6\% \\ 6{,}000 - x &= \$2{,}500 \textit{ at } 8\% \end{aligned}$$

15. Let fathers' tickets = x
Let sons' tickets = 75 - x

$$2.00x + 1.50(75 - x) = 127.50$$
$$2x + 112.50 - 1.50x = 127.50$$
$$112.50 + .50x = 127.50$$
$$.50x = 15$$
$$x = 30 \text{ Fathers' tickets}$$
$$75 - x = 45 \text{ Sons' tickets}$$

16. Let x = mother's tickets
62 - x = daughter's tickets

$$4.00x + 3.00(62 - x) = 216$$
$$4x + 186 - 3x = 216$$
$$186 + x = 216$$
$$x = 30 \text{ Mother's tickets}$$
$$62 - x = 32 \text{ Daughter's tickets}$$

18. Let x = items sold

$$x + .06x = 3{,}392$$
$$1.06x = 3{,}392$$
$$x = \$3{,}200$$
$$.06x = \$192 \text{ Sales tax}$$

19. Let x = additional minutes

$$.40 + .30x + .50 = 13.80$$
$$.90 + .30x = 13.80$$
$$.30x = 12.90$$
$$x = 43$$

Patrick talked 43 + 1 (at .40) = 44 minutes.

20. Let x = additional minutes

$$.41 + .32x + 3.00 = 6.29$$
$$3.41 + .32x = 6.29$$
$$.32x = 2.88$$
$$x = 9$$

The person talked 9 + 1 (at .41) = 10 minutes.

22.

23.

24.

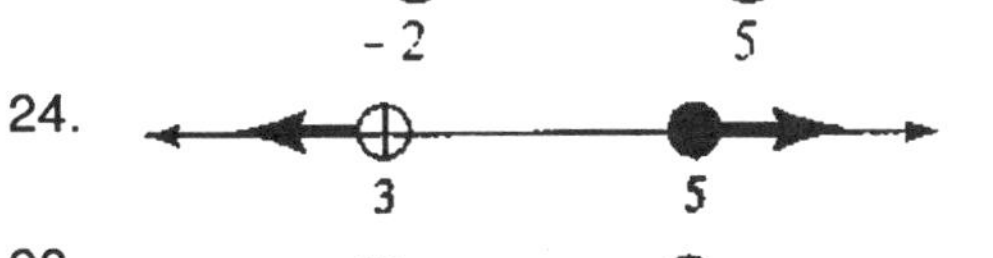

26.

27.

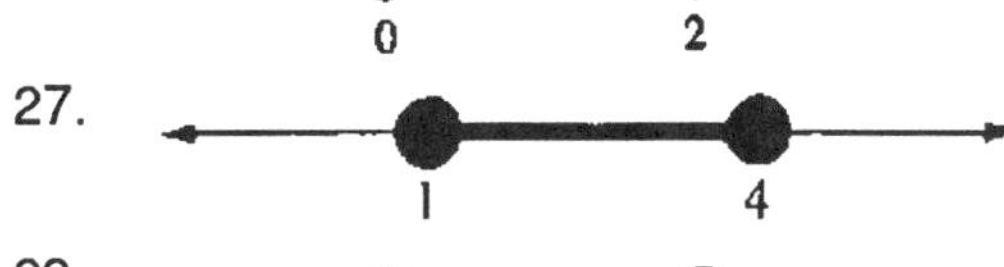

28.

## Section 2.6

2. $5x \geq -115$
$x \geq -23$

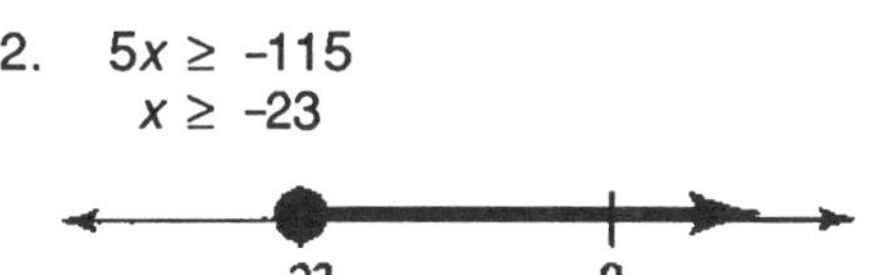


3. $\frac{1}{2}x > 2$

$x > 4$

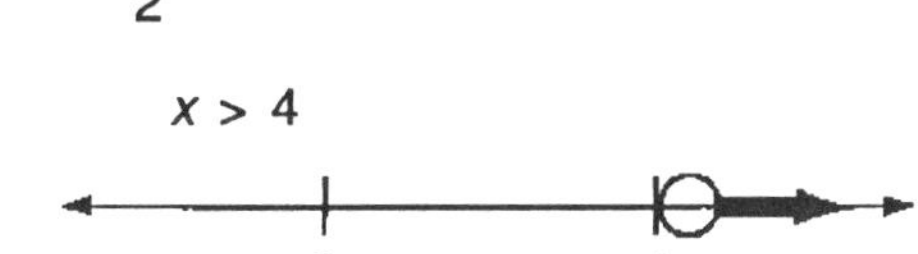

4. $\frac{1}{3}x > 4$

$x > 12$

6. $-7x \geq 35$
$x \leq -5$

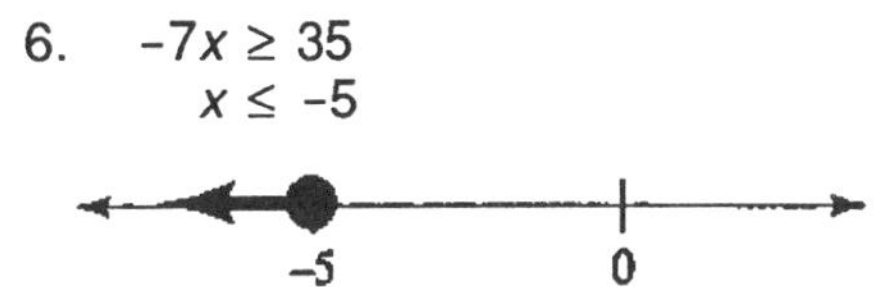

7. $-\frac{3}{2}x > -6$

$x < 4$

8. $-\frac{2}{3}x < -8$

$x > 12$

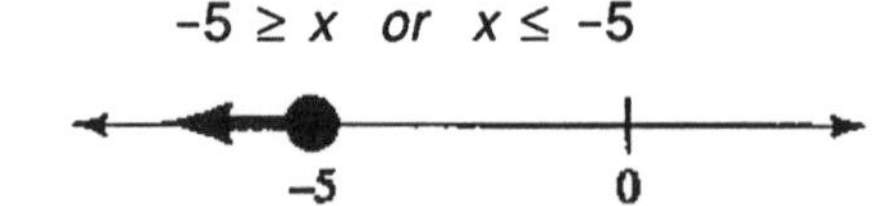

10. $-20 \geq 4x$
$-5 \geq x$ or $x \leq -5$

11. $-1 \geq -\frac{1}{4}x$

$4 \leq x$ or $x \geq 4$

12. $-1 \leq -\frac{1}{5}x$

$5 \geq x$ or $x \leq 5$

14. $-2x - 5 \leq 15$
$-2x \leq 20$
$x \geq -10$

15. $\frac{1}{2} - \frac{m}{12} \leq \frac{7}{12}$ $LCD = 12$

$6 - m \leq 7$
$-m \leq 1$
$m \geq -1$

16. $\frac{1}{2} - \frac{m}{10} > -\frac{1}{5}$ $LCD = 10$

$5 - m > -2$
$-m > -7$
$m < 7$

18. $\frac{9}{5} > -\frac{1}{5} - \frac{1}{2}x$ $LCD = 10$

$18 > -2 - 5x$
$20 > -5x$
$-4 < x$ or $x > -4$

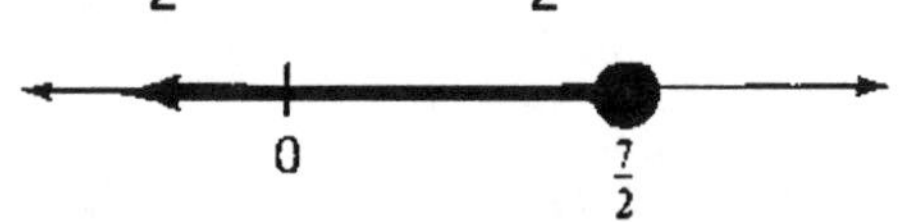

19. $-40 \leq 30 - 20y$
$-70 \leq -20y$

$\frac{7}{2} \geq y$ or $y \leq \frac{7}{2}$

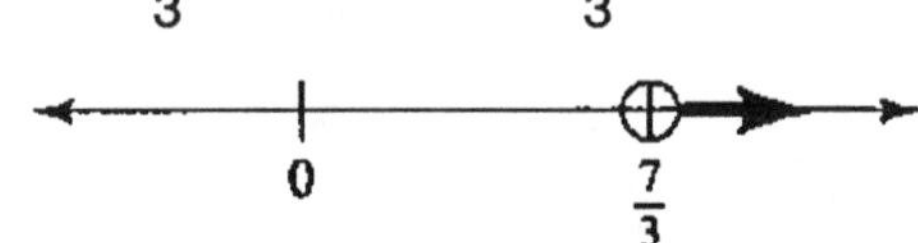

20. $-20 > 50 - 30y$
$-70 > -30y$

$\frac{7}{3} < y$ or $y > \frac{7}{3}$

22. $\frac{3}{4}x - 2 > 7$

$\frac{3}{4}x > 9$

$x > 12$

23. $10 - \frac{1}{2}y \leq 36$

$-\frac{1}{2}y \leq 26$

$y \geq -52$

−52 0

24. $8 - \frac{1}{3}y \geq 20$

$-\frac{1}{3}y \geq 12$

$y \leq -36$

−36 0

26. $3(2y - 4) > 0$
$6y - 12 > 0$
$6y > 12$
$y > 2$

$(2, \infty)$

27. $-(a+1) - 4a \leq 2a - 8$
$-a - 1 - 4a \leq 2a - 8$
$-5a - 1 \leq 2a - 8$
$-1 \leq 7a - 8$
$7 \leq 7a$
$1 \leq a$ or $a \geq 1$

$[1, \infty)$

28. $-(a - 2) - 5a \leq 3a + 7$
$-a + 2 - 5a \leq 3a + 7$
$-6a + 2 \leq 3a + 7$
$2 \leq 9a + 7$
$-5 \leq 9a$

$-\frac{5}{9} \leq a$ or $a \geq -\frac{5}{9}$

$\left[-\frac{5}{9}, \infty\right)$

30. $\frac{1}{4}t - \frac{1}{3}(2t - 5) < 0$ $\quad LCD = 12$
$3t - 4(2t - 5) \leq 0$
$3t - 8t + 20 \leq 0$
$-5t + 20 \leq 0$
$-5t \leq -20$
$t \geq 4$

$(4, \infty)$

31. $-2 \leq 5 - 7(2a + 3)$
$-2 \leq 5 - 14a - 21$
$-2 \leq -14a - 16$
$14 \leq -14a$
$-1 \geq a$ or $a \leq -1$

$(-\infty, -1]$

32. $1 < 3 - 4(3a - 1)$
$1 < 3 - 12a + 4$
$1 < -12a + 7$
$-6 < -12a$

$\frac{1}{2} > a$ or $a < \frac{1}{2}$

$\left(-\infty, \frac{1}{2}\right)$

34. $-\frac{1}{2}(2x + 1) \leq -\frac{3}{8}(x + 2)$ $\quad LCD = 8$

$-4(2x + 1) \leq -3(x + 2)$
$-8x - 4 \leq -3x - 6$
$2 \leq 5x$

$\frac{2}{5} \leq x$ or $x \geq \frac{2}{5}$

$\left[\frac{2}{5}, \infty\right)$

35. $5(y + 3) + 4 < 6y - 1 - 5y$
$5y + 15 + 4 < y - 1$
$5y + 19 < y - 1$
$4y < -20$
$y < -5$

$(-\infty, -5)$

36. $4(y - 1) + 2 \geq 3y + 8 - 2y$
$4y - 4 + 2 \geq y + 3$
$4y - 2 \geq y + 8$
$3y \geq 10$

$y \geq \frac{10}{3}$

$\left[\frac{10}{3}, \infty\right)$

38. $-3 \le m + 1 \le 3$
$-4 \le m \le 2$

$[-4,2]$

39. $-60 < 20a + 20 < 60$
$-80 < 20a < 40$
$-4 < a < 2$

$(-4,2)$

40. $-60 < 50a - 40 < 60$
$-20 < 50a < 100$

$-\frac{2}{5} < a < 2$

$\left(-\frac{2}{5},2\right)$

42. $.1 \le .4a + .1 \le .3$
$0 \le .4a \le .2$
$0 \le a \le .5$

$\left[0,\frac{1}{2}\right]$

0 $\frac{1}{2}$

43. $3 < \frac{1}{2}x + 5 < 6$

$-2 < \frac{1}{2}x < 1$

$-4<x<2$

$(-4,2)$

44. $5 < \frac{1}{4}x + 1 < 9$

$4 < \frac{1}{4}x < 8$

$16 < x < 32$

$(16,32)$

46. $3 < 7 + \frac{4}{5}x < 15$

$-4 < \frac{4}{5}x < 8$

$-5 < x < 10$

$(-5,10)$

47. $x + 5 \le -2$ *or* $x + 5 \ge 2$
$x \le -7$ *or* $x \ge -3$

$(-\infty,-7] \cup [-3,\infty)$

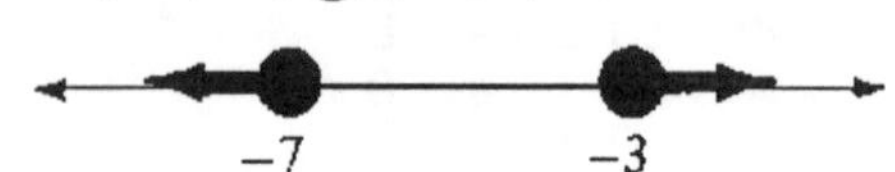


48. $3x + 2 < -3$ *or* $3x + 2 > 3$

$3x < -5$ *or* $3x > 1$

$x < -\frac{5}{3}$ *or* $x > \frac{1}{3}$

$\left(-\infty,-\frac{5}{3}\right) \cup \left(\frac{1}{3},\infty\right)$

$-\frac{5}{3}$ $\frac{1}{3}$

50. $7y - 5 \le -2$ *or* $7y - 5 \ge 2$
$7y \le 3$ *or* $7y \ge 7$

$y \le \frac{3}{7}$ *or* $y \ge 1$

$\left(-\infty, \frac{3}{7}\right] \cup [1, \infty)$

51. $2x + 5 < 3x - 1$ *or* $x - 4 > 2x + 6$
$5 < x - 1$ *or* $-4 > x + 6$
$6 < x$ *or* $-10 > x$
$x < -10$ *or* $x > 6$

$(-\infty, -10) \cup (6, \infty)$

52. $3x - 1 > 2x + 4$ *or* $5x - 2 < 3x + 4$
$x - 1 > 4$ *or* $2x - 2 < 4$
$x > 5$ *or* $2x < 6$
$x < 3$

$(-\infty, 3) \cup (5, \infty)$

54. *Let* $x = 600$,
$x < 900 - 300p$
$600 < 900 - 300p$
$-300 < -300p$
$1 > p$ *or* $p < 1$

Charge less than $1.00 per pad.

55. $x = 525$
$x = 900 - 300p$
$525 > 900 - 300p$
$-375 > -300p$
$1.25 < p$ *or* $p > 1.25$

Charge more than $1.25 per pad.

56. $x = 375$
$x = 900 - 300p$
$375 \ge 900 - 300p$
$-525 \ge -300p$
$1.75 \le p$ *or* $p \ge 1.75$

Charge $1.75 or more per pad.

58. $2x + 3y > 6$
$3y > -2x + 6$

$y > -\frac{2}{3}x + 2$

59. $4x - 5y \ge 20$
$-5y \ge -4x + 20$

$y \le \frac{4}{5}x - 4$

60. $5x - 3y \le 15$
$-3y \le -5x + 15$

$y \ge \frac{5}{3}x - 5$

62. $68° \le \frac{9}{5}c + 32 \le 86°$

$36° \le \frac{9}{5}c \le 54°$

$\frac{5}{9}(36°) \le \frac{5}{9}\left(\frac{9}{5}c\right) \le \frac{5}{9}(54°)$

$20° \le c \le 30°$
20° *to* 30° *Celsius*

63. $-13° \le \frac{9}{5}c + 32 \le 14°$

$-45° \le \frac{9}{5}c \le -18°$

$\frac{5}{9}(-45°) \le \frac{5}{9}\left(\frac{9}{5}c\right) \le \frac{5}{9}(-18°)$

$-25° \le c \le -10°$
-25° *to* -10° *Celsius*

64. $-4° \le \frac{9}{5}c + 32 \le 23°$

$-36 \le \frac{9}{5}c \le -9°$

$\frac{5}{9}(-36°) \le \frac{5}{9}\left(\frac{9}{5}c\right) \le \frac{5}{9}(-9°)$

$-20° \le c \le -5°$
-20° *to* -5° *Celsius*

66. $-3 < -x < 2$

67. $|x| < 2$
$|-5| < 2$
$5 < 2$ *No*

68. $|x| > 2$
$|-3| > 2$
$3 > 2$ *Yes*

70. $|7 - 9| = |-2| = 2$

71. $|-4 - 7| = |-11| = 11$

72. $|-4| = |-7| = 4 - 7 = -3$

74. $|x| = \begin{cases} x \text{ if } x \geq 0 \\ -x \text{ if } x < 0 \end{cases}$

75. $ax + b < c$
$ax < c - b$
$x < \dfrac{c - b}{a}$

76. $\dfrac{x}{a} + \dfrac{y}{b} < 1$

$ab\left(\dfrac{x}{a}\right) + ab\left(\dfrac{y}{b}\right) < ab(1)$

$bx + ay < ab$
$bx < ab - ay$

$x < \dfrac{ab - ay}{b}$

$x < -\dfrac{a}{b}y + a$

78. $-1 < \dfrac{ax + b}{c} < 1$

$-c < ax + b < c$
$-c - b < ax < c - b$

$\dfrac{-c - b}{a} < x < \dfrac{c - b}{a}$

79. $-1.96 < \dfrac{x - \mu}{s} < 1.96$

$-1.96s < x - \mu < 1.96s$
$-1.96s + \mu < x < 1.96s + \mu$

80. $-2.58 < \dfrac{x - \mu}{s} < 2.58$

$-2.58s < x - \mu < 2.58s$
$-2.58s + \mu < x < 2.58s + \mu$

82. $\dfrac{x}{a} + \dfrac{y}{b} < 1$

$ab\left(\dfrac{x}{a}\right) + ab\left(\dfrac{y}{b}\right) < ab(1)$

$bx + ay < ab$
$bx < ab - ay$

$x > \dfrac{ab - ay}{b}$

$x > -\dfrac{a}{b}y + a$

*for a is negative*

## Section 2.7

2. x = 7 or -7

3. a = 2 or -2

4. a = 5 or -5

6. x = ∅

7. $|a| + 2 = 3$
$|a| = 1$
$a = 1$ *or* $-1$

8. $|a| - 5 = 2$
$|a| = 7$
$a = 7$ *or* $-7$

10. $|y| + 3 = 1$
$|y| = -2$
$y = \varnothing$

11. $4 = |x| - 2$
$6 = |x|$
$6$ *or* $-6 = x$

12. $3 = |x| - 5$
$8 = |x|$
$8$ *or* $-8 = x$

14. $|x + 1| = 2$

$x + 1 = 2$ *or* $x + 1 = -2$
$x = 1$ $\quad x = -3$

15. $|a - 4| = \frac{5}{3}$

$a - 4 = \frac{5}{3}$ *or* $a - 4 = -\frac{5}{3}$

$a = \frac{5}{3} + \frac{12}{3}$ $\quad a = -\frac{5}{3} + \frac{12}{3}$

$a = \frac{17}{3}$ $\quad a = \frac{7}{3}$

16. $|a + 2| = \frac{7}{5}$

$a + 2 = \frac{7}{5}$ *or* $a + 2 = -\frac{7}{5}$

$a = \frac{7}{5} - \frac{10}{5}$ $\quad a = -\frac{7}{5} - \frac{10}{5}$

$a = -\frac{3}{5}$ $\quad a = -\frac{17}{5}$

18. $2 = |4 - x|$
$2 = 4 - x$ *or* $-2 = 4 - x$
$-2 = -x$ $\quad -6 = -x$
$2 = x$ $\quad 6 = x$

19. $\left|\frac{3}{5}a + \frac{1}{2}\right| = 1$

$\frac{3}{5}a + \frac{1}{2} = 1$ *or* $\frac{3}{5}a + \frac{1}{2} = -1$

$\frac{3}{5}a = +\frac{1}{2}$ $\quad \frac{3}{5}a = -\frac{3}{2}$

$a = +\frac{5}{6}$ $\quad a = -\frac{5}{2}$

20. $|\frac{2}{7}a + \frac{3}{4}| = 1$

$\frac{2}{7}a + \frac{3}{4} = 1$ *or* $\frac{2}{7}a + \frac{3}{4} = -1$

$\frac{2}{7}a = \frac{1}{4}$ $\quad \frac{2}{7}a = -\frac{7}{4}$

$a = \frac{7}{8}$ $\quad a = -\frac{49}{8}$

22. $800 = |400x - 200|$
$800 = 400x - 200$ *or* $-800 = 400x - 200$
$1000 = 400x$ $\quad -600 = 400x$

$\frac{5}{2} = x$ $\quad -\frac{3}{2} = x$

23. $|2x + 1| = -3$
$\varnothing$

24. $|2x - 5| = -7$
$\varnothing$

26. $|\frac{4}{5}x - 5| = 15$

$\frac{4}{5}x - 5 = 15$ *or* $\frac{4}{5}x - 5 = -15$

$\frac{4}{5}x = 20$ $\quad \frac{4}{5}x = -10$

$x = 25$ $\quad x = -\frac{25}{2}$

27. $|1 - \frac{1}{2}a| = 3$

$1 - \frac{1}{2}a = 3$ *or* $1 - \frac{1}{2}a = -3$

$-\frac{1}{2}a = 2$ $\quad -\frac{1}{2}a = -4$

$a = -4$ $\quad a = 8$

28. $|2 - \frac{1}{3}a| = 10$

$2 - \frac{1}{3}a = 10$ *or* $2 - \frac{1}{3}a = -10$

$-\frac{1}{3}a = 8$ $\quad$ $-\frac{1}{3}a = -12$

$a = -24$ $\quad$ $a = 36$

30. $|5x - 3| - 4 = 3$
$|5x - 3| = 7$
$5x - 3 = 7$ *or* $5x - 3 = -7$
$5x = 10$ $\quad$ $5x = -4$

$x = 2$ $\quad$ $x = -\frac{4}{5}$

31. $|3 - 2y| + 4 = 3$
$|3 - 2y| = -1$
$\varnothing$

32. $|8 - 7y| + 9 = 1$
$|8 - 7y| = -8$
$\varnothing$

34. $2 + |2t - 6| = 10$
$|2t - 6| = 8$
$2t - 6 = 8$ *or* $2t - 6 = -8$
$2t = 14$ $\quad$ $2t = -2$
$t = 7$ $\quad$ $t = -1$

35. $\left|9 - \frac{3}{5}x\right| + 6 = 12$

$\left|9 - \frac{3}{5}x\right| = 6$

$9 - \frac{3}{5}x = 6$ *or* $9 - \frac{3}{5}x = -6$

$-\frac{3}{5}x = -3$ $\quad$ $-\frac{3}{5}x = -15$

$x = 5$ $\quad$ $x = 25$

36. $|4 - \frac{2}{7}x| + 2 = 14$

$|4 - \frac{2}{7}x| = 12$

$4 - \frac{2}{7}x = 12$ *or* $4 - \frac{2}{7}x = -12$

$-\frac{2}{7}x = 8$ $\quad$ $-\frac{2}{7}x = -16$

$x = -28$ $\quad$ $x = 56$

38. $7 = \left|\frac{3x}{5} + \frac{1}{5}\right| + 2$

$5 = \left|\frac{3x + 1}{5}\right|$

$5 = \frac{3x + 1}{5}$ *or* $-5 = \frac{3x + 1}{5}$

$25 = 3x + 1$ $\quad$ $-25 = 3x + 1$
$24 = 3x$ $\quad$ $-26 = 3x$

$8 = x$ $\quad$ $-\frac{26}{3} = x$

39. $2 = -8 + \left|4 - \frac{1}{2}y\right|$

$10 = \left|4 + \frac{1}{2}y\right|$

$10 = 4 + \frac{1}{2}y$ *or* $-10 = 4 + \frac{1}{2}y$

$y = \frac{1}{2}y$ $\quad$ $-14 = \frac{1}{2}y$

$12 = y$ $\quad$ $-28 = y$

40. $1 = -3 + |2 - \frac{1}{4}y|$

$4 = |2 - \frac{1}{4}y|$

$4 = 2 - \frac{1}{4}y$ *or* $-4 = 2 - \frac{1}{4}y$

$2 = -\frac{1}{4}y$ $\quad$ $-6 = -\frac{1}{4}y$

$-8 = y$ $\quad$ $24 = y$

42. $|2(x-4)+3| = 7$
$$2(x-4)+3 = 7$$
$$2x-8+3 = 7$$
$$2x-5 = 7$$
$$2x = 12$$
$$x = 6 \quad \textit{or}$$

$$2(x-4)+3 = -7$$
$$2x-8+3 = -7$$
$$2x-5 = -7$$
$$2x = -2$$
$$x = -1$$

43. $|1+2(x-1)| = 7$
$$1+2(x-1) = 7$$
$$1+2x-2 = 7$$
$$2x-1 = 7$$
$$2x = 8$$
$$x = 4 \quad \textit{or}$$

$$1+2(x-1) = -7$$
$$1+2x-2 = -7$$
$$2x-1 = -7$$
$$2x = -6$$
$$x = -3$$

44. $|3+4(x+2)| = 5$
$$3+4(x+2) = 5$$
$$3+4x+8 = 5$$
$$4x+11 = 5$$
$$4x = -6$$
$$x = -\frac{6}{4}$$
$$x = -\frac{3}{2} \quad \textit{or}$$

$$3+4(x+2) = -5$$
$$3+4x+8 = -5$$
$$4x+11 = -5$$
$$4x = -16$$
$$x = -4$$

46. $4 = |3(K-2)+1|$
$$4 = 3\ (K-2)+1$$
$$4 = 3k-6+1$$
$$4 = 3k-5$$
$$9 = 3k$$
$$3 = k \quad \textit{or}$$

$$-4 = 3(k-2)+1$$
$$-4 = 3k-6+1$$
$$-4 = 3k-5$$
$$1 = 3k$$
$$\frac{1}{3} = k$$

47. $|3a+1| = |2a-4|$

*Equals*

$$3a+1 = 2a-4$$
$$a+1 = -4$$
$$a = -5$$

*Opposites*

$$3a+1 = -(2a-4)$$
$$3a+1 = -2a+4$$
$$5a+1 = 4$$
$$5a = 3$$
$$a = \frac{3}{5}$$

48. $|5a+2| = |4a+7|$

*Equals*

$$5a+2 = 4a+7$$
$$a+2 = 7$$
$$a = 5$$

*Opposites*

$$5a+2 = -(4a+7)$$
$$5a+2 = -4a-7$$
$$9a+2 = -7$$
$$9a = -9$$
$$a = -1$$

50. $\left|\frac{1}{10}x - \frac{1}{2}\right| = \left|\frac{1}{5}x + \frac{1}{10}\right|$

*Equals*

$$\frac{1}{10}x - \frac{1}{2} = \frac{1}{5}x + \frac{1}{10}$$
$$x-5 = 2x+1$$
$$-5 = x+1$$
$$-6 = x$$

*Opposites*

$$\frac{1}{10}x - \frac{1}{2} = -\left(\frac{1}{5}x + \frac{1}{10}\right) \quad LCD = 10$$
$$x-5 = -(2x+1)$$
$$x-5 = -2x-1$$
$$3x-5 = -1$$
$$3x = 4$$
$$x = \frac{4}{3}$$

51. $|y - 2| = |y + 3|$

*Equals*

$$y - 2 = y + 3$$
$$-2 = 3$$
*No solution*

*Opposites*

$$y - 2 = -(y + 3)$$
$$y - 2 = -y - 3$$
$$2y - 2 = -3$$
$$2y = -1$$
$$y = -\frac{1}{2}$$

52. $|y - 5| = |y - 4|$

*Equals*

$$y - 5 = y - 4$$
$$-5 = -4$$
*No solution*

*Opposites*

$$y - 5 = -(y - 4)$$
$$y - 5 = -y + 4$$
$$2y - 5 = 4$$
$$2y = 9$$
$$y = \frac{9}{2}$$

54. $|5x - 8| = |5x + 8|$

*Equals*

$$5x - 2 = 5x + 8$$
$$-8 = 8$$
*No solution*

*Opposites*

$$5x - 8 = -(5x + 8)$$
$$5x - 8 = -5x - 8$$
$$10x - 8 = -8$$
$$10x = 0$$
$$x = 0$$

55. $|3 - m| = |m + 4|$

*Equals*

$$3 - m = m + 4$$
$$3 = 2m + 4$$
$$-1 = 2m$$
$$-\frac{1}{2} = m$$

*Opposites*

$$3 - m = -(m + 4)$$
$$3 - m = -m - 4$$
$$3 = -m$$
*No solution*

56. $|5 - m| = |m + 8|$

*Equals*

$$5 - m = m + 8$$
$$5 = 2m + 8$$
$$-3 = 2m$$
$$-\frac{3}{2} = m$$

*Opposites*

$$5 - m = -(m + 8)$$
$$5 - m = -m - 8$$
$$5 = -8$$
*No solutions*

58. $|0.07 - 0.01x| = |0.08 - 0.02x|$

*Equals*

$$0.07 - 0.01x = 0.08 - 0.02x$$
$$7 - x = 8 - 2x$$
$$x = 1$$

*Opposites*

$$0.07 - 0.01x = -(0.08 - 0.02x)$$
$$0.07 - 0.01x = -0.08 + 0.02x$$
$$7 - x = -8 + 2x$$
$$15 = 3x$$
$$5 = x$$

59. $|x - 2| = |2 - x|$

*Equals*

$$\begin{aligned} x - 2 &= 2 - x \\ 2x - 2 &= 2 \\ 2x &= 4 \\ x &= 2 \end{aligned}$$

*Opposites*

$$\begin{aligned} x - 2 &= -(2 - x) \\ x - 2 &= -2 + x \\ -2 &= -2 \end{aligned}$$

*All real numbers*

60. $|x - 4| = |4 - x|$

*Equals*

$$\begin{aligned} x - 4 &= 4 - x \\ 2x - 4 &= 4 \\ 2x &= 8 \\ x &= 4 \end{aligned}$$

*Opposites*

$$\begin{aligned} x - 4 &= -(4 - x) \\ x - 4 &= -4 + x \\ -4 &= -4 \end{aligned}$$

*All real numbers*

62. $\left|\frac{x}{3} - 1\right| = \left|1 - \frac{x}{3}\right|$

*Equals*

$$\frac{x}{3} - 1 = 1 - \frac{x}{3}$$

$$\begin{aligned} x - 3 &= 3 - x \\ 2x - 3 &= 3 \\ 2x &= 6 \\ x &= 3 \end{aligned}$$

*Opposites*

$$\frac{x}{3} - 1 = -\left(1 - \frac{x}{3}\right) \quad LCD = 3$$

$$\begin{aligned} x - 3 &= -(3 - x \\ x - 3 &= -3 + x \\ -3 &= -3 \end{aligned}$$

*All real numbers*

64. $|ab| = |a|\,|b|$ *when* $a = 3,\ b = -6$

$$\begin{aligned} |3(-6)| &= |3|\,|-6| \\ |-18| &= 3 \cdot 6 \\ 18 &= 18 \end{aligned}$$

$|ab| = |a|\,|b|$ *when* $a = -8,\ b = -2$

$$\begin{aligned} |-8(-2)| &= |-8|\,|-2| \\ |16| &= 8 \cdot 2 \\ 16 &= 16 \end{aligned}$$

66. $|x - 2| = x - 2$

$$\begin{aligned} x - 2 &= x - 2 \\ -2 &= -2 \end{aligned}$$

*All real numbers* *OR*

$$\begin{aligned} x - 2 &= -(x - 2) \\ x - 2 &= -x + 2 \\ 2x - 2 &= 2 \\ 2x &= 4 \\ x &= 2 \end{aligned}$$

The solution set is {2,3,4} because when all the other values are substituted the absolute value becomes negative.

67. $|x - 2| = x - 2$ *if* $x - 2 \geq 0$

$$\begin{aligned} x - 2 &\geq 0 \\ x &\geq 2 \end{aligned}$$

68. $|x + 3| = x + 3$ *if* $x + 3 \geq 0$

$$\begin{aligned} x + 3 &\geq 0 \\ x &\geq -3 \end{aligned}$$

70. $1 < x < 4$

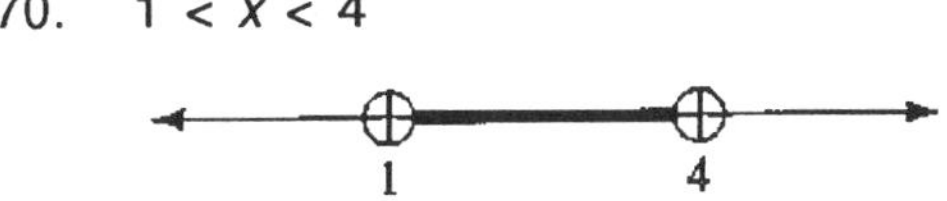


71. $-2 \leq x \leq 1$

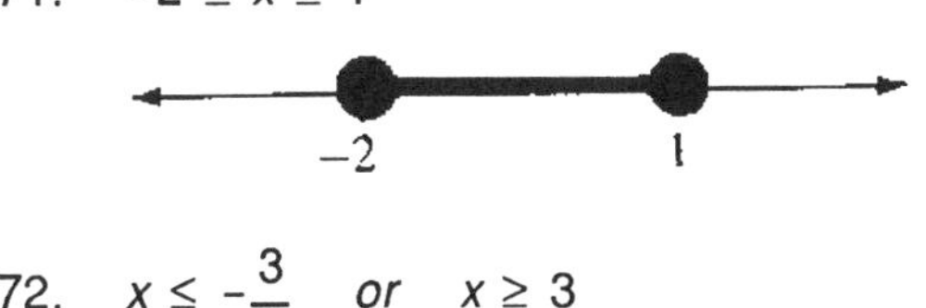


72. $x \leq -\frac{3}{2}$ *or* $x \geq 3$

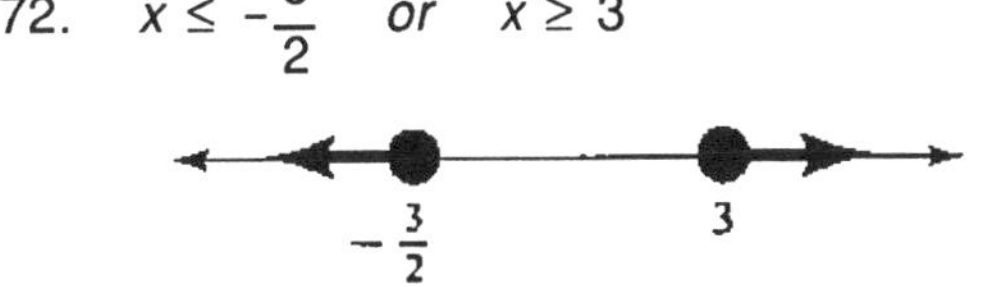

74. $-3 < 2a - 5 < 3$
$2 < 2a < 8$
$1 < a < 4$

75. $-3x > 15$
$x < -5$

76. $-2x \le 10$
$x \ge -5$

78. $\frac{3}{7}a + 2 < \frac{1}{4}$

$12a + 56 < 7$ *LCD* = 28
$12a < -49$

$a < -\frac{49}{12}$

79. $|x - a| = b$
$x - a = b$
$x = a + b$ *or*

$x - a = -b$
$x = a - b$

80. $|x + a| - b = 0$
$|x + a| = b$
$x + a = b$
$x = -a + b$ *or*
$x + a = -b$
$x = -a - b$

82. $|ax - b| - c = 0$
$|ax - b| = c$
$ax - b = c$
$ax = b + c$

$x = \frac{b + c}{a}$ *or*

$ax - b = -c$
$ax = b - c$

$x = \frac{b - c}{a}$

83. $|\frac{x}{a} + \frac{y}{b}| = 1$ *LCD* = *ab*

$\frac{x}{a} + \frac{y}{b} = 1$

$bx + ay = ab$
$bx = -ay + ab$

$x = -\frac{a}{b}y + a$ *or*

$\frac{x}{a} + \frac{y}{b} = -1$

$bx + ay = -ab$
$bx = -ay - ab$

$x = -\frac{a}{b}y - a$

84. $\left|\frac{x}{a} + \frac{y}{b}\right| = c$

$\frac{x}{a} + \frac{y}{b} = c$ *LCD* = *ab*
$bx + ay = abc$
$bx = -ay + abc$

$x = -\frac{a}{b}y + ac$ *or*

$\frac{x}{a} + \frac{y}{b} = -c$

$bx + ay = -abc$
$bx = -ay - abc$

$x = -\frac{a}{b}y - ac$

**Section 2.8**

2. $|x| \le 7$
$-7 \le x \le 7$

−7 7

3. $|x| \ge 2$
$x \le -2$ *or* $x \ge 2$

−2 2

4. $|x| > 4$
$x < -4$ *or* $x > 4$

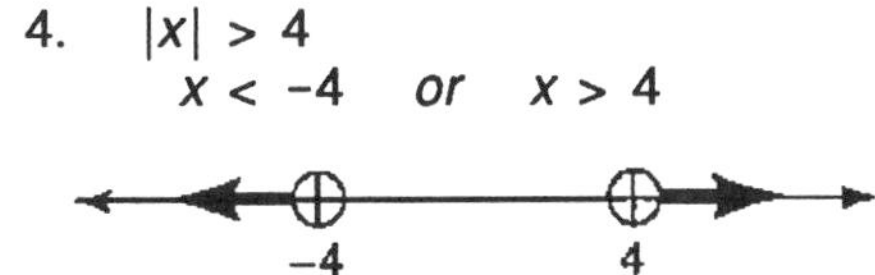


6. $|x| - 3 < -1$
$|x| < 2$
$-2 < x < 2$

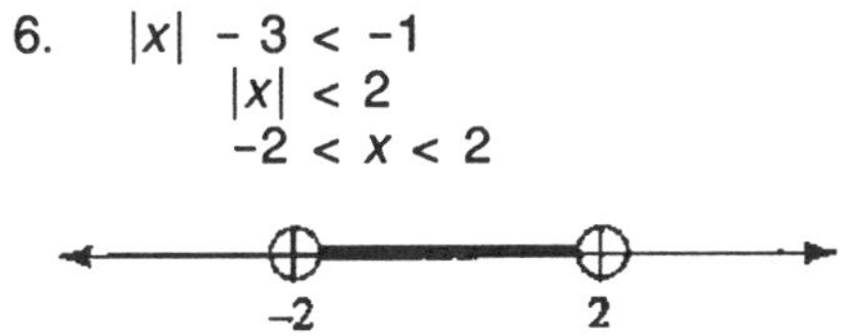


7. $|t| - 3 > 4$
$|t| > 7$
$t < -7$ *or* $t > 7$

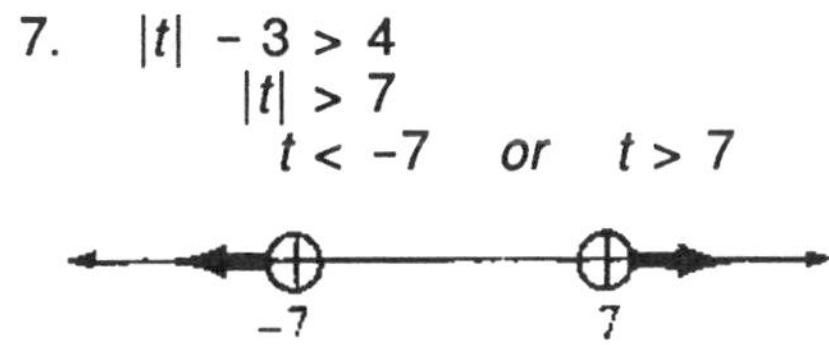


8. $|t| + 5 > 8$
$|t| > 3$

$t < -3$ *or* $t > 3$

10. $|y| > -3$
$y < 3$ *or* $y > -3$
*All real numbers*

11. $|x| \geq -2$
$x \leq 2$ *or* $x \geq -2$
*All real numbers*

12. $|x| \leq -4$
$\varnothing$

14. $|x + 4| < 2$
$-2 < x + 4 < 2$
$-6 < x < -2$

15. $|a + 5| \geq 4$
$a + 5 \leq -4$ *or* $a + 5 \geq 4$
$a \leq -9$ $\quad$ $a \geq -1$

16. $|a - 6| \geq 3$
$a - 6 \leq -3$ *or* $a - 6 \geq 3$
$a \leq 3$ $\quad$ $a \geq 9$

18. $|a + 2| \geq -5$
$a + 2 \leq 5$ *or* $a + 2 \geq -5$
$a \leq 3$ $\quad$ $a + 2 \geq -7$
*All real numbers*

19. $|2x - 4| < 6$
$-6 < 2x - 4 < 6$
$-2 < 2x < 10$
$-1 < x < 5$

20. $|2x + 6| < 2$
$-2 < 2x + 6 < 2$
$-8 < 2x < -4$
$-4 < x < -2$

22. $|5y - 1| \geq 4$
$5y - 1 \leq -4$ *or* $5y - 1 \geq 4$
$5y \leq -3$ $\quad$ $5y \geq 5$

$y \leq -\frac{3}{5}$ $\quad$ $y \geq 1$

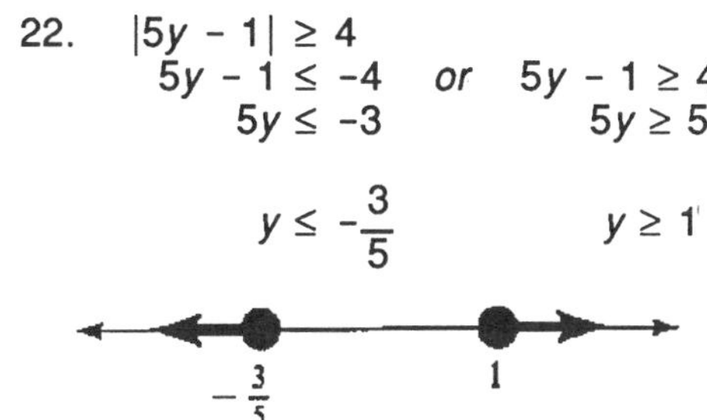


23. $|2k + 3| \geq 7$
$2k + 3 \leq -7$ *or* $2k + 3 \geq 7$
$2k \leq -10$ $\quad$ $2k \geq 4$
$k \leq -5$ $\quad$ $k \geq 2$

24. $|2k - 5| \geq 3$
$2k - 5 \leq -3$ *or* $2k - 5 \geq 3$
$2k \leq 2$ $\quad$ $2k \geq 8$
$k \leq 1$ $\quad$ $k \geq 4$

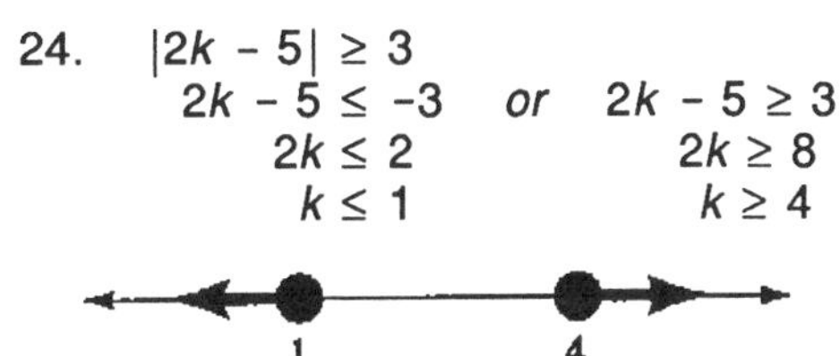

26. $|x + 4| - 3 < -1$
$|x + 4| < 2$
$-2 < x + 4 < 2$
$-6 < x < -2$

27. $|2a + 1| + 4 \geq 7$
$|2a + 1| \geq 3$
$2a + 1 \leq -3$ or $2a + 1 \geq 3$
$2a \leq -4$ $\quad$ $2a \geq 2$
$a \leq -2$ $\quad$ $a \geq 1$

28. $|2a - 6| - 1 \geq 2$
$|2a - 6| \geq 3$
$2a - 6 \leq -3$ or $2a - 6 \geq 3$
$2a \leq 3$ $\quad$ $2a \geq 9$
$a \leq \frac{3}{2}$ $\quad$ $a \geq \frac{9}{2}$

30. $|6x - 1| - 4 \leq 2$
$|6x - 1| \leq 6$
$-6 \leq 6x - 1 \leq 6$
$-5 \leq 6x \leq 7$
$-\frac{5}{6} \leq x \leq \frac{7}{6}$

31. $|5 - x| > 3$
$5 - x < -3$ or $5 - x > 3$
$-x < -8$ $\quad$ $-x > -2$
$x > 8$ $\quad$ $x < 2$

32. $|7 - x| > 2$
$7 - x < -2$ or $7 - x > 2$
$-x < -9$ $\quad$ $-x > -5$
$x > 9$ $\quad$ $x < 5$

34. $\left|3 - \frac{3}{4}x\right| \geq 9$

$3 - \frac{3}{4}x \leq -9$ $\quad$ LCD = 4

$12 - 3x \leq -36$
$-3x \leq -48$
$x \geq 16$ $\quad$ or

$3 - \frac{3}{4}x \geq 9$

$12 - 3x \geq 36$
$-3x \geq 24$
$x \leq -8$

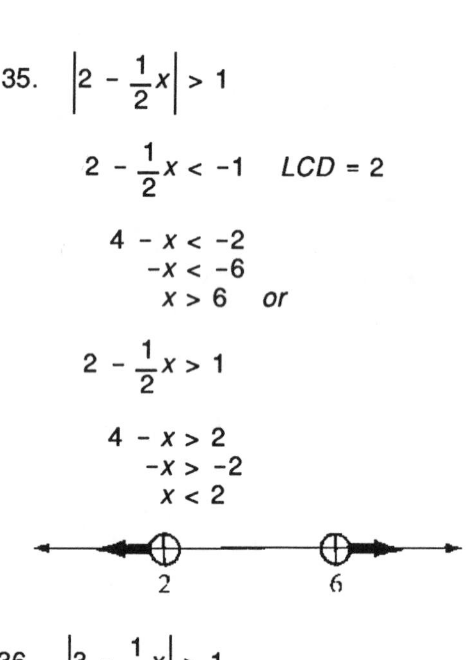

35. $\left|2 - \frac{1}{2}x\right| > 1$

$2 - \frac{1}{2}x < -1$ $\quad$ LCD = 2

$4 - x < -2$
$-x < -6$
$x > 6$ $\quad$ or

$2 - \frac{1}{2}x > 1$

$4 - x > 2$
$-x > -2$
$x < 2$

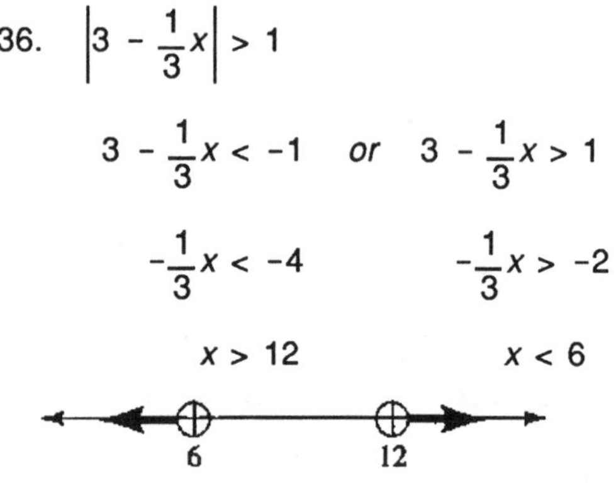

36. $\left|3 - \frac{1}{3}x\right| > 1$

$3 - \frac{1}{3}x < -1$ or $3 - \frac{1}{3}x > 1$

$-\frac{1}{3}x < -4$ $\quad$ $-\frac{1}{3}x > -2$

$x > 12$ $\quad$ $x < 6$

38. $|x + 1| < .01$

$-.01 < x + 1 < .01$

$-1.01 < x < -.99$

39. $|2x + 1| \ge \frac{1}{5}$

$2x + 1 \le -\frac{1}{5}$ *LCD = 5*

$10x + 5 \le -1$

$10x \le -6$

$x \le -\frac{6}{10}$

$x \le -\frac{3}{5}$ *or*

$2x + 1 \ge \frac{1}{5}$

$10 + 5 \ge 1$

$10x \ge -4$

$x \ge -\frac{4}{10}$

$x \ge -\frac{2}{5}$

40. $|2x - 1| \ge \frac{1}{8}$

$2x - 1 \le -\frac{1}{8}$

$16x - 8 \le -1$

$16x \le 7$

$x \le \frac{7}{16}$ *or*

$2x - 1 \ge \frac{1}{8}$

$16x - 8 \ge 1$

$16x \ge 9$

$x \ge \frac{9}{16}$

41. $-\frac{1}{2} \le \frac{3x - 2}{5} \le \frac{1}{2}$ *LCD = 10*

$-5 \le 6x - 4 \le 5$

$-1 \le 6x \le 9$

$-\frac{1}{6} \le x \le \frac{9}{6}$

$-\frac{1}{6} \le x \le \frac{3}{2}$

42. $\left|\frac{4x - 3}{2}\right| \le \frac{1}{3}$

$-\frac{1}{3} \le \frac{4x - 3}{2} \le \frac{1}{3}$ *LCD = 6*

$-2 \le 3(4x - 3) \le 2$

$-2 \le 12x - 9 \le 2$

$7 \le 12x \le 11$

$\frac{7}{12} \le x \le \frac{11}{12}$

43. $\left|2x - \frac{1}{5}\right| < 0.3$

$-0.3 < 2x - \frac{1}{5} < 0.3$ *LCD = 10*

$-3 < 20x - 2 < 3$

$-1 < 20x < 5$

$-0.05 < x < 0.25$

44. $-1 < 15x - 3 < 1$

$2 < 15x < 4$

$\frac{2}{15} < x < \frac{4}{15}$

46. *The continued inequality $-8 \le x \le 8$ as an absolute value becomes $|x| \le 8$.*

47. $|x - 5| \le 1$

48. $|x + 2| \le 3$

50. $-\frac{4}{5} \div (-4) = -\frac{4}{5} \cdot \left(-\frac{1}{4}\right)$

$= \frac{1}{5}$

51. $3 - 7(-6 - 3) = 3 - 7(-9)$
$= 3 + 63$
$= 66$

52. $(3 - 7)(-6 - 3) = (-4)(-9) = 36$

54. $4(2 - 5)^3 - 3(4 - 5)^5$
$= 4(-3)^3 - 3(-1)^5$
$= 4(-27) - 3(-1)$
$= -108 + 3$
$= -105$

55. $-2(-3 + 8) - 7(-9 + 6)$
$= -2(5) - 7(-3)$
$= -10 + 21$
$= -11$

56. $-3 - 6[5 - 2(-3 - 1)]$
$= -3 - 6[5 - 2(-4)]$
$= -3 - 6[5 + 8]$
$= -3 - 6[13]$
$= -3 - 78$
$= -81$

58. $\dfrac{4 - 8(3 - 5)}{2 - 4(3 - 5)} = \dfrac{4 - 8(-2)}{2 - 4(-2)}$

$= \dfrac{4 + 16}{2 + 8}$

$= \dfrac{20}{10}$

$= 2$

59. $|x - a| < b$
$-b < x - a < b$
$a - b < x < a + b$

60. $|x - a| > b$
$x - a < -b$ or $x - a > b$
$x < a - b$    $x > a + b$

61. $|ax - b| > c$
$ax - b < -c$ or $ax - b > c$
$ax < b - c$    $ax > b + c$

$x < \dfrac{b - c}{a}$    $x > \dfrac{b + c}{a}$

62. $|ax - b| < c$
$-c < ax - b < c$
$b - c < ax < b + c$

$\dfrac{b - c}{a} < x < \dfrac{b + c}{a}$

63. $\left|\dfrac{x}{a} + \dfrac{y}{b}\right| < 1$

$-1 < \dfrac{x}{a} + \dfrac{y}{b} < 1$    $LCD = ab$

$-ab < bx + ay < ab$
$-ab - ay < bx < ab - ay$

$-a - \dfrac{a}{b}y < x < a - \dfrac{a}{b}y$

64. $\left|\dfrac{x}{a} + \dfrac{y}{b}\right| > 1$

$\dfrac{x}{a} + \dfrac{y}{b} > 1$    $LCD = ab$

$bx + ay > ab$
$bx > ab - ay$

$x > a - \dfrac{a}{b}y$   or

$\dfrac{x}{a} + \dfrac{y}{b} < -1$

$bx + ay < -ab$
$bx < -ab - ay$

$x < -a - \dfrac{a}{b}y$

66. $\left|\dfrac{x}{a} + \dfrac{y}{b}\right| > c$

$\dfrac{x}{a} + \dfrac{y}{b} > c$    $LCD = ab$

$bx + ay > abc$
$bx > abc - ay$

$x > ac - \dfrac{a}{b}y$   or

$\dfrac{x}{a} + \dfrac{y}{b} < -c$

$bx + ay < -abc$
$bx < -abc - ay$

$x < -ac - \dfrac{a}{b}y$

# Chapter 3

## Section 3.1

2. $(-4)^2 = 16$

3. $-4^2 = -4 \cdot 4 = -16$

4. $-(-4)^2 = -(16)$
$= -16$

6. $(-0.3)^3 = -0.027$

7. $2^5 = 32$

8. $2^4 = 16$

10. $\left(\frac{3}{4}\right)^2 = \frac{9}{16}$

11. $\left(-\frac{5}{6}\right)^2 = \frac{25}{36}$

12. $\left(-\frac{7}{8}\right)^2 = \frac{49}{64}$

14. $x^6 \cdot x^3 = x^9$

15. $(2^3)^2 = 2^6 = 64$

16. $(3^2)^2 = 3^4 = 81$

18. $\left(-\frac{3}{5}x^4\right)^3 = \left(-\frac{3}{5}\right)^3(x^4)^3$
$= -\frac{27}{125}x^{12}$

19. $-3a^2(2a^4) = -6a^6$

20. $5a^7(-4a^6) = -20a^{13}$

22. $(5x^3)(-7x^4)(-2x^6) = 70x^{13}$

23. $(-\frac{1}{3}n)^4(2n^3)^2\left(\frac{3}{2}n^6\right)^4$
$= \left(\frac{n^4}{81}\right)\left(\frac{4n^6}{1}\right)\left(\frac{81n^{24}}{16}\right)$
$= \frac{1}{4}n^{34}$

24. $\left(\frac{1}{8}n^6\right)^2(-2n^3)^2(-3n^7)^2$
$= \left(\frac{n^{12}}{64}\right)\left(\frac{4n^6}{1}\right)\left(\frac{9n^{14}}{1}\right)$
$= \frac{9}{16}n^{32}$

26. $(-5)^{-2} = \frac{1}{(-5)^2} = \frac{1}{25}$

27. $(-2)^{-5} = \frac{1}{(-2)^5} = -\frac{1}{32}$

28. $2^{-5} = \frac{1}{2^5} = \frac{1}{32}$

30. $(-7)^{-2} = \frac{1}{(-7)^2} = \frac{1}{49}$

31. $\left(\frac{3}{4}\right)^{-2} = \frac{1}{\left(\frac{3}{4}\right)^2}$
$= \frac{1}{\left(\frac{9}{16}\right)}$
$= \frac{16}{9}$

32. $\left(\frac{3}{5}\right)^{-2} = \frac{1}{\left(\frac{3}{5}\right)^2}$

$= \frac{1}{\left(\frac{9}{25}\right)}$

$= \frac{25}{9}$

34. $\left(\frac{1}{2}\right)^{-2} + \left(\frac{1}{3}\right)^{-3} = \frac{1}{\left(\frac{1}{2}\right)^2} + \frac{1}{\left(\frac{1}{3}\right)^3}$

$= \frac{1}{\left(\frac{1}{4}\right)} + \frac{1}{\left(\frac{1}{27}\right)}$

$= \frac{4}{1} + \frac{27}{1}$

$= 31$

35. $\left(\frac{2}{3}\right)^{-2} - \left(\frac{2}{5}\right)^{-2} = \frac{1}{\left(\frac{2}{3}\right)^2} - \frac{1}{\left(\frac{2}{5}\right)^2}$

$= \frac{1}{\left(\frac{4}{9}\right)} - \frac{1}{\left(\frac{4}{25}\right)}$

$= \frac{9}{4} - \frac{25}{4}$

$= -\frac{16}{4}$

$= -4$

36. $\left(\frac{3}{2}\right)^{-2} - \left(\frac{3}{4}\right)^{-2} = \frac{1}{\left(\frac{3}{2}\right)^2} - \frac{1}{\left(\frac{3}{4}\right)^2}$

$= \frac{1}{\frac{9}{4}} - \frac{1}{\frac{9}{16}}$

$= \frac{4}{9} - \frac{16}{9}$

$= -\frac{12}{9}$

$= -\frac{4}{3}$

38. $x^{-3}x^{8} = x^{5}$

39. $(a^2b^{-5})^3 = a^6b^{-15}$

$= \frac{a^6}{b^{15}}$

40. $(a^4b^{-3})^3 = a^{12}b^{-9}$

$= \frac{a^{12}}{b^9}$

42. $(4x^{-4})^3\left(\frac{1}{8}x^8\right) = \frac{4^3}{x^{12}} \cdot \frac{x^8}{8}$

$= \frac{8}{x^4}$

43. $(5y^4)^{-3}(2y^{-2})^3 = 5^{-3}y^{-12}2^3y^{-6}$

$= \frac{2^3}{5^3y^{12}y^6}$

$= \frac{8}{125y^{18}}$

44. $(3y^5)^{-2}(2y^{-4})^3 = 3^{-2}y^{-10}2^3y^{-12}$

$= \frac{2^3}{3^2y^{10}y^{12}}$

$= \frac{8}{9y^{22}}$

46. $\left(\frac{1}{7}x^{-3}\right)\left(\frac{7}{8}x^{-5}\right)\left(\frac{8}{9}x^{8}\right) = \left(\frac{1}{7x^3}\right)\left(\frac{7}{8x^5}\right)\left(\frac{8x^8}{9}\right)$

$= \frac{1}{9}$

47. $(0.2a^3)^2(5a^{-4})^2(4a^3)$

$= (0.04a^6)(25a^{-8})(4a^3)$

$= \frac{4a^9}{a^8}$

$= 4a$

48. $(0.3a^{-4})^2(3a^4)^{-2}\left(\frac{1}{10}a^{16}\right)$

$= (0.09a^{-8})(3^{-2}a^{-8})\left(\frac{1}{10}a^{16}\right)$

$= \frac{0.09a^{16}}{3^2 \cdot a^8 \cdot a^8 \cdot 10}$

$= \frac{.09a^{16}}{90a^{16}}$

$= .001$

$= \frac{1}{1000}$

50. $(4x^7y^{-2})(8x^3y^{-4}) = \frac{4x^7}{y^2} \cdot \frac{8x^3}{y^4}$

$= \frac{32x^{10}}{y^6}$

51. $(3x^2y^5z^{-3})(5x^7y^{-2}z^5)$

$= \frac{3x^2y^5}{z^3} \cdot \frac{5x^7z^5}{y^2}$

$= 15x^9y^3z^2$

52. $(9x^{-3}y^4z^{-2})(7x^5y^{-1}z^4)$

$= \frac{9y^4}{x^3z^2} \cdot \frac{7x^5z^4}{y}$

$= 63x^2y^3z^2$

54. $(3a^{-2}c^3)(5b^{-6}c^5)(4a^6b^{-2})$

$= \frac{3c^3}{a^2} \cdot \frac{5c^5}{b^6} \cdot \frac{4a^6}{b^2}$

$= \frac{60a^4c^8}{b^8}$

55. $(2x^2y^{-5})^3(3x^{-4}y^2)^{-4}$

$= (2^3x^6y^{-15})(3^{-4}x^{16}y^{-8})$

$= \frac{8x^6}{y^{15}} \cdot \frac{x^{16}}{81y^8}$

$= \frac{8x^{22}}{81y^{23}}$

56. $(4x^{-4}y^9)^{-2}(5x^4y^{-3})^2$

$= (4^{-2}x^8y^{-18})(5^2x^8y^{-6})$

$= \frac{x^8}{16y^{18}} \cdot \frac{25x^8}{y^6}$

$= \frac{25x^{16}}{16y^{24}}$

58. $(8r^{-2}s^4)^2(4r^{-3}s)^{-2}$

$= (8^2r^{-4}s^8)(4^{-2}r^6s^{-4})$

$= \frac{64s^8}{r^4} \cdot \frac{r^6}{16s^4}$

$= 4r^2s^4$

59. $378{,}000 = 3.78 \times 10^4$

60. $3{,}780{,}000 = 3.78 \times 10^6$

62. $490 = 4.9 \times 10^2$

63. $0.00037 = 3.7 \times 10^{-4}$

64. $0.000037 = 3.7 \times 10^{-5}$

66. $0.0495 = 4.95 \times 10^{-2}$

67. $0.562 = 5.62 \times 10^{-1}$

68. $0.0562 = 5.62 \times 10^{-2}$

70. $5.34 \times 10^2 = 534$

71. $7.8 \times 10^6 = 7{,}800{,}000$

72. $7.8 \times 10^4 = 78{,}000$

74. $3.44 \times 10^{-5} = 0.0000344$

75. $4.9 \times 10^{-1} = 0.49$

76. $4.9 \times 10^{-2} = 0.049$

78. $\frac{1}{3^{-2}} = \frac{1}{\frac{1}{3^2}}$

$= 1 \cdot \frac{3^2}{1}$

$= 3^2$
$= 9$

79. $\frac{1}{5^{-2}} = \frac{1}{\frac{1}{5^2}}$

$= 1 \cdot \frac{5^2}{1}$

$= 5^2$
$= 25$

80. $\frac{1}{3^{-4}} = \frac{1}{\frac{1}{3^4}}$

$= 1 \cdot \frac{3^4}{1}$

$= 3^4$
$= 81$

82. $(3^4)^2 = 3^8$

$3^{4^2} = 3^{16}$ *larger*

83. $d = vt + \frac{1}{2}gt^2$

$d = 174,\ v = 10,\ t = 3$

$174 = 10(3) + \frac{1}{2}g(3)^2$

$174 = 30 + \frac{1}{2}g(9)$

$144 = \frac{9}{2}g$

$\frac{288}{9} = g$

$32 = g$

84. $d = vt - \frac{1}{2}gt^2$

$d = 36,\ v = 60,\ 5 = 3$

$36 = 60(3) - \frac{1}{2}g(3)^2$

$36 = 180 - \frac{9}{2}g$

$-144 = -\frac{9}{2}g$

$\frac{288}{9} = g$

$32 = g$

86. $(a + b)^2 = a^2 + b^2 \quad a = 2,\ b = 3$
$(2 + 3)^2 = 2^2 + 3^2$
$5^2 = 4 + 9$
$25 = 13$ *False*

87. $237 \times 10^4 = 2.37 \times 10^2 \times 10^4$
$= 2.37 \times 10^6$

88. $46.2 \times 10^{-3} = 4.62 \times 10^1 \times 10^{-3}$
$= 4.62 \times 10^{-2}$

90. *In 20 yrs* = 680,000,000 *seconds*
*So in 40 yrs* = 2(630,000,000)
= 1,260,000,000
= $1.26 \times 10^9$

91. 22 *zeros because* 98 *takes two of the* 24 *places.*

92. 29 *digits to the right of the decimal.*

94. $-6 - (-8) = -6 + 8 = 2$

95. $8 - (-6) = 8 + 6 = 14$

96. $-8 - (-6) = -8 + 6 = -2$

98. $4 - (-3) = 4 + 3 = 7$

99. $-4 - (-9) = -4 + 9 = 5$

100. $4 - (-9) = 4 + 9 = 13$

102. $x^{m-4}x^{m+9}x^{-2m} = x^{m-4+m+9-2m}$
$= x^5$

103. $(y^m)^2(y^{-3})^m(y^{m+3})$
$= y^{2m}y^{-3m}y^{m+3}$
$= y^{2m-3m+m+3}$
$= y^3$

104. $(y^m)^{-4}(y^3)^m(y^{m+6})$
$= y^{-4m}y^{3m}y^{m+6}$
$= y^6$

106. $(4x^{3m}y^{2n})^{-4}(2x^{-6m}y^{-4n})^2$
$= 4^{-4}x^{-12m}y^{-8n}2^2x^{-12m}y^{-8n}$

$$= \frac{2^2}{4^4x^{12m}y^{8n}x^{12m}y^{8n}}$$

$$= \frac{4}{256x^{24m}y^{16n}}$$

$$= \frac{1}{64x^{24m}y^{16n}}$$

**Section 3.2**

2. $\left(\frac{x^5}{y^2}\right)^3 = \frac{(x^5)^3}{(y^2)^3} = \frac{x^{15}}{y^6}$

3. $\left(\frac{2a^{-2}}{b^{-1}}\right)^2 = \frac{(2a^{-2})^2}{(b^{-1})^2}$

$$= \frac{2^2a^{-4}}{b^{-2}}$$

$$= \frac{4b^2}{a^4}$$

4. $\left(\frac{2a^{-3}}{b^{-2}}\right)^3 = \frac{(2a^{-3})}{(b^{-2})^3}$

$$= \frac{2^3a^{-9}}{b^{-6}}$$

$$= \frac{8b^6}{a^9}$$

6. $\frac{3^6}{3^4} = 3^2 = 9$

7. $\frac{2^{-2}}{2^{-5}} = \frac{2^5}{2^2} = 2^3 = 8$

8. $\frac{2^{-5}}{2^{-2}} = \frac{2^2}{2^5} = 2^{2-5} = 2^{-3} = \frac{1}{2^3} = \frac{1}{8}$

10. $\frac{x^{-3}}{x^5} = \frac{1}{x^3x^5} = \frac{1}{x^8}$

11. $\frac{a^4}{a^{-6}} = a^4a^6 = a^{10}$

12. $\frac{a^5}{a^{-2}} = a^5a^2 = a^7$

14. $\frac{t^{-8}}{t^{-5}} = t^{-8-(-5)} = t^{-8+5} = t^{-3} = \frac{1}{t^3}$

15. $\left(\frac{x^5}{x^3}\right)^6 = \frac{(x^5)^6}{(x^3)^6} = \frac{x^{30}}{x^{18}} = x^{12}$

16. $\left(\frac{x^7}{x^4}\right)^5 = \frac{(x^7)^5}{(x^4)^5} = \frac{x^{35}}{x^{20}} = x^{15}$

18. $\frac{(a^5)^3}{a^{10}} = \frac{a^{15}}{a^{10}} = a^5$

19. $\frac{a^7}{(a^3)^4} = \frac{a^7}{a^{12}} = a^{7-12} = a^{-5} = \frac{1}{a^5}$

20. $\frac{a^{10}}{(a^5)^3} = \frac{a^{10}}{a^{15}} = a^{10-15} = a^{-5} = \frac{1}{a^5}$

22. $\frac{(x^7)^3}{(x^4)^5} = \frac{x^{21}}{x^{20}} = x$

23. $\frac{x^5x^6}{x^3} = \frac{x^{11}}{x^3} = x^8$

24. $\frac{x^7x^8}{x^4} = \frac{x^{15}}{x^4} = x^{11}$

26. $\frac{a^4}{a^7a^8} = \frac{a^4}{a^{15}} = a^{4-15} = a^{-11} = \frac{1}{a^{11}}$

27. $\frac{(m^3)^2m^5}{(m^4)^3} = \frac{m^6m^5}{m^{12}}$

$= \frac{m^{11}}{m^{12}}$

$= m^{11-12}$
$= m^{-1}$

$= \frac{1}{m}$

28. $\frac{(m^6)^2m^4}{(m^5)^8} = \frac{m^{12}m^4}{m^{40}}$

$= \frac{m^{16}}{m^{40}}$

$= m^{16-40}$
$= m^{-24}$

$= \frac{1}{m^{24}}$

30. $\frac{(x^{-4})^3(x^3)^{-4}}{x^{10}} = \frac{x^{-12}x^{-12}}{x^{10}}$

$= \frac{x^{-24}}{x^{10}}$

$= x^{-24-10}$
$= x^{-34}$

$= \frac{1}{x^{34}}$

31. $\frac{15x^6y^7}{5x^4y^3} = 3x^{6-4}y^{7-3} = 3x^2y^4$

32. $\frac{24x^8y^6}{8x^5y^2} = 3x^{8-5}y^{6-2} = 3x^3y^4$

34. $\frac{7a^6b^{-2}}{21a^2b^{-5}} = \frac{1}{3}a^{6-2}b^{-2-(-5)}$

$= \frac{1}{3}a^4b^3$

$= \frac{a^4b^3}{3}$

35. $\frac{27x^3y^{-4}z}{9x^7y^{-6}z^4} = 3x^{3-7}y^{-4-(-6)}z^{1-4}$

$= 3x^{-4}y^2z^{-3}$

$= \frac{3y^2}{x^4z^3}$

36. $\frac{28x^5y^{-2}z}{14x^8y^{-5}z^6} = 2x^{5-8}y^{-2-(-5)}z^{1-6}$

$= 2x^{-3}y^3z^{-5}$

$= \frac{2y^3}{x^3z^5}$

38. $\frac{18r^{-8}s^{-2}t^0}{6r^{-10}s^{-4}t^{-3}}$

$= 3r^{-8-(-10)}s^{-2-(-4)}t^{0-(-3)}$
$= 3r^2s^2t^3$

39. $\frac{(2x^3y^4)^5}{(x^2y^3)^3} = \frac{2^5x^{15}y^{20}}{x^6y^9} = 32x^9y^{11}$

40. $\dfrac{(5x^8y^{10})^2}{(x^3y^4)^3} = \dfrac{5^2x^{16}y^{20}}{x^9y^{12}} = 25x^7y^8$

42. $\dfrac{(6x^{-3}y^{-5})^2}{(3x^{-4}y^{-3})^4} = \dfrac{6^2x^{-6}y^{-10}}{3^4x^{-16}y^{-12}}$

$= \dfrac{36}{81} \cdot x^{-6-(-16)}y^{-10-(-12)}$

$= \dfrac{4x^{10}y^2}{9}$

43. $\dfrac{(2a^3b^{-2}c)^5}{(a^{-2}b^4c^{-3})^{-2}} = \dfrac{2^5a^{15}b^{-10}c^5}{a^4b^{-8}c^6}$

$= 32a^{15-4}b^{-10-(-8)}c^{5-6}$
$= 32a^{11}b^{-2}c^{-1}$

$= \dfrac{32a^{11}}{b^2c}$

44. $\dfrac{(4a^{-2}bc^4)^3}{(a^5b^{-2}c^{-7})^{-3}} = \dfrac{4^3a^{-6}b^3c^{12}}{a^{-15}b^6c^{21}}$

$= 64a^{-6-(-15)}b^{3-6}c^{12-21}$
$= 64a^9b^{-3}c^{-9}$

$= \dfrac{64a^9}{b^3c^9}$

46. $\left(\dfrac{5x^4y^5}{10xy^{-2}}\right)^3 = \dfrac{5^3x^{12}y^{15}}{10^3x^3y^{-6}}$

$= \dfrac{125}{1000}x^{12-3}y^{15-(-6)}$

$= \dfrac{1}{8}x^9y^{21}$

$= \dfrac{x^9y^{21}}{8}$

47. $\left(\dfrac{x^{-5}y^2}{x^{-3}y^5}\right)^{-2} = \dfrac{x^{10}y^{-4}}{x^6y^{-10}}$

$= x^{10-6}y^{-4-(-10)}$
$= x^4y^6$

48. $\left(\dfrac{x^{-8}y^{-3}}{x^{-5}y^6}\right)^{-1} = \dfrac{x^8y^3}{x^5y^{-6}}$

$= x^{8-5}y^{3-(-6)}$
$= x^3y^9$

50. $\left(\dfrac{2x^6y^4z^0}{8x^{-3}y^0z^{-5}}\right)^{-1} = \dfrac{2^{-1}x^{-6}y^{-4}z^0}{8^{-1}x^3y^0z^5}$

$= \dfrac{8}{2}x^{-6-3}y^{-4-0}z^{0-5}$

$= 4x^{-9}y^{-4}z^{-5}$

$= \dfrac{4}{x^9y^4z^5}$

51. $\left(\dfrac{ab^{-3}c^{-2}}{a^{-3}b^0c^{-5}}\right)^{-1} = \dfrac{a^{-1}b^3c^2}{a^3b^0c^5}$

$= a^{-1-3}b^{3-0}c^{2-5}$
$= a^{-4}b^3c^{-3}$

$= \dfrac{b^3}{a^4c^3}$

52. $\left(\dfrac{a^3b^2c^1}{a^{-1}b^{-2}c^{-3}}\right)^{-2} = \dfrac{a^{-6}b^{-4}c^{-2}}{a^2b^4c^6}$

$= a^{-6-2}b^{-4-4}c^{-2-6}$
$= a^{-8}b^{-8}c^{-8}$

$= \dfrac{1}{a^8b^8c^8}$

54. $\left(\dfrac{x^{-1}y^4}{x^{-5}y^0}\right)^{-1}\left(\dfrac{x^3y^{-1}}{xy^{-3}}\right)$

$= \dfrac{x^1y^{-4}}{x^5y^0}\left(\dfrac{x^3y^{-1}}{xy^{-3}}\right)$

$= \dfrac{x^4y^{-5}}{x^6y^{-3}}$

$= x^{4-6}y^{-5-(-3)}$
$= x^{-2}y^{-2}$

$= \dfrac{1}{x^2y^2}$

55. $2x^2y^3\left(\frac{7xy^4}{14x^3y^6}\right)^{-2} = 2x^2y^3\left(\frac{7^{-2}x^{-2}y^{-8}}{14^{-2}x^{-6}y^{-12}}\right)$

$= 2x^2y^3\left(\frac{14^2}{7^2}x^{-2-(-6)}y^{-8-(-12)}\right)$

$= 2x^2y^3\left(\frac{196}{49}x^4y^4\right)$

$= \frac{392x^6y^7}{49}$

$= 8x^6y^7$

56. $3xy^5\left(\frac{2x^4y}{6x^5y^3}\right)^{-2} = 3xy^5\left(\frac{2^{-2}x^{-8}y^{-2}}{6^{-2}x^{-10}y^{-6}}\right)$

$= 3xy^5\left(\frac{6^2}{2^2}x^{-8-(-10)}x^{-2-(-6)}\right)$

$= 3xy^5\left(\frac{36}{4}x^2y^4\right)$

$= 27x^3y^9$

58. $8x^4y^{-3}\left(\frac{12x^{-3}y^{-2}}{24x^4y^{-5}}\right)^{-3}$

$= 8x^4y^{-3}\left(\frac{12^{-3}x^9y^6}{24^{-3}x^{-12}y^{15}}\right)$

$= 8x^4y^{-3}\left(\frac{24^3}{12^3}x^{9-(-12)}y^{6-15}\right)$

$= 8x^4y^{-3}(8x^{21}y^{-9})$

$= 64x^{25}y^{-12}$

$= \frac{64x^{25}}{y^{12}}$

59. $(4.5 \times 10^6)(2 \times 10^4)$
$= (4.5 \times 2)(10^6 \times 10^4)$
$= 9.0 \times 10^{10}$

60. $(4.3 \times 10^8)(2 \times 10^5)$
$= (4.3 \times 2)(10^8 \times 10^5)$
$= 8.6 \times 10^{13}$

62. $\frac{9.6 \times 10^{11}}{4.8 \times 10^{15}} = 2 \times 10^{11-15} = 2 \times 10^{-4}$

63. $\frac{(5 \times 10^6)(4 \times 10^{-8})}{8 \times 10^4} = 2.5 \times 10^{-2} \times 10^{-4}$

$= 2.5 \times 10^{-6}$

64. $\frac{(6 \times 10^{-7})(3 \times 10^9)}{5 \times 10^6} = 3.6 \times 10^2 \times 10^{-6}$

$= 3.6 \times 10^{-4}$

66. $\frac{(7.5 \times 10^{-6})(1.5 \times 10^9)}{(1.8 \times 10^4)(2.5 \times 10^{-2})} = 2.5 \times 10^3 \times 10^{-2}$

$= 2.5 \times 10^1$

67. $(2{,}000{,}000)(0.0000249)$
$= (2.0 \times 10^6)(2.49 \times 10^{-5})$
$= 4.98 \times 10^1$

68. $(30{,}000)(0.000192)$
$= (3.0 \times 10^4)(1.92 \times 10^{-4})$
$= 5.76$

70. $\frac{0.000545}{1{,}090{,}000} = \frac{5.45 \times 10^{-4}}{1.09 \times 10^6}$

$= 5.0 \times 10^{-4-6}$
$= 5 \times 10^{-10}$

71. $\frac{(40{,}000)(0.0007)}{0.0014}$

$= \frac{(4.0 \times 10^4)(7.0 \times 10^{-4})}{1.4 \times 10^{-3}}$

$= \frac{28 \times 10^0}{1.4 \times 10^{-3}}$

$= 20 \times 10^3$
$= 2.0 \times 10^1 \times 10^3$
$= 2 \times 10^4$

72. $\dfrac{(800{,}000)(0.00002)}{4000} = \dfrac{(8.0 \times 10^5)(2.0 \times 10^{-5})}{4.0 \times 10^3}$

$= \dfrac{16 \times 10^0}{4 \times 10^3}$

$= 4 \times 10^{-3}$

74. $(4^3)^x = 4^9$
$4^{3x} = 4^9$ *The exponents become:*
$3x = 9$
$x = 3$

75. $\dfrac{3^x}{3^5} = 3^4$

$3^{x-5} = 3^4$ *The exponents become:*
$x - 5 = 4$
$x = 9$

76. $\dfrac{3^x}{3^5} = 3^{-4}$

$3^{x-5} = 3^{-4}$ *The exponents become:*
$x - 5 = -4$
$x = 1$

78. $(2^x)^3 = \dfrac{1}{8}$

$2^{3x} = 2^{-3}$ *The exponents become:*
$3x = -3$
$x = -1$

79. $(5.9 \times 10^{12})(1.7 \times 10^6) = 10.03 \times 10^{18}$
$= 1.003 \times 10^{19}$

80. $\dfrac{9.3 \times 10^7}{1.2 \times 10^7} = 7.75$ *min.*

82. $8 + 3(x + 4) = 8 + 3x + 12$
$= 3x + 20$

83. $3(2a + 1) - 6a = 6a + 3 - 6a = 3$

84. $5(3a + 3) - 8a = 15a + 15 - 8a$
$= 7a + 15$

86. $\dfrac{1}{5}(5y - 10) - \dfrac{1}{3}(3y + 6)$

$= (y - 2) - (y + 2)$
$= y - 2 - y - 2$
$= -4$

87. $3 - 7(x - 5) + 3x$
$= 3 - 7x + 35 + 3x$
$= -4x + 38$

88. $4 - 9(x - 3) + 5x$
$= 4 - 9x + 27 + 5x$
$= -4x + 31$

90. $\dfrac{1}{2} - \dfrac{1}{4} + \dfrac{1}{3}$

$= \dfrac{6}{12} - \dfrac{3}{12} + \dfrac{4}{12}$ *LCD* = 12

$= \dfrac{7}{12}$

91. $\dfrac{5}{12} + \dfrac{9}{14} - \dfrac{1}{7} + \dfrac{1}{2}$

$= \dfrac{35}{84} + \dfrac{54}{84} - \dfrac{12}{84} + \dfrac{42}{84}$ *LCD* = 84

$= \dfrac{119}{84}$

$= \dfrac{17}{12}$

92. $\dfrac{4}{15} + \dfrac{3}{10} - \dfrac{1}{5} - \dfrac{1}{2}$

$= \dfrac{8}{30} + \dfrac{9}{30} - \dfrac{6}{30} - \dfrac{15}{30}$ *LCD* = 30

$= -\dfrac{4}{30}$

$= -\dfrac{2}{15}$

94. $\dfrac{(1.43 \times 10^{33})(1.87 \times 10^{47})}{2.21 \times 10^{50}} = \dfrac{2.6741 \times 10^{80}}{2.21 \times 10^{50}}$

$= 1.21 \times 10^{30}$

95. $\dfrac{(1.05 \times 10^{-18})(5.25 \times 10^{23})}{3.15 \times 10^{-37}} = \dfrac{5.5125 \times 10^{5}}{3.15 \times 10^{-37}}$

$= 1.75 \times 10^{42}$

96. $\dfrac{(3.51 \times 10^{-51})(5.13 \times 10^{37})}{2.47 \times 10^{-18}} = \dfrac{18.0063 \times 10^{-14}}{2.47 \times 10^{-18}}$

$= 7.29 \times 10^{4}$

98. $\dfrac{x^{n-3}}{x^{n-7}} = x^{n-3-(n-7)}$

$= x^{n-3-n+7}$
$= x^4$

99. $\dfrac{a^{3m}a^{m+1}}{a^{4m}} = \dfrac{a^{3m+m+1}}{a^{4m}}$

$= a^{4m+1-4m}$
$= a$

100. $\dfrac{a^{2m}a^{m-5}}{a^{3m-7}} = a^{2m+m-5-(3m-7)}$

$= a^{3m-5-3m+7}$
$= a^2$

**Section 3.3**

2. $2x^2 + 4x - 1$

Trinomial, degree 2,
leading coefficient 2.

3. $3x - 5$

Binomial, degree 1,
leading coefficient 3.

4. $5y + 3$

Binomial, degree 1,
leading coefficient 5.

6. $9a^2 - 8a - 4$

Trinomial, degree 2,
leading coefficient 9.

7. $4x^3 - 6x^2 + 5x - 3$

Polynomial, degree 3,
leading coefficient 4.

8. $9x^4 + 4x^3 - 2x^2 + x$

Polynomial, degree 4,
leading coefficient 9.

10. $-16$

Monomial, degree 0
leading coefficient -16.

11. $4x - 5 + 6x^3 = 6x^3 + 4x - 5$

Trinomial, degree 3,
leading coefficient 6.

12. $9x + 2 + 3x^3 = 3x^3 + 9x + 2$

Trinomial, degree 3,
leading coefficient 3.

14. $(8x - 5) + (-5x + 4) = 3x - 1$

15. $2x^2 - 3x + 10x - 15 = 2x^2 + 7x - 15$

16. $6x^2 - 4x - 15x + 10 = 6x^2 - 19x + 10$

18. $28a^2 - 8ab + 7ab - 2b^2 = 28a^2 - ab - 2b^2$

19. $(5x^2 - 6x + 1) - (4x^2 + 7x - 2)$
$= 5x^2 - 6x + 1 - 4x^2 - 7x + 2$
$= x^2 - 13x + 3$

20. $(11x^2 - 8x) - (4x^2 - 2x - 7)$
$= 11x^2 - 8x - 4x^2 + 2x + 7$
$= 7x^2 - 6x + 7$

22. $\left(\frac{2}{3}x^2 - \frac{1}{2}x\right) - \left(\frac{1}{4}x^2 + \frac{1}{6}x + \frac{1}{12}\right) - \left(\frac{1}{2}x^2 + \frac{1}{4}\right)$

$= \frac{2}{3}x^2 - \frac{1}{2}x - \frac{1}{4}x^2 - \frac{1}{6}x - \frac{1}{12} - \frac{1}{2}x^2 - \frac{1}{4}$

$= \frac{8}{12}x^2 - \frac{6}{12}x - \frac{3}{12}x^2 - \frac{2}{12}x - \frac{1}{12} - \frac{6}{12}x^2 - \frac{3}{12}$ *LCD* = 12

$= -\frac{1}{12}x^2 - \frac{8}{12}x - \frac{4}{12}$

$= -\frac{1}{12}x^2 - \frac{2}{3}x - \frac{1}{3}$

23. $(y^3 - 2y^2 - 3y + 4) - (2y^3 - y^2 + y - 3)$
$= y^3 - 2y^2 - 3y + 4 - 2y^3 + y^2 - y + 3$
$= y^3 - y^2 - 4y + 7$

24. $(8y^3 - 3y^2 + 7y + 2) - (-4y^3 + 6y^2 - 5y - 8)$
$= 8y^3 - 3y^2 + 7y + 2 + 4y^3 - 6y^2 + 5y + 8$
$= 12y^3 - 9y^2 + 12y + 10$

26. $(x^3 - x) - (x^2 + x) + (x^3 - 1) - (-3x + 2)$
$= x^3 - x - x^2 - x + x^3 - 1 + 3x - 2$
$= 2x^3 - x^2 + x - 3$

27. $\left(\frac{4}{7}x^2 - \frac{1}{7}xy + \frac{1}{14}y^2\right) - \left(\frac{1}{2}x^2 - \frac{2}{7}xy - \frac{9}{14}y^2\right)$

$= \frac{8}{14}x^2 - \frac{2}{14}xy + \frac{1}{14}y^2 - \frac{7}{14}x^2 + \frac{4}{14}xy + \frac{9}{14}y^2 \quad LCD = 14$

$= \frac{1}{14}x^2 + \frac{1}{7}xy + \frac{5}{7}y^2$

28. $\left(\frac{1}{5}x^2 - \frac{1}{2}xy + \frac{1}{10}y^2\right) - \left(-\frac{3}{10}x^2 + \frac{2}{5}xy - \frac{1}{2}y^2\right)$

$= \frac{2}{10}x^2 - \frac{5}{10}xy + \frac{1}{10}y^2 + \frac{3}{10}x^2 - \frac{4}{10}xy + \frac{5}{10}y^2 \quad LCD = 10$

$= \frac{1}{2}x^2 - \frac{9}{10}xy + \frac{3}{5}y^2$

30. $(a^3 - 3a^2b + 3ab^2 - b^3) - (a^3 + 3a^2b + 3ab^2 + b^3)$
$= a^3 - 3a^2b + 3ab^2 - b^3 - a^3 - 3a^2b - 3ab^2 - b^3$
$= -6a^2b - 2b^3$

31. $(2x^2 - 7x) - (2x^2 - 4x) = 2x^2 - 7x - 2x^2 + 4x = -3x$

32. $(-3x + 9) - (-3x + 6) = -3x + 9 + 3x - 6 = 3$

34. $(9x^3 - 6x^2 + 2) + (3x^2 - 5x + 4) = 9x^3 - 3x^2 - 5x + 6$

35. $(9x^5 - 4x^3 - 6) - (-8x^5 - 4x^3 + 6)$
$= 9x^5 - 4x^3 - 6 + 8x^5 + 4x^3 - 6$
$= 17x^5 - 12$

36. $(2x^4 + 3x^3 + 4x^2) - (4x^4 - 3x^3 - 2x^2)$
$= 2x^4 + 3x^3 + 4x^2 - 4x^4 + 3x^3 + 2x^2$
$= -2x^4 + 6x^3 + 6x^2$

38. $(a^2 - ab - b^2) + (a^2 + ab - b^2) + (a^2 + 2ab + b^2)$
$= 3a^2 + 2ab - b^2$

39. $-[2 - (4 - x)] = -[2 - 4 + x] = -[-2 + x] = 2 - x$

40. $-[-3 - (x - 6)] = -[-3 - x + 6]$
$= -[3 - x]$
$= x - 3$

42. $-6[(2x - 5) - 3(8x - 2)]$
$= -6[2x - 5 - 24x + 6]$
$= -6[-22x + 1]$
$= 132x - 6$

43. $4x - 5[3 - (x - 4)] = 4x - 5[3 - x + 4]$
$= 4x - 5[-x + 7]$
$= 4x + 5x - 35$
$= 9x - 35$

44. $x - 7[3x - (2 - x)] = x - 7[3x - 2 + x]$
$= x - 7[4x - 2]$
$= x - 28x + 14$
$= -27x + 14$

46. $(8x - y) - [-(2x + y) - (-3x - 6y)]$
$= 8x - y - [-2x - y + 3x + 6y]$
$= 8x - y - [x + 5y]$
$= 8x - y - x - 5y$
$= 7x - 6y$

47. $4a - \{3a + 2[a - 5(a + 1) + 4]\}$
$= 4a - \{3a + 2[a - 5a - 5 + 4]\}$
$= 4a - \{3a + 2[-4a - 1]\}$
$= 4a - \{3a - 8a - 2\}$
$= 4a - \{-5a - 2\}$
$= 4a + 5a + 2$
$= 9a + 2$

48. $6a - \{-2a - 6[2a + 3(a - 1) - 6]\}$
$= 6a - \{-2a - 6[2a + 3a - 3 - 6]\}$
$= 6a - \{-2a - 6[5a - 9]\}$
$= 6a - \{-2a - 30a + 54\}$
$= 6a - \{-32a + 54\}$
$= 6a + 32a - 54$
$= 38a - 54$

50. $4x^2 + 3x - 2 \qquad x = -1$
$= 4(-1)^2 + 3(-1) - 2$
$= 4 - 3 - 2$
$= -1$

51. $\frac{3}{2}x^2 - \frac{3}{4}x + 1$ *when* $x = 12$

$= \frac{3}{2}(12)^2 - \frac{3}{4}(12) + 1$

$= 216 - 9 + 1$
$= 208$

52. $\frac{2}{5}x^2 - \frac{1}{10}x + 2$ *when* $x = 10$

$= \frac{2}{5}(10)^2 - \frac{1}{10}(10) + 2$

$= 40 - 1 + 2$
$= 41$

54. $x^3 + x^2 + x + 1$ *when* $x = -2$
$= (-2)^3 + (-2)^2 + (-2) + 1$
$= -8 + 4 - 2 + 1$
$= -5$

55. $(a + 4)^2$ *when* $a = 3$
$= (3 + 4)^2$
$= 7^2$
$= 49$

$a^2 + 16$ *when* $a = 3$
$= 3^2 + 16$
$= 9 + 16$
$= 25$

$a^2 + 8a + 16$ *when* $a = 3$
$= 3^2 + 8(3) + 16$
$= 9 + 24 + 16$
$= 49$

56. $(2a - 3)^2$ *when* $a = 2$
$= (2 \cdot 2 - 3)^2$
$= (4 - 3)^2$
$= 1^2$
$= 1$

$4a^2 - 9$ *when* $a = 2$
$= 4(2^2) - 9$
$= 4(4) - 9$
$= 16 - 9$
$= 7$

$4a^2 - 12a + 9$ *when* $a = 2$
$= 4(2)^2 - 12(2) + 9$
$= 4(4) - 24 + 9$
$= 16 - 24 + 9$
$= 1$

58. $h = -16t^2 + 64t \qquad t = 1$ *sec.*
$h = -16(1)^2 + 64(1)$
$h = -16 + 64$
$h = 48$ *ft*

$h = -16t^2 + 64t \qquad t = 3$ *sec*
$h = -16(3)^2 + 64(3)$
$h = -16(9) + 192$
$h = -144 + 192$
$h = 48$ *ft.*

59. $P = R - C$
$C = 60x + 300,\ R = 100x - .5x^2$
$P = (100x - .5x^2) - (60x + 300)$
$P = 100x - .5x^2 - 60x - 300$

$P = -300 + 40x - .5x^2 \qquad x = 60$
$P = -300 + 40(60) - .5(60)^2$
$P = -300 + 2400 - .5(3600)$
$P = 2100 - 1800$
$P = \$300$

60. $P = R - C$
$C = 200x + 1600,\ R = 300x - .6x^2$
$P = (300x - .6x^2) - (200x + 1600)$
$P = 300x - .6x^2 - 200x - 1600$
$P = -1600 + 100x - .6x^2$

$P = -1600 + 100(50) - .6(50)^2 \qquad x = 50$
$P = -1600 + 5000 - .6(2500)$
$P = 3400 - 1500.0$
$P = \$1900$

62. $P = R - C$
$C = 1200 + 3.5x,\ R = 9x - .003x^2$
$P = 9x - .003x^2 - (1200 + 3.5x)$
$P = 9x - .003x^2 - 1200 - 3.5x$
$P = -1200 + 5.5x - .003x^2$

$P = -1200 + 5.5(1000) - .003(1000)^2 \qquad x = 1000$
$P = -1200 + 5500 - 3000$
$P = \$1300$

63. $4x^3(-3x) = -12x^4$

64. $4x^3(-3x) = -12x^4$

66. $2a^2b(-6a^2b) = -12a^4b^2$

67. $2x(3x^2) = 6x^3$

68. $-3y(4y^2) = -12y^3$

70. $\frac{1}{2} - \frac{y}{5} = -\frac{9}{10} + \frac{y}{2} \qquad LCD = 10$

$5 - 2y = -9 + 5y$
$5 = -9 + 7y$
$14 = 7y$
$2 = y$

71. $3 - \frac{2}{3}y = -9$

$-\frac{2}{3}y = -12$

$y = 18$

72. $5 = -\frac{3}{4}y - 4$

$9 = -\frac{3}{4}y$

$-12 = y$

74. $3(5t - 1) - (3 - 2t) = 5t - 8$
$15t - 3 - 3 + 2t = 5t - 8$
$17t - 6 = 5t - 8$
$12t - 6 = -8$
$12t = -2$

$t = -\frac{1}{6}$

## Section 3.4

2. $-3x(5x^2 - 6x - 4) = -15x^3 + 18x^2 + 12x$

3. $-3a^2(a^3 - 6a^2 + 7) = -3a^5 + 18a^4 - 21a^2$

4. $4a^3(3a^2 - a + 1) = 12a^5 - 4a^4 + 4a^3$

6. $5a^2b^2(8a^2 - 2ab + b^2)$
$= 40a^4b^2 - 10a^3b^3 + 5a^2b^4$

7. $-4x^2y^3(7x^2 - 3xy + 6y^2)$
$= -28x^4y^3 + 12x^3y^4 - 24x^2y^5$

8. $-3x^3y^2(6x^2 - 3xy + 4y^2)$
$= -18x^5y^2 + 9x^4y^3 - 12x^3y^4$

10. $5r^2s^3(2r^3 + 3r^2s - 4rs^2 + 5s^3)$
$= 10r^5s^3 + 15r^4s^4 - 20r^3s^5 + 25r^2s^6$

11.
$$\begin{array}{r} x - 5 \\ x + 3 \\ \hline 3x - 15 \\ x^2 - 5x \phantom{- 15} \\ \hline x^2 - 2x - 15 \end{array}$$

12.
$$\begin{array}{r} x + 4 \\ x + 6 \\ \hline 6x + 24 \\ x^2 + 4x \phantom{+ 24} \\ \hline x^2 + 10x + 24 \end{array}$$

14.
$$\begin{array}{r} 3x^2 + 4 \\ 2x^2 - 5 \\ \hline -15x^2 - 20 \\ 6x^4 + 8x^2 \phantom{- 20} \\ \hline 6x^4 - 7x^2 - 20 \end{array}$$

15.
$$\begin{array}{r} x^2 + 6x + 5 \\ + 9x^2 + 18x + 3 \\ \hline 3x^2 + 18x + 15 \\ x^3 + 6x^2 + 5x \phantom{+ 15} \\ \hline x^3 + 9x^2 + 23x + 15 \end{array}$$

16.
$$\begin{array}{r} x^2 - 5x + 7 \\ x - 2 \\ \hline - 2x^2 + 10x - 14 \\ x^3 - 5x^2 + 7x \phantom{- 14} \\ \hline x^3 - 7x^2 + 17x - 14 \end{array}$$

18.
$$\begin{array}{r} 3a^2 - 5a + 1 \\ 2a - 3 \\ \hline - 9a^2 + 15a - 3 \\ 6a^3 - 10a^2 + 2a \phantom{- 3} \\ \hline 6a^3 - 19a^2 + 17a - 3 \end{array}$$

19.
$$\begin{array}{r} a^2 + ab + b^2 \\ a - b \\ \hline - a^2b - ab^2 - b^3 \\ a^3 + a^2b + ab^2 \phantom{- b^3} \\ \hline a^3 \phantom{+ a^2b + ab^2} - b^3 \end{array}$$

20.
$$\begin{array}{r} a^2 - ab + b^2 \\ a + b \\ \hline a^2b - ab^2 + b^3 \\ a^3 - a^2b + ab^2 \phantom{+ b^3} \\ \hline a^3 \phantom{- a^2b + ab^2} + b^3 \end{array}$$

22.
$$\begin{array}{r} x^2 + 3xy + 9y^2 \\ x - 3y \\ \hline - 3x^2y - 9xy^2 - 27y^3 \\ x^3 + 3x^2y + 9xy^2 \phantom{- 27y^3} \\ \hline x^3 \phantom{+ 3x^2y + 9xy^2} - 27y^3 \end{array}$$

23.
$$\begin{array}{r} a^2 + ab + b^2 \\ 2a - 3b \\ \hline - 3a^2b - 3ab^2 - 3b^3 \\ 2a^3 + 2a^2b + 2ab^2 \phantom{- 3b^3} \\ \hline 2a^3 - a^2b - ab^2 - 3b^3 \end{array}$$

24.
$$\begin{array}{r} a^2 - ab - b^2 \\ 5a - 2b \\ \hline - 2a^2b + 2ab^2 + 2b^3 \\ 5a^3 - 5a^2b - 5ab^2 \phantom{+ 2b^3} \\ \hline 5a^3 - 7a^2b - 3ab^2 + 2b^3 \end{array}$$

26.
$$\begin{array}{r} 7x^2 - 6xy + 3y^2 \\ 2x - 6y \\ \hline - 42x^2y + 36xy^2 - 18y^3 \\ 14x^3 - 12x^2y + 6xy^2 \phantom{- 18y^3} \\ \hline 14x^3 - 54x^2y + 42xy^2 - 18y^3 \end{array}$$

27. $2x^2(x - 5) = 2x^3 - 10x^2$

$$\begin{array}{r} 2x^3 - 10x^2 \\ 3x - 7 \\ \hline - 14x^3 + 70x^2 \\ 6x^4 - 30x^3 \phantom{+ 70x^2} \\ \hline 6x^4 - 44x^3 + 70x^2 \end{array}$$

28. $-5x^3(3x - 2) = -15x^4 + 10x^3$

$$\begin{array}{r} -15x^4 + 10x^3 \\ \underline{x + 4} \\ -60x^4 + 40x^3 \\ \underline{-15x^5 + 10x^4 \phantom{+ 40x^3}} \\ -15x^5 - 50x^4 + 40x^3 \end{array}$$

$(x - 2)(2x + 3)(3x - 4)$
$= 6x^3 - 11x^2 - 14x + 24$

30.
$$\begin{array}{r} x + 5 \\ \underline{-2x - 6} \\ -6x - 30 \\ \underline{2x^2 + 10x \phantom{- 30}} \\ 2x^2 + 4x - 30 \end{array}$$

$$\begin{array}{r} 2x^2 + 4x - 30 \\ \underline{x - 3} \\ -6x^2 - 12x + 90 \\ \underline{2x^3 + 4x^2 - 30x \phantom{+ 90}} \\ 2x^3 - 2x^2 - 4xx + 90 \end{array}$$

$(x + 5)(2x - 6)(x - 3)$
$= 2x^3 + 2x^2 - 42x + 90$

32. $(x + 2)(x - 3) = x^2 - 3x + 2x - 6$
$= x^2 - x - 6$

34. $(x^2 + 2)(x^2 - 3) = x^4 - 3x^2 + 2x^2 - 6$
$= x^4 - x^2 - 6$

35. $(2a + 3)(3a + 2) = 6a^2 + 4a + 9a + 6$
$= 6a^2 + 13a + 6$

36. $(5a - 4)(2a + 1) = 10a^2 + 5a - 8a - 4$
$= 10a^2 - 3a - 4$

38. $(7 - t)(6 - 3t) = 42 - 21t - 6t + 3t^2$
$= 42 - 27t + 3t^2$

39. $(x^3 + 3)(x^3 - 5) = x^6 - 5x^3 + 3x^3 - 15$
$= x^6 - 2x^3 - 15$

40. $(x^3 + 4)(x^3 - 7) = x^6 - 7x^3 + 4x^3 - 28$
$= x^6 - 3x^3 - 28$

42. $(3a - 1)(2a - 1) = 6a^2 - 3a - 2a + 1$
$= 6a^2 - 5a + 1$

43. $(5x - 6y)(4x + 3y)$
$= 20x^2 + 15xy - 24xy - 18y^2$
$= 20x^2 - 9xy - 18y^2$

44. $(6x - 5y)(2x - 3y)$
$= 12x^2 - 18xy - 10xy + 15y^2$
$= 12x^2 - 28xy + 15y^2$

46. $\left(5t - \frac{1}{5}\right)\left(10t + \frac{3}{5}\right)$
$= 50t^2 + 3t - 2t - \frac{3}{25}$

$= 50t^2 + t - \frac{3}{25}$

47. $(b - 4a^2)(b + 3a^2)$
$= b^2 + 3a^2b - 4a^2b - 12a^4$
$= b^2 - a^2b - 12a^4$

48. $(b + 5a^2)(b - 2a^2)$
$= b^2 - 2a^2b + 5a^2b - 10a^4$
$= b^2 + 3a^2b - 10a^4$

50. $(3x - 4y)^2 = (3x)^2 + 2(3x)(-4y) + (-4y)^2$
$= 9x^2 - 24xy + 16y^2$

51. $(5 - 3t^3)^2 = (5)^2 + 2(5)(-3t^3) + (-3t^3)^2$
$= 25 - 30t^3 + 9t^6$

52. $(7 - 2t^4)^2 = (7)^2 + 2(7)(-2t^4) + (-2t^4)^2$
$= 49 - 28t^4 + 4t^8$

54. $(6a - 1)(6a + 1) = (6a)^2 - (1)^2$
$= 36a^2 - 1$

55. $(3r^2 + 7s)(3r^2 - 7s) = (3r^2)^2 - (7s)^2$
$= 9r^4 - 49s^2$

56. $(5r^2 - 2s)(5r^2 + 2s) = (5r^2)^2 - (2s)^2$
$= 25r^4 - 4s^2$

58. $\left(\frac{3}{4}x - \frac{1}{7}\right)\left(\frac{3}{4}x + \frac{1}{7}\right) = \left(\frac{3}{4}x\right)^2 - \left(\frac{1}{7}\right)^2$
$= \frac{9}{16}x^2 - \frac{1}{49}$

59. $(x - 2)^3 = (x - 2)(x - 2)(x - 2)$
$= (x^2 - 4x + 4)(x - 2)$ *then*

$$\begin{array}{r} x^2 - 4x + 4 \\ \underline{-2x^2 + 12x - 2} \\ x^3 - 2x^2 + 8x - 8 \\ \underline{x^3 - 4x^2 + 4x \phantom{- 8}} \\ x^3 - 6x^2 + 12x - 8 \end{array}$$

60. $(x + 4)^3$
$= (x + 4)(x + 4)(x + 4)$
$= (x^2 + 8x + 16)(x + 4)$ *then*

$$\begin{array}{r} x^2 + 8x + 16 \\ \underline{x + 4} \\ 4x^2 + 32x + 64 \\ \underline{x^3 + 8x^2 + 16x \phantom{+ 64}} \\ x^3 + 12x^2 + 48x + 64 \end{array}$$

62. $(4x + 1)^3$
$= (4x + 1)(4x + 1)(4x + 1)$
$= (16x^2 + 8x + 1)(4x + 1)$ *then*

$$\begin{array}{r} 16x^2 + 8x + 1 \\ \underline{4x + 1} \\ 16x^2 + 8x + 1 \\ \underline{64x^3 + 32x^2 + 4x \phantom{+ 1}} \\ 64x^3 + 48x^2 + 12x + 1 \end{array}$$

63. $\left(x - \frac{1}{2}\right)^3 = \left(x - \frac{1}{2}\right)\left(x - \frac{1}{2}\right)\left(x - \frac{1}{2}\right)$
$= \left(x^2 - x + \frac{1}{4}\right)\left(x - \frac{1}{2}\right)$ *then*

$$\begin{array}{r} x^2 - x + \frac{1}{4} \\ \underline{x - \frac{1}{2}} \\ -\frac{1}{2}x^2 + \frac{1}{2}x - \frac{1}{8} \\ \underline{x^3 - x^2 + \frac{1}{4}x \phantom{- \frac{1}{8}}} \\ x^3 - \frac{3}{2}x^2 + \frac{3}{4}x - \frac{1}{8} \end{array}$$

64. $\left(x + \frac{1}{4}\right)^3 = \left(x + \frac{1}{4}\right)\left(x + \frac{1}{4}\right)\left(x + \frac{1}{4}\right)$
$= \left(x^2 + \frac{1}{2}x + \frac{1}{16}\right)\left(x + \frac{1}{4}\right)$ *then*

$$\begin{array}{r} x^2 + \frac{1}{2}x + \frac{1}{16} \\ \underline{x + \frac{1}{4}} \\ \frac{1}{4}x^2 + \frac{1}{8}x + \frac{1}{64} \\ \underline{x^3 + \frac{1}{2}x^2 + \frac{1}{16}x \phantom{+ \frac{1}{64}}} \\ x^3 + \frac{3}{4}x^2 + \frac{3}{16}x + \frac{1}{64} \end{array}$$

66. $2(x + 1)(x + 2)(x + 3)$
$= (2x + 2)(x + 2)(x + 3)$
$= (2x^2 + 6x + 4)(x + 3)$ *then*

$$\begin{array}{r} 2x^2 + 6x + 4 \\ \underline{x + 3} \\ 6x^2 + 18x + 12 \\ \underline{2x^3 + 6x^2 + 4x \phantom{+ 12}} \\ 2x^3 + 12x^2 + 22x + 12 \end{array}$$

67. $(b^2 + 8)(a^2 + 1)$
$= a^2b^2 + b^2 + 8a^2 + 8$

68. $(b^2 + 1)(a^4 - 5)$
$= a^4b^2 - 5b^2 + a^4 - 5$

70. $(x - 4)(2y^3 + 1)$
$= 2xy^3 + x - 8y^3 - 4$

71. $(x + 1)^2 + (x + 2)^2 + (x + 3)^2$
$= (x^2 + 2x + 1) + (x^2 + 4x + 4) + (x^2 + 6x + 9)$
$= 3x^2 + 12x + 14$

72. $(x - 1)^2 + (x - 2)^2 + (x - 3)^2$
$= (x^2 - 2x + 1) + (x^2 - 4x + 4) + (x^2 - 6x + 9)$
$= 3x^2 - 12x + 14$

74. $(5x - 4)^2 - (5x + 4)^2$
$= (25x^2 - 40x + 16) - (25x^2 + 40x + 16)$
$= 25x^2 - 40x + 16 - 25x^2 - 40x - 16$
$= -80x$

75. $(x - 1)^3 - (x + 1)^3$
$= (x^2 - 2x + 1)(x - 1) - (x^2 + 2x + 1)(x + 1)$
$= (x^3 - 3x^2 + 3x - 1) - (x^3 + 3x^2 + 3x + 1)$
$= x^3 - 3x^2 + 3x - 1 - x^3 - 3x^2 - 3x - 1$
$= -6x^2 - 2$

76. $(x - 3)^3 - (x + 3)^3$
$= (x^2 - 6x + 9)(x - 3) - (x^2 + 6x + 9)(x + 3)$
$= (x^3 - 9x^2 + 27x - 27) - (x^3 + 9x^2 + 27x + 27)$
$= x^3 - 9x^2 + 27x - 27 - x^3 - 9x^2 - 27x - 27$
$= -18x^2 - 54$

78. $[(x - 5) - y][(x - 5) + y]$
$= (x - 5)^2 - (y)^2$
$= x^2 - 10x + 25 - y^2$

79. $[(x + y) + z]^2 = (x + y)^2 + 2(x + y)(z) + (z)^2$
$= x^2 + 2xy + y^2 + 2xz + 2yz + z^2$

80. $[x + (y + z)]^2 = (x)^2 + 2(x)(y + z) + (y + z)^2$
$= x^2 + 2xy + 2xz + y^2 + 2yz + z^2$

82. *If we expand* $(p + 1)^2 = p^2 + 2pq + a^2$,
*we find the middle term is* $2pq$.

*When* $p = \frac{1}{2}$ *and* $q = \frac{1}{2}$

*the expression* $2pq$

*becomes* $2(\frac{1}{2})(\frac{1}{2})$

$= \frac{1}{2}$ *of the next generation will have pink flowers.*

83. $a^4 - b^4 \quad a = 2,\ b = 3$
$= 2^4 - 3^4$
$= 16 - 81$
$= -65$

$(a - b)^4 \quad a = 2,\ b = 3$
$= (2 - 3)^4$
$= (-1)^4$
$= 1$

$(a^2 + b^2)(a + b)(a - b) \quad a = 2,\ b = 3$
$= (2^2 + 3^2)(2 + 3)(2 - 3)$
$= (13)(5)(-1)$
$= -65$

84. $a^3 + b^3 \quad a = 2,\ b = 3$
$= 2^3 + 3^3$
$= 8 + 27$
$= 35$

$(a + b)^3 \quad a = 2,\ b = 3$
$= (2 + 3)^3$
$= 125$

$a^3 + 3a^2b + 3ab^2 + b^3 \quad a = 2,\ b = 3$
$= (2)^3 + 3(2)^2(3) + 3(2)(3)^2 + (3)^3$
$= 8 + 36 + 54 + 27$
$= 125$

86. $R = xp \quad x = 800 - 100p,\ p = \$3.80$
$R = (800 - 100p)p$
$R = 800p - 100p^2$
$R = 800(3.80) - 100(3.80)^2$
$R = \$1,596$

87. $R = xp \quad x = 350 - 10p,\ 0 = \$28.50$
$R = (350 - 10p)p$
$R = 350p - 10p^2$
$R = 350(28.50) - 10(28.50)^2$
$R = \$1,852.50$

88. $R = xp \quad x = 1,475 - 250p,\ 0 = \$5.10$
$R = (1475 - 250p)p$
$R = 1475p - 250p^2$
$R = 1475(5.10) - 250(5.10)^2$
$R = \$1,020$

90. If we let x = the first of the odd integers, then x + 2 is the next consecutive odd integer, and x + 4 is the one after that.

| Total Surface Area | Area of two sides | Area of the the top and bottom | Area of the front and back |
|---|---|---|---|
| S | = 2(x + 2)(x + 4) | + 2x(x + 4) | + 2x(x + 2) |

$$S = 2(x+2)(x+4) + 2x(x+4) + 2x(x+2)$$
$$= 2x^2 + 12x + 16 + 2x^2 + 8x + 2x^2 + 4x$$
$$= 6x^2 + 24x + 16$$

The surface area of a rectangle box having odd or even consecutive numbers as their sides give the same formula.

91. $A = 100(1 + r)^4$
$a = 100(1 + 4r + 6r^2 + 4r^3 + r^4)$
$A = 100 + 400r + 600r^2 + 400r^3 + 100r^4$

92. $A = P\left(1 + \frac{r}{2}\right)^2$

$A = P\left(1 + r + \frac{r^2}{4}\right)$

$A = P + Pr + \frac{Pr^2}{4}$

94. $|0.04 - 0.03x| = 0.02$

$0.04 - 0.03x = 0.02$ *or* $0.04 - 0.03x = -0.02$
$-0.03x = -0.02$ $\qquad -0.03x = -0.06$

$x = \frac{2}{3}$ $\qquad x = 2$

95. $|4y + 2| - 8 = -2$

$|4y + 2| = 6$

$4y + 2 = 6$ *or* $4y + 2 = -6$
$4y = 4$ $\qquad 4y = -8$
$y = 1$ $\qquad y = -2$

96. $4 = |3 - 2y| - 5$

$9 = |3 - 2y|$

$9 = 3 - 2y$ *or* $-9 = 3 - 2y$
$6 = -2y$ $\qquad -12 = -2y$
$-3 = y$ $\qquad 6 = y$

98. $7 + \left|3 - \frac{3}{4}t\right| = 10$

$\left|3 - \frac{3}{4}t\right| = 3$

$3 - \frac{3}{4}t = 3$ *or* $3 - \frac{3}{4}t = -3$

$3 - \frac{3}{4}t = 0$ $\qquad -\frac{3}{4}t = -6$

$5 = 0$ $\qquad t = 8$

99. $\left|\frac{1}{10}x - \frac{1}{5}\right| = \left|\frac{1}{2} - \frac{1}{10}x\right|$

*Equal*

$$\frac{1}{10}x - \frac{1}{5} = \frac{1}{2} - \frac{1}{10}x$$

$$\frac{1}{5}x - \frac{1}{5} = \frac{1}{2}$$

$$\frac{1}{5}x = \frac{7}{10}$$

$$x = \frac{7}{2}$$

*Opposite*

$$\frac{1}{10}x = \frac{1}{5} = -\left(\frac{1}{2} - \frac{1}{10}x\right)$$

$$\frac{1}{10}x - \frac{1}{5} = -\frac{1}{2} + \frac{1}{10}x$$

$$-\frac{1}{5} = -\frac{1}{2}$$

$$\varnothing$$

100. $|3x + 4| = |2 - 5x|$

*Equal*

$$3x + 4 = 2 - 5x$$
$$8x + 4 = 2$$
$$8x = -2$$

$$x = -\frac{1}{4}$$

*Opposite*

$$3x - 4 = -(2 - 5x)$$
$$3x + 4 = -2 + 5x$$
$$-2x + 4 = -2$$
$$-2x = -6$$
$$x = 3$$

102. $(x^n + 4)(x^n - 1)$
$= x^{2n} + 3x^n - 4$

103. $(x^{2n} + 3)(x^{2n} - 3)$
$= x^{4n} - 9$

104. $(x^{3n} + 4)(x^{3n} - 4)$
$= x^{6n} - 16$

106. $(4x^n - 3)(7x^n + 2)$
$= 28x^{2n} - 13x^n - 6$

107. $(x^n + 5)^2 = (x^n)^2 + 2(x^n)(5) + 5^2$
$= x^{2n} + 10x^n + 25$

108. $(x^n - 3)^2 = (x^n)^2 + 2(x^n)(-3) + (-3)^2$
$= x^{2n} - 6x^n + 9$

110. $(x^n - 1)^3 = (x^n - 1)^2(x^n - 1)$
$= (x^{2n} - 2x^n + 1)(x^n - 1)$
$= x^{3n} + 3x^{2n} + 3x^n - 1$

## Section 3.5

2. $12x^5 + 18x^7 = 6x^5(2 + 3x^2)$

3. $9y^6 + 18y^3 = 9y^3(y^3 + 2)$

4. $24y^4 - 8y^2 = 8y^2(3y^2 - 1)$

6. $30a^3b^4 + 20a^4b^3 = 10a^3b^3(3b + 2a)$

7. $21xy^4 + 7x^2y^2 = 7xy^2(3y^2 + x)$

8. $14x^6y^3 - 6x^2y^4 = 2x^2y^3(7x^4 - 3y)$

10. $3a^2 - 3a - 6 = 3(a^2 - a - 2)$

11. $4x^3 - 16x^2 - 20x = 4x(x^2 - 4x - 5)$

12. $2x^3 - 14x^2 + 20x = 2x(x^2 - 7x + 10)$

14. $6x^4y^2 + 18x^3y^3 - 24x^2y^4$
$= 6x^2y^2(x^2 + 3xy - 4y^2)$

15. $-x^2y + xy^2 - x^2y^2 = xy(-x + y - xy)$

16. $-x^3y^2 - x^2y^3 - x^2y^2$
$= x^2y^2(-x - y - 1)$

18. $7x^4y^3z^2 - 21x^2y^2z^2 - 14x^2y^3z^4$
$= 7x^2y^2z^2(x^2y - 3 - 2yz^2)$

19. $20a^2b^2c^2 - 30ab^2c + 25a^2bc^2$
$= 5abc(4abc - 6b + 5ac)$

20. $8a^3bc^5 - 48a^2b^4c + 16ab^3c^5$
$= 8abc(a^2c^4 - 6ab^3 + 2b^2c^4)$

22. $3a(x - y) - 7b(x - y)$
$= (x - y)(3a - 7b)$

23. $3x^2(x + y)^2 - 6y^2(x + y)^2$
$= (x+y)^2(3x^2 - 6y^2)$
$= 3(x + y)^2(x^2 - 2y^2)$

24. $10x^3(2x - 3y) - 15x^2(2x - 3y)$
$= (2x - 3y)(10x^3 - 15x^2)$
$= 5x^2(2x - 3y)(2x - 3)$

26. $2x^2(x + 2) + 13x(x + 2) + 15(x + 2)$
$= (x + 2)(2x^2 + 13x + 15)$

27. $3xy + 3y + 2ax + 2a$
$= 3y(x + 1) + 2a(x + 1)$
$= (x + 1)(3y + 2a)$

28. $5xy^2 + 5y^2 + 3ax + 3a$
$= 5y^2(x + 1) + 3a(x + 1)$
$= (x + 1)(5y^2 + 3a)$

30. $x^3y^3 + 2x^3 + 5x^2y^3 + 10x^2$
$= x^3(y^3 + 2) + 5x^2(y^3 + 2)$
$= (x^3 + 5x^2)(y^3 + 2)$
$= x^2(y^3 + 2)(x + 5)$

31. $3xy^2 - 6y^2 + 4x - 8$
$= 3y^2(x - 2) + 4(x - 2)$
$= (x - 2)(3y^2 + 4)$

32. $8x^2y - 4x^2 + 6y - 3$
$= 4x^2(2y - 1) + 3(2y - 1)$
$= (2y - 1)(4x^2 + 3)$

34. $ax - x^2 - bx + ab$
$= x(a - x) + b(-x + a)$
$= (a - x)(x + b)$

35. $ab + 5a - b - 5$
$= a(b + 5) - 1(b + 5)$
$= (b + 5)(a - 1)$

36. $x^2 - xy - ax + ay$
$= x(x - y) - a(x - y)$
$= (x - y)(x - a)$

38. $2a^2 - a^2b - bc^2 + 2c^2$
$= a^2(2 - b) + c^2(-b + 2)$
$= (2 - b)(a^2 + c^2)$

39. $x^3 + 3x^2 - 4x - 12$
$= x^2(x + 3) - 4(x + 3)$
$= (x + 3)(x^2 - 4)$

40. $x^3 + 5x^2 - 4x - 20$
$= x^2(x + 5) - 4(x + 5)$
$= (x + 5)(x^2 - 4)$

42. $x^3 + 4x^2 - 9x - 36$
$= x^2(x + 4) - 9(x + 4)$
$= (x + 4)(x^2 - 9)$

43. $2x^3 + 3x^2 - 8x - 12$
$= x^2(2x + 3) - 4(2x + 3)$
$= (2x + 3)(x^2 - 4)$

44. $3x^3 + 2x^2 - 27x - 18$
$= x^2(3x + 2) - 9(3x + 2)$
$= (3x + 2)(x^2 - 9)$

46. $9x^3 + 18x^2 - 4x - 8$
$= 9x^2(x + 2) - 4(x + 2)$
$= (x + 2)(9x^2 - 4)$

47. $(3x - 9)(6x - 2) = 18x^2 - 60x + 18$

Greatest common factor is 6.

48. $(5x - 10)(2x + 4) = 10x^2 - 40$

Greatest common factor is 10.

50. $P(1 + r)^2 + P(1 + r)^2r$
$= (1 + r)^2(P + Pr)$
$= (1 + r)^2P(1 + r)$
$= P(1 + r)^3$

51. $R = xp \quad R = 11.5x - .05x^2 \quad x = 125$
$xp = 11.5x - .05x^2$
$p = 11.5 - .05x$
$p = 11.5 - .05(125)$
$p = 11.5 - 6.25$
$p = \$5.25$

52. $R = xp \quad R = 8x - .01x^2 \quad x = 420$
$xp = 8x - .01x^2$
$p = 8 - .01x$
$p = 8 - .01(420)$
$p = 8 - 4.20$
$p = \$3.80$

54. $R = xp \quad R = 5.9x - .004x^2 \quad x = 200$
$xp = 5.9x - .004x^2$
$p = 5.9 - .004x$
$p = 5.9 - .004(200)$
$p = 5.9 - .8$
$p = \$5.10$

55. $(x + 2)(x + 3) = x^2 + 3x + 2x + 6$
$= x^2 + 5x + 6$

56. $(x - 2)(x - 3) = x^2 - 3x - 2x + 6$
$= x^2 - 5x + 6$

58. $(2y - 5)(3y + 7)$
$= 6y^2 + 14y - 15y - 35$
$= 6y^2 - y - 35$

59. $(4 - 3a)(5 - a)$
$= 20 - 4a - 15a + 3a^2$
$= 20 - 19a + 3a^2$

60. $(4 - 3a)(5 + a)$
$= 20 + 4a - 15a - 3a^2$
$= 20 - 11a - 3a^2$

62. $-\frac{2}{5}x > 12$

$x < -30$

63. $\frac{1}{3} + \frac{y}{5} \leq \frac{26}{15}$

$5 + 3y \leq 26$
$3y \leq 21$
$y \leq 7$

64. $-\frac{1}{3} \geq \frac{1}{6} - \frac{y}{2}$

$-2 \geq 1 - 3y$
$-3 \geq -3y$
$1 \leq y$
$y \geq 1$

66. $-3(t - 2) < 6 - 5(t + 1)$
$-3t + 6 < 6 - 5t - 5$
$-3t + 6 < 1 - 5t$
$2t + 6 < 1$
$2t < -5$

$t < -\frac{5}{2}$

67. $-9 < -4 + 5t < 6$
$-5 < 5t < 10$
$-1 < t < 2$

68. $-3 < 2t + 1 < 3$
$-4 < 2t < 2$
$-2 < t < 1$

70. $x^{n+4} + x^{n+2} + x^n$
$= x^n x^4 + x^n x^2 + x^n$
$= x^n(x^4 + x^2 + x)$

71. $x^{n+5} + x^{n+4} + x^{n+3}$
$= x^{n+3}(x^2 + x + 1)$

72. $x^{n+3} + x^{n+2} + x^{n+1}$
$= x^{n+1}(x^2 + x + 1)$

## Section 3.6

2. $x^2 - 7x + 12 = (x - 3)(x - 4)$

3. $x^2 - x - 12 = (x + 3)(x - 4)$

4. $x^2 + x - 12 = (x + 4)(x - 3)$

6. $y^2 - y - 6 = (y + 2)(y - 3)$

7. $16 - 6x - x^2 = (2 - x)(8 + x)$

8. $3 + 2x - x^2 = (3 - x)(1 + x)$

10. $15 - 2x - x^2 = (5 + x)(3 - x)$

11. $3a^2 - 21a + 30$
$= 3(a^2 - 7a + 10)$
$= 3(a - 2)(a - 5)$

12. $3a^2 - 3a - 6$
$= 3(a^2 - a - 2)$
$= 3(a + 1)(a - 2)$

14. $2x^3 - 14x^2 + 20x$
$= 2x(x^2 - 7x + 10)$
$= 2x(x - 2)(x - 5)$

15. $x^2 + 3xy + 2y^2 = (x + 2y)(x + y)$

16. $x^2 - 5xy - 24y^2 = (x + 3y)(x - 8y)$

18. $a^2 - 8ab - 9b^2 = (a + b)(a - 9b)$

19. $x^2 - 2xa - 48a^2 = (x + 6a)(x - 8a)$

20. $x^2 + 14xa + 48a^2 = (x + 6a)(x + 8a)$

22. $x^2 + 10xb + 25b^2$
$= (x + 5b)(x + 5b)$
$= (x + 5b)^2$

23. $3x^2 - 6xy - 9y^2$
$= 3(x^2 - 2xy - 3y^2)$
$= 3(x + y)(x - 3y)$

24. $5x^2 + 25xy + 20y^2$
$= 5(x^2 + 5xy + 4y^2$
$= 5(x + y)(x + 4y)$

26. $3a^4 - 18a^3b + 27a^2b^2$
$= 3a^2(a^2 - 6ab + 9b^2)$
$= 3a^2(a - 3b)(a - 3b)$
$= 3a^2(a - 3b)^2$

27. $10x^4y^2 + 20x^3y^3 - 30x^2y^4$
$= 10x^2y^2(x^2 + 2xy - 3y^2)$
$= 10x^2y^2(x + 3y)(x - y)$

28. $6x^4y^2 + 18x^3y^3 - 24x^2y^4$
$= 6x^2y^2(x^2 + 3xy - 4y^2)$
$= 6x^2y^2(x + 4y)(x - y)$

30. $2x^2 - 7x - 15 = (2x + 3)(x - 5)$

31. $2x^2 + x - 15 = (2x - 5)(x + 3)$

32. $2x^2 - x - 15 = (2x + 5)(x - 3)$

34. $2x^2 + 13x + 15 = (2x + 3)(x + 5)$

35. $2x^2 - 11x + 15 = (2x - 5)(x - 3)$

36. $2x^2 + 11x + 15 = (2x + 5)(x + 3)$

38. $2x^2 + x + 15$ *Prime*

39. $2 + 7a + 6a^2 = (2 + 3a)(1 + 2a)$

40. $2 - 7a + 6a^2 = (2 - 3a)(1 - 2a)$

41. $60y^2 - 15y - 45$
$= 15(4y^2 - y - 3)$
$= 15(4y + 3)(y - 1)$

42. $72y^2 + 60y - 72$
$= 12(6y^2 + 5y - 6)$
$= 12(2y + 3)(3y - 2)$

43. $6x^4 - x^3 - 2x^2$
$= x^2(6x^2 - x - 2)$
$= x^2(3x - 2)(2x + 1)$

44. $3x^4 + 2x^3 - 5x^2$
$= x^2(3x^2 + 2x - 5)$
$= x^2(3x + 5)(x - 1)$

46. $40r^3 + 200r^2 + 250r$
$= 10r(4r^2 + 20r + 25)$
$= 10r(2r + 5)(2r + 5)$
$= 10r(2r + 5)^2$

47. $4x^2 - 11xy - 3y^2$
$= (4x + y)(x - 3y)$

48. $3x^2 + 19xy - 14y^2$
$= (3x - 2y)(x + 7y)$

50. $9x^2 + 9xa - 10a^2$
$= (3x + 5a)(3x - 2a)$

51. $18a^2 + 3ab - 28b^2$
$= (3a + 4b)(6a - 7b)$

52. $6a^2 - 7ab - 5b^2$
$= (2a + b)(3a - 5b)$

54. $200 - 600t - 350t^2$
$= 50(4 - 12t - 7t^2)$
$= 50(2 - 7t)(2 + t)$

55. $9x^4 + 9y^3 - 10y^2$
$= y^2(9y^2 + 9y - 10)$
$= y^2(3y - 2)(3y + 5)$

56. $4y^5 + 7y^4 - 2y^3$
$= y^3(4y^2 + 7y - 2)$
$= y^3(4y - 1)(y + 2)$

58. $60a^2 + 65a^3 - 20a^4$
$= 5a^2(12 + 13a - 4a^2)$
$= 5a^2(4 - a)(3 + 4a)$

59. $8x^4y^2 - 2x^3y^3 - 6x^2y^4$
$= 2x^2y^2(4x^2 - xy - 3y^2)$
$= 2x^2y^2(4x + 3y)(x - y)$

60. $8x^4y^2 - 47x^3y^3 - 6x^2y^4$
$= x^2x^2(8x^2 - 47xy - 6y^2)$
$= x^2y^2(8x + y)(x - 6y)$

62. $600x^4 - 100x^2 - 200$
$= 100(6x^4 - x^2 - 2)$
$= 100(3x^2 - 2)(2x^2 + 1)$

63. $20a^4 + 37a^2 + 15$
$= (5a^2 + 3)(4a^2 + 5)$

64. $20a^4 + 13a^2 - 15$
$= (4a^2 + 5)(5a^2 - 3)$

66. $2 - 4r^2 - 30r^4$
$= 2(1 - 2r^2 - 15r^4)$
$= 2(1 + 3r^2)(1 - 5r^2)$

67. $2x^2(x + 5) + 7x(x + 5) + 6(x + 5)$
$= (x + 5)(2x^2 + 7x + 6)$
$= (x + 5)(2x + 3)(x + 2)$

68. $2x^2(x + 2) + 13x(x + 2) + 15(x + 2)$
$= (x + 2)(2x^2 + 13x + 15)$
$= (x + 2)(2x + 3)(x + 5)$

70. $2x^2(x + 1) + 7x(x + 1) + 6(x + 1)$
$= (x + 1)(2x^2 + 7x + 6)$
$= (x + 1)(2x + 3)(x + 2)$

71. $9x^2 - 25y^2$

72. $49x^2 - 4y^2$

74. $a^2 - 75a - 2500 = (a + 25)(a - 100)$
*The other factor is* $(a - 100)$.

75. $y = 4x^2 + 18x - 10$
$y = 2(2x^2 + 9x - 4)$
$y = 2(2x - 1)(x + 5)$

$y = 2(2 \cdot \frac{1}{2} - 1)(\frac{1}{2} + 5)$ $\quad x = \frac{1}{2}$

$y = 2(1 - 1)(5\frac{1}{2})$

$y = 2(0)(5\frac{1}{2})$

$y = 0$

$y = 2(2 \cdot -5 - 1)(-5 + 5)$ $\quad x = -5$
$y = 2(-11)(0)$
$y = 0$

$y = 2(2 \cdot 2 - 1)(2 + 5)$ $\quad x = 2$
$y = 2(3)(7)$
$y = 42$

76. $y = 9x^2 + 33x - 12$
$y = 3(3x^2 + 11x - 4)$
$y = 3(x + 4)(3x - 1)$

$y = 3(\frac{1}{3} + 4)(3 \cdot \frac{1}{3} - 1)$ $\quad x = \frac{1}{3}$

$y = 3(4\frac{1}{3})(0)$
$y = 0$

$y = 3(-4 + 4)(3 \cdot -4 - 1)$ $\quad x = -4$
$y = 3(0)(-13)$
$y = 0$

$y = 3(3 + 4)(3 \cdot 3 - 1)$ $\quad x = 3$
$y = 3(7)(8)$
$y = 168$

78. $h = 32 + 16t - 16t^2$
$h = 16(2 + t - t^2)$
$h = 16(2 - t)(1 + t)$

$h = 16(2 - 2)(1 + 2)$ $\quad t = 2$
$h = 16(0)(3)$
$h = 0$

$h = 16(2 - 1)(1 + 1)$ $\quad t = 1$
$h = 16(1)(2)$
$h = 32$

When t is 2 seconds, h is 0 feet and when t is 1 second, h is 32 feet.

79. $(2x - 3)(2x + 3) = 4x^2 - 9$

80. $(4 - 5x)(4 + 5x) = 16 - 25x^2$

82. $(4 - 5x)^2 = (4 - 5x)(4 - 5x)$
$= 16 - 40x + 25x^2$

83.
$$\begin{array}{r} 4x^2 + 6x + 9 \\ \underline{2x - 3} \\ -12x^2 - 18x - 27 \\ \underline{8x^3 + 12x^2 + 18x \phantom{- 27}} \\ 8x^3 \phantom{+ 12x^2 + 18x} - 27 \end{array}$$

84.
$$\begin{array}{r} 4x^2 - 6x + 9 \\ \underline{2x + 3} \\ 12x^2 - 18x + 27 \\ \underline{8x^3 - 12x^2 + 18x \phantom{+ 27}} \\ 8x^3 \phantom{- 12x^2 + 18x} + 27 \end{array}$$

86. $|x - 6| \geq .01$
$x - 6 \leq -.01$
$x \leq 5.99$ *or*

$x - 6 \geq .01$
$x \geq 6.01$

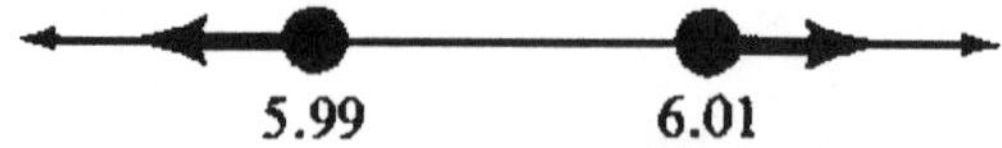


87. $|3 - 4t| > -5$
$3 - 4t < 5$
$-4t < 2$

$t > -\frac{1}{2}$ *or*

$3 - 4t > -5$
$-4t > -8$
$t < 2$

All real numbers.

88. $|2 - 6t| < -5$

$\varnothing$

90. $|6y - 1| - 4 \leq 2$
$|6y - 1| \leq 6$

$-6 < 6y - 1 \leq 6$
$-5 < 6y \leq 7$

$-\frac{5}{6} < y \leq \frac{7}{6}$

$-\frac{5}{6}$ $\frac{7}{6}$

91. $8x^6 + 26x^3y^2 + 15y^4$
$= (2x^3 + 5y^2)(4x^3 + 3y^2)$

92. $24x^4 + 6x^2y^3 - 45y^6$
$= 3(8x^4 + 2x^2y^3 - 15y^6)$
$= 3(4x^2 - 5y^3)(2x^2 + 3y^3)$

94. $3x^2 + 594x - 1200$
$= 3(x^2 + 198x - 400)$
$= 3(x + 200)(x - 2)$

95. $\frac{1}{8}x^2 + x + 2$

$= \left(\frac{1}{4}x + 1\right)\left(\frac{1}{2}x + 2\right)$

96. $\frac{1}{9}x^2 + x + 2$

$= \left(\frac{1}{3}x + 1\right)\left(\frac{1}{3}x + 2\right)$

98. $6x^2 + 2x + 0.16$
$= 2(3x^2 + x + 0.08)$
$= 2(3x + 0.4)(x + 0.2)$

## Section 3.7

2. $x^2 + 10x + 25$
$= (x + 5)(x + 5)$
$= (x + 5)^2$

3. $a^2 - 12a + 36$
$= (a - 6)(a - 6)$
$= (a - 6)^2$

4. $36 - 12a + a^2$
$= (6 - a)(6 - a)$
$= (6 - a)^2$

6. $64 + 16t + t^2$
$= (8 + t)(8 + t)$
$= (8 + t)^2$

7. $\frac{1}{9}x^2 + 2x + 9$

$= \left(\frac{1}{3}x + 3\right)\left(\frac{1}{3}x + 3\right)$

$= \left(\frac{1}{3}x + 3\right)^2$

8. $\frac{1}{4}x^2 - 2x + 4$

$= \left(\frac{1}{2}x - 2\right)\left(\frac{1}{2}x - 2\right)$

$= \left(\frac{1}{2}x - 2\right)^2$

10. $9y^4 + 12y^2 + 4$
$= (3y^2 + 2)(3y^2 + 2)$
$= (3y^2 + 2)^2$

11. $16a^2 + 40ab + 25b^2$
$= (4a + 5b)(4a + 5b)$
$= (4a - 5b)^2$

12. $25a^2 - 40ab + 16b^2$
$= (5a - 4b)(5a - 4b)$
$= (5a - 4b)^2$

14. $\frac{1}{9} - \frac{1}{3}t^3 + \frac{1}{4}t^6$

$= \left(\frac{1}{3} - \frac{1}{2}t^3\right)\left(\frac{1}{3} - \frac{1}{2}t^3\right)$

$= \left(\frac{1}{3} - \frac{1}{2}t^3\right)^2$

15. $16^2 - 48x + 36$
$= 4(4x^2 - 12x + 9)$
$= 4(2x - 3)(2x - 3)$
$= 4(2x - 3)^2$

16. $36x^2 + 48x + 16$
$= 4(9x^2 + 12x + 4)$
$= 4(3x + 2)(3x + 2)$
$= 4(3x + 2)^2$

18. $45a^4 - 30a^3 + 5a^2$
$= 5a^2(9a^2 - 6a + 1)$
$= 5a^2(3a - 1)(3a - 1)$
$= 5a^2(3a - 1)^2$

19. $(x + 2)^2 + 6(x + 2) + 9$
$= [(x + 2) + 3][(x + 2) + 3]$
$= (x + 5)(x + 5)$
$= (x + 5)^2$

20. $(x + 5)^2 + 4(x + 5) + 4$
$= [(x + 5) + 2][(x + 5) + 2]$
$= (x + 7)(x + 7)$
$= (x + 7)^2$

22. $x^2 - 16 = (x + 4)(x - 4)$

23. $49x^2 - 64y^2 = (7x + 8y)(7x - 8y)$

24. $81x^2 - 49y^2 = (9x + 7y)(9x - 7y)$

26. $25a^2 - \frac{1}{25} = \left(5a + \frac{1}{5}\right)\left(5a - \frac{1}{5}\right)$

27. $x^2 - \frac{9}{25} = \left(x + \frac{3}{5}\right)\left(x - \frac{3}{5}\right)$

28. $x^2 - \frac{25}{36} = \left(x + \frac{5}{6}\right)\left(x - \frac{5}{6}\right)$

30. $25x^2 - 49y^2$
$= (5x + 7y)(5x - 7y)$

31. $250 - 10t^2$
$= 10(25 - t^2)$
$= 10(5 + t)(5 - t)$

32. $640 - 10t^2$
$= 10(64 - t^2)$
$= 10(8 + t)(8 - t)$

34. $x^4 - 16$
$= (x^2 + 4)(x^2 - 4)$
$= (x^2 + 4)(x + 2)(x - 2)$

35. $9x^6 - 1 = (3x^3 + 1)(3x^3 - 1)$

36. $25x^6 - 1 = (5x^3 + 1)(5x^3 - 1)$

38. $81a^4 - 16b^4$
$= (9a^2 + 4b^2)(9a^2 - 4b^2)$
$= (9a^2 + 4b^2)(3a + 2b)(3a - 2b)$

39. $\dfrac{1}{81} - \dfrac{y^4}{16}$

$= \left(\dfrac{1}{9} + \dfrac{y^2}{4}\right)\left(\dfrac{1}{9} - \dfrac{y^2}{4}\right)$

$= \left(\dfrac{1}{9} + \dfrac{y^2}{4}\right)\left(\dfrac{1}{3} + \dfrac{y}{2}\right)\left(\dfrac{1}{3} - \dfrac{y}{2}\right)$

40. $\dfrac{1}{25} - \dfrac{y^4}{64} = \left(\dfrac{1}{5} + \dfrac{y^2}{8}\right)\left(\dfrac{1}{5} - \dfrac{y^2}{8}\right)$

42. $x^6 - 1 = (x^3 + 1)(x^3 - 1)$
$= (x + 1)(x^2 - x + 1)(x - 1)(x^2 + x + 1)$
$= (x + 1)(x - 1)(x^2 - x + 1)(x^2 + x + 1)$

43. $2a^7 - 128a$
$= 2a(a^6 - 64)$
$= 2a(a^3 - 8)(a^3 + 8)$
$= 2a(a - 2)(a^2 + 2a + 4)(a + 2)(a^2 - 2a + 4)$
$= 2a(a - 2)(a + 2)(a^2 + 2a + 4)(a^2 - 2a + 4)$

44. $128a^8 - 2a^2$
$= 2a^2(64a^6 - 1)$
$= 2a^2(8a^3 + 1)(8a^3 - 1)$
$= 2a^2(2a + 1)(4a^2 - 2a + 1)(2a - 1)(4a^2 + 2a + 1)$
$= 2a^2(2a + 1)(2a - 1)(4a^2 - 2a + 1)(4a^2 + 2a + 1)$

46. $(x + 2)^2 - 9$
$= [(x + 2) + 3][(x + 2) - 3]$
$= (x + 5)(x - 1)$

47. $(y + 4)^2 - 16$
$= [(y + 4) - 4][(y + 4) + 4]$
$= y(y + 8)$

48. $(y - 4)^2 - 16$
$= [(y - 4) + 4][(y - 4) - 4]$
$= y(y - 8)$

50. $x^2 - 6x + 9 - y^2$
$= (x - 3)^2 - y^2$
$= [(x - 3) + y][(x - 3) - y]$
$= (x - 3 + y)(x - 3 - y)$

51. $a^2 + 8a + 16 - b^2$
$= (a + 4)^2 - b^2$
$= [(a + 4) + b][(a + 4) - b]$
$= (a + 4 + b)(a + 4 - b)$

52. $a^2 + 12a + 3b - b^2$
$= (a + 6)^2 - b^2$
$= [(a + 6) + b][(a + 6) - b]$
$= (a + 6 + b)(a + 6 - b)$

54. $a^2 + 2ab + b^2 - y^2$
$= (a + b)^2 - y^2$
$= [(a + b) + y][(a + b) - y]$
$= (a + b + y)(a + b - y)$

55. $x^3 + 3x^2 - 4x - 12$
$= x^2(x + 3) - 4(x + 3)$
$= (x + 3)(x^2 - 4)$
$= (x + 3)(x + 2)(x - 2)$

56. $x^3 + 5x^2 - 4x - 20$
$= x^2(x + 5) - 4(x + 5)$
$= (x + 5)(x^2 - 4)$
$= (x + 5)(x + 2)(x - 2)$

58. $x^3 + 4x^2 - 9x - 36$
$= x^2(x + 4) - 9(x + 4)$
$= (x + 4)(x^2 - 9)$
$= (x + 4)(x + 3)(x - 3)$

59. $2x^3 + 3x^2 - 8x - 12$
$= x^2(2x + 3) - 4(2x + 3)$
$= (2x + 3)(x^2 - 4)$
$= (2x + 3)(x + 2)(x - 2)$

60. $3x^3 + 2x^2 - 27x - 18$
$= x^2(3x + 2) - 9(3x + 2)$
$= (3x + 2)(x^2 - 9)$
$= (3x + 2)(x + 3)(x - 3)$

62. $9x^3 + 18x^2 - 4x - 8$
$= 9x^2(x + 2) - 4(x + 2)$
$= (x + 2)(9x^2 - 4)$
$= (x + 2)(3x + 2)(3x - 2)$

63. $x^3 - y^3 = (x - y)(x^2 + xy + y^2)$

64. $x^3 + y^3 = (x + y)(x^2 - xy + y^2)$

66. $a^3 - 8 = a^3 - 2^3$
$= (a - 2)(a^2 + 2a + 4)$

67. $27 + x^3 = 3^3 + x^3$
$= (3 + x)(9 - 3x + x^2)$

68. $27 - x^3 = 3^3 - x^3$
$= (3 - x)(9 + 3x + x^2)$

70. $y^3 + 1 = (y + 1)(y^2 - y + 1)$

71. $10r^3 - 1{,}250 = 10(r^3 - 125)$
$= 10(r^3 - 5^3)$
$= 10(r - 5)(r^2 + 5r + 25)$

72. $10r^3 + 1{,}250 = 10(r^3 + 125)$
$= 10(r^3 + 5^3)$
$= 10(r + 5)(r^2 - 5r + 25)$

74. $27 - 64a^3 = 3^3 - (4a)^3$
$= (3 - 4a)(9 + 12a + 16a^2)$

75. $8x^3 - 27y^3 = (2x)^3 - (3y)^3$
$= (2x - 3y)(4x^2 + 6xy + 9y^2)$

76. $27x^3 - 8y^3 = (3x)^3 - (2y)^3$
$= (3x - 2y)(9x^2 + 6xy + 4y^2)$

78. $t^3 - \dfrac{1}{27} = t^3 - \left(\dfrac{1}{3}\right)^3$
$= \left(t - \dfrac{1}{3}\right)\left(t^2 + \dfrac{1}{3}t + \dfrac{1}{9}\right)$

79. $27x^3 - \dfrac{1}{27} = (3x)^3 - \left(\dfrac{1}{3}\right)^3$
$= \left(3x - \dfrac{1}{3}\right)\left(9x^2 + x + \dfrac{1}{9}\right)$

80. $8x^3 + \dfrac{1}{8} = (2x)^3 + \left(\dfrac{1}{2}\right)^3$
$= \left(2x + \dfrac{1}{2}\right)\left(4x^2 - x + \dfrac{1}{4}\right)$

82. $125a^3 - 27b^3$
$= (5a)^3 - (3b)^3$
$= (5a - 3b)(25a^2 + 15ab + 9b^2)$

83. $9x^2 + 30x + 25 \qquad b = 30$
$9x^2 - 30x + 25 \qquad b = -30$

84. $49x^2 - 42x + 9 \qquad c = 9$

86. $A = 100\left(1 + r + \dfrac{r^2}{4}\right)$

$A = 100\left(1 + \dfrac{r}{2}\right)^2$

$A = 100\left(1 + \dfrac{.12}{2}\right)^2$

$A = 100(1 + .06)^2$
$A = 100(1.06)^2$
$A = 100(1.1236)$
$A = \$112.36$

87. $3x + 2y = 12$
$x = 4$
$3(4) + 2y = 12$
$12 + 2y = 12$
$2y = 0$
$y = 0$

88. $y = 3x - 1 \qquad y = 0$
$0 = 3x - 1$
$1 = 3x$

$\dfrac{1}{3} = x$

90. $y = 3x - 1$
$y + 1 = 3x$
$\frac{y+1}{3} = x$
$x = \frac{1}{3}y + \frac{1}{3}$

91. $A = P + Prt$
$A - P = Prt$
$\frac{A-P}{Pr} = t$

92. $S = \pi r^2 + 2\pi rh$
$S - \pi r^2 = 2\pi rh$
$\frac{S - \pi r^2}{2\pi r} = h$

94. $x^{4n} - y^{4n}$
$= (x^{2n} + y^{2n})(x^{2n} - y^{2n})$
$= (x^{2n} + y^{2n})(x^n + y^n)(x^n - y^n)$

95. $x^{2n} + 2x^ny^m + y^{2m}$
$= (x^n + y^m)(x^n + y^m)$
$= (x^n + y^m)^2$

96. $x^{4n} + 2x^{2n}y^m + y^{2m}$
$= (x^{2n} + y^m)(x^{2n} + y^m)$
$= (x^{2n} + y^m)^2$

98. $27x^{3n} - 1 = 3^3x^{3n} - 1^3$
$= (3x^n - 1)(9x^{2n} + 3x^n + 1)$

99. $x^{3n} - y^{3n}$
$= (x^n - y^n)(x^{2n} + x^ny^n + y^{2n})$

100. $x^{3n} + y^{3m}$
$= (x^n + y^m)(x^{2n} - x^ny^m + y^{2m})$

## Section 3.8

2. $x^2 - 18x + 81 = (x - 9)(x - 9)$
$= (x - 9)^2$

3. $x^2 + 2x - 15 = (x + 5)(x - 3)$

4. $15x^2 + 13x - 6 = (5x + 6)(3x - 1)$

6. $12x^2 - 11x + 2 = (4x - 1)(3x - 2)$

7. $x^2y^2 + 2y^2 + x^2 + 2$
$= y^2(x^2 + 2) + x^2 + 2$
$= (x^2 + 2)(y^2 + 1)$

8. $21y^2 - 25y - 4 = (7y + 1)(3y - 4)$

10. $6a^2 - ab - 15b^2$
$= (2a + 3b)(3a - 5b)$

11. $x^2 + x + 1$ *Prime*

12. $x^2y + 3y + 2x^2 + 6$
$= y(x^2 + 3) + 2(x^2 + 3)$
$= (x^2 + 3)(y + 2)$

14. $18a^2 - 50 = 2(9a^2 - 25)$
$= 2(3a + 5)(3a - 5)$

15. $9x^2 - 12xy + 4y^2 = (3x - 2y)^2$

16. $x^3 - x^2 = x^2(x - 1)$

18. $t^2 + 4t + 4 - y^2$
$= (t + 2)^2 - y^2$
$= (t + 2 + y)(t + 2 - y)$

19. $4x^3 + 16xy^2 = 4x(x^2 + 4y^2)$

20. $16x^2 + 49y^2$ *Prime*

22. $x^2 + 5bx - 2ax - 10ab$
$= x(x + 5b) - 2a(x + 5b)$
$= (x + 5b)(x - 2a)$

23. $a^7 + 8a^4b^3 = a^4(a^3 + 8b^3)$
$= a^4(a + 2b)(a^2 - 2ab + 4b^2)$

24. $5a^2 - 45b^2 = 5(a^2 - 9b^2)$
$= 5(a + 3b)(a - 3b)$

26. $36 + 12t + t^2 = (6 + t)^2$

27. $x^3 + 5x^2 - 9x - 45$
$= x^2(x + 5) - 9(x + 5)$
$= (x + 5)(x^2 - 9)$
$= (x + 5)(x + 3)(x - 3)$

28. $x^3 + 5x^2 - 16x - 80$
$= x^2(x + 5) - 16(x + 5)$
$= (x + 5)(x^2 - 16)$
$= (x + 5)(x + 4)(x - 4)$

30. $3a^3b^2 + 15a^2b^2 + 3ab^2$
$= 3ab^2(a^2 + 5a + 1)$

31. $x^2 + 49$ *Prime*

32. $16 - x^4 = (4 + x^2)(4 - x^2)$
$= (4 + x^2)(2 + x)(2 - x)$

34. $3x^2 + 27xy + 54y^2$
$= 3(x^2 + 9xy + 18y^2)$
$= 3(x + 3y)(x + 6y)$

35. $9a^2 + 2a + \frac{1}{9} = \left(3a + \frac{1}{3}\right)^2$

36. $18 - 2a^2 = 2(9 - a)^2$
$= 2(3 + a)(3 - a)$

38. $x^2 + 3ax - 2bx - 6ab$
$= x(x + 3a) - 2b(x + 3a)$
$= (x + 3a)(x - 2b)$

39. $x^2 - 64 = (x + 8)(x - 8)$

40. $9x^2 - 4 = (3x + 2)(3x - 2)$

42. $5x^4 + 14x^2 - 3 = (5x^2 - 1)(x^2 + 3)$

43. $49a^7 - 9a^5 = a^5(49a^2 - 9)$
$= a^5(7a + 3)(7a - 3)$

44. $a^6 - b^6$
$= (a^3 + b^3)(a^3 - b^3)$
$= (a + b)(a^2 - ab + b^2)(a - b)(a^2 + ab + b^2)$
$= (a + b)(a - b)(a^2 - ab + b^2)(a^2 + ab + b^2)$

46. $27 - r^3 = 3^3 - r^3$
$= (3 - r)(9 + 3r + r^2)$

47. $49x^2 + 9y^2$ *Prime*

48. $12x^4 - 62x^3 + 70x^2$
$= 2x^2(6x^2 - 31x + 35)$
$= 2x^2(3x - 5)(2x - 7)$

50. $100x^2 - 100x - 1200$
$= 100(x^2 - x - 12)$
$= 100(x - 4)(x + 3)$

51. $25a^3 + 20a^2 + 3a$
$= a(25a^2 + 20a + 3)$
$= a(5a + 1)(5a + 3)$

52. $16a^5 - 54a^2$
$= 2a^2(8a^3 - 27)$
$= 2a^2(2a - 3)(4a^2 + 6a + 9)$

54. $8 - 2x - 15x^2 = (4 + 5x)(2 - 3x)$

55. $24a^5b - 3a^2b$
$= 3a^2b(8a^3 - 1)$
$= 3a^2b(2a - 1)(4a^2 + 2a + 1)$

56. $18a^4b^2 - 24a^3b^3 + 8a^2b^4$
$= 2a^2b^2(9a^2 - 12ab + 4b^2)$
$= 2a^2b^2(3a - 2b)^2$

58. $r^2 - \frac{1}{9} = \left(r + \frac{1}{3}\right)\left(r - \frac{1}{3}\right)$

59. $20x^4 - 45x^2 = 5x^2(4x^2 - 9)$
$= 5x^2(2x + 3)(2x - 3)$

60. $16x^3 + 16x^2 + 3x$
$= x(16x^2 + 16x + 3)$
$= x(4x + 1)(4x + 3)$

62. $900 - 400t^2 = 100(9 - 4t^2)$
$= 100(3 + 2t)(3 - 2t)$

63. $16x^5 - 44x^4 + 30x^3$
$= 2x^3(8x^2 - 22x + 15)$
$= 2x^3(4x - 5)(2x - 3)$

64. $16x^2 + 16x - 1$ *Prime*

66. $25y^7 - 16y^5 = y^5(25y^2 - 16)$
$= y^5(5y + 4)(5y - 4)$

67. $50 - 2a^2 = 2(25 - a^2)$
$= 2(5 + a)(5 - a)$

68. $4a^2 + 2a + \frac{1}{4} = \left(2a + \frac{1}{2}\right)^2$

70. $16x^3y^2 - 4xy^2 = 4xy^2(4x^2 - 1)$
$= 4xy^2(2x + 1)(2x - 1)$

71. $x^2 - 4x + 4 - y^2 = (x - 2)^2 - y^2$
$= (x - 2 + y)(x - 2 - y)$

72. $x^2 - 12x + 36 - b^2 = (x - 6)^2 - b^2$
$= (x - 6 + b)(x - 6 - b)$

73. Let x = the smaller consecutive even integer and x + 2 = the larger consecutive even integer.

$$\begin{aligned}(x + 2) + 2x &= 26\\ 3x + 2 &= 26\\ 3x &= 24\\ x &= 8\end{aligned}$$

The smaller consecutive even integer is x = 8, and the larger consecutive even integer is x + 2 = 10.

74. Let x = width, 4x + 3 = length, perimeter = 56 in.

$$\begin{aligned}P &= 2L + 2W\\ 56 &= 2(4x + 3) + 2x\\ 56 &= 8x + 6 + 2x\\ 56 &= 10x + 6\\ 50 &= 10x\\ 5 &= x\\ 23 &= 4x + 3\end{aligned}$$

Width = 5 in.
Length = 23 in.

75. $x + 4x - 10 = 90°$ *(complementary)*

$$\begin{aligned}5x &= 100°\\ x &= 20°\\ 4x - 10 &= 70°\end{aligned}$$

$x + 4x - 10 = 180°$ *(supplementary)*

$$\begin{aligned}5x &= 190°\\ x &= 38°\\ 4x - 10 &= 142°\end{aligned}$$

76. The two numbers are x, 24 - x

$$\begin{aligned}x &= 2(24 - x) - 3\\ x &= 48 - 2x - 3\\ 3x &= 45\\ x &= 15\\ 24 - x &= 9\end{aligned}$$

78.

| | Dollars at 6% | Dollars at 7% | Total |
|---|---|---|---|
| Number of | x | 1800 - x | 1800 |
| Interest on | .06x | .07(1800 - x) | 118 |

$$\begin{aligned}.06x + .07(1800 - x) &= 118\\ .06x + 126 - .07x &= 118\\ 126 - .01x &= 118\\ -.01x &= -8\\ x &= \$800 \quad \textit{at 6\%}\\ 1800 - x &= \$1000 \quad \textit{at 7\%}\end{aligned}$$

**Section 3.9**

2. $(x - 1)(x + 6) = 0$

$x - 1 = 0$

$x = 1$ *or*

$x + 6 = 0$

$x = -6$

3. $x^3 - 5x^2 + 6x = 0$

$x(x^2 - 5x + 6) = 0$

$x(x - 2)(x - 3) = 0$

$x = 0$ *or*

$x - 2 = 0$

$x = 2$ *or*

$x - 3 = 0$

$x = 3$

4.
$$x^3 + 5x^2 + 6x = 0$$
$$x(x^2 + 5x + 6) = 0$$
$$x(x + 2)(x + 3) = 0$$
$$x = 0 \quad or$$

$$x + 2 = 0$$
$$x = -2 \quad or$$

$$x + 3 = 0$$
$$x = -3$$

6.
$$3y^2 - y - 4 = 0$$
$$(y + 1)(3y - 4) = 0$$
$$y + 1 = 0$$
$$y = -1 \quad or$$

$$3y - 4 = 0$$
$$3y = 4$$
$$y = \frac{4}{3}$$

7.
$$60x^2 - 130x + 60 = 0$$
$$10(6x^2 - 13x + 6) = 0$$
$$10(3x - 2)(2x - 3) = 0$$
$$3x - 2 = 0$$
$$3x = 2$$
$$x = \frac{2}{3} \quad or$$

$$2x - 3 = 0$$
$$2x = 3$$
$$x = \frac{3}{2}$$

8.
$$90x^2 + 60x - 80 = 0$$
$$10(9x^2 + 6x - 8) = 0$$
$$10(3x + 4)(3x - 2) = 0$$
$$3x + 4 = 0$$
$$3x = -4$$
$$x = -\frac{4}{3} \quad or$$

$$3x - 2 = 0$$
$$3x = 2$$
$$x = \frac{2}{3}$$

10.
$$\frac{2}{7}t^2 - \frac{7}{2} = 0 \quad LCD = 14$$

$$4t^2 - 49 = 0$$
$$(2t + 7)(2t - 7) = 0$$
$$2t + 7 = 0$$
$$2t = -7$$
$$t = -\frac{7}{2} \quad or$$

$$2t - 7 = 0$$
$$2t = 7$$
$$t = \frac{7}{2}$$

11.
$$100x^4 = 400x^3 + 2{,}100x^2$$
$$100x^4 - 400x^3 - 2{,}100x^2 = 0$$
$$100x^2(x^2 - 4x - 21) = 0$$
$$100x^2(x + 3)(x - 7) = 0$$
$$100x^2 = 0$$
$$x^2 = 0$$
$$x = 0 \quad or$$

$$x = 3 = 0$$
$$x = -3 \quad or$$

$$x - 7 = 0$$
$$x = 7$$

12.
$$100x^4 = -400x^3 + 2100x^2$$
$$100x^4 + 400x^3 - 2100x^2 = 0$$
$$100x^2(x^2 + 4x - 21) = 0$$
$$100x^2(x + 7)(x - 3) = 0$$
$$100x^2 = 0$$
$$x^2 = 0$$
$$x = 0 \quad or$$

$$x + 7 = 0$$
$$x = -7 \quad or$$

$$x - 3 = 0$$
$$x = 3$$

14. $\frac{1}{2}y^2 + \frac{5}{3} = \frac{17}{6}y$

$\frac{1}{2}y^2 - \frac{17}{6}y + \frac{5}{3} = 0 \quad LCD = 6$

$3y^2 - 17y + 10 = 0$
$(y - 5)(3y - 2) = 0$
$y - 5 = 0$
$y = 5$ *or*

$3y - 2 = 0$
$3y = 2$

$y = \frac{2}{3}$

15. $9x^2 - 12x = 0$
$3x(3x - 4) = 0$
$3x = 0$
$x = 0$ *or*

$3x - 4 = 0$
$3x = 4$

$x = \frac{4}{3}$

16. $4x^2 + 4x = 0$
$4x(x + 1) = 0$
$4x = 0$
$x = 0$ *or*

$x + 1 = 0$
$x = -1$

18. $0.02r - 0.01 = -0.08r^2$
$0.08r^2 + 0.02r - 0.01 = 0 \quad LCD = 100$
$8r^2 + 2r - 1 = 0$
$(2r + 1)(4r - 1) = 0$
$2r + 1 = 0$
$2r = -1$

$r = -\frac{1}{2}$ *or*

$4r - 1 = 0$
$4r = 1$

$r = \frac{1}{4}$

19. $9a^3 = 16a$
$9a^3 - 16a = 0$
$a(9a^2 - 16) = 0$
$a(3a + 4)(3a - 4) = 0$
$a = 0$ *or*

$3a + 4 = 0$
$3a = -4$

$a = -\frac{4}{3}$ *or*

$3a - 4 = 0$
$3a = 4$

$a = \frac{4}{3}$

20. $16a^3 = 25a$
$16a^3 - 25a = 0$
$a(16a^2 - 25) = 0$
$a(4a + 5)(4a - 5) = 0$
$a = 0$ *or*

$4a + 5 = 0$
$4a = -5$

$a = -\frac{5}{4}$ *or*

$4a - 5 = 0$
$4a = 5$

$a = \frac{5}{4}$

22. $800x = 100x^2$
$0 = 100x^2 - 800x$
$0 = 100x(x - 8)$
$100x = 0$
$x = 0$ *or*

$x - 8 = 0$
$x = 8$

23. $(x + 6)(x - 2) = -7$
$x^2 + 4x - 12 + 7 = 0$
$x^2 + 4x - 5 = 0$
$(x + 5)(x - 1) = 0$
$x + 5 = 0$
$x = -5$ *or*

$x - 1 = 0$
$x = 1$

24.
$$\begin{aligned}(x-7)(x+5)&=-20\\x^2-2x-35+20&=0\\x^2-2x-15&=0\\(x+3)(x-5)&=0\\x+3&=0\\x&=-3 \quad \textit{or}\\[1ex] x-5&=0\\x&=5\end{aligned}$$

26.
$$\begin{aligned}(y-6)(y+1)&=-12\\y^2-5y-6+12&=0\\y^2-5y+6&=0\\(y-2)(y-3)&=0\\y-2&=0\\y&=2 \quad \textit{or}\\[1ex] y-3&=0\\y&=3\end{aligned}$$

27.
$$\begin{aligned}(x+1)^2&=3x+7\\x^2+2x+1-3x-7&=0\\x^2-x-6&=0\\(x+2)(x-3)&=0\\x+2&=0\\x&=-2 \quad \textit{or}\\[1ex] x-3&=0\\x&=3\end{aligned}$$

28.
$$\begin{aligned}(x+2)^2&=9x\\x^2+4x+4-9x&=0\\x^2-5x+4&=0\\(x-1)(x-4)&=0\\x-1&=0\\x&=1 \quad \textit{or}\\[1ex] x-4&=0\\x&=4\end{aligned}$$

30.
$$\begin{aligned}(3r+2)(r-1)&=-(7r-7)\\3r^2-r-2&=-7r+7\\3r^2-r-2+7r-7&=0\\3r^2+6r-9&=0\\3(r^2+2r-3)&=0\\3(r+3)(r-1)&=0\\r+3&=0\\r&=-3 \quad \textit{or}\\[1ex] r-1&=0\\r&=1\end{aligned}$$

31.
$$\begin{aligned}x^3+3x^2-4x-12&=0\\x^2(x+3)-4(x+3)&=0\\(x+3)(x^2-4)&=0\\(x+3)(x+2)(x-2)&=0\\x+3&=0\\x&=-3 \quad \textit{or}\\[1ex] x+2&=0\\x&=-2 \quad \textit{or}\\[1ex] x-2&=0\\x&=2\end{aligned}$$

32.
$$\begin{aligned}x^3+5x^2-4x-20&=0\\x^2(x+5)-4(x+5)&=0\\(x+5)(x^2-4)&=0\\(x+5)(x+2)(x-2)&=0\\x+5&=0\\x&=-5 \quad \textit{or}\\[1ex] x+2&=0\\x&=-2 \quad \textit{or}\\[1ex] x-2&=0\\x&=2\end{aligned}$$

34.
$$\begin{aligned}x^3+4x^2-9x-36&=0\\x^2(x+4)-9(x+4)&=0\\(x+4)(x^2-9)&=0\\(x+4)(x+3)(x-3)&=0\\x+4&=0\\x&=-4 \quad \textit{or}\\[1ex] x+3&=0\\x&=-3 \quad \textit{or}\\[1ex] x-3&=0\\x&=3\end{aligned}$$

35.
$$\begin{aligned}2x^3+3x^2-8x-12&=0\\x^2(2x+3)-4(2x+3)&=0\\(2x+3)(x^2-4)&=0\\(2x+3)(x+2)(x-2)&=0\\2x+3&=0\\2x&=-3\\x&=-\frac{3}{2} \quad \textit{or}\\[1ex] x+2&=0\\x&=-2 \quad \textit{or}\\[1ex] x-2&=0\\x&=2\end{aligned}$$

36.
$$3x^3 + 2x^2 - 27x - 18 = 0$$
$$x^2(3x + 2) - 9(3x + 2) = 0$$
$$(3x + 2)(x^2 - 9) = 0$$
$$(3x + 2)(x + 3)(x - 3) = 0$$
$$3x + 2 = 0$$
$$3x = -2$$
$$x = -\frac{2}{3} \quad \textit{or}$$
$$x + 3 = 0$$
$$x = -3 \quad \textit{or}$$
$$x - 3 = 0$$
$$x = 3$$

38.
$$9x^3 + 18x^2 - 4x - 8 = 0$$
$$9x^2(x + 2) - 4(x + 2) = 0$$
$$(x + 2)(9x^2 - 4) = 0$$
$$(x + 2)(3x + 2)(3x - 2) = 0$$
$$x + 2 = 0$$
$$x = -2 \quad \textit{or}$$
$$3x + 2 = 0$$
$$3x = -2$$
$$x = -\frac{2}{3} \quad \textit{or}$$
$$3x - 2 = 0$$
$$3x = 2$$
$$x = \frac{2}{3}$$

39.
$$x^2 + (x + 2)^2 = 34$$
$$x^2 + x^2 + 4x + 4 - 34 = 0$$
$$2x^2 + 4x - 30 = 0$$
$$2(x^2 + 2x - 15) = 0$$
$$2(x + 5)(x - 3) = 0$$
$$x + 5 = 0$$
$$x = -5$$
$$x + 2 = -3 \quad \textit{or}$$
$$x - 3 = 0$$
$$x = 3$$
$$x + 2 = 5$$

40.
$$x^2 + (x + 2)^2 = 100$$
$$x^2 + x^2 + 4x + 4 - 100 = 0$$
$$2x^2 + 4x - 96 = 0$$
$$2(x^2 + 2x - 48) = 0$$
$$2(x + 8)(x - 6) = 0$$
$$x + 8 = 0$$
$$x = -8$$
$$x + 2 = -6 \quad \textit{or}$$
$$x - 6 = 0$$
$$x = 6$$
$$x + 2 = 8$$

42.
$$[x + (x + 2)]^2 = 100$$
$$[2x + 2]^2 = 100$$
$$4x^2 + 8x + 4 - 100 = 0$$
$$4x^2 + 8x - 96 = 0$$
$$4(x^2 + 2x - 24) = 0$$
$$4(x + 6)(x - 4) = 0$$
$$x + 6 = 0$$
$$x = -6$$
$$x + 2 = -4 \quad \textit{or}$$
$$x - 4 = 0$$
$$x = 4$$
$$x + 2 = 6$$

43.
$$x(2x + 3) = 65$$
$$2x^2 + 3x - 65 = 0$$
$$(x - 5)(2x + 13) = 0$$
$$x - 5 = 0$$
$$x = 5$$
$$2x + 3 = 13 \quad \textit{or}$$
$$2x + 13 = 0$$
$$2x = -13$$
$$x = -\frac{13}{2} \quad \textit{Not an integer}$$

44.
$$x(2x - 5) = 150$$
$$2x^2 - 5x - 150 = 0$$
$$(2x + 15)(x - 10) = 0$$
$$2x + 15 = 0$$
$$2x = -15$$
$$x = -\frac{15}{2} \quad \textit{Not an integer} \quad \textit{or}$$
$$x - 10 = 0$$
$$x = 10$$
$$2x - 5 = 15$$

46. Shortest side - x,
Longest side - 2x - 3,
Third side = 12

$$a^2 + b^2 = c^2$$
$$x^2 + 12^2 = (2x - 3)^2$$
$$x^2 + 144 = 4x^2 - 12x + 9$$
$$x^2 + 144 = 4x^2 - 12x + 9$$
$$0 = 3x^2 - 12x - 135$$
$$0 = (3x + 15)(x - 9)$$
$$3x + 15 = 0$$
$$3x = -15$$
$$x = -5$$
*No solution* *or*
$$x - 9 = 0$$
$$x = 9$$

The shortest side is 9 in.

47. Let x = width, 3x + 2 = length,
area = 16 sq. ft.

$$A = LW$$
$$16 = (3x + 2)x$$
$$16 = 3x^2 + 2x$$
$$0 = 3x^2 + 2x - 16$$
$$0 = (3x + 8)(x - 2)$$
$$3x + 8 = 0$$
$$3x = -8$$
$$x = -\frac{8}{3}$$
*No solution* *or*
$$x - 2 = 0$$
$$x = 2 \quad \textit{ft (width)}$$
$$3x + 2 = 8 \quad \textit{ft (length)}$$

48. Let x = width, 2x + 4 = length,
area = 70 sq. in.

$$A = LW$$
$$70 = (2x + 4)x$$
$$70 = 2x^2 + 4x$$
$$0 = 2x^2 + 4x - 70$$
$$0 = 2(x^2 + 2x - 35)$$
$$0 = 2(x + 7)(x - 5)$$
$$x + 7 = 0$$
$$x = -7$$
*No solution* *or*
$$x - 5 = 0$$
$$x = 5 \quad \textit{in. (width)}$$
$$2x + 4 = 14 \quad \textit{in. (length)}$$

50. Let x = base,
2x - 4 = height,
area = 48 sq. ft.

$$A = \frac{1}{2}bh$$
$$48 = \frac{1}{2}(x)(2x - 4)$$
$$48 = (x)(x - 2)$$
$$0 = x^2 - 2x - 48$$
$$0 = (x - 8)(x + 6)$$
$$x - 8 = 0$$
$$x = 8 \quad \textit{ft. (base)}$$
$$2x - 4 = 12 \quad \textit{ft. (height)}$$ *or*
$$x + 6 = 0$$
$$x = -6$$
*No solution*

52. $h = 64t - 16t^2$, $h = 0$ (*on the ground*)
$$0 = 64t - 16t^2$$
$$0 = 16t(4 - t)$$
$$16t = 0$$
$$t = 0$$
$$4 - t = 0$$
$$4 = t$$

0 *and* 4 *seconds*

53. Let v = 48 ft/sec
and height = 32 ft.

$$h = vt - 16t^2$$
$$32 = 48t - 16t^2$$
$$16t^2 - 48t + 32 = 0$$
$$16(t^2 - 3t + 2) = 0$$
$$16(t - 1)(t - 2) = 0$$
$$t - 1 = 0$$
$$t = 1 \quad or$$

$$t - 2 = 0$$
$$t = 2$$

1 *second and* 2 *seconds*

54.
$$h = vt - 16t^2$$
$$v = 80 \text{ ft/sec}$$
$$h = 64 \text{ ft}$$
$$64 = 80t - 16t^2$$
$$16t^2 - 80t + 64 = 0$$
$$16(t^2 - 5t + 4) = 0$$
$$16(t - 1)(t - 4) = 0$$
$$t - 1 = 0$$
$$t = 1 \quad or$$

$$t - 4 = 0$$
$$t = 4$$

1 *and* 4 *seconds*

56.
$$h = vt - 16t^2$$
$$v = 20 \text{ ft/sec}$$
$$h = 0$$
$$0 = 20t - 16t^2$$
$$0 = 4t(5 - 4t)$$
$$4t = 0$$
$$t = 0$$

$$5 - 4t = 0$$
$$5 = 4t$$

$$\frac{5}{4} = t$$

0 *and* $\frac{5}{4}$ *seconds*

57. v = 80 ft/sec and
h = 192 ft.

$$h = 96 + 80t - 16t^2$$
$$192 = 96 + 80t - 16t^2$$
$$16t^2 - 80t + 96 = 0$$
$$16(t^2 - 5t + 6) = 0$$
$$16(t - 2)(t - 3) = 0$$
$$t - 2 = 0$$
$$t = 2 \quad or$$

$$t - 3 = 0$$
$$t = 3$$

2 *and* 3 *seconds*

58.
$$h = 32 + 48t - 16t^2, \; h = 64 \text{ ft}$$
$$64 = 32 + 48t - 16t^2$$
$$0 = -32 + 48t - 16t^2$$
$$0 = -16(t^2 - 3t + 2)$$
$$0 = -16(t - 2)(t - 1)$$
$$t - 2 = 0$$
$$t = 2 \quad or$$

$$t - 1 = 0$$
$$t = 1$$

1 *and* 2 *seconds*

59.
$$R = xp$$
$$x = 1200 - 100p$$
$$R = 3200$$

$$3200 = (1200 - 100p)p$$
$$3200 = 1200p - 100p^2$$
$$100p^2 - 1200p + 3200 = 0$$
$$100(p^2 - 12p + 32) = 0$$
$$100(p - 4)(p - 8) = 0$$
$$p - 4 = 0$$
$$p = 4$$

$$p - 8 = 0$$
$$p = 8$$

The price should be \$4 or \$8.

60.
$$R = xp$$
$$x = 800 - 100p$$
$$R = \$1{,}200$$

$$1200 = (800 - 100p)p$$
$$1200 = 800p - 100p^2$$
$$100p^2 - 800p + 1200 = 0$$
$$100(p^2 - 8p + 12) = 0$$
$$100(p - 2)(p - 6) = 0$$
$$p - 2 = 0$$
$$p = 2 \quad OR$$

$$p - 6 = 0$$
$$p = 6$$

The price should be \$2 or \$6.

62.
$$R = xp$$
$$x = 1800 - 100p$$
$$R = 7200$$

$$7200 = (1800 - 100p)p$$
$$7200 = 1800p - 100p^2$$
$$100p^2 - 1800p + 7200 = 0$$
$$100(p^2 - 18p + 72) = 0$$
$$100(p - 6)(p - 12) = 0$$
$$p - 6 = 0$$
$$p = 6 \quad OR$$

$$p - 12 = 0$$
$$p = 12$$

The price should be \$6 or \$12.

63. $|x| + 4 = 6$
$$|x| = 2$$
$$x = 2 \quad or \quad x = -2$$

64. $|4 - 3x| = 5$
$$4 - 3x = 5 \quad or \quad 4 - 3x = -5$$
$$-3x = 1 \qquad -3x = -9$$
$$x = -\frac{1}{3} \qquad x = 3$$

66. $2 = |5 - 3a| + 8$
$$-6 = |5 - 3a|$$
$$\varnothing$$

67. $|1 - 5y| = |4y + 10|$

*Equal*

$$1 - 5y = 4y + 10$$
$$-9 = 9y$$
$$-1 = y$$

*Opposites*

$$1 - 5y = -(4y + 10)$$
$$1 - 5y = -4y - 10$$
$$11 = y$$

68. $\left|\frac{y}{3} - 1\right| = \left|1 - \frac{y}{3}\right|$

*Equal*

$$\frac{y}{3} - 1 = 1 - \frac{y}{3}$$
$$\frac{2y}{3} = 2$$
$$2y = 6$$
$$y = 3$$

*Opposites*

$$\frac{y}{3} - 1 = -\left(1 - \frac{y}{3}\right)$$
$$\frac{y}{3} - 1 = -1 + \frac{y}{3}$$
$$-1 = -1 \quad (True)$$

*All real numbers*

70. $|x| > 0.01$
$$x > 0.01 \quad or \quad x < -0.01$$

71. $|2y + 1| > -5$

$$2y + 1 > -5$$
$$2y > -6$$
$$y > -3 \quad or$$

$$2y + 1 < 5$$
$$2y < 4$$
$$y < 2$$

*All real numbers*

72. $|2y + 1| < -5$

$$\varnothing$$

74. $|3t - 1| \le 5$
$$-5 \le 3t - 1 \le 5$$
$$-4 \le 3t \le 6$$
$$-\frac{4}{3} \le t \le 2$$

# CHAPTER 4

## Section 4.1

2. $-\dfrac{45}{60} = -\dfrac{3}{4}$

3. $\dfrac{2a^3b^3}{4a^2} = \dfrac{b^3}{2}$

4. $\dfrac{3a^3b^2}{6b^2} = \dfrac{a^3}{2}$

6. $-\dfrac{36x^5y^3}{24x^3y^9} = -\dfrac{3x^3}{2y}$

7. $\dfrac{144a^2b^3c^4}{56a^4b^3c^2} = \dfrac{18c^2}{7a^2}$

8. $\dfrac{108a^5b^2c^5}{27a^2b^5a^2} = \dfrac{4a^3c^3}{b^3}$

10. $\dfrac{5x + 25}{x^2 - 25} = \dfrac{5(x + 5)}{(x + 5)(x - 5)}$
$$= \frac{5}{x - 5}$$

11. $\dfrac{12x - 9y}{3x^2 + 3xy} = \dfrac{3(4x - 3y)}{3x(x + y)}$
$$= \frac{4x - 3y}{x(x + y)}$$

12. $\dfrac{x^3 - xy^2}{4x + 4y} = \dfrac{x(x^2 - y^2)}{4(x + y)}$
$$= \frac{x(x + y)(x - y)}{4\ (x + y)}$$
$$= \frac{x(x - y)}{4}$$

14. $\dfrac{a + 4}{a^2 - 16} = \dfrac{a + 4}{(a + 4)(a - 4)}$
$$= \frac{1}{a - 4}$$

15. $\dfrac{a^2 - 4a - 12}{a^2 + 8a + 12} = \dfrac{(a + 2)(a - 6)}{(a + 2)(a + 6)}$
$$= \frac{a - 6}{a + 6}$$

16. $\dfrac{a^2 - 7a + 12}{a^2 - 9a + 20} = \dfrac{(a - 3)(a - 4)}{(a - 4)(a - 5)}$
$$= \frac{a - 3}{a - 5}$$

18. $\dfrac{54y^2 - 6}{18y^2 - 60y + 18} = \dfrac{6(9y^2 - 1)}{6(3y^2 - 10y + 3)}$
$$= \frac{6(3y + 1)(3y - 1)}{6(3y - 1)(y - 3)}$$
$$= \frac{3y + 1}{y - 3}$$

19. $\dfrac{20x^2 - 93x + 34}{4x^2 - 9x - 34} = \dfrac{(5x - 2)(4x - 17)}{(x + 2)(4x - 17)}$
$$= \frac{5x - 2}{x + 2}$$

20. $\dfrac{15x^2 - 59x + 52}{5x^2 - 33x + 52} = \dfrac{(5x - 13)(3x - 4)}{(5x - 13)(x - 4)}$
$$= \frac{3x - 4}{x - 4}$$

22. $\dfrac{250a + 100ax + 10ax^2}{50a - 2ax^2}$

$= \dfrac{10a(25 + 10x + x^2)}{2a(25 - x^2)}$

$= \dfrac{10a(5 + x)(5 + x)}{2a(5 + 2)(5 - x)}$

$= \dfrac{5(5 + x)}{5 - x}$

23. $\dfrac{(x - 3)^2(x + 2)}{(x + 2)^2(x - 3)} = \dfrac{x - 3}{x + 2}$

24. $\dfrac{(x - 4)^3(x + 3)}{(x + 3)^2(x - 4)} = \dfrac{(x - 4)^2}{x + 3}$

26. $\dfrac{a^2 - b^2}{a^3 - b^3} = \dfrac{(a + b)(a - b)}{(a - b)(a^2 + ab + b^2)}$

$= \dfrac{a + b}{a^2 + ab + b^2}$

27. $\dfrac{8x^4 - 8x}{4x^4 + 4x^3 + 4x^2}$

$= \dfrac{8x(x^3 - 1)}{4x^2(x^2 + x + 1)}$

$= \dfrac{8x(x - 1)(x^2 + x + 1)}{4x^2(x^2 + x + 1)}$

$= \dfrac{2(x - 1)}{x}$

28. $\dfrac{6x^5 - 48x^2}{12x^3 + 24x^2 + 48x}$

$= \dfrac{6x^2(x^3 - 8)}{12x(x^2 + 2x + 4)}$

$= \dfrac{6x^2(x - 2)(x^2 + 2x + 4)}{12x(x^2 + 2x + 4)}$

$= \dfrac{x(x - 2)}{2}$

30. $\dfrac{4x^2 - y^2}{4x^2 - 8xy - 5y^2} = \dfrac{(2x + y)(2x - y)}{(2x + y)(2x - 5y)}$

$= \dfrac{2x - y}{2x - 5y}$

31. $\dfrac{ax + 2x + 3a + 6}{ay + 2y - 4a - 8}$

$= \dfrac{x(a + 2) + 3(a + 2)}{y(a + 2) - 4(a + 2)}$

$= \dfrac{(a + 2)(x + 3)}{(a + 2)(y - 4)}$

$= \dfrac{x + 3}{y - 4}$

32. $\dfrac{ax - x - 5a + 5}{ax + x - 5a - 5}$

$= \dfrac{x(a - 1) - 5(a - 1)}{x(a + 1) - 5(a + 1)}$

$= \dfrac{(a - 1)(x - 5)}{(a + 1)(x - 5)}$

$= \dfrac{a - 1}{a + 1}$

34. $\dfrac{x^2 - 3ax - 2x + 6a}{x^2 - 3ax + 2x - 6a}$

$= \dfrac{x(x - 3a) - 2(x - 3a)}{x(x - 3a) + 2(x - 3a)}$

$= \dfrac{(x - 3a)(x - 2)}{(x - 3a)(x + 2)}$

$= \dfrac{x - 2}{x + 2}$

35. $\dfrac{x^3 + 3x^2 - 4x - 12}{x^2 + x - 6}$

$= \dfrac{x^2(x + 3) - 4(x + 3)}{(x + 3)(x - 2)}$

$= \dfrac{(x + 3)(x^2 - 4)}{(x + 3)(x - 2)}$

$= \dfrac{(x + 3)(x - 2)(x + 2)}{(x + 3)(x - 2)}$

$= x + 2$

36. $\dfrac{x^3 + 5x^2 - 4x - 20}{x^2 + 7x + 10}$

$= \dfrac{x^2(x + 5) - 4(x + 5)}{(x + 2)(x + 5)}$

$= \dfrac{(x + 5)(x^2 - 4)}{(x + 2)(x + 5)}$

$= \dfrac{(x + 5)(x + 2)(x - 2)}{(x + 2)(x + 5)}$

$= x - 2$

38. $\dfrac{2x^4 + 14x^3 + 20x^2}{2x^5 + 4x^4 - 50x^3 - 100x^2}$

$= \dfrac{2x^2(x^2 + 7x + 10)}{2x^4(x + 2) - 50x^2(x + 2)}$

$= \dfrac{2x^2(x + 5)(x + 2)}{(x + 2)(2x^4 - 50x^2)}$

$= \dfrac{2x^2(x + 5)(x + 2)}{(x + 2)2x^2(x^2 - 25)}$

$= \dfrac{2x^2(x + 5)(x + 2)}{2x^2(x + 2)(x + 5)(x - 5)}$

$= \dfrac{1}{x - 5}$

39. $\dfrac{4x^4 - 25}{6x^3 - 5x^2 + 15x - 10}$

$= \dfrac{(2x^2 + 5))(2x^2 - 5)}{2x^2(3x - 2) + 5(3x - 2)}$

$= \dfrac{(2x^2 + 5)(2x^2 - 5)}{(3x - 2)(2x^2 + 5)}$

$= \dfrac{2x^2 - 5}{3x - 2}$

40. $\dfrac{16x^4 - 49}{8x^3 - 12x^2 + 14x - 21}$

$= \dfrac{(4x^2 + 7)(4x^2 - 7)}{4x^2(2x - 3) + 7(2x - 3)}$

$= \dfrac{(4x^2 + 7)(4x^2 - 7)}{(2x - 3)(4x^2 + 7)}$

$= \dfrac{4x^2 - 7}{2x - 3}$

42. $\dfrac{6 - x}{x - 6} = \dfrac{-1(x - 6)}{x - 6} = -1$

43. $\dfrac{y^2 - 36}{6 - y} = \dfrac{(y + 6)(y - 6)}{-1(y - 6)} = -(y + 6)$

44. $\dfrac{1 - y}{y^2 - 1} = \dfrac{-1(y - 1)}{(y + 1)(y - 1)} = -\dfrac{1}{y + 1}$

46. $\dfrac{1 - a^2}{a^2 - 2a + 1} = \dfrac{(1 + a)(1 - a)}{(a - 1)(a - 1)}$

$= \dfrac{(a + 1)(-1)(a - 1)}{(a - 1)(a - 1)}$

$= -\dfrac{a + 1}{a - 1}$

47. $\dfrac{28x^2 - 4ax + 15}{7x - 5} - \dfrac{12x^2 - 4ax + 24}{3x - 8}$

$= \dfrac{(7x - 5)(4x - 3)}{7x - 5} - \dfrac{(3x - 8)(4x - 3)}{3x - 8}$

$= 4x - 3 - (4x - 3)$
$= 4x - 3 - 4x + 3$
$= 0$

48. $\dfrac{42x^2 + 47x - 55}{7x - 5} - \dfrac{18x^2 - 15x - 88}{3x - 8}$

$= \dfrac{(7x - 5)(6x + 11)}{7x - 5} - \dfrac{(3x - 8)(6x + 11)}{3x - 8}$

$= 6x + 11 - (6x + 11)$
$= 6x + 11 - 6x - 11$
$= 0$

50. $\frac{x^4 - 16}{x + 2} - \frac{x^4 - 16}{x - 2}$

$= \frac{(x^2 + 4)(x + 2)(x - 2)}{x + 2} - \frac{(x^2 + 4)(x + 2)(x - 2)}{x - 2}$

$= (x^2 + 4)(x - 2) - [(x^2 + 4)(x + 2)]$
$= x^3 - 2x^2 + 4x - 8 - [x^3 + 2x^2 + 4x + 8]$
$= x^3 - 2x^2 + 4x - 8 - x^3 - 2x^2 - 4x - 8$
$= -4x^2 - 16$

51., 52., 53. *You can only divide out common factors. You cannot divide out common terms.*

55. $\frac{x^3 - 1}{x - 1}$ $\quad x = 3$

$= \frac{3^3 - 1}{3 - 1}$

$= \frac{27 - 1}{2}$

$= \frac{26}{2}$

$= 13$

$x^2 + x + 1 \quad x = 3$
$= 3^2 + 3 + 1$
$= 9 + 3 + 1$
$= 13$

56. $\frac{x - 4}{4 - x}$ $\quad x = 7$

$= \frac{7 - 4}{4 - 7}$

$= \frac{3}{-3}$

$= -1$

*Do not replace $x = 0$, undefined*

$\frac{x - 4}{4 - x}$ $\quad x = 10$

$= \frac{10 - 4}{4 - 10}$

$= \frac{6}{-6}$

$= -1$

*4 would not give the same results*

58. $E = \frac{7L}{88d^2}$

*Let $d = 1$*

$E = \frac{7(1,540)}{88(1)^2}$

$E = 122.5$

*Let $d = 2$*

$E = \frac{7(1,540)}{88(2)^2}$

$E = 30.6$

*Let $d = 3$*

$E = \frac{7(1,540)}{88(3)^2}$

$E = 13.6$

*Let $d = 4$*

$E = \frac{7)1,540)}{88(4)^2}$

$E = 7.7$

*Let $d = 5$*

$E = \frac{7(1,540)}{88(5)^2}$

$E = 4.9$

*Let $d = 6$*

$E = \frac{7(1,540)}{88(6)^2}$

$E = 3.4$

59. $E = \dfrac{7L}{88d^2}$

Let $d = 1$

$E = \dfrac{7(780)}{88(1)^2}$

$E = 62.0$

Let $d = 1.5$

$E = \dfrac{7(780)}{88(1.5)^2}$

$E = 27.6$

Let $d = 2$

$E = \dfrac{7(780)}{88(2)^2}$

$E = 15.5$

Let $d = 2.5$

$E = \dfrac{7(780)}{88(2.5)^2}$

$E = 9.9$

Let $d = 3$

$E = \dfrac{7(780)}{88(3)^2}$

$E = 6.9$

Let $d = 3.5$

$E = \dfrac{7(780)}{88(3.5)}$

$E = 5.1$

60. $E = \dfrac{7L}{88d^2}$

Let $d = 1$

$E = \dfrac{7(480)}{88(1)^2}$

$E = 38.2$

Let $d = 1.5$

$E = \dfrac{7(480)}{88(1.5)}$

$E = 17.0$

Let $d = 2$

$E = \dfrac{7(480)}{88(2)^2}$

$E = 9.5$

Let $d = 2.5$

$E = \dfrac{7(480)}{88(2.5)^2}$

$E = 6.1$

Let $d = 3$

$E = \dfrac{7(480)}{88(3)^2}$

$E = 4.2$

Let $d = 3.5$

$E = \dfrac{7(480)}{88(3.5)^2}$

$E = 3.1$

62. $\dfrac{4{,}750}{3.2} = 1{,}484.4$ *feet/second*

63. $\dfrac{175.8}{16.3} = 10.8$ *miles/gallon*

64. $\dfrac{200}{16.5} = 12.1$ *miles/gallon*

66. $C = \pi d$

$C = 3.14(102) = 320.28$ *feet*

$\dfrac{320.28}{3.5} = 91.5$ *feet/minute*

67. $C = 2\pi r,\ r = 2$
$C = 2(3.14)(2) = 12.56$ *inches*

$d = \dfrac{12.57}{\frac{1}{300}} = 3.768$ *ft*/min

$C = 2\pi r,\ r = 1.5$
$C = 2(3.14)(1.5) = 9.42$ *inches*

$d = \dfrac{9.42}{\frac{1}{300}} = 2.826$ *ft*/min

68. $C = 2\pi r, r=2$
$C = 2(3.14)(2) = 12.56$ *inches*

$d = \dfrac{12.56}{\frac{1}{3,600}} = 45,216$ *in*/min

$C = 2\pi r, r=1.5$
$C = 2(3.14)(1.5) = 9.42$ *inches*

$d = \dfrac{9.42}{\frac{1}{3,600}} = 33,912$ *in*/min.

70. $R_1 = 6$ *ohms and* $R_2 = 18$ *ohms*

$$\frac{1}{R} = \frac{R_1 + R_2}{R_1 R_2}$$

$$\frac{1}{R} = \frac{6 + 18}{6(18)}$$

$$\frac{1}{R} = \frac{24}{108}$$

$$\frac{1}{R} = \frac{2}{9} \text{ then } R = \frac{9}{2} \text{ ohms}$$

71. $(4x^2 - 5x + 5) - (x^2 + 2x + 1)$
$= 4x^2 - 5x + 5 - x^2 - 2x - 1$
$= 3x^2 - 7x + 4$

72. $(7x^2 + 6x + 4) - (3x^2 - 5x + 2)$
$= 7x^2 + 6x + 4 - 3x^2 + 5x - 2$
$= 4x^2 + 11x + 2$

74. $(-6x + 5) - (-6x - 18)$
$= -6x + 5 + 6x + 18$
$= 23$

75. $4x^3 - (5x^3 - 8x^2)$
$= 4x^3 - 4x^3 + 8x^2$
$= 8x^2$

76. $2x^2 - (2x^2 + 6x)$
$= 2x^2 - 2x^2 - 6x$
$= -6x$

78. $$\frac{\frac{1}{3}x^2 + \frac{5}{12}x - \frac{1}{2}}{\frac{2}{3}x^2 - x + \frac{3}{8}}$$

$$= \frac{24\left(\frac{1}{3}x^2\right) + 24\left(\frac{5}{12}x\right) - 24\left(\frac{1}{2}\right)}{24\left(\frac{2}{3}x^2\right) - 24(x) + 24\left(\frac{3}{8}\right)} \qquad LCD = 24$$

$$= \frac{8x^2 + 10x - 12}{16x^2 - 24x + 9}$$

$$= \frac{2(4x^2 + 5x - 6)}{(4x - 3)(4x - 3)}$$

$$= \frac{2(4x - 3)(x + 2)}{(4x - 3)(4x - 3)}$$

$$= \frac{2(x + 2)}{4x - 3}$$

79. $\dfrac{6x^{2n} - 5x^{n} - 21}{9x^{2n} - 49}$

$= \dfrac{(3x^{n} - 7)(2x^{n} + 3)}{(3x^{n} + 7)(3x^{n} - 7)}$

$= \dfrac{2x^{n} + 3}{3x^{n} + 7}$

80. $\dfrac{30x^{2n} - 19x^{n} - 4}{36x^{2n} - 1}$

$= \dfrac{(5x^{n} - 4)(6x^{n} - 1)}{(2x^{n} + 1)(2x^{n} - 1)}$

$= \dfrac{5x^{n} - 4}{6x^{n} - 1}$

82. $\dfrac{x^{3n} + 5x^{2n} - 4x^{n} - 20}{x^{2n} + 10x^{n} + 25}$

$= \dfrac{x^{2n}(x^{n} + 5) - 4(x^{n} + 5)}{(x^{n} + 5)(x^{n} + 5)}$

$= \dfrac{(x^{2n} - 4)(x^{n} + 5)}{(x^{n} + 5)(x^{n} + 5)}$

$= \dfrac{x^{2n} - 4}{x^{n} + 5}$

$= \dfrac{(x^{n} + 2)(x^{n} - 2)}{x^{n} + 5}$

83. $\dfrac{(4x^2 + 3)(x - 3) + (29x + 4)(x - 3)}{4x^2 - 11x - 3}$

$= \dfrac{(4x^2 + 3)(x - 3) + (29x + 4)(x - 3)}{(4x + 1)(x - 3)}$

$= \dfrac{4x^2 + 3 + 29x + 4}{4x + 1}$

$= \dfrac{4x^2 + 29x + 7}{4x + 1}$

$= \dfrac{(x + 7)(4x + 1)}{(4x + 1)}$

$= x + 7$

84. $\dfrac{(5x^2 + 21)(x - 4) + (43x + 3)(x - 4)}{5x^2 - 17x - 12}$

$= \dfrac{(5x^2 + 21 + 43x + 3)(x - 4)}{(5x + 3)(x - 4)}$

$= \dfrac{5x^2 + 43x + 24}{5x + 3}$

$= \dfrac{(x + 8)(5x + 3)}{5x + 3}$

$= x + 8$

## Section 4.2

2. $\dfrac{6x^3 + 12x^2 - 9x}{3x} = \dfrac{6x^3}{3x} + \dfrac{12x^2}{3x} - \dfrac{9x}{3x}$

$= 2x^2 + 4x - 3$

3. $\dfrac{10x^4 + 15x^3 - 20x^2}{-5x^2} = \dfrac{10x^4}{-5x^2} + \dfrac{15x^3}{-5x^2} - \dfrac{20x^2}{-5x^2}$

$= -2x^2 - 3x + 4$

4. $\dfrac{12x^5 - 18x^4 - 6x^3}{6x^3} = \dfrac{12x^5}{6x^3} - \dfrac{18x^4}{6x^3} - \dfrac{6x^3}{6x^3}$

$= 2x^2 - 3x - 1$

6. $\dfrac{6y^4 - 3y^3 + 18y^2}{9y^2} = \dfrac{6y^4}{9y^2} - \dfrac{3y^3}{9y^2} + \dfrac{18y^2}{9y^2}$

$= \dfrac{2}{3}x^2 - \dfrac{1}{3}y + 2$

7. $\dfrac{5x^3 - 8x^2 - 6x}{-2x^2} = \dfrac{5x^3}{-2x^2} - \dfrac{8x^2}{-2x^2} - \dfrac{6x}{-2x^2}$

$= -\dfrac{5}{2}x + 4 + \dfrac{3}{x}$

8. $\dfrac{-9x^5 + 10x^3 - 12x}{-6x^4} = \dfrac{-9x^5}{-6x^4} + \dfrac{10x^3}{-6x^4} - \dfrac{12x}{-6x^4}$

$= \dfrac{3}{2}x - \dfrac{5}{3}x + \dfrac{2}{x^3}$

10. $$\frac{a^2b + ab^2}{ab} = \frac{a^2b}{ab} + \frac{ab^2}{ab}$$

$$= a + b$$

11. $$\frac{10x^3y^2 - 20x^2y^3 - 30x^3y^3}{-10x^2y}$$

$$= \frac{10x^3y^2}{-10x^2y} - \frac{20x^2y^3}{-10x^2y} - \frac{30x^3y^3}{-10x^2y}$$

$$= -xy + 2y^2 + 3xy^2$$

12. $$\frac{9x^4y^4 + 18x^3y^4 - 27x^2y^4}{-9xy^3}$$

$$= \frac{9x^4y^4}{-9xy^3} + \frac{18x^3y^4}{-9xy^3} - \frac{27x^2y^4}{-9xy^3}$$

$$= -x^3y - 2x^2y + 3xy$$

14. $$\frac{x^2 - x - 6}{x + 2} = \frac{(x + 2)(x - 3)}{x + 2}$$

$$= x - 3$$

15. $$\frac{2a^2 - 3a - 9}{2a + 3} = \frac{(2a + 3)(a - 3)}{2a + 3}$$

$$= a - 3$$

16. $$\frac{2a^2 + 3a - 9}{2a - 3} = \frac{(2a - 3)(a + 3)}{2a + 3}$$

$$= a + 3$$

18. $$\frac{5x^2 - 26xy - 24y^2}{5x + 4y} = \frac{(5x + 4y)(x - 6y)}{5x + 4y}$$

$$= x - 6y$$

19. $$\frac{x^3 - y^3}{x - y} = \frac{(x - y)(x^2 + xy + y^2)}{x - y}$$

$$= x^2 + xy + y^2$$

20. $$\frac{x^3 + 8}{x + 2} = \frac{(x + 2)(x^2 - 2x + 4)}{x + 2}$$

$$= x^2 - 2x + 4$$

22. $$\frac{y^4 - 81}{y - 3} = \frac{(y^2 + 9)(y + 3)(y - 3)}{y - 3}$$

$$= (y^2 + 9)(y + 3)$$

23. $$\frac{x^3 + 2x^2 - 25x - 50}{x - 5}$$

$$= \frac{x^2(x + 2) - 25(x + 2)}{x - 5}$$

$$= \frac{(x + 2)(x + 5)(x - 5)}{x - 5}$$

$$= (x + 2)(x + 5)$$

24. $$\frac{x^3 + 2x^2 - 25x - 50}{x + 5}$$

$$= \frac{x^2(x + 2) - 25(x + 2)}{x + 5}$$

$$= \frac{(x + 2)(x + 5)(x - 5)}{x + 4}$$

$$= (x + 2)(x - 5)$$

26. $$\frac{9x^3 + 18x^2 - 4x - 8}{x + 2}$$

$$= \frac{(x^2(x + 2) - 4(x + 2)}{x + 2}$$

$$= \frac{(x + 2)(3x + 2)(3x - 2)}{x + 2}$$

$$= (3x + 2)(3x - 2)$$

27.
$$\begin{array}{r|l} & \phantom{-}x - 7 \\ x + 2) & x^2 - 5x - 7 \\ & -\ \ - \\ & \underline{x^2 + 2x} \\ & -7x - 7 \\ & +\ \ + \\ & \underline{-7x - 14} \\ & 7 \end{array}$$

$$\frac{x^2 - 5x - 7}{x + 2} = x - 7 + \frac{7}{x + 2}$$

28.
$$\begin{array}{r} x + 7 \\ x - 3\overline{)\, x^2 + 4x - 8} \\ + \quad + \\ \underline{x^2 - 3x} \\ 7x - 8 \\ + \quad + \\ \underline{7x - 21} \\ 13 \end{array}$$

$$\frac{x^2 + 4x - 8}{x - 3} = x + 7 + \frac{13}{x - 3}$$

30.
$$\begin{array}{r} 4x + 1 \\ 2x - 7\overline{)\, 8x^2 - 26x - 9} \\ - \quad + \\ \underline{8x^2 - 28x} \\ 2x - 9 \\ - \quad + \\ \underline{2x - 7} \\ -2 \end{array}$$

$$\frac{8x^2 - 26x - 9}{2x - 7} = 4x + 1 + \frac{-2}{2x - 7}$$

31.
$$\begin{array}{r} 2x^2 - 5x + 1 \\ x + 1\overline{)\, 2x^3 - 3x^2 - 4x + 5} \\ - \quad - \\ \underline{2x^3 + 2x^2} \\ -5x^2 - 4x \\ + \quad + \\ \underline{-5x^2 - 5x} \\ x + 5 \\ - \quad - \\ \underline{x + 1} \\ 4 \end{array}$$

$$\frac{2x^3 - 3x^2 - 4x + 5}{x + 1}$$

$$= 2x^2 - 5x + 1 + \frac{4}{x + 1}$$

32.
$$\begin{array}{r} 3x^2 + x + 4 \\ x - 2\overline{)\, 3x^3 - 5x^2 + 2x - 1} \\ - \quad + \\ \underline{3x^3 - 6x^2} \\ x^2 + 2x \\ - \quad + \\ \underline{x^2 - 2x} \\ 4x - 1 \\ - \quad + \\ \underline{4x - 8} \\ 7 \end{array}$$

$$\frac{3x^3 - 5x^2 + 2x - 1}{x - 2}$$

$$= 3x^2 + x + 4 + \frac{7}{x - 2}$$

34.
$$\begin{array}{r} y^2 - 5y - 1 \\ 3y - 4\overline{)\, 3y^3 - 19y^2 + 17y + 4} \\ - \quad + \\ \underline{3y^3 - 4y^2} \\ -15y^2 + 17y \\ + \quad - \\ \underline{-15y^2 + 20y} \\ -3y + 4 \\ + \quad - \\ \underline{+3y + 4} \\ 0 \end{array}$$

$$\frac{3y^3 - 19y^2 + 17y + 4}{3y - 4} = y^2 - 5y - 1$$

35.
$$\begin{array}{r} x - 3 \\ 2x^2 - 3x + 2\overline{)\, 2x^3 - 9x^1 + 11x - 6} \\ - \quad + \quad - \\ \underline{2x^3 - 3x^2 + 2x} \\ -6x^2 + 9x - 6 \\ + \quad - \quad + \\ \underline{-6x^2 + 9x - 6} \\ 0 \end{array}$$

$$\frac{2x^3 - 9x^2 + 11x - 6}{2x^2 - 3x + 2} = x - 3$$

36.

$$\begin{array}{r} 2x + 3 \\ 3x^2 - x + 1 \overline{)\; 6x^3 + 7x^2 - x + 3} \\ - \quad + \quad - \\ \underline{6x^3 - 2x^2 + 2x} \\ 9x^1 - 3x + 3 \\ - \quad + \quad - \\ \underline{9x^2 - 3x + 3} \\ 0 \end{array}$$

$$\frac{6x^3 + 7x^2 - x + 3}{3x^2 - x + 1} = 2x + 3$$

38.

$$\begin{array}{r} 3y^2 + y + 1 \\ 3y - 3 \overline{)\; 9y^3 - 6y^2 + 0y + 8} \\ - \quad + \\ \underline{9y^3 - 9y^3} \\ 3y^2 + 0y \\ - \quad + \\ \underline{3y^2 - 3y} \\ 3y + 8 \\ - \quad + \\ \underline{3y - 3} \\ 11 \end{array}$$

$$\frac{9x^3 - 6y^2 + 8}{3y - 3}$$

$$= 3y^2 + y + 1 + \frac{11}{3y - 3}$$

39.

$$\begin{array}{r} a^3 + 2a^2 + 4a + 6 \\ a - 2 \overline{)\; a^4 + 0a^3 + 0a^2 - 2a + 5} \\ - \quad + \\ \underline{a^4 - 2a^3} \\ 2a^3 + 0a^2 \\ - \quad + \\ \underline{2a^3 - 4a^2} \\ 4a^2 - 2a \\ - \quad + \\ \underline{4a^2 - 8a} \\ 6a + 5 \\ - \quad + \\ \underline{6a - 12} \\ 17 \end{array}$$

$$\frac{a^4 - 2a + 5}{a - 2}$$

$$= a^3 + 2a^2 + 4a + 6 + \frac{17}{a - 2}$$

40.

$$\begin{array}{r} a^3 - a^2 + 2a - 4 \\ a + 2 \overline{)\; a^4 + a^3 + 0a^2 + 0a - 1} \\ - \quad - \\ \underline{a^4 + 3a^3} \\ - a^3 + 0a^2 \\ + \quad + \\ \underline{- a^3 - 3a^2} \\ 2a^2 + 0a \\ - \quad - \\ \underline{2a^2 + 4a} \\ - 4a - 1 \\ + \quad + \\ \underline{- 4a - 8} \\ 7 \end{array}$$

$$\frac{a^4 + a^3 - 1}{a + 2}$$

$$= a^3 - a^2 + 2a - 4 + \frac{7}{a + 2}$$

42.

$$\begin{array}{r} y^3 + 3y^2 + 9y + 27 \\ y - 3 \overline{)\; y^4 + 0y^3 + 0y^2 + 0y - 81} \\ - \quad + \\ \underline{y^4 - 3y^3} \\ 3y^3 + 0y^2 \\ - \quad + \\ \underline{3y^3 - 9y^2} \\ 9y^2 + 0y \\ - \quad + \\ \underline{9y^2 - 27} \\ 27y - 81 \\ - \quad + \\ \underline{27y - 81} \\ 0 \end{array}$$

$$\frac{y^4 - 81}{y - 3} = y^3 + 3y^2 + 9y + 27$$

43.

$$\begin{array}{r} x^2 - 2x + 1 \\ x^2 + 3x + 2 \overline{\big) x^4 + x^3 - 3x^2 - x + 1} \\ - \quad - \quad - \\ \underline{x^4 + 3x^3 + 2x^2} \\ -2x^3 - 5x^1 - x \\ + \quad + \quad + \\ \underline{-2x^3 - 6x^2 - 4x} \\ x^2 + 3x + 2 \\ - \quad - \quad - \\ \underline{x^2 + 3x + 2} \\ 0 \end{array}$$

$$\frac{x^4 + x^3 - 3x^2 - x + 2}{x^2 + 3x + 2} = x^2 - 2x + 1$$

44.

$$\begin{array}{r} x^2 + x - 1 \\ 2x^2 - x + 3 \overline{\big) 2x^4 + x^3 + 0x^2 + 4x - 3} \\ - \quad + \quad - \\ \underline{2x^4 - x^3 + 3x^2} \\ +2x^3 = 3x^2 + 4x \\ - \quad + \quad - \\ \underline{2x^3 - x^2 + 3x} \\ -2x^2 + x - 3 \\ + \quad + \quad + \\ \underline{-2x^2 - x - 3} \\ 3 \end{array}$$

$$\frac{2x^4 + x^3 + 4x - 3}{2x^2 - x + 3} = x^2 + x - 1$$

46. *The answer to problem 22 is*

$(x^2 + 9(y + 3)$

*which is the answer to problem 42.*

47. $\frac{3}{5} \div \frac{2}{7} = \frac{3}{5} \cdot \frac{7}{2} = \frac{21}{10}$

48. $\frac{2}{7} \div \frac{3}{5} = \frac{2}{7} \cdot \frac{5}{3} = \frac{10}{21}$

50. $\frac{6}{8} \div \frac{3}{5} = \frac{6}{8} \cdot \frac{5}{3} = \frac{10}{8} = \frac{5}{4}$

51. $\frac{4}{9} \div 8 = \frac{4}{9} \cdot \frac{1}{8} = \frac{4}{72} = \frac{1}{18}$

52. $\frac{3}{7} \div 6 = \frac{3}{7} \cdot \frac{1}{6} = \frac{1}{14}$

54. $12 \div \frac{2}{3} = \frac{12}{1} \cdot \frac{3}{2} = \frac{36}{2} = 18$

55. $\left(\frac{1}{3}\right)^{-2} + \left(\frac{1}{2}\right)^{-3}$

$= \frac{1}{\left(\frac{1}{3}\right)^2} + \frac{1}{\left(\frac{1}{2}\right)^3}$

$= \frac{1}{\frac{1}{9}} + \frac{1}{\frac{1}{8}}$

$= \frac{9}{1} + \frac{8}{1}$

$= 17$

56. $\left(\frac{1}{2}\right)^{-3} - \left(\frac{1}{3}\right)^{-3}$

$= \left(\frac{2}{1}\right)^3 - \left(\frac{3}{1}\right)^3$

$= 8 - 27$

$= -19$

58. $(4x^4y^{-3})^2(2x^{-6}y^4)^{-3}$

$$= 4^2x^8y^{-6}x^{-3}x^{18}y^{-12}$$

$$= \frac{4^2x^8x^{18}}{2^3y^6y^{12}}$$

$$= \frac{2x^{26}}{y^{18}}$$

59.

$$\begin{array}{r}
4x^3 - x^2 + 3 \\
x^2 - 5\overline{)\ 4x^5 - x^4 - 20x^3 + 8x^2 - 15} \\
- \quad\quad + \quad\quad\quad\quad \\
\underline{4x^5 \quad\quad - 20x^3} \quad\quad\quad\quad \\
- x^4 \quad\quad + 8x^2 \quad\quad \\
+ \quad\quad\quad - \quad\quad\quad \\
\underline{- x^4 \quad\quad + 5x^2} \quad\quad \\
3x^2 - 15 \\
+ \quad\quad - \quad \\
\underline{3x^2 - 15} \\
0
\end{array}$$

60.

$$\begin{array}{r}
4x^2 + 2x + 1 \\
x^3 + 0x^2 + 0x - 5\overline{)\ 4x^5 + 2x^4 + x^3 - 20x^2 - 10x - 5} \\
- \quad - \quad - \quad + \quad\quad\quad\quad\quad\quad \\
\underline{4x^5 + 0x^4 + 0x^3 - 20x^2} \quad\quad\quad\quad\quad \\
2x^4 + x^3 + 0x^2 - 10x \quad\quad \\
- \quad - \quad - \quad + \quad\quad\quad \\
\underline{2x^4 + 0x^3 + 0x^2 - 10x} \quad\quad \\
x^3 + 0x^2 + 0x - 5 \\
- \quad - \quad - \quad + \\
\underline{x^3 + 0x^2 + 0x - 5} \\
0
\end{array}$$

62.

$$\begin{array}{r}
2.0x^2 - 5.0x + 3 \\
.3x + .2\overline{)\ .6x^3 - 1.1x^2 - .1x + .6} \\
\underline{.6x^3 - .4x^2} \quad\quad\quad\quad \\
- 1.5x^2 - .1x \quad\quad \\
- \quad\quad + \quad\quad\quad \\
\underline{1.5x^2 - 1.0x} \quad\quad \\
+ .9x + .6 \\
- \quad\quad - \\
\underline{+ .9x + .6} \\
0
\end{array}$$

63.

$$\begin{array}{r}
\frac{3}{2}x - \frac{5}{2} + \frac{1}{2x + 4} \\
2x + 4\overline{)\ 3x^2 + x - 9} \\
- \quad - \quad\quad\quad \\
\underline{3x^2 + 6x} \quad\quad \\
- 5x - 9 \\
+ \quad + \\
\underline{- 5x - 10} \\
1
\end{array}$$

$$\frac{3x^2 + x - 9}{2x + 4} = \frac{3}{2}x + \frac{5}{2} + \frac{1}{2x + 4}$$

64.
$$\begin{array}{r}
\frac{2}{3}x - \frac{5}{3} \\
3x + 6 \overline{) \; 2x^2 - x - 9} \\
- \quad - \qquad\qquad \\
\underline{2x^2 + 4x} \qquad \\
-5x - 9 \\
+ \quad + \\
\underline{-5x - 10} \\
1
\end{array}$$

$$\frac{2x^2 - x - 9}{3x + 6} = \frac{2}{3}x - \frac{5}{3} + \frac{1}{3x + 6}$$

66.
$$\begin{array}{r}
\frac{1}{5}x + \frac{1}{5} \\
5x - 2 \overline{) \; x^2 + \frac{3}{5}x + \frac{8}{5}} \\
- \quad + \qquad\qquad \\
\underline{x^3 - \frac{2}{5}x} \qquad \\
x + \frac{8}{5} \\
- \quad + \\
\underline{x - \frac{2}{5}} \\
2
\end{array}$$

$$\frac{x^2 + \frac{3}{5}x + \frac{8}{5}}{5x - 2} = \frac{1}{5}x + \frac{1}{5} + \frac{2}{5x - 2}$$

## Section 4.3

2. $\frac{5}{6} \cdot \frac{7}{8} = \frac{35}{48}$

3. $\frac{3}{4} \div \frac{1}{3} = \frac{3}{4} \cdot \frac{3}{1} = \frac{9}{4}$

4. $\frac{3}{8} \div \frac{5}{4} = \frac{3}{8} \cdot \frac{4}{5} = \frac{3}{10}$

6. $\frac{6}{5} \cdot \frac{10}{36} \div \frac{3}{4} = \frac{6}{5} \cdot \frac{10}{36} \cdot \frac{4}{3}$

$= \frac{8}{18}$

$= \frac{4}{9}$

7. $\frac{10x^2}{5y^2} \cdot \frac{15y^3}{2x^4} = \frac{15y}{x^2}$

8. $\frac{8x^3}{7y^4} \cdot \frac{14y^6}{16x^2}$

$= \frac{112x^3y^6}{112x^2y^4}$

$= xy^2$

10. $\frac{8ab^3}{9a^2b} \div \frac{16a^2b^2}{18ab^3}$

$= \frac{8ab^3}{9a^2b} \cdot \frac{18ab^3}{16a^2b^2}$

$= \frac{144a^2b^6}{144a^4b^3}$

$= \frac{b^3}{a^2}$

11. $\frac{6x^2}{5y^3} \cdot \frac{11z^2}{2x^2} \div \frac{33z^5}{10y^8}$

$= \frac{6x^2}{5y^3} \cdot \frac{11z^2}{2x^2} \cdot \frac{10y^8}{33z^5}$

$= \frac{660x^2y^8a^2}{330x^2y^3a^5}$

$= \frac{2y^5}{a^3}$

12. $\frac{4x^3}{7y^2} \cdot \frac{6a^5}{5x^6} \div \frac{24z^2}{35x^6}$

$= \frac{4x^3}{7y^2} \cdot \frac{6z^5}{5x^6} \cdot \frac{35x^6}{24z^2}$

$= \frac{840x^9z^5}{840x^6y^2z^2}$

$= \frac{x^3z^3}{y^2}$

14. $\dfrac{x^2 - 16}{x^2 - 25} \cdot \dfrac{x - 5}{x - 4}$

$= \dfrac{(x + 4)(x - 4)}{(x + 5)(x - 5)} \cdot \dfrac{x - 5}{x - 4}$

$= \dfrac{x + 4}{x + 5}$

15. $\dfrac{y^2 - 1}{y + 2} \cdot \dfrac{y^2 + 5y + 6}{y^2 + 2y - 3}$

$= \dfrac{(y + 1)(y - 1)}{y + 2} \cdot \dfrac{(y + 2)(y + 3)}{(y + 3)(y - 1}$

$= y + 1$

16. $\dfrac{y - 1}{y^2 - y - 6} \cdot \dfrac{y^2 + 5y + 6}{y^2 - 1}$

$= \dfrac{y - 1}{(y + 2)(y - 3)} \cdot \dfrac{(y + 2)(y + 3)}{(y + 1)(y - 1)}$

$= \dfrac{y + 3}{(y - 3)(y + 1)}$

18. $\dfrac{x^2 + 5x + 1}{4x - 4} \cdot \dfrac{x - 1}{x^2 + 5x + 1}$

$= \dfrac{x^2 + 5x + 1}{4(x - 1)} \cdot \dfrac{x - 1}{x^2 + 5x + 1}$

$= \dfrac{1}{4}$

19. $\dfrac{5x + 2y}{25x^2 - 5xy - 6y^2} \cdot \dfrac{20x^2 - 7xy - 3y^2}{4x + y}$

$= \dfrac{5x + 2y}{(5x + 2y)(5x - 3y)} \cdot \dfrac{(4x + y)(5x - 3y)}{4x + y}$

$= 1$

20. $\dfrac{7x + 3y}{12x^2 - 17xy - 15y^2} \cdot \dfrac{12x^2 - 4xy - 5y^2}{2x + y}$

$= \dfrac{7x + 3y}{(7x + 3y)(6x - 5y)} \cdot \dfrac{(2x + y)(6x - 5y)}{2x + y}$

$= 1$

22. $\dfrac{a^2 + 7a + 12}{a - 5} \div \dfrac{a^2 + 9a + 18}{a^2 - 7a + 10}$

$= \dfrac{(a + 3)(a + 4)}{a - 5} \cdot \dfrac{(a + 2)(a - 5)}{(a + 3)(a + 6)}$

$= \dfrac{(a + 4)(a - 2)}{a + 6}$

23. $\dfrac{4t^2 - 1}{6t^2 + t - 2} \div \dfrac{8t^3 + 1}{27t^3 + 8}$

$= \dfrac{(2t + 1)(2t - 1)}{(2t - 1)(2t + 2)} \cdot \dfrac{(3t + 2)(9t^2 - 6t + 4)}{(2t + 1)(4t^2 - 2t + 1)}$

$= \dfrac{9t^2 - 6t + 4}{4t^2 - 2t + 1}$

24. $\dfrac{9t^2 - 1}{6t^2 + 7t - 3} \div \dfrac{27t^3 + 1}{8t^3 + 24}$

$= \dfrac{(3t + 1)(3t - 1)}{(2t + 3)(3t - 1)} \cdot \dfrac{(2t + 3)(4t^2 - 6t + 9)}{(3t + 1)(9t^2 - 3t + 1)}$

$= \dfrac{4t^2 - 6t + 9}{9t^2 - 3t + 1}$

26. $\dfrac{x^2 - 2x + 1}{3x^2 + 7x - 20} \div \dfrac{x^2 + 3x - 4}{3x^2 - 2x - 5}$

$= \dfrac{(x - 1)(x - 1)}{(3x - 5)(x + 4)} \cdot \dfrac{(x + 1)(3x}{(x + 4)(x}$

$= \dfrac{(x - 1)(x + 1)}{(x + 4)^2}$

27. $$\frac{6a^2b + 2ab^2 - 20b^3}{4a^2b - 16b^3} \cdot \frac{10a^2 - 22ab + 4b^2}{27a^3 - 125b^3}$$

$$= \frac{2b(3a^2 + ab - 10b^2)}{4b(a^2 - 4b^2)} \cdot \frac{2(5a^2 - 11ab + 2b^2)}{(3a)^3 - (5b)^3}$$

$$= \frac{2b(a + 2b)(3a - 5b)}{4b(a + 2b)(a - 2b)} \cdot \frac{2(5a - b)(a - 2b)}{(3a - 5b)(9a^2 + 15ab + 25b^2)}$$

$$= \frac{5a - b}{9a^2 + 15ab + 25b^2}$$

28. $$\frac{12a^2b - 3ab^2 - 42b^3}{9a^2 - 36b^2} \cdot \frac{6a^2 - 15ab + 6b^2}{8a^3b - b^4}$$

$$= \frac{3b(4a^2 - ab - 14b^2)}{9(a^2 - 4b^2)} \cdot \frac{3(2a^2 - 5ab + 2b^2)}{b(8a^3 - b^3)}$$

$$= \frac{3b(4a + 7b)(a - 2b)}{9(a + 2b)(a - 2b)} \cdot \frac{3(a - 2b)(2a - b)}{b(2a - b)(4a^2 + 2ab + b^2)}$$

$$= \frac{(4a + 7b)(a - 2b)}{(a + 2b)(4a^2 + 2ab + b^2)}$$

30. $$\frac{490x^2 - 640}{49x^2 - 112x + 64} \cdot \frac{28x^2 - 95x + 72}{56x^3 - 62x^2 - 144x}$$

$$= \frac{10(49x^2 - 64)}{(7x - 8)(7x - 8)} \cdot \frac{(7x - 8)(4x - 9)}{2x(28x^2 - 31x - 72)}$$

$$= \frac{10(7x + 8)(7x - 8)}{(7x - 8)(7x - 8)} \cdot \frac{(7x - 8)(4x - 9)}{2x(7x + 8)(4x - 9)}$$

$$= \frac{5}{x}$$

31. $$\frac{x^5 - x^2}{5x^5 - 5x} \cdot \frac{10x^4 - 10x^2}{2x^4 + 2x^3 + 2x^2}$$

$$= \frac{x^2(x^3 - 1)}{5x(x^4 - 1)} \cdot \frac{10x^2(x^2 - 1)}{2x^2(x^2 + x + 1)}$$

$$= \frac{x^2(x - 1)(x^2 + x + 1)}{5x(x^2 + 1)(x + 1)(x - 1)} \cdot \frac{10x^2(x + 1)(x - 1)}{2x^2(x^2 + x + 1)}$$

$$= \frac{x(x - 1)}{x^2 + 1}$$

32. $\dfrac{2x^4 - 16x}{3x^6 - 48x^2} \cdot \dfrac{6x^5 + 24x^3}{4x^4 + 8x^3 + 13x^2}$

$$= \frac{2x(x^3 - 8)}{3x^2(x^4 - 16)} \cdot \frac{6x^3(x^2 + 4)}{4x^2(x^2 + 2x + 4)}$$

$$= \frac{2x(x - 2)(x^2 + 2x + 4)}{3x^2(x^2 + 4)(x + 2)(x - 2)} \cdot \frac{6x^3(x^2 + 4)}{4x^2(x^2 + 2x + 4)}$$

$$= \frac{1}{x + 2}$$

34. $\dfrac{a^2 - 6ab + 9b^2}{a^2 - 4b^2} \cdot \dfrac{a^2 - 5ab + 6b^2}{(a - 3b)^2} \div \dfrac{a^2 - 9b^2}{a^2 - ab - 6b^2}$

$$= \frac{(a - 3b)(a - 3b)}{(a + 2b)(a - 2b)} \cdot \frac{(a - 2b)(a - 3b)}{(a - 3b)(a - 3b)} \cdot \frac{(a - 3b)(a + 2b)}{(a + 3b)(a - 3b)}$$

$$= \frac{a - 3b}{a + 3b}$$

35. $\dfrac{2y^2 - 7y - 15}{42y^2 - 29y - 5} \cdot \dfrac{12y^2 - 16y + 5}{7y^2 - 36y + 5} \div \dfrac{4y^2 - 9}{49y^2 - 1}$

$$= \frac{(2y + 3)(y - 5)}{(7y + 1)(6y - 5)} \cdot \frac{(2y - 1)(6y - 5)}{(7y - 1)(y - 5)} \cdot \frac{(7y + 1)(7y - 1)}{(2y + 3)(2y - 3)}$$

$$= \frac{2y - 1}{2y - 3}$$

36. $\dfrac{8y^2 + 18y - 5}{21y^2 - 16y + 3} \cdot \dfrac{35y^2 - 22y + 3}{6y^2 + 17y + 5} \div \dfrac{16y^2 - 1}{9y^2 - 1}$

$$= \frac{(2y + 5)(4y - 1)}{(7y - 3)(3y - 1)} \cdot \frac{(5y - 1)(7y - 3)}{(3y + 1)(2y + 5)} \cdot \frac{(3y + 1)(3y - 1)}{(4y + 1)(4y - 1)}$$

$$= \frac{5y - 1}{4y + 1}$$

38. $\dfrac{ax + bx + 2a + 2b}{ax - 3a + bx - 3b} \cdot \dfrac{ax - bx - 3a + 3b}{ax - bx - 2a + 2b}$

$$= \frac{x(a + b) + 2(a + b)}{a(x - 3) + b(x - 3)} \cdot \frac{x(a - b) - 3(a - b)}{x(a - b) - 2(a - b)}$$

$$= \frac{(a + b)(x + 2)}{(x - 3)(a + b)} \cdot \frac{(a - b)(x - 3)}{(a - b)(x - 2)}$$

$$= \frac{x + 2}{x - 2}$$

39. $$\frac{xy^2 - y^2 + 4xy - 4y}{xy - 3y + 4x - 12} \div \frac{xy^3 + 2xy^2 + y^3 + 2y^2}{xy^2 - 3y^2 + 2xy - 6y}$$

$$= \frac{y^2(x - 1) + 4y(x - 1)}{y(x - 3) + 4(x - 3)} \cdot \frac{y^2(x - 3) - 2y(x - 3)}{xy^2(y + 2) + y^2(y + 2)}$$

$$= \frac{(x - 1)(y^2 + 4y)}{(x - 3)(x + 4)} \cdot \frac{(x - 3)(y^2 + 2y)}{(y + 2)(xy^2 + y^2)}$$

$$= \frac{(x - 1)y(y + 4)}{(x - 3)(y + 4)} \cdot \frac{(x - 3)y(y + 2)}{(y + 2)y^2(x + 1)}$$

$$= \frac{x - 1}{x + 1}$$

40. $$\frac{4xb - 8b + 12x - 24}{xb^2 + 3b^2 + 3xb + 9b} \div \frac{4xb - 8b - 8x + 16}{xb^2 + 3b^2 - 2xb - 6b}$$

$$= \frac{4b(x - 2) + 12(x - 2)}{b^2(x + 3) + 3b(x + 3)} \cdot \frac{b^2(x + 3) - 2b(x + 3)}{4b(x - 2) - 8(x - 2)}$$

$$= \frac{(x - 2)(4b + 12)}{(x + 3)(b^2 + 3b)} \cdot \frac{(x + 3)(b^2 - 2b)}{(x - 2)(4b - 8)}$$

$$= \frac{(x - 2)4(b + 3)}{(x + 3)b(b + 3)} \cdot \frac{(x + 3)b(b - 2)}{(x - 2)4(b - 2)}$$

$$= 1$$

42. $$\frac{x^3 + 2x^2 - 9x - 18}{x^4 + 3x^3 - 4x^2 - 12x} \cdot \frac{x^3 + 5x^2 + 6x}{x^2 - x - 6}$$

$$= \frac{x^2(x + 2) - 9(x + 2)}{x^3(x + 3) - 4x(x + 3)} \cdot \frac{x(x^2 + 5x + 6)}{(x + 2)(x - 3)}$$

$$= \frac{(x + 2)(x + 3)(x - 3)}{(x + 3)x(x + 2)(x - 3)} \cdot \frac{x(x + 2)(x + 3)}{(x + 2)(x - 3)}$$

$$= \frac{x + 3}{x - 2}$$

43. $$\frac{(3x - 6)}{1} \cdot \frac{x}{x - 2}$$

$$= \frac{3(x - 2)}{1} \cdot \frac{x}{x - 2}$$

$$= 3x$$

44. $\dfrac{(4x + 8)}{1} \cdot \dfrac{x}{x + 2}$

$= \dfrac{4(x + 2)}{1} \cdot \dfrac{x}{x + 2}$

$= 4x$

46. $(x^2 - 49) \cdot \dfrac{5}{x + 7}$

$= \dfrac{(x + 7)(x - 7)}{1} \cdot \dfrac{5}{x + 7}$

$= 5(x - 7)$

47. $(x^2 - 3x + 2) \cdot \dfrac{3}{3x - 3}$

$= \dfrac{(x - 1)(x - 2)}{1} \cdot \dfrac{3}{3(x - 1)}$

$= x - 2$

48. $(x^2 - 3x + 2) \cdot \dfrac{-1}{x - 2}$

$= \dfrac{(x - 1)(x - 2)}{1} \cdot \dfrac{-1}{x - 2}$

$= -1(x - 1)$ *or* $1 - x$

50. $(y + 1)(y + 4)(y - 1) \cdot \dfrac{3}{y^2 - 1}$

$= \dfrac{(y + 1)(y + 4)(y - 1)}{1} \cdot \dfrac{3}{(y + 1)(y - 1)}$

$= 3(y + 4)$

51. $a(a + 5)(a - 5) \cdot \dfrac{a + 1}{a^2 + 5a}$

$= \dfrac{a(a + 5)(a - 5)}{1} \cdot \dfrac{a + 1}{a(a + 5)}$

$= (a - 5)(a + 1)$

52. $a(a + 3)(a - 3) \cdot \dfrac{a - 1}{a^2 - 3a}$

$= \dfrac{a(a + 3)(a - 3)}{1} \cdot \dfrac{a - 1}{a(a - 3)}$

$= (a + 3)(a - 1)$

54. $3x^3(7x^2 - 4x - 8)$
$= 21x^5 - 12x^4 - 24x^3$

55. $(3a - 1)(4a + 5) = 12a^2 + 11a - 5$

56. $(6a - 3)(2a + 1) = 12a^2 - 3$

58.
$$\begin{array}{r} 4x^2 + 6x + 9 \\ 2x - 3 \\ \hline 8x^3 + 12x^2 + 18x \qquad \\ - 12x^2 - 18x - 27 \\ \hline 8x^3 \qquad\qquad\qquad - 27 \end{array}$$

59. $(4y - 5)^2 = (4y - 5)(4y - 5)$
$= 16y^2 - 40y + 25$

60. $\left(2y - \dfrac{1}{2}\right)^2$

$= \left(2y - \dfrac{1}{2}\right)\left(2y - \dfrac{1}{2}\right)$

$= 4y^2 - 2y + \dfrac{1}{4}$

62. $(x + 2a)(2 - 3b)$
$= 2x - 3xb + 4a - 6ab$

63. $(3 - t^2)^2$
$= (3 - t^2)(3 - t^2)$
$= 9 - 6t^2 + t^4$

64. $(2 - t^3)^2$
$= (2 - t^3)(2 - t^3)$
$= 4 - 4t^3 + t^6$

66. $4(x - 1)(x - 2)(x - 3)$
$4(x - 1) = 4x - 4$
$(x - 2)(x - 3) = x^2 - 5x + 6$

$$\begin{array}{r} x^2 - 5x + 6 \\ 4x - 4 \\ \hline 4x^3 - 20x^2 + 24x \qquad \\ - 4x^2 + 20x - 24 \\ \hline 4x^3 - 24x^2 + 44x - 24 \end{array}$$

67. $\dfrac{3}{14} + \dfrac{7}{30}$

$= \dfrac{45}{210} + \dfrac{49}{210}$

$= \dfrac{94}{210}$

$= \dfrac{47}{105}$

68. $\frac{5}{12} + \frac{7}{18}$

$= \frac{15}{36} + \frac{14}{36}$

$= \frac{29}{36}$

70. $\frac{3}{14} - \frac{5}{22}$

$= \frac{33}{154} - \frac{35}{154}$

$= -\frac{2}{154}$

$= -\frac{1}{77}$

71. $(1 + 2^{-1})(1 + 3^{-1})(1 + 4^{-1})(1 + 5^{-1})$

$= \left(1\frac{1}{2}\right)\left(1\frac{1}{3}\right)\left(1\frac{1}{4}\right)\left(1\frac{1}{5}\right)$

$= \left(\frac{3}{2}\right)\left(\frac{4}{3}\right)\left(\frac{5}{4}\right)\left(\frac{6}{5}\right)$

$= 3$

72. $(1 - 2^{-1})(1 - 3^{-1})(1 - 4^{-1})(1 - 5^{-1})$

$= \left(\frac{1}{2}\right)\left(\frac{2}{3}\right)\left(\frac{3}{4}\right)\left(\frac{4}{5}\right)$

$= \frac{1}{5}$

74. $(1 - 2^{-1})(1 - 3^{-1})(1 - 4^{-1})\cdots(1 - 99^{-1})(1 - 100^{-1})$

$= \left(\frac{1}{2}\right)\left(\frac{2}{3}\right)\left(\frac{3}{4}\right)\cdots\left(\frac{98}{99}\right)\left(\frac{99}{100}\right)$

$= \frac{1}{100}$

## Section 4.4

2. $\frac{5}{6} + \frac{1}{3} = \frac{5}{6} + \frac{2}{6} = \frac{7}{6}$

3. $\frac{2}{5} - \frac{1}{15} = \frac{6}{15} - \frac{1}{15}$

$= \frac{5}{15}$

$= \frac{1}{3}$

4. $\frac{5}{8} - \frac{1}{4} = \frac{5}{8} - \frac{2}{8} = \frac{3}{8}$

6. $\frac{3}{4} + \frac{2}{3} = \frac{9}{12} + \frac{8}{12} = \frac{17}{12}$

7. $\frac{9}{48} - \frac{3}{54} = \frac{81}{432} - \frac{24}{432}$

$= \frac{57}{432}$

$= \frac{19}{144}$

8. $\frac{6}{28} - \frac{5}{42} = \frac{18}{84} - \frac{10}{84}$

$= \frac{8}{84}$

$= \frac{2}{21}$

10. $\frac{1}{3} - \frac{5}{6} + \frac{5}{12}$

$= \frac{4}{12} - \frac{10}{12} + \frac{5}{12}$

$= -\frac{1}{12}$

11. $\frac{x}{x + 3} + \frac{3}{x + 3} = \frac{x + 3}{x + 3} = 1$

12. $\frac{5x}{5x + 2} + \frac{2}{5x + 2} = \frac{5x + 2}{5x + 2} = 1$

14. $\frac{8}{y + 8} + \frac{y}{y + 8} = \frac{y + 8}{y + 8} = 1$

15. $\dfrac{x}{x^2 - y^2} - \dfrac{y}{x^2 - y^2}$

$= \dfrac{x - y}{(x + y)(x - y)}$

$= \dfrac{1}{x + y}$

16. $\dfrac{x}{x^2 - y^2} + \dfrac{y}{x^2 - y^2}$

$= \dfrac{x + y}{(x + y)(x - y)}$

$= \dfrac{1}{x - y}$

18. $\dfrac{2x - 4}{x + 2} - \dfrac{x - 6}{x + 2}$

$= \dfrac{2x - 4 - (x - 6)}{x + 2}$

$= \dfrac{2x - 4 - x + 6}{x + 2}$

$= \dfrac{x + 2}{x + 2}$

$= 1$

19. $\dfrac{1}{1} + \dfrac{1}{a^2} - \dfrac{3}{1^3}$

$= \dfrac{a^2}{a^3} + \dfrac{a}{a^3} - \dfrac{3}{a^3}$

$= \dfrac{a^2 + a - 3}{a^3}$

20. $\dfrac{3}{a} + \dfrac{2}{a^2} - \dfrac{1}{a^3}$

$= \dfrac{3a^2}{a^3} + \dfrac{2a}{a^3} - \dfrac{1}{a^3}$

$= \dfrac{3a^2 + 2a - 1}{a^3}$

22. $\dfrac{7x - 1}{3x + 2} - \dfrac{4x - 3}{3x + 2}$

$= \dfrac{7x - 1 - (4x - 3)}{3x + 2}$

$= \dfrac{7x - 1 - 4x + 3}{3x + 2}$

$= \dfrac{3x + 2}{3x + 2}$

$= 1$

23. $\dfrac{2}{t^2} - \dfrac{3}{2t} = \dfrac{4}{2t^2} - \dfrac{3t}{2t^2}$

$= \dfrac{4 - 3t}{2t^2}$

24. $\dfrac{5}{3t} - \dfrac{4}{t^2} = \dfrac{5t}{3t^2} - \dfrac{12}{3t^2}$

$= \dfrac{5t - 12}{3t^2}$

26. $\dfrac{x + 1}{x - 2} - \dfrac{4x + 7}{5x - 10}$

$= \dfrac{x + 1}{x - 2} - \dfrac{4x + 7}{5(x - 2)}$ $\quad LCD = 5(x - 2)$

$= \dfrac{x + 1}{x - 2} \cdot \dfrac{5}{5} - \dfrac{4x + 7}{5(x - 2)}$

$= \dfrac{5x + 5 - (4x + 7)}{5(x - 2)}$

$= \dfrac{5x + 5 - 4x - 7}{5(x - 2)}$

$= \dfrac{x - 2}{5(x - 2)}$

$= \dfrac{1}{5}$

27. $\dfrac{6x + 5}{5x - 25} - \dfrac{x + 2}{x - 5}$

$$= \frac{6x + 5}{5(x - 5)} - \frac{x + 2}{x - 5} \qquad LCD = 5(x - 25)$$

$$= \frac{6x + 5}{5(x - 5)} - \frac{x + 2}{x - 5} \cdot \frac{5}{5}$$

$$= \frac{6x + 5 - [5(x + 2)]}{5(x-5)}$$

$$= \frac{6x + 5 - 5x - 10}{5(x - 5)}$$

$$= \frac{x - 5}{5(x - 5)}$$

$$= \frac{1}{5}$$

28. $\dfrac{4x + 2}{3x + 12} - \dfrac{x - 2}{x + 4}$

$$= \frac{4x + 2}{3(x + 4)} - \frac{x - 2}{x + 4} \qquad LCD = 3(x + 4)$$

$$= \frac{4x + 2}{3(x + 4)} - \frac{x - 2}{x + 4} \cdot \frac{3}{3}$$

$$= \frac{4x + 2 - [3(x - 2)]}{3(x + 4)}$$

$$= \frac{4x + 2 - 3x + 6}{3(x + 4)}$$

$$= \frac{x + 8}{3(x + 4)}$$

30. $\dfrac{x + 7}{2x + 12} + \dfrac{6}{x^2 - 36}$

$$= \frac{x + 7}{2(x + 6)} + \frac{6}{(x + 6)(x - 6)} \qquad LCD = 2(x + 6)(x - 6)$$

$$= \frac{x + 7}{2(x + 6)} \cdot \frac{x - 6}{x - 6} + \frac{6}{(x + 6)(x - 6)} \cdot \frac{2}{2}$$

$$= \frac{x^2 + x - 42 + 12}{2(x + 6)(x - 6)}$$

$$= \frac{x^2 + x - 30}{2(x + 6)(x - 6)}$$

$$= \frac{(x + 6)(x - 5)}{2(x + 6)(x - 6)}$$

$$= \frac{x - 5}{2(x - 6)}$$

31. $\dfrac{1}{a - b} - \dfrac{3ab}{a^3 - b^3}$

$$= \frac{1}{a - b} - \frac{3ab}{(a - b)(a^2 + ab + b^2)} \qquad LCD = (a - b)(a^2 + ab + b^2)$$

$$= \frac{1}{a - b} \cdot \frac{a^2 + ab + b^2}{a^2 + ab + b^2} - \frac{3ab}{(a - b)(a^2 + ab + b^2)}$$

$$= \frac{a^2 + ab + b^2 - 3ab}{(a - b)(a^2 + ab + b^2)}$$

$$= \frac{a^2 - 2ab + b^2}{(a - b)(a^2 + ab + b^2)}$$

$$= \frac{(a - b)\ (a - b)}{(a - b)(a^2 + ab + b^2)}$$

$$= \frac{a - b}{a^2 + ab + b^2}$$

32. $\dfrac{1}{a + b} + \dfrac{3ab}{a^3 + b^3}$

$$= \frac{1}{a + b} + \frac{3ab}{(a + b)(a^2 - ab + b^2)} \qquad LCD = (a + b)(a^2 - ab + b^2)$$

$$= \frac{1}{(a + b)} \cdot \frac{a^2 - ab + b^2}{a^2 - ab + b^2} + \frac{3ab}{(a + b)(a^2 - ab + b^2)}$$

$$= \frac{a^2 - ab + b^2 + 3ab}{(a + b)(a^2 - ab + b^2)}$$

$$= \frac{a^2 + 2ab + b^2}{(a + b)(a^2 - ab + b^2)}$$

$$= \frac{(a + b)(a + b)}{(a + b)(a^2 - ab + b^2)}$$

$$= \frac{a + b}{a^2 - ab + b^2}$$

34. $\dfrac{1}{3y - 2} - \dfrac{18y}{27y^3 - 8}$

$$= \frac{1}{3y - 2} - \frac{18y}{(3y - 2)(9y^2 + 6y + 4)} \qquad LCD = (3y - 2)(9y^2 + 6y + 4)$$

$$= \frac{1}{3y - 2} \cdot \frac{9y^2 + 6y + 4}{9y^2 + 6y + 4} - \frac{18y}{(3y - 2)(9y^2 + 6y + 4)}$$

$$= \frac{9y^2 + 6y + 4 - 18y}{(3y - 2)(9y^2 + 6y + 4)}$$

$$= \frac{9y^2 - 12y + 4}{(3y - 2)(9y^2 + 6y + 4)}$$

$$= \frac{(3y - 2)(3y - 2)}{(3y - 2)(9y^2 + 6y + 4)}$$

$$= \frac{3y - 2}{9y^2 + 6y + 4}$$

35. $\dfrac{x}{x^2 - 5x + 6} - \dfrac{3}{3 - x}$

$$= \frac{x}{(x - 2)(x - 3)} - \frac{3}{-1(x - 3)} \qquad LCD = (x - 2)(x - 3)$$

$$= \frac{x}{(x - 2)(x - 3)} + \frac{3}{x - 3} \cdot \frac{x - 2}{x - 2}$$

$$= \frac{x + 3x - 6}{(x - 2)(x - 3)}$$

$$= \frac{4x - 6}{(x - 2)(x - 3)}$$

$$= \frac{2(2x - 3)}{(x - 2)(x - 3)}$$

36. $\dfrac{x}{x^2 + 4x + 4} - \dfrac{2}{2 + x}$

$$= \frac{x}{(x + 2)(x + 2)} - \frac{2}{x + 2} \cdot \frac{x + 2}{x + 2} \qquad LCD = (x + 2)(x + 2)$$

$$= \frac{x - 2x - 4}{(x + 2)(x + 2)}$$

$$= \frac{-x - 4}{(x + 2)^2}$$

$$= \frac{-(x + 4)}{(x + 2)^2}$$

38. $\dfrac{3}{2t - 5} + \dfrac{21}{8t^2 - 14t - 15}$

$$= \frac{3}{2t - 5} + \frac{21}{(2t - 5)(4t + 3)} \qquad LCD = (2t - 5)(4t + 3)$$

$$= \frac{3}{2t - 5} \cdot \frac{4t + 3}{4t + 3} + \frac{21}{(2t - 5)(4t + 3)}$$

$$= \frac{12t + 9 + 21}{(2t - 5)(4t + 3)}$$

$$= \frac{12t + 30}{(2t - 5)(4t + 3)}$$

$$= \frac{6(2t + 5)}{(2t - 5)(4t + 3)}$$

39. $\dfrac{1}{a^2 - 5a + 6} + \dfrac{3}{a^2 - a - 2}$

$$= \frac{1}{(a-2)(a-3)} + \frac{3}{(a+1)(a-2)} \qquad LCD = (a-2)(a-3)(a+1)$$

$$= \frac{1}{(a-2)(a-3)} \cdot \frac{a+1}{a+1} + \frac{3}{(a+1)(a-2)} \cdot \frac{a-3}{a-3}$$

$$= \frac{a + 1 + 3a - 9}{(a-2)(a-3)(a+1)}$$

$$= \frac{4a - 8}{(a-2)(a-3)(a+1)}$$

$$= \frac{4(a-2)}{(a-2)(a-3)(a+1)}$$

$$= \frac{4}{(a-3)(a+1)}$$

40. $\dfrac{-3}{a^2 + a - 2} + \dfrac{5}{a^2 - a - 6}$

$$= \frac{-3}{(a+2)(a-1)} + \frac{5}{(a+2)(a-3)} \qquad LCD = (a+2)(a-1)(a-3)$$

$$= \frac{-3}{(a+2)(a-1)} \cdot \frac{a-3}{a-3} + \frac{5}{(a+2)(a-3)} \cdot \frac{a-1}{a-1}$$

$$= \frac{-3a + 9 + 5a - 5}{(a+2)(a-1)(a-3)}$$

$$= \frac{2a + 4}{(a+2)(a-1)(a-3)}$$

$$= \frac{2(a+2)}{(a+2)(a-1)(a-3)}$$

$$= \frac{2}{(a-1)(a-3)}$$

42. $\dfrac{1}{27x^3 - 1} - \dfrac{1}{9x^2 - 1}$

$$= \frac{1}{(3x-1)(9x^2+3x+1)} - \frac{1}{(3x+1)(3x-1)} \qquad LCD = (3x-1)(3x+1)(9x^2-3x+1)$$

$$= \frac{1}{(3x-1)(9x^2+3x+1)} \cdot \frac{3x+1}{3x+1} - \frac{1}{(3x+1)(3x-1)} \cdot \frac{9x^2+3x+1}{9x^2+3x+1}$$

$$= \frac{3x+1-9x^2-3x-1}{(3x-1)(3x+1)(9x^2-3x+1)}$$

$$= \frac{-9x^2}{(3x-1)(3x+1)(9x^2-3x+1)}$$

43. $\dfrac{4}{4x^2 - 9} - \dfrac{6}{8x^2 - 6x - 9}$

$$= \frac{4}{(2x+3)(2x-3)} - \frac{6}{(4x+3)(2x-3)} \qquad LCD = (2x+3)(2x-3)(4x+3)$$

$$= \frac{4}{(2x+3)(2x-3)} \cdot \frac{4x+3}{4x+3} - \frac{6}{(4x+3)(2x-3)} \cdot \frac{2x+3}{2x+3}$$

$$= \frac{16x+12-12x-18}{(2x+3)(2x-3)(4x+3)}$$

$$= \frac{4x-6}{(2x+3)(2x-3)(4x+3)}$$

$$= \frac{2(2x-3)}{(2x+3)(2x-3)(4x+3)}$$

$$= \frac{2}{(2x+3)(4x+3)}$$

44. $\dfrac{9}{9x^2 + 6x - 8} - \dfrac{6}{9x^2 - 4}$

$$= \frac{9}{(3x + 4)(3x - 2)} - \frac{6}{(3x + 2)(3x - 2)} \qquad LCD = (3x + 4)(3x - 2)(3x + 2)$$

$$= \frac{9}{(3x + 4)(3x - 2)} \cdot \frac{3x + 2}{3x + 2} - \frac{6}{(3x + 2)(3x - 2)} \cdot \frac{3x + 4}{3x + 4}$$

$$= \frac{27x + 18 - 18x - 24}{(3x + 4)(3x - 2)(3x + 2)}$$

$$= \frac{9x - 6}{(3x + 4)(3x - 2)(3x + 2)}$$

$$= \frac{3(3x - 2)}{(3x + 4)(3x - 2)(3x + 2)}$$

$$= \frac{3}{(3x + 2)(3x + 4)}$$

46. $\dfrac{3a}{a^2 + 7a + 10} - \dfrac{2a}{a^2 + 6a + 8}$

$$= \frac{3a}{(a + 2)(a + 5)} - \frac{2a}{(a + 2)(a + 4)} \qquad LCD = (a + 2)(a + 5)(a + 4)$$

$$= \frac{3a}{(a + 2)(a + 5)} \cdot \frac{a + 4}{a + 4} - \frac{2a}{(a + 2)(a + 4)} \cdot \frac{a + 5}{a + 5}$$

$$= \frac{3a^2 + 12a - 2a^2 - 10a}{(a + 2)(a + 5)(a + 4)}$$

$$= \frac{a^2 + 2a}{(a + 2)(a + 5)(a + 4)}$$

$$= \frac{a(a + 2)}{(a + 2)(a + 5)(a + 4)}$$

$$= \frac{a}{(a + 5)(a + 4)}$$

47. $\dfrac{2x-1}{x^2+x-6} - \dfrac{x+2}{x^2+5x+6}$

$$= \frac{2x-1}{(x+3)(x-2)} - \frac{x+2}{(x+3)(x+2)} \qquad LCD = (x+3)(x-2)(x+2)$$

$$= \frac{2x-1}{(x+3)(x-2)} \cdot \frac{x+2}{x+2} - \frac{x+2}{(x+3)(x+2)} \cdot \frac{x-2}{x-2}$$

$$= \frac{2x^2+3x-2-x^2+4}{(x+3)(x-2)(x+2)}$$

$$= \frac{x^2+3x+2}{(x+3)(x-2)(x+2)}$$

$$= \frac{(x+1)(x+2)}{(x+3)(x-2)(x+2)}$$

$$= \frac{x+1}{(x+3)(x-2)}$$

48. $\dfrac{4x+1}{x^2+5x+4} - \dfrac{x+3}{x^2+4x+3}$

$$= \frac{4x+1}{(x+1)(x+4)} - \frac{x+3}{(x+1)(x+3)} \qquad LCD = (x+1)(x+4)(x+3)$$

$$= \frac{4x+1}{(x+1)(x+4)} \cdot \frac{x+3}{x+3} - \frac{x+3}{(x+1)(x+3)} \cdot \frac{x+4}{x+4}$$

$$= \frac{4x^2+13x+3-x^2-7x-12}{(x+1)(x+4)(x+3)}$$

$$= \frac{3x^2+6x-9}{(x+1)(x+4)(x+3)}$$

$$= \frac{3(x^2+2x-3)}{(x+1)(x+4)(x+3)}$$

$$= \frac{3(x-1)(x+3)}{(x+1)(x+4)(x+3)}$$

$$= \frac{3(x-1)}{(x+1)(x+4)}$$

50. $\dfrac{5x + 3}{2x^2 + 5x + 3} - \dfrac{3x + 9}{2x^2 + 7x + 6}$

$$= \frac{5x + 3}{(2x + 3)(x + 1)} - \frac{3x + 9}{(2x + 3)(x + 2)} \qquad LCD = (2x + 3)(x + 1)(x + 2)$$

$$= \frac{5x + 3}{(2x + 3)(x + 1)} \cdot \frac{x + 2}{x + 2} - \frac{3x + 9}{(2x + 3)(x + 2)} \cdot \frac{x + 1}{x + 1}$$

$$= \frac{5x^2 + 13x + 6 - 3x^2 - 12x - 9}{(2x + 3)(x + 1)(x + 2)}$$

$$= \frac{2x^2 + x - 3}{(2x + 3)(x + 1)(x + 2)}$$

$$= \frac{(2x + 3)(x - 1)}{(2x + 3)(x + 1)(x + 2)}$$

$$= \frac{x - 1}{(x + 1)(x + 2)}$$

51. $\dfrac{2}{x^2 + 5x + 6} - \dfrac{4}{x^2 + 4x + 3} + \dfrac{3}{x^2 + 3x + 2}$

$$= \frac{2}{(x + 2)(x + 3)} - \frac{4}{(x + 1)(x + 3)} + \frac{3}{(x + 2)(x + 1)} \qquad LCD = (x + 2)(x + 3)(x + 1)$$

$$= \frac{2}{(x + 2)(x + 3)} \cdot \frac{x + 1}{x + 1} - \frac{4}{(x + 1)(x + 3} \cdot \frac{x + 2}{x + 2} + \frac{3}{(x + 2)(x + 1)} \cdot \frac{x + 3}{x + 3}$$

$$= \frac{2x + 2 - 4x - 8 + 3x + 9}{(x + 2)(x + 3)(x + 1)}$$

$$= \frac{x + 3}{(x + 2)(x + 3)(x + 1)}$$

$$= \frac{1}{(x + 1)(x + 2)}$$

52. $\dfrac{-5}{x^2 + 3x - 4} + \dfrac{5}{x^2 + 2x - 3} + \dfrac{1}{x^2 + 7x + 12}$

$= \dfrac{-5}{(x + 4)(x - 1)} + \dfrac{5}{(x + 3)(x - 1)} + \dfrac{1}{(x + 4)(x + 3)}$ $\quad LCD = (x + 4)(x + 3)(x - 1)$

$= \dfrac{-5}{(x + 4)(x - 1)} \cdot \dfrac{x + 3}{x + 3} + \dfrac{5}{(x + 3)(x - 1)} \cdot \dfrac{x + 4}{x + 4} + \dfrac{1}{(x + 4)(x + 3)} \cdot \dfrac{x - 1}{x - 1}$

$= \dfrac{-5x - 15 + 5x + 20 + x - 1}{(x + 4)(x - 1)(x + 3)}$

$= \dfrac{x + 4}{(x + 4)(x - 1)(x + 3)}$

$= \dfrac{1}{(x - 1)(x + 3)}$

54. $\dfrac{2x + 11}{x^2 + 9x + 20} - \dfrac{x + 1}{x^2 + 7x + 12} - \dfrac{x + 6}{x^2 + 8x + 15}$

$= \dfrac{2x + 11}{(x + 4)(x + 5)} - \dfrac{x + 1}{(x + 3)(x + 4)} - \dfrac{x + 6}{(x + 3)(x + 5)}$ $\quad LCD = (x + 4)(x + 5)(x + 3)$

$= \dfrac{2x + 11}{(x + 4)(x + 5)} \cdot \dfrac{x + 3}{x + 3} - \dfrac{x + 1}{(x + 3)(x + 4)} \cdot \dfrac{x + 5}{x + 5} - \dfrac{x + 6}{(x + 3)(x + 5)} \cdot \dfrac{x + 4}{x + 4}$

$= \dfrac{2x^2 + 17x + 33 - x^2 - 6x - 5 - x^2 - 10x - 24}{(x + 4)(x + 5)(x + 3)}$

$= \dfrac{x + 4}{(x + 4)(x + 5)(x + 3)}$

$= \dfrac{1}{(x + 3)(x + 5)}$

55. $2 + \dfrac{3}{2x + 1}$ $\quad LCD = 2x + 1$

$= \dfrac{2}{1} \cdot \dfrac{2x + 1}{2x + 1} + \dfrac{3}{2x + 1}$

$= \dfrac{4x + 2 + 3}{2x + 1}$

$= \dfrac{4x + 5}{2x + 1}$

56. $3 - \dfrac{2}{2x + 3}$ $\quad LCD = 2x + 3$

$= \dfrac{3}{1} \cdot \dfrac{2x + 3}{2x + 3} - \dfrac{2}{2x + 3}$

$= \dfrac{6x + 9 - 2}{2x + 3}$

$= \dfrac{6x + 7}{2x + 3}$

58. $7 + \dfrac{3}{5 - t}$ $\quad LCD = 5 - t$

$= \dfrac{7}{1} \cdot \dfrac{5 - t}{5 - t} + \dfrac{3}{5 - t}$

$= \dfrac{35 - 7t + 3}{5 - t}$

$= \dfrac{38 - 7t}{5 - t}$

59. $x - \dfrac{4}{2x + 3}$ $\quad LCD = 2x + 3$

$= \dfrac{x}{1} \cdot \dfrac{2x + 3}{2x + 3} - \dfrac{4}{2x + 3}$

$= \dfrac{2x^2 + 3x - 4}{2x + 3}$

60. $x - \dfrac{5}{3x + 4} + 1$

$= \dfrac{x}{1} \cdot \dfrac{3x + 4}{3x + 4} - \dfrac{5}{3x + 4} + \dfrac{1}{1} \cdot \dfrac{3x + 4}{3x + 4}$

$= \dfrac{3x^2 + 4x - 5 + 3x + 4}{3x + 4}$

$= \dfrac{3x^2 + 7x - 1}{3x + 4}$

62. $\dfrac{x}{x+3} + \dfrac{7}{3x+9} - \dfrac{2}{x^2+3x}$

$= \dfrac{x}{x+3} + \dfrac{7}{3(x+3)} - \dfrac{2}{x(x+3)}$ $\quad LCD = 3x(x+3)$

$= \dfrac{x}{x+3} \cdot \dfrac{3x}{3x} + \dfrac{7}{3(x+3)} \cdot \dfrac{x}{x} - \dfrac{2}{x(x+3)} \cdot \dfrac{3}{3}$

$= \dfrac{3x^2 + 7x - 6}{3x(x+3)}$

$= \dfrac{(3x-2)(x+3)}{3x(x+3)}$

$= \dfrac{3x-2}{3x}$

63. $\dfrac{1}{x} + \dfrac{x}{2x+4} - \dfrac{2}{x^2+2x}$

$= \dfrac{1}{x} + \dfrac{x}{2(x+2)} - \dfrac{2}{x(x+2)}$ $\quad LCD = 2x(x+2)$

$= \dfrac{1}{x} \cdot \dfrac{2(x+2)}{2(x+2)} + \dfrac{x}{2(x+2)} \cdot \dfrac{x}{x} - \dfrac{2}{x(x+2)} \cdot \dfrac{2}{2}$

$= \dfrac{2x + 4 + x^2 - 4}{2x(x+2)}$

$= \dfrac{x^2 + 2x}{2x(x+2)}$

$= \dfrac{x(x+2)}{2x(x+2)}$

$= \dfrac{1}{2}$

64. $\dfrac{1}{x} + \dfrac{x}{3x + 9} - \dfrac{3}{x^2 + 3x}$

$= \dfrac{1}{x} + \dfrac{x}{3(x + 3)} - \dfrac{3}{x(x + 3)}$ $\quad LCD = 3x(x + 3)$

$= \dfrac{1}{x} \cdot \dfrac{3(x + 3)}{3(x + 3)} + \dfrac{x}{3(x + 3)} \cdot \dfrac{x}{x} - \dfrac{3}{x(x + 3)} \cdot \dfrac{3}{3}$

$= \dfrac{3x + 9 + x^2 - 9}{3x(x + 3)}$

$= \dfrac{x^2 + 3x}{3x(x + 3)}$

$= \dfrac{x(x + 3)}{3x(x + 3)}$

$= \dfrac{1}{3}$

66. $P = \dfrac{1}{a} + \dfrac{1}{b}$ $\quad LCD = ab$

$P = \dfrac{1}{a} \cdot \dfrac{b}{b} + \dfrac{1}{b} \cdot \dfrac{a}{a}$

$P = \dfrac{b}{ab} + \dfrac{a}{ab}$

$P = \dfrac{a+b}{ab}$ $\quad a = 10 \quad b = 0.2$

$P = \dfrac{10 + 02.}{10(0.2)}$

$P = \dfrac{10.2}{2.0}$

$P = 5.1$ *or* $\dfrac{51}{10}$

67. $(3 + 4)^{-1} = 7^{-1} = \dfrac{1}{7}$

$3^{-1} + 3^{-1} = \dfrac{1}{3} + \dfrac{1}{4} = \dfrac{7}{12}$

68. $(x + y)^{-1} = x^{-1} + y^{-1}$

$$\frac{1}{x + y} = \frac{1}{x} + \frac{1}{y}$$

$$\frac{1}{x + y} = \frac{1}{x} \cdot \frac{y}{y} + \frac{1}{y} \cdot \frac{x}{x}$$

$$\frac{1}{x + y} = \frac{x + y}{xy} \quad \textit{False}$$

70. $(1 - 5^{-2}) \div (1 - 5^{-1})$

$$= \left(1 - \frac{1}{5^2}\right) \div \left(1 - \frac{1}{5}\right)$$

$$= \frac{24}{25} \div \frac{4}{5}$$

$$= \frac{24}{25} \cdot \frac{5}{4}$$

$$= \frac{6}{5}$$

71. $(1 - x^{-2}) \div (1 - x^{-1})$

$$= \left(1 - \frac{1}{x^2}\right) \div \left(1 - \frac{1}{x}\right)$$

$$= \left(\frac{x^2}{x^2} - \frac{1}{x^2}\right) \div \left(\frac{x}{x} - \frac{1}{x}\right)$$

$$= \frac{x^2 - 1}{x^2} \div \frac{x - 1}{x}$$

$$= \frac{(x + 1)(x - 1)}{x^2} \cdot \frac{x}{x - 1}$$

$$= \frac{x + 1}{x}$$

72. $(1 - x^{-3}) \div (1 - x^{-2})$

$$= \left(1 - \frac{1}{x^3}\right) \div \left(1 - \frac{1}{x^2}\right)$$

$$= \left(\frac{x^3}{x^3} - \frac{1}{x^3}\right) \div \left(\frac{x^2}{x^2} - \frac{1}{x^2}\right)$$

$$= \frac{x^3 - 1}{x^3} \div \frac{x^2 - 1}{x^2}$$

$$= \frac{(x - 1)(x^2 + x + 1)}{x^3} \cdot \frac{x^2}{(x + 1)(x - 1)}$$

$$= \frac{x^2 + x + 1}{x(x + 1)}$$

74. *Let x = a number, then the reciprocal*

*of a number would be* $\frac{1}{x}$

*The sum of a number and three times its reciprocal*

$$x + 3\left(\frac{1}{x}\right) = \frac{x}{1} + \frac{3}{x} \qquad LCD = x$$

$$= \frac{x}{1} \cdot \frac{x}{x} + \frac{3}{x}$$

$$= \frac{x^2}{x} + \frac{3}{x}$$

$$= \frac{x^2 + 3}{x}$$

75. *Let x = a number and x + 1 = the second number then the reciprocals of the numbers would be*

$$\frac{1}{x} \text{ and } \frac{1}{x + 1}.$$

*The sum of the reciprocals of two consecutive even integers*

$$\frac{1}{x} + \frac{1}{x + 2} = \frac{1}{x} \cdot \frac{x + 2}{x + 2} + \frac{1}{x + 2} \cdot \frac{x}{x} \qquad LCD = x(x + 2)$$

$$= \frac{x + 2}{x(x + 2)} + \frac{x}{x(x + 2)}$$

$$= \frac{2x + 2)}{x(x + 2)}$$

76. *Let $x$ = a number and $x + 2$ = the second number, then the reciprocals of the numbers would be*

$$\frac{1}{x} \text{ and } \frac{1}{x + 2} .$$

*The sum of the reciprocals of two consecutive even integers*

$$\frac{1}{x} + \frac{1}{x + 2} = \frac{1}{x} \cdot \frac{x + 2}{x + 2} + \frac{1}{x + 2} \cdot \frac{x}{x} \qquad LCD = x(x + 2)$$

$$= \frac{x + 2}{x(x + 2)} + \frac{x}{x(x + 2)}$$

$$= \frac{2(x + 1)}{x(x + 2)}$$

78. $768{,}000 = 7.68 \times 10^5$

79. $0.00034 = 3.4 \times 10^{-4}$

80. $0.0359 = 3.59 \times 10^{-2}$

82. $2.5 \times 10^2 = 250$

83. $6.44 \times 10^{-3} = 0.00644$

84. $2.5 \times 10^{-2} = 0.025$

86. $(6 \times 10^3)(3 \times 10^{-7})$
 $= 18 \times 10^{-4}$
 $= 1.8 \times 10^1 \times 10^{-4}$
 $= 1.8 \times 10^{-3}$

87. $\dfrac{8 \times 10^{-3}}{4 \times 10^{-6}} = 2 \times 10^{-3} \times 10^6$

 $= 2 \times 10^3$

88. $\dfrac{8 \times 10^5}{2 \times 10^{-8}} = 4 \times 10^5 \times 10^8$

 $= 4 \times 10^{13}$

90. $\left(1 + \frac{1}{x}\right)\left(1 + \frac{1}{x+1}\right)\left(1 + \frac{1}{x+2}\right)\left(1 + \frac{1}{x+3}\right)$

$= \left(\frac{x}{x} + \frac{1}{x}\right)\left(\frac{x+1}{x+1} + \frac{1}{x+1}\right)\left(\frac{x+2}{x+2} + \frac{1}{x+2}\right)\left(\frac{x+3}{x+3} + \frac{1}{x+3}\right)$

$= \left(\frac{x+1}{x}\right)\left(\frac{x+2}{x+1}\right)\left(\frac{x+3}{x+2}\right)\left(\frac{x+4}{x+3}\right)$

$= \frac{x+4}{x}$

91. $\left(1 - \frac{1}{x}\right)\left(1 - \frac{1}{x+1}\right)\left(1 - \frac{1}{x+2}\right)\cdots\left(1 - \frac{1}{x+49}\right)\left(1 - \frac{1}{x+50}\right)$

$= \left(\frac{x}{x} - \frac{1}{x}\right)\left(\frac{x+1}{x+1} - \frac{1}{x+1}\right)\left(\frac{x+2}{x+2} - \frac{1}{x+2}\right)\cdots\left(\frac{x+49}{x+49} - \frac{1}{x+49}\right)\left(\frac{x+50}{x+50} - \frac{1}{x+50}\right)$

$= \left(\frac{x-1}{x}\right)\left(\frac{x}{x+1}\right)\left(\frac{x+1}{x+2}\right)\cdots\left(\frac{x+48}{x+49}\right)\left(\frac{x+49}{x+50}\right)$

$= \frac{x-1}{x+50}$

92. $\left(1 + \frac{1}{x}\right)\left(1 + \frac{1}{x+1}\right)\left(1 + \frac{1}{x+2}\right)\cdots\left(1 + \frac{1}{x+98}\right)\left(1 + \frac{1}{x+99}\right)$

$= \left(\frac{x}{x} + \frac{1}{x}\right)\left(\frac{x+1}{x+1} + \frac{1}{x+1}\right)\left(\frac{x+2}{x+2} + \frac{1}{x+2}\right)\cdots\left(\frac{x+98}{x+98}\right)\left(\frac{x+99}{x+99} + \frac{1}{x+99}\right)$

$= \left(\frac{x+1}{x}\right)\left(\frac{x+2}{x+1}\right)\left(\frac{x+3}{x+2}\right)\cdots\left(\frac{x+99}{x+98}\right)\left(\frac{x+100}{x+99}\right)$

$= \frac{x+100}{x}$

94. $\left(1 - \frac{1}{x-1}\right)\left(1 - \frac{1}{x-2}\right)\left(1 - \frac{1}{x-3}\right)\cdots\left(1 - \frac{1}{x-48}\right)\left(1 - \frac{1}{x-49}\right)$

$= \left(\frac{x-1}{x-1} - \frac{1}{x-1}\right)\left(\frac{x-2}{x-2} - \frac{1}{x-2}\right)\left(\frac{x-3}{x-3} - \frac{1}{x-3}\right)\cdots$

$\left(\frac{x-48}{x-48} - \frac{1}{x-48}\right)\left(\frac{x-49}{x-49} - \frac{1}{x-49}\right)$

$= \left(\frac{x-2}{x-1}\right)\left(\frac{x-3}{x-2}\right)\left(\frac{x-4}{x-3}\right)\cdots\left(\frac{x-49}{x-48}\right)\left(\frac{x-50}{x-49}\right)$

$= \frac{x-50}{x-1}$

## Section 4.5

2. *Method* 1

$$\frac{\frac{5}{9}}{\frac{7}{12}} = \frac{\frac{5}{9} \cdot 36}{\frac{7}{12} \cdot 36} = \frac{20}{21} \qquad LCD = 36$$

*Method* 2

$$\frac{\frac{5}{9}}{\frac{7}{12}} = \frac{5}{9} \cdot \frac{12}{7} = \frac{60}{63} = \frac{20}{21}$$

3. *Method* 1

$$\frac{\frac{1}{3} - \frac{1}{4}}{\frac{1}{2} + \frac{1}{8}} = \frac{\frac{1}{12}}{\frac{5}{8}} \qquad LCD = 24$$

$$= \frac{\frac{1}{12} \cdot 24}{\frac{5}{8} \cdot 24}$$

$$= \frac{2}{15}$$

*Method* 2

$$\frac{\frac{1}{3} - \frac{1}{4}}{\frac{1}{2} + \frac{1}{8}} = \frac{\frac{1}{12}}{\frac{5}{8}}$$

$$= \frac{1}{12} \cdot \frac{8}{5}$$

$$= \frac{8}{60}$$

$$= \frac{2}{15}$$

4. *Method* 1

$$\frac{\frac{1}{6} - \frac{1}{3}}{\frac{1}{4} - \frac{1}{8}} = \frac{-\frac{1}{6}}{\frac{1}{8}} \qquad LCD = 24$$

$$= \frac{-\frac{1}{6} \cdot 24}{\frac{1}{8} \cdot 24}$$

$$= -\frac{4}{3}$$

*Method* 2

$$\frac{\frac{1}{6} - \frac{1}{3}}{\frac{1}{4} - \frac{1}{8}} = \frac{-\frac{1}{6}}{\frac{1}{8}}$$

$$= -\frac{1}{6} \cdot \frac{8}{1}$$

$$= -\frac{8}{6}$$

$$= -\frac{4}{3}$$

6. *Method* 2

$$\frac{2 + \frac{5}{6}}{1 - \frac{7}{8}} = \frac{\frac{17}{6}}{\frac{1}{8}}$$

$$= \frac{17}{6} \cdot \frac{8}{1}$$

$$= \frac{136}{6}$$

$$= \frac{68}{3}$$

7. *Method* 1

$$\frac{\frac{1}{x}}{1+\frac{1}{x}} = \frac{\frac{1}{x}\cdot x}{\left(1+\frac{1}{x}\right)\cdot x} \qquad LCD = x$$

$$= \frac{1}{x+1}$$

8. *Method* 1

$$\frac{1-\frac{1}{x}}{\frac{1}{x}} = \frac{\left(1-\frac{1}{x}\right)x}{\left(\frac{1}{x}\right)x} \qquad LCD = x$$

$$= \frac{x-1}{1}$$

$$= x - 1$$

10. *Method* 1

$$\frac{1-\frac{2}{a}}{1-\frac{3}{a}} = \frac{\left(1-\frac{2}{a}\right)a}{\left(1-\frac{3}{a}\right)a} \qquad LCD = a$$

$$= \frac{a-2}{a-3}$$

11. *Method* 1

$$\frac{\frac{1}{x}-\frac{1}{y}}{\frac{1}{x}+\frac{1}{y}} = \frac{\left(\frac{1}{x}-\frac{1}{y}\right)xy}{\left(\frac{1}{x}+\frac{1}{y}\right)xy} \qquad LCD = xy$$

$$= \frac{y-x}{y+x}$$

12. *Method* 1

$$\frac{\frac{1}{x}+\frac{2}{y}}{\frac{2}{x}+\frac{1}{y}} = \frac{\left(\frac{1}{x}+\frac{2}{y}\right)xy}{\left(\frac{2}{x}+\frac{1}{y}\right)xy} \qquad LCD = xy$$

$$= \frac{2x+y}{x+2y}$$

14. *Method* 2

$$\frac{\frac{3x+1}{x^2-49}}{\frac{9x^2-1}{x-7}} = \frac{3x+1}{x^2-49}\cdot\frac{x-7}{9x^2-1}$$

$$= \frac{3x+1}{(x+7)(x-7)}\cdot\frac{x-7}{(3x+1)(3x-1)}$$

$$= \frac{1}{(x+7)(3x-1)}$$

15. *Method* 2

$$\frac{\frac{4a}{2a^3+2}}{\frac{8a}{4a+4}} = \frac{4a}{2(a^3+1)}\cdot\frac{4(a+1)}{8a}$$

$$= \frac{4a}{2(a+1)(a^2-a+1)}\cdot\frac{4(a+1)}{8a}$$

$$= \frac{1}{a^2-a+1}$$

16. *Method* 2

$$\frac{\frac{2a}{3a^3-3}}{\frac{4a}{6a-6}} = \frac{2a}{3a^3-3}\cdot\frac{6a-6}{4a}$$

$$= \frac{2a}{3(a-1)(a^2+a+1)}\cdot\frac{6(a-1)}{4a}$$

$$= \frac{1}{a^2+a+1}$$

18. *Method* 1

$$\frac{4 - \frac{1}{x^2}}{4 + \frac{4}{x} + \frac{1}{x^2}} = \frac{\left(4 - \frac{1}{x^2}\right)x^2}{\left(4 + \frac{4}{x} + \frac{1}{x^2}\right)x^2} \qquad LCD = x^2$$

$$= \frac{4x^2 - 1}{4x^2 + 4x + 1}$$

$$= \frac{(2x + 1)(2x - 1)}{(2x + 1)(2x + 1)}$$

$$= \frac{2x - 1}{2x + 1}$$

19. *Method* 1

$$\frac{2 + \frac{5}{a} - \frac{3}{a^2}}{2 - \frac{5}{a} + \frac{2}{a^2}} = \frac{\left(2 + \frac{5}{a} - \frac{3}{a^2}\right)a^2}{\left(2 - \frac{5}{a} - \frac{2}{a^2}\right)a^2} \qquad LCD = a^2$$

$$= \frac{2a^2 + 5a - 3}{2a^2 - 5a + 2}$$

$$= \frac{(2a - 1)(a + 3)}{(2a - 1)(a - 2)}$$

$$= \frac{a + 3}{a - 2}$$

20. *Method* 1

$$\frac{3 + \frac{5}{a} - \frac{3}{a^2}}{3 - \frac{10}{a} + \frac{3}{a^2}} = \frac{\left(3 + \frac{5}{a} - \frac{2}{a^2}\right)a^2}{\left(3 - \frac{10}{a} + \frac{3}{a^2}\right)a^2} \qquad LCD = a^2$$

$$= \frac{3a^2 + 5a - 2}{3a^2 - 10a + 3}$$

$$= \frac{(3a - 1)(a + 2)}{(3a - 1)(a - 3)}$$

$$= \frac{a + 2}{a - 3}$$

22. *Method* 1

$$\frac{3 + \frac{5}{x} - \frac{12}{x^2} - \frac{20}{x^3}}{3 + \frac{11}{x} + \frac{10}{x^2}} \qquad LCD = x^3$$

$$= \frac{\left(3 + \frac{5}{x} - \frac{12}{x^2} - \frac{20}{x^3}\right)x^3}{\left(3 + \frac{11}{x} + \frac{10}{x^2}\right)x^3}$$

$$= \frac{3x^3 + 5x^2 - 12x - 20}{3x^3 + 11x^2 + 10x}$$

$$= \frac{x^2(3x + 5) - 4(3x + 5)}{x(3x^2 + 11x + 10)}$$

$$= \frac{(3x + 5)(x + 2)(x - 2)}{x(3x + 5)(x + 2)}$$

$$= \frac{x - 2}{x}$$

23. *Method* 1

$$\frac{1 + \frac{1}{x + 3}}{1 - \frac{1}{x + 3}} \qquad LCD = x + 3$$

$$= \frac{\left(1 + \frac{1}{x + 3}\right)x + 3}{\left(1 - \frac{1}{x + 3}\right)x + 3}$$

$$= \frac{x + 3 + 1}{x + 3 - 1}$$

$$= \frac{x + 4}{x + 2}$$

24. *Method 1* $\dfrac{a + \dfrac{a}{x - 2}}{1 - \dfrac{1}{x - 2}}$ *LCD* $= x - 2$

$$= \frac{\left(1 + \dfrac{1}{x - 2}\right)(x - 2)}{\left(1 - \dfrac{1}{x - 2}\right)(x - 2)}$$

$$= \frac{x - 2 + 1}{x - 2 - 1}$$

$$= \frac{x - 1}{x - 3}$$

26. *First, we simplify the numerator and denominator separately, Method 2*

*Numerator* $1 + \dfrac{1}{x - 2}$

$$= 1 \cdot \frac{x - 2}{x - 2} + \frac{1}{x - 2}$$

$$= \frac{x - 1}{x - 2}$$

*Denominator* $1 - \dfrac{3}{x + 2}$

$$= 1 \cdot \frac{x + 2}{x + 2} - \frac{3}{x + 2}$$

$$= \frac{x - 1}{x + 2}$$

*Therefore*: $\dfrac{1 + \dfrac{1}{x - 2}}{1 - \dfrac{3}{x + 2}}$

$$= \frac{\dfrac{x - 1}{x - 2}}{\dfrac{x - 1}{x + 2}}$$

$$= \frac{x - 1}{x - 2} \cdot \frac{x + 2}{x - 1}$$

$$= \frac{x + 2}{x - 2}$$

27. *Method 2* $\dfrac{1 - \dfrac{1}{a + 1}}{1 + \dfrac{1}{a - 1}}$

$$= \frac{1 \cdot \dfrac{a + 1}{a + 1} - \dfrac{1}{a + 1}}{1 \cdot \dfrac{a - 1}{a - 1} + \dfrac{1}{a - 1}}$$

$$= \frac{\dfrac{a + 1 - 1}{a + 1}}{\dfrac{a - 1 + 1}{a - 1}}$$

$$= \frac{a}{a + 1} \cdot \frac{a - 1}{a}$$

$$= \frac{a - 1}{a + 1}$$

28. *Method 2* $\dfrac{\dfrac{1}{a - 1} + 1}{\dfrac{1}{a + 1} - 1}$

$$= \frac{\dfrac{1}{a - 1} + 1 \cdot \dfrac{a - 1}{a - 1}}{\dfrac{1}{a + 1} - 1 \cdot \dfrac{a + 1}{a + 1}}$$

$$= \frac{\dfrac{1 + a - 1}{a - 1}}{\dfrac{1 - a - 1}{a + 1}}$$

$$= \frac{1}{a - 1} \cdot \frac{a + 1}{-a}$$

$$= -\frac{a + 1}{a - 1} \quad \textit{or} \quad \frac{1 + a}{1 - a}$$

30. *Applying Method 1, we find the LCD for both fractions, which in this case is* $(x + a)(x - a)$:

$$\frac{\dfrac{1}{x+a} + \dfrac{1}{x-a}}{\dfrac{1}{x+a} - \dfrac{1}{x-a}}$$

$$= \frac{(x+a)(x-a)\left(\dfrac{1}{x+a}\right) + (x+a)(x-a)\left(\dfrac{1}{x-a}\right)}{(x+a)(x-a)\left(\dfrac{1}{x+a}\right) - (x+a)(x-a)\left(\dfrac{1}{x-a}\right)}$$

$$= \frac{x - a + x + a}{x - a - (x + a)}$$

$$= \frac{2x}{x - a - x - a}$$

$$= \frac{2x}{-2a}$$

$$= -\frac{x}{a}$$

31. *Method* 1 $\dfrac{\dfrac{y+1}{y-1} + \dfrac{y-1}{y+1}}{\dfrac{y+1}{y-1} - \dfrac{y-1}{y+1}}$ $LCD = (y - 1)(y + 1)$

$$= \frac{\left(\dfrac{y+1}{y-1} + \dfrac{y-1}{y+1}\right)(y-1)(y+1)}{\left(\dfrac{y+1}{y-1} - \dfrac{y-1}{y+1}\right)(y-1)(y+1)}$$

$$= \frac{(y+1)(y+1) + (y-1)(y-1)}{(y+1)(y+1) - (y-1)(y-1)}$$

$$= \frac{y^2 + 2y + 1 + y^2 - 2y + 1}{y^2 + 2y + 1 - y^2 + 2y - 1}$$

$$= \frac{2y^2 + 2}{4y}$$

$$= \frac{2(y^2 + 1)}{4y}$$

$$= \frac{y^2 + 1}{2y}$$

32. *Method* 1 $\dfrac{\dfrac{y-1}{y+1} - \dfrac{y+1}{y-1}}{\dfrac{y-1}{y+1} + \dfrac{y+1}{y-1}}$ $LCD = (y = 1)(y - 1)$

$$= \frac{\left(\dfrac{y-1}{y+1} - \dfrac{y+1}{y-1}\right)(y+1)(y-1)}{\left(\dfrac{y-1}{y+1} + \dfrac{y+1}{y-1}\right)(y+1)(y-1)}$$

$$= \frac{(y-1)(y-1) - (y+1)(y+1)}{(y-1)(y-1) + (y+1)(y+1)}$$

$$= \frac{y^2 - 2y + 1 - y^2 - 2y - 1}{y^2 - 2y + 1 + y^2 + 2y + 1}$$

$$= \frac{-4y}{2y^2 + 2}$$

$$= \frac{-4y}{2(y^2 + 1)}$$

$$= -\frac{2y}{y^2 + 1}$$

34. $x - \cfrac{1}{x - \cfrac{1}{2}}$

$= x - \dfrac{2 \cdot 1}{2\left(x - \frac{1}{2}\right)}$

$= x - \dfrac{2}{2x - 1}$

$= \dfrac{x}{1} \cdot \dfrac{2x - 1}{2x - 1} - \dfrac{2}{2x - 1}$

$= \dfrac{2x^2 - x - 2}{2x - 1}$

35. $1 + \cfrac{1}{1 + \cfrac{1}{1 + 1}}$

$= 1 + \cfrac{1}{1 + \cfrac{1}{2}}$

$= 1 + \cfrac{1}{\cfrac{3}{2}}$

$= 1 + \dfrac{2}{3}$

$= \dfrac{5}{3}$

36. $1 - \cfrac{1}{1 - \cfrac{1}{1 - \cfrac{1}{2}}}$

$= 1 - \cfrac{1}{1 - \cfrac{1}{\cfrac{1}{2}}}$

$= 1 - \dfrac{1}{1 - 2}$

$= 1 - \dfrac{1}{-1}$

$= 1 + 1$
$= 2$

38. *First, we simplify the numerator and denominatlr separately:*

*Numerator* $2 + \cfrac{1}{x - \cfrac{1}{3}}$

$= 2 + \dfrac{3(1)}{3\left(x - \frac{1}{3}\right)}$

$= 2 + \dfrac{3}{3x - 1}$

$= \dfrac{2}{1} \cdot \dfrac{3x - 1}{3x - 1} + \dfrac{3}{3x - 1}$

$= \dfrac{6x - 2 + 3}{3x - 1}$

$= \dfrac{6x + 1}{3x - 1}$

*Denominator* $2 - \dfrac{1}{x - \dfrac{1}{3}}$

$$= 2 - \frac{3(1)}{3\left(x - \dfrac{1}{3}\right)}$$

$$= 2 - \frac{3}{3x - 1}$$

$$= \frac{2}{1} \cdot \frac{3x - 1}{3x - 1} - \frac{3}{3x - 1}$$

$$= \frac{6x - 2 - 3}{3x - 1}$$

$$= \frac{6x - 5}{3x - 1}$$

*Therefore:* $\dfrac{2 + \dfrac{1}{x - \dfrac{1}{3}}}{2 - \dfrac{1}{x - \dfrac{1}{3}}}$

$$= \frac{\dfrac{6x + 1}{3x - 1}}{\dfrac{6x - 5}{3x - 1}}$$

$$= \frac{6x + 1}{3x - 1} \cdot \frac{3x - 1}{6x - 5}$$

$$= \frac{6x + 1}{6x - 5}$$

39. $F = (a^{-1} + b^{-1})^{-1}$

$$F = \frac{1}{a^{-1} + b^{-1}}$$

$$F = \frac{1}{\dfrac{1}{a} + \dfrac{1}{b}}$$

$$F = \frac{1}{\dfrac{1}{a} \cdot \dfrac{b}{b} + \dfrac{1}{b} \cdot \dfrac{a}{a}}$$

$$F = \frac{1}{\dfrac{b}{ab} + \dfrac{a}{ab}}$$

$$F = \frac{1}{\dfrac{a + b}{ab}}$$

$$F = \frac{ab}{a + b}$$

*Look at answer key in the back of the textbook for another method.*

40. $(a^{-1} - b^{-1})^{-1} = \left(\dfrac{1}{a} - \dfrac{1}{b}\right)^{-1}$

$$= \left(\frac{b - a}{ab}\right)^{-1}$$

$$= \frac{ab}{b - a}$$

42. $(1 + x^{-1})^{-1} = \left(1 + \dfrac{1}{x}\right)^{-1}$

$$= \left(\frac{x + 1}{x}\right)^{-1}$$

$$= \frac{x}{x + 1}$$

43. *First 3 terms:* $\dfrac{3}{2}, \dfrac{5}{3}, \dfrac{8}{5}$

*Next 3 terms:* $\dfrac{13}{8}, \dfrac{21}{13}, \dfrac{24}{21}$

44. 1.500, 1.667, 1.600, 1.625, 1.615, 1.619

46. 1.33, 1.429, 1.412

47, 48, 50, 51 *and* 52. *See answers in back of the book.*

54.
$$\begin{aligned} 3x - 18 &= 4 \\ 3x &= 22 \\ x &= \frac{22}{3} \end{aligned}$$

55.
$$\begin{aligned} 3(y - 3) &= 2(y - 2) \\ 3y - 9 &= 2y - 4 \\ y - 9 &= -4 \\ y &= 5 \end{aligned}$$

56.
$$\begin{aligned} 5(y + 2) &= 4(y + 1) \\ 5y + 10 &= 4y + 4 \\ y + 10 &= 4 \\ y &= -6 \end{aligned}$$

58.
$$\begin{aligned} 15 - 3(x - 1) &= x - 2 \\ 15 - 3x + 3 &= x - 2 \\ -3x + 18 &= x - 2 \\ 18 &= 4x - 2 \\ 20 &= 4x \\ 5 &= x \end{aligned}$$

59.
$$\begin{aligned} x^2 - x - 12 &= 0 \\ (x + 3)(x - 4) &= 0 \\ x + 3 &= 0 \\ x &= -3 \quad \textit{or} \end{aligned}$$
$$\begin{aligned} x - 4 &= 0 \\ x &= 4 \end{aligned}$$

60.
$$\begin{aligned} x^2 + x - 12 &= 0 \\ (x + 4)(x - 3) &= 0 \\ x + 4 &= 0 \\ x &= -4 \quad \textit{or} \end{aligned}$$
$$\begin{aligned} x - 3 &= 0 \\ x &= 3 \end{aligned}$$

62.
$$\begin{aligned} 10x^2 - x - 3 &= 0 \\ (2x + 1)(5x - 3) &= 0 \\ 2x + 1 &= 0 \\ 2x &= -1 \\ x &= -\frac{1}{2} \quad \textit{or} \end{aligned}$$
$$\begin{aligned} 5x - 3 &= 0 \\ 5x &= 3 \\ x &= \frac{3}{5} \end{aligned}$$

63.
$$\begin{aligned} (x + 1)(x - 6) &= -12 \\ x^2 - 5x - 6 + 12 &= 0 \\ x^2 - 5x + 6 &= 0 \\ (x - 2)(x - 3) &= 0 \\ x - 2 &= 0 \\ x &= 2 \quad \textit{or} \end{aligned}$$
$$\begin{aligned} x - 3 &= 0 \\ x &= 3 \end{aligned}$$

64.
$$\begin{aligned} (x + 1)(x - 4) &= -6 \\ x^2 - 3x - 4 + 6 &= 0 \\ x^2 - 3x + 2 &= 0 \\ (x - 1)(x - 2) &= 0 \\ x - 1 &= 0 \\ x &= 1 \quad \textit{or} \end{aligned}$$
$$\begin{aligned} x - 2 &= 0 \\ x &= 2 \end{aligned}$$

66.
$$\frac{1 + \dfrac{1}{x + 2}}{x - \dfrac{10}{x - 2}}$$

$$= \frac{\dfrac{1}{1} \cdot \dfrac{x + 2}{x + 2} + \dfrac{1}{x + 2}}{\dfrac{x}{1} \cdot \dfrac{x - 2}{x - 2} - \dfrac{10}{x - 2}}$$

$$= \frac{\dfrac{x + 3}{x + 2}}{\dfrac{x^2 - 2x - 10}{x - 2}}$$

$$= \frac{x + 3}{x + 2} \cdot \frac{x - 2}{x^2 - 2x - 10}$$

$$= \frac{(x + 3)(x - 2)}{(x + 2)(x^2 - 2x - 10)}$$

67. $$\frac{1 + \frac{1}{x + a}}{1 + \frac{2a + 1}{x - a}}$$

$$= \frac{\frac{1}{1} \cdot \frac{x + a}{x + a} + \frac{1}{x + a}}{\frac{1}{1} \cdot \frac{x - a}{x - a} + \frac{2a + 1}{x - a}}$$

$$= \frac{\frac{x + a + 1}{x + a}}{\frac{x + a + 1}{x - a}}$$

$$= \frac{x + a + 1}{x + a} \cdot \frac{x - a}{x + a + 1}$$

$$= \frac{x - a}{x + a}$$

68. $$\frac{1 + \frac{1}{x - a}}{1 - \frac{2a - 1}{x + a}}$$

$$= \frac{\frac{1}{1} \cdot \frac{x - a}{x - a} + \frac{1}{x - a}}{\frac{1}{1} \cdot \frac{x + a}{x + a} - \frac{2a - 1}{x + a}}$$

$$= \frac{\frac{x - a + 1}{x - a}}{\frac{x - a + 1}{x + a}}$$

$$= \frac{x - a + 1}{x - a} \cdot \frac{x + a}{x - a + 1}$$

$$= \frac{x + a}{x - a}$$

## Section 4.6

2. $\frac{x}{5} = \frac{x}{2} - 9 \quad LCD = 10$

$$10\left(\frac{x}{5}\right) = 10\left(\frac{x}{2} - 9\right)$$

$$2x = 5x - 90$$
$$90 = 3x$$
$$30 = x$$

3. $\frac{a}{3} + 2 = \frac{4}{5} \quad LCD = 15$

$$15\left(\frac{a}{3} + 2\right) = 15\left(\frac{4}{5}\right)$$

$$5a + 30 = 12$$
$$5a = -18$$
$$a = -\frac{18}{5}$$

4. $\frac{a}{4} + \frac{1}{2} = \frac{2}{3} \quad LCD = 12$

$$12\left(\frac{1}{4} + \frac{1}{2}\right) = 12\left(\frac{2}{3}\right)$$

$$3a + 6 = 8$$
$$3a = 2$$
$$a = \frac{2}{3}$$

6. $\frac{y}{3} - \frac{y}{6} + \frac{y}{2} = 1 \quad LCD = 6$

$$6\left(\frac{y}{3} - \frac{y}{6} + \frac{y}{2}\right) = 6(1)$$

$$2y - y + 3y = 6$$
$$4y = 6$$
$$y = \frac{3}{2}$$

7. $$\frac{5}{2x} = \frac{1}{x} + \frac{3}{4} \qquad LCD = 4x$$

$$4x\left(\frac{5}{2x}\right) = 4x\left(\frac{1}{x} + \frac{3}{4}\right)$$
$$10 = 4 + 3x$$
$$6 = 3x$$
$$2 = x$$

8. $$\frac{1}{2a} = \frac{2}{a} - \frac{3}{8} \qquad LCD = 8a$$

$$8a\left(\frac{1}{2a}\right) = 8a\left(\frac{2}{a} - \frac{3}{8}\right)$$
$$4 = 16 - 3a$$
$$-12 = -3a$$
$$4 = a$$

10. $$\frac{5}{2x} = \frac{2}{x} - \frac{1}{12}$$

$$12x\left(\frac{5}{2x}\right) = 12x\left(\frac{2}{x} - \frac{1}{12}\right) \qquad LCD = 12x$$
$$30 = 24 - x$$
$$6 = -x$$
$$-6 = x$$

11. $$\frac{2x}{x-3} + 2 = \frac{2}{x-3} \qquad LCD = x - 3$$

$$x - 3\left(\frac{2x}{x-3} + 2\right) = x - 3\left(\frac{2}{x-3}\right)$$
$$2x + 2x - 6 = 2$$
$$4x - 6 = 2$$
$$4x = 8$$
$$x = 2$$

12. $$\frac{2}{x+5} = \frac{2}{5} - \frac{2}{x+5} \qquad LCD = 5(x + 5)$$

$$5(x + 5)\left(\frac{2}{x+5}\right) = 5(x + 5)\left(\frac{2}{5} - \frac{x}{x+5}\right)$$
$$10 = 2x + 10 - 5x$$
$$0 = -3x$$
$$0 = x$$

14. $$2 + \frac{5}{x} = \frac{3}{x^2} \qquad LCD = x^2$$

$$x^2\left(2 + \frac{5}{x}\right) = x^2\left(\frac{3}{x^2}\right)$$
$$2x^2 + 5x = 3$$
$$2x^2 + 5x - 3 = 0$$
$$(x + 3)(2x - 1) = 0$$
$$x + 3 = 0$$
$$x = -3 \quad \textit{or}$$
$$2x - 1 = 0$$
$$x = \frac{1}{2}$$

15. $$y - \frac{4}{3y} = -\frac{1}{3} \qquad LCD = 3y$$

$$3y\left(y - \frac{4}{3y}\right) = 3y\left(-\frac{1}{3}\right)$$
$$3y^2 - 4 = -y$$
$$3y^2 + y - 4 = 0$$
$$(3y + 4)(y - 1) = 0$$
$$3y + 4 = 0$$
$$y = -\frac{4}{3} \quad \textit{or}$$
$$y - 1 = 0$$
$$y = 1$$

16. $$\frac{y}{2} - \frac{4}{y} = -\frac{7}{2} \qquad LCD = 2y$$

$$2y\left(\frac{y}{2} - \frac{4}{y}\right) = 2y\left(-\frac{7}{2}\right)$$
$$y^2 - 8 = -7y$$
$$y^2 + 7y - 8 = 0$$
$$(y + 8)(y - 1) = 0$$
$$y + 8 = 0$$
$$y = -8 \quad \textit{or}$$
$$y - 1 = 0$$
$$y = 1$$

18. $$\frac{x+6}{x+3} = \frac{3}{x+3} + 2 \quad LCD = x + 3$$

$$x + 3\left(\frac{x+6}{x+3}\right) = x + 3\left(\frac{3}{x+3} + 2\right)$$

$$\begin{aligned} x + 6 &= 3 + 2x + 6 \\ 6 &= x + 9 \\ -3 &= x \end{aligned}$$

*Possible solution −3 which does not check;* ∅

19. $$\frac{3}{a-2} = \frac{2}{a-3} \quad LCD = (a-2)(a-3)$$

$$(a-2)(a-3)\left(\frac{3}{a-2}\right) = (a-2)(a-3)\left(\frac{2}{a-3}\right)$$

$$\begin{aligned} 3a - 9 &= 2a - 4 \\ a - 9 &= -4 \\ a &= 5 \end{aligned}$$

20. $$\frac{5}{a+1} = \frac{4}{a+2} \quad LCD = (a+1)(a+2)$$

$$(a+1)(a+2)\left(\frac{5}{a+1}\right) = (a+1)(a+2)\left(\frac{4}{a+2}\right)$$

$$\begin{aligned} 5a + 10 &= 4a + 4 \\ a + 10 &= 4 \\ a &= -6 \end{aligned}$$

22. $$10 - \frac{3}{x^2} = -\frac{1}{x} \quad LCD = x^2$$

$$x^2\left(10 - \frac{3}{x^2}\right) = x^2\left(-\frac{1}{x}\right)$$

$$\begin{aligned} 10x^2 - 3 &= -x \\ 10x^2 + x - 3 &= 0 \\ (5x + 3)(2x - 1) &= 0 \\ 5x + 3 &= 0 \end{aligned}$$

$$x = -\frac{3}{5} \quad or$$

$$2x - 1 = 0$$

$$x = \frac{1}{2}$$

23. $$\frac{1}{x-1} - \frac{1}{x+1} = \frac{3x}{x^2-1} \qquad LCD = (x-1)(x+1)$$

$$(x-1)(x+1)\left(\frac{1}{x-1} - \frac{1}{x+1}\right) = (x-1)(x+1)\left(\frac{3x}{(x+1)(x-1)}\right)$$

$$x + 1 - x + 1 = 3x$$
$$2 = 3x$$
$$\frac{2}{3} = x$$

24. $$\frac{5}{x-1} + \frac{2}{x-1} = \frac{4}{x+1} \qquad LCD = (x+1)(x-1)$$

$$(x+1)(x-1)\left(\frac{5}{x-1} + \frac{2}{x-1}\right) = (x+1)(x-1)\left(\frac{4}{x+1}\right)$$

$$5x + 5 + 2x + 2 = 4x - 4$$
$$7x + 7 = 4x - 4$$
$$3x = -11$$
$$x = -\frac{11}{3}$$

26. $$\frac{2}{x+5} + \frac{3}{x+4} = \frac{2x}{x^2+9x+20} \qquad LCD = (x+5)(x+4)$$

$$(x+5)(x+4)\left(\frac{2}{x+5} + \frac{3}{x+4}\right) = (x+5)(x+4)\left(\frac{2x}{(x+5)(x+4)}\right)$$

$$2x + 8 + 3x + 15 = 2x$$
$$5x + 23 = 2x$$
$$23 = -3x$$
$$-\frac{23}{3} = x$$

27. $$\frac{3}{2} - \frac{1}{x-4} = \frac{-2}{2x-8} \qquad LCD = 2(x-4)$$

$$2(x-4)\left(\frac{3}{2} - \frac{1}{x-4}\right) = 2(x-4)\left(\frac{-2}{2(x-4)}\right)$$

$$3x - 12 - 2 = -2$$
$$3x = 12$$
$$x = 4$$

*Possible solution 4 which does not check ;* $\varnothing$

28. $$\frac{2}{x} - \frac{1}{x + 1} = \frac{-2}{5x + 5} \qquad LCD = 5x(x + 1)$$

$$5x(x + 1)\left(\frac{2}{x} - \frac{1}{x + 1}\right) = 5x(x + 1)\left(\frac{-2}{5(x + 1)}\right)$$

$$\begin{aligned} 10x + 10 - 5x &= -2x \\ 5x + 10 &= -2x \\ 10 &= -7x \\ -\frac{10}{7} &= x \end{aligned}$$

30. $$\frac{t + 3}{t^2 - 2t} = \frac{10}{t^2 - 4} \qquad LCD = t(t + 2)(t - 2)$$

$$t(t + 2)(t - 2)\left(\frac{t + 3}{t(t - 2)}\right) = t(t + 2)(t - 2)\left(\frac{10}{(t + 2)(t - 2)}\right)$$

$$\begin{aligned} t^2 + 5t + 6 &= 10t \\ t^2 - 5t + 6 &= 0 \\ (t - 2)(t - 3) &= 0 \\ t - 2 &= 0 \\ t &= 2 \quad \textit{or} \\ t - 3 &= 0 \\ t &= 3 \end{aligned}$$

*Possible solutions* 2 *and* 3; *but only* 3 *checks*: 3

31. $$\frac{3}{y - 4} - \frac{2}{y + 1} = \frac{5}{y^2 - 3y - 4} \qquad LCD = (y + 1)(y - 4)$$

$$(y + 1)(y - 4)\left(\frac{3}{y - 4} - \frac{2}{y + 1}\right) = (y + 1)(y - 4)\left(\frac{5}{(y + 1)(y - 4)}\right)$$

$$\begin{aligned} 3y + 3 - 2y + 8 &= 5 \\ y &= -6 \end{aligned}$$

32. $$\frac{1}{y + 2} - \frac{2}{y - 3} = \frac{-2y}{y^2 - y - 6} \qquad LCD = (y + 2)(y - 3)$$

$$(y + 2)(y - 3)\left(\frac{1}{y + 2} - \frac{2}{y - 3}\right) = (y + 2)(y - 3)\left(\frac{-2y}{(y + 2)(y - 3)}\right)$$

$$\begin{aligned} y - 3 - 2y - 4 &= -2y \\ -y - 7 &= -2y \\ -7 &= -y \\ 7 &= y \end{aligned}$$

34. $$\frac{1}{a+3} - \frac{a}{a^2-9} = \frac{2}{3-a} \qquad LCD = (a+3)(a-3)$$

$$(a+3)(a-3)\left(\frac{1}{a+3} - \frac{a}{(a+3)(a-3)}\right) = (a+3)(a-3)\left(\frac{2}{-1(a-3)}\right)$$

$$a - 3 - a = -2a - 6$$
$$3 = -2a$$
$$-\frac{3}{2} = a$$

35. $$\frac{3}{2x-6} - \frac{x+1}{4x-12} = 4 \qquad LCD = 4(x-3)$$

$$4(x-3)\left(\frac{3}{2(x-3)} - \frac{x+1}{4(x-3)}\right) = 4(x-3)4$$
$$6 - x - 1 = 16x - 48$$
$$53 = 17x$$
$$\frac{53}{17} = x$$

36. $$\frac{2x-3}{5x+10} + \frac{3x-2}{4x+8} = 1 \qquad LCD = 20(x+2)$$

$$20(x+2)\left(\frac{2x-3}{5(x+2)} + \frac{3x-2}{4(x+2)}\right) = 20(x+2)1$$

$$8x - 12 + 15x - 10 = 20x + 40$$
$$23x - 22 = 20x + 40$$
$$3x = 62$$
$$x = \frac{62}{3}$$

38. $$\frac{y+3}{y^2-y} - \frac{8}{y^2-1} = 0 \qquad LCD = y(y+1)(y-1)$$

$$y(y+1)(y-1)\left(\frac{y+3}{y(y-1)} - \frac{8}{(y+1)(y-1)}\right) = y(y+1)(y-1)0$$

$$y^2 + 4y + 3 - 8y = 0$$
$$y^2 - 4y + 3 = 0$$
$$(y-1)(y-3) = 0$$
$$y - 1 = 0$$
$$y = 1 \quad or$$
$$y - 3 = 0$$
$$y = 3$$

*Possible solutions* 1 *and* 3, *but only* 3 *checks:* 3

39. $$\frac{4}{2x - 6} - \frac{12}{4x + 12} = \frac{12}{x^2 - 9} \qquad LCD = 4(x + 3)(x - 3)$$

$$4(x + 3)(x - 3)\left(\frac{4}{2(x - 3)} - \frac{12}{4(x + 3)}\right) = 4(x + 3)(x - 3)\left(\frac{12}{(x + 3)(x - 3)}\right)$$

$$\begin{aligned} 8x + 24 - 12x + 36 &= 48 \\ -4x + 60 &= 48 \\ -4x &= -12 \\ x &= 3 \end{aligned}$$

*Possible solution 3, which does not check:* ∅

40. $$\frac{1}{x + 2} + \frac{1}{x - 2} = \frac{4}{x^2 - 4} \qquad LCD = (x + 2)(x - 2)$$

$$(x + 2)(x - 2)\left(\frac{1}{x + 2} + \frac{1}{x - 2}\right) = (x + 2)(x - 2)\left(\frac{1}{(x + 2)(x - 2)}\right)$$

$$\begin{aligned} x - 2 + x + 2 &= 4 \\ 2x &= 4 \\ x &= 2 \end{aligned}$$

*Possible solution 2, which does not check:* ∅

42. $$\frac{1}{y^2 + 5y + 4} + \frac{3}{y^2 - 1} = \frac{-1}{y^2 + 3y - 4} \qquad LCD = (y + 1)(y + 4)(y - 1)$$

$$(y + 1)(y + 4)(y - 1)\left(\frac{1}{(y + 1)(y + 4)} + \frac{3}{(y + 1)(y - 1)}\right)$$

$$= (y + 1)(y + 4)(y - 1)\left(\frac{-1}{(y + 4)(y - 1)}\right)$$

$$\begin{aligned} y - 1 + 3y + 12 &= -y - 1 \\ 4y + 11 &= -y - 1 \\ 5y &= -12 \\ y &= -\frac{12}{5} \end{aligned}$$

43. $$\begin{aligned} 6x^{-1} + 4 &= 7 \\ x(6x^{-1} + 4) &= x(7) \\ 6 + 4x &= 7x \\ 6 &= 3x \\ 2 &= x \end{aligned}$$

44. $$\begin{aligned} 3x^{-1} - 5 &= 2x^{-1} - 3 \\ x(3x^{-1} - 5) &= x(2x^{-1} - 3) \\ 3 - 5x &= 2 - 3x \\ 1 &= 2x \\ \frac{1}{2} &= x \end{aligned}$$

46.
$$\begin{aligned} 1 + 3x^{-2} &= 4x^{-1} \\ x^2(1 + 3x^{-2}) &= x^2(4x^{-1}) \\ x^2 + 3 &= 4x \\ x^2 - 4x + 3 &= 0 \\ (x - 1)(x - 3) &= 0 \\ x - 1 &= 0 \\ x &= 1 \quad \textit{or} \\ x - 3 &= 0 \\ x &= 3 \end{aligned}$$

47.
$$\frac{1}{x} = \frac{1}{b} - \frac{1}{a} \qquad LCD = abx$$

$$abx\left(\frac{1}{x}\right) = abx\left(\frac{1}{b} - \frac{1}{a}\right)$$

$$\begin{aligned} ab &= ax - bx \\ ab &= (a - b)x \end{aligned}$$

$$\frac{ab}{a - b} = x$$

48.
$$\frac{1}{x} = \frac{1}{a} - \frac{1}{b} \qquad LCD = abx$$

$$abx\left(\frac{1}{x}\right) = abx\left(\frac{1}{a} - \frac{1}{b}\right)$$

$$\begin{aligned} ab &= bx - ax \\ ab &= (b - a)x \end{aligned}$$

$$\frac{ba}{b - a} = x$$

50.
$$\frac{1}{R} = \frac{1}{R_1} + \frac{1}{R_2} + \frac{1}{R_3} \qquad LCD = RR_1R_2R_3$$

$$RR_1R_2R_3\left(\frac{1}{R}\right) = RR_1R_2R_3\left(\frac{1}{R_1} + \frac{1}{R_2} + \frac{1}{R_3}\right)$$

$$\begin{aligned} R_1R_2R_3 &= RR_2R_3 + RR_1R_3 + RR_1R_2 \\ R_1R_2R_3 &= R(R_2R_3 + R_1R_3 + R_1R_2) \end{aligned}$$

$$\frac{R_1R_2R_3}{R_2R_3 + R_1R_3 + R_1R_2} = R$$

51. $x = \dfrac{y-3}{y-1}$ $\quad LCD = y - 1$

$$x(y-1) = y-3$$
$$xy - x = y - 3$$
$$xy - y = x - 3$$
$$(x-1)y = x - 3$$

$$y = \frac{x-3}{x-1}$$

52. $x = \dfrac{y-2}{y-3}$ $\quad LCD = y - 3$

$$x(y-3) = y - 2$$
$$xy - 3x = y - 2$$
$$xy - y = 3x - 2$$
$$(x-1)y = 3x - 2$$

$$y = \frac{3x-2}{x-1}$$

54. $x = \dfrac{3y+2}{5y+1}$ $\quad LCD = 5y + 1$

$$x(5y+1) = 3y + 2$$
$$5xy + x = 3y + 2$$
$$5xy - 3y = 2 - x$$
$$(5x-3)y = 2 - x$$

$$y = \frac{2-x}{5x-3}$$

55. $x$ = *the number*

$$2(x+3) = 16$$
$$2x + 6 = 16$$
$$2x = 10$$
$$x = 5$$

56. $x$ = *1st odd integer*
$x + 2$ =*2nd odd integer*

$$x + (x+2) = 48$$
$$2x + 2 = 48$$
$$2x = 46$$
$x = 23$ (*1st*)
$x + 2 = 25$ (*2nd*)

58. $x$ = *smallest angle*
$4x$ = *largest angle*
$x + 9$ = *third angle*

$$x + 4x + x + 9 = 180$$
$$6x = 171$$
$$x = 28.5°$$
$$4x = 114°$$
$$x + 9 = 37.5°$$

59. $x$ = *1st integer*
$x + 1$ = *2nd integer*

$$(x)^2 + (x+1)^2 = 61$$
$$x^2 + x^2 + 2x + 1 - 61 = 0$$
$$2x^2 + 2x - 60 = 0$$
$$2(x^2 + x - 30) = 0$$
$$(x+6)(x-5) = 0$$
$$x + 6 = 0$$
$x = -6$ (*1st*)
$x + 1 = -5$ (*2nd*) *or*

$$x - 5 = 0$$
$x = 5$ (*1st*)
$x + 1 = 6$ (*2nd*)

60. $(x + x + 1)^2 = 121$

$$(2x+1)^2 = 121$$
$$4x^2 + 4x + 1 = 121$$
$$4x^2 + 4x - 120 = 0$$
$$4(x^2 + x - 30) = 0$$
$$4(x-5)(x+6) = 0$$
$$x - 5 = 0$$
$$x = 5$$
$x + 1 = 6$ *or*

$$x + 6 = 0$$
$$x = -6$$
$$x + 1 = -5$$

62. Let $x$ = shortest side
$x + 7$ = other side
$x + 8$ = longest side

$$c^2 = a^2 + b^2$$
$$(x + 8)^2 = x^2 + (x + 7)^2$$
$$x^2 + 16x + 64 = x^2 + x^2 + 14x + 49$$
$$0 = x^2 - 2x - 15$$
$$0 = (x + 3)(x - 5)$$
$$x + 3 = 0$$
$$x = -3$$
Extraneous root or

$$x - 5 = 0$$
$$x = 5 \text{ in.}$$
$$x + 7 = 12 \text{ in.}$$
$$x + 8 = 13 \text{ in.}$$

63. $$\frac{12}{x} + \frac{8}{x^2} - \frac{75}{x^3} - \frac{50}{x^4} = 0 \quad LCD = x^4$$

$$x^4\left(\frac{12}{x} + \frac{8}{x^2} - \frac{75}{x^3} - \frac{50}{x^4}\right) = x^4(0)$$

$$12x^3 + 8x^2 - 75x - 50 = 0$$
$$4x^2(3x + 2) - 25(3x + 2) = 0$$
$$(3x + 2)(2x + 5)(2x - 5) = 0$$
$$3x + 2 = 0$$

$$x = -\frac{2}{3} \quad \text{or}$$

$$2x + 5 = 0$$

$$x = -\frac{5}{2} \quad \text{or}$$

$$2x - 5 = 0$$

$$x = \frac{5}{2}$$

64. $$\frac{45}{x} + \frac{18}{x^2} - \frac{80}{x^3} - \frac{32}{x^4} = 0 \quad LCD = x^4$$

$$x^4\left(\frac{45}{x} + \frac{18}{x^2} - \frac{80}{x^3} - \frac{32}{x^4}\right) = x^4(0)$$

$$45x^3 + 18x^2 - 80x - 32 = 0$$
$$9x^2(5x + 2) - 16(5x + 2) = 0$$
$$(5x + 2)(3x + 4)(3x - 4) = 0$$
$$5x + 2 = 0$$

$$x = -\frac{2}{5} \quad \text{or}$$

$$3x + 4 = 0$$

$$x = -\frac{4}{3} \quad \text{or}$$

$$3x - 4 = 0$$

$$x = \frac{4}{3}$$

66. $$\frac{1}{x^3} - \frac{1}{2x^2} - \frac{1}{9x} + \frac{1}{18} = 0 \quad LCD = 18x^3$$

$$18x^3\left(\frac{1}{x^3} - \frac{1}{2x^2} - \frac{1}{9x} + \frac{1}{18}\right) = 18x^3(0)$$

$$18 - 9x - 2x^2 + x^3 = 0$$
$$9(2 - x) - x^2(2 - x) = 0$$
$$(2 - x)(3 + x)(3 - x) = 0$$
$$2 - x = 0$$
$$2 = x \quad \text{or}$$
$$3 + x = 0$$
$$x = -3 \quad \text{or}$$
$$3 - x = 0$$
$$3 = x$$

## Section 4.7

2. $\frac{1}{x} + \frac{1}{3x} = \frac{4}{9}$ $\quad LCD = 9x$

$$9x\left(\frac{1}{x} + \frac{1}{3x}\right) = 9x\left(\frac{4}{9}\right)$$

$$\begin{aligned} 9 + 3 &= 4x \\ 12 &= 4x \\ 3 &= x \\ 9 &= 3x \end{aligned}$$

3. $x + \frac{1}{x} = \frac{10}{3}$ $\quad LCD = 3x$

$$3x\left(x + \frac{1}{x}\right) = 3x\left(\frac{10}{3}\right)$$

$$\begin{aligned} 3x^2 + 3 &= 10x \\ 3x^2 - 10x + 3 &= 0 \\ (3x - 1)(x - 3) &= 0 \\ 3x - 1 &= 0 \end{aligned}$$

$$x = \frac{1}{3}$$

$$\frac{1}{x} = 3 \quad \textit{or}$$

$$\begin{aligned} x - 3 &= 0 \\ x &= 3 \end{aligned}$$

$$\frac{1}{x} = \frac{1}{3}$$

4. $x + 2\left(\frac{1}{x}\right) = \frac{27}{5}$ $\quad LCD = 5x$

$$5x\left(x + \frac{2}{x}\right) = 5x\left(\frac{27}{5}\right)$$

$$\begin{aligned} 5x^2 + 10 &= 27x \\ 5x^2 - 27x + 10 &= 0 \\ (5x - 2)(x - 5) &= 0 \\ 5x - 2 &= 0 \end{aligned}$$

$$x = \frac{2}{5} \quad \textit{or}$$

$$\begin{aligned} x - 5 &= 0 \\ x &= 5 \end{aligned}$$

6. $\frac{1}{x} + \frac{1}{x+2} = \frac{3}{4}$ $\quad LCD = 4x(x + 2)$

$$4x(x + 2)\left(\frac{1}{x} + \frac{1}{x+2}\right) = 4x(x + 2)\frac{3}{4}$$

$$\begin{aligned} 4x + 8 + 4x &= 3x^2 + 6x \\ 0 &= 3x^2 - 2x - 8 \\ 0 &= (3x + 4)(x - 2) \\ 3x + 4 &= 0 \end{aligned}$$

$$x = -\frac{4}{3}$$

*Not an integer* *or*

$$\begin{aligned} x - 2 &= 0 \\ x &= 2 \\ x + 2 &= 4 \end{aligned}$$

7. $\frac{7 + x}{9 + x} = \frac{5}{6}$ $\quad LCD = 6(9 + x)$

$$6(9 + x)\left(\frac{7 + x}{9 + x}\right) = 6(9 + x)\frac{5}{6}$$

$$\begin{aligned} 42 + 6x &= 45 + 5x \\ x &= 3 \end{aligned}$$

8. $\frac{8 + x}{11 + x} = \frac{6}{7}$ $\quad LCD = 7(11 + x)$

$$7(11 + x)\left(\frac{8 + x}{11 + x}\right) = 7(11 + x)\frac{6}{7}$$

$$\begin{aligned} 56 + 7x &= 66 + 6x \\ x &= 10 \end{aligned}$$

10. $\frac{14}{18 + x} = \frac{10}{18 - x}$ $\quad LCD = (18 + x)(18 - x)$

$$\begin{aligned} 14(18 - x) &= 10(18 + x) \\ 252 - 14x &= 180 + 10x \\ 72 &= 24x \\ x &= 3 \text{ mph for the current} \end{aligned}$$

11. $$\frac{8}{x+2} + \frac{8}{x-2} = 3 \qquad LCD = (x+2)(x-2)$$

$$8x - 16 + 8x + 16 = 3x^2 - 12$$
$$0 = 3x^2 - 16x - 12$$
$$0 = (3x+2)(x-6)$$
$$3x + 2 = 0$$
$$x = -\frac{2}{3}$$

*Speed cannot be negative* *or*

$$x - 6 = 0$$
$$x = 6 \text{ miles/hour}$$

12. $$\frac{12}{4-x} + \frac{12}{4+x} = 8 \qquad LCD = (4-x)(4+x)$$

$$48 + 12x + 48 - 12x = 128 - 8x^2$$
$$8x^2 - 32 = 0$$
$$8(x+2)(x-2) = 0$$
$$x + 2 = 0$$
$$x = -2$$

*Speed cannot be negative*

$$x - 2 = 0$$
$$x = 2 \text{ mph}$$

14. $$\frac{120}{x+30} = \frac{80}{x} \qquad LCD = x(x+30)$$

$$120x = 80x + 2400$$
$$40x = 2400$$
$$x = 60 \text{ mph (car)}$$
$$x + 30 = 90 \text{ mph (train)}$$

15. *Let $r$ = avg. speed of 747*

$810 \div 270 = 3$ *hrs for small plane*

$$810 = \left(3 - 1\frac{1}{2}\right)r$$

$$810 = 1\frac{1}{2}r$$

$$r = 540 \text{ miles/hour}$$

16. *Let $r$ = speed of car*

$30 \div 20 = 1.5$ *hrs for Lou*

$$30 = (1.5 - .25)r$$
$$r = 24 \text{ miles/hour}$$

18. $$\frac{140}{x - \frac{1}{2}} - \frac{140}{x} = 5$$

$$104x - 140\left(x - \frac{1}{2}\right) = 5x\left(x - \frac{1}{2}\right)$$

$$70 = 5x^2 - \frac{5}{2}x$$

$$\begin{aligned} 10x^2 - 5x - 140 &= 0 \\ 2x^2 - x - 28 &= 0 \\ (2x + 7)(x - 4) &= 0 \\ x &= 4 \end{aligned}$$

$$\frac{140}{4} = 35 \textit{ miles/hour}$$

19. $$\frac{1}{3} + \frac{1}{6} = \frac{1}{x} \qquad LCD = 6x$$

$$\begin{aligned} 2x + x &= 6 \\ 3x &= 6 \\ x &= 2 \textit{ days} \end{aligned}$$

20. $$\frac{1}{10} + \frac{1}{8} = \frac{1}{x} \qquad LCD = 40x$$

$$\begin{aligned} 4x + 5x &= 40 \\ 9x &= 40 \end{aligned}$$

$$x = \frac{40}{9} \textit{ hr.} \quad \textit{or} \quad 4\frac{4}{9} \textit{ hours}$$

22. $$\frac{1}{3x} + \frac{1}{x} = \frac{1}{3} \qquad LCD = 3x$$

$$\begin{aligned} 1 + 3 &= x \\ 4 &= x \\ 3x &= 12 \textit{ hrs (slow worker)} \end{aligned}$$

23. $$\frac{1}{8} - \frac{1}{16} = \frac{1}{x} \qquad LCD = 16x$$

$$\begin{aligned} 2x - x &= 16 \\ x &= 16 \textit{ hours} \end{aligned}$$

24. $$\frac{1}{3} - \frac{1}{5} = \frac{1}{x} \qquad LCD = 15x$$

$$\begin{aligned} 5x - 3x &= 15 \\ 2x &= 15 \end{aligned}$$

$$x = \frac{15}{2} \textit{ min.}$$

26. $\frac{1}{6} - \frac{1}{8} = \frac{3}{4}\left(\frac{1}{x}\right)$

$\frac{1}{6} - \frac{1}{8} = \frac{3}{4x}$ $\quad LCD = 24x$

$4x - 3x = 18$
$x = 18\ min.$

27. $\frac{1}{3.5} + \frac{1}{x} = \frac{1}{2.1}$

$2.1x + (3.5)(2.1) = 3.5x$
$7.35 = 1.4x$

$x = 5\frac{1}{4}$ *or* 5.25 *minutes*

28. $\frac{1}{4\frac{1}{2}} + \frac{1}{B} = \frac{1}{2}$

$2b + \left(4\frac{1}{2}\right)(2) = 4\frac{1}{2}B$

$9 = 2\frac{1}{2}B$

$B = 3.6\ hours$

30. $\frac{4.9l}{1} \cdot \frac{1\ cu\ in}{0.0164l} = 298.8\ in^3$

31. $\frac{5{,}750\ feet}{11\ minutes} \cdot \frac{1\ mile}{5{,}280\ ft} \cdot \frac{60\ \text{min}}{1\ h4}$

$= 5.9\ miles/hour$

32. $\frac{790\ feet}{2.2\ \text{min}} \cdot \frac{1\ mile}{5{,}280\ ft} \cdot \frac{60\ \text{min}}{1\ hr}$

$= 4.1\ miles/hour$

34. $\frac{40\ meters}{49.8\ seconds} \cdot \frac{3.28\ ft}{1\ meter} \cdot \frac{1\ mi}{5{,}280\ ft} \cdot \frac{60\ seconds}{1\ \text{min}} \cdot \frac{60\ \text{min}}{1\ hour} = 18.0\ miles/hour$

35. $C = \pi d = 3.14(65\ ft) = 204.1\ ft$

$\frac{204.1\ ft}{30\ seconds} \cdot \frac{1\ mi}{5{,}280\ ft} \cdot \frac{60\ seconds}{1\ \text{min.}} \cdot \frac{60\ \text{min}}{1\ hour} = 4.6\ miles/hour$

36. $C = \pi d = 3.14(102\ ft) = 320.28\ ft$

$\frac{320.28\ ft}{3.5\ \text{min}} \cdot \frac{1\ mi}{5{,}280\ ft} \cdot \frac{60\ \text{min}}{1\ hour} = 1.0\ miles/hour$

38. $C = 2\pi r = 2(3.14)(2) = 12.56$ *inches*

$$d = \frac{12.56}{\frac{1}{3{,}600}} = 45{,}216 \text{ in/min}$$

$$\frac{45{,}216 \textit{ in}}{\text{min}} \cdot \frac{1 \textit{ foot}}{12 \textit{ in}} \cdot \frac{1 \textit{ mi}}{5{,}280 \textit{ feet}} \cdot \frac{60 \text{ min}}{1 \textit{ hour}} = 42.8 \textit{ miles/hour}$$

39. $\dfrac{2a + 10}{x^3} \cdot \dfrac{a^2}{3a + 15}$

$$= \frac{2(a + 5)}{a^3} \cdot \frac{a^2}{3(a + 5)}$$

$$= \frac{2}{3a}$$

40. $\dfrac{4a + 8}{a^2 - a - 6} \div \dfrac{a^2 + 7a + 12}{a^2 - 9}$

$$= \frac{4(a + 2)}{(a + 2)(a - 3)} \cdot \frac{(a + 3)(a - 3)}{(a + 3)(a + 4)}$$

$$= \frac{4}{a + 4}$$

42. $\dfrac{1}{x + 4} + \dfrac{8}{x^2 - 16}$ $\quad LCD = (x + 4)(x - 4)$

$$= \frac{x - 4}{(x + 4)(x - 4)} + \frac{8}{(x + 4)(x - 4)}$$

$$= \frac{x + 4}{(x + 4)(x - 4)}$$

$$= \frac{1}{x - 4}$$

43. $\dfrac{2x - 7}{x - 2} - \dfrac{x - 5}{x - 2}$

$$= \frac{2x - 7 - x + 5}{x - 2}$$

$$= \frac{x - 2}{x - 2}$$

$$= 1$$

44. $2 + \dfrac{25}{5x - 1}$

$= \dfrac{10x - 2}{5x - 1} + \dfrac{25}{5x - 1}$

$= \dfrac{10x + 23}{5x - 1}$

46. $\dfrac{1 - \dfrac{9}{x^2}}{1 - \dfrac{1}{x} - \dfrac{6}{x^2}}$ *LCD* = $x^2$

$= \dfrac{x^2 - 9}{x^2 - x - 6}$

$= \dfrac{(x + 3)(x - 3)}{(x + 2)(x - 3)}$

$= \dfrac{x + 3}{x + 2}$

47. $\dfrac{x}{x - 3} + \dfrac{3}{2} = \dfrac{3}{x - 3}$ *LCD* = $2(x - 3)$

$$2x + 3x - 9 = 6$$
$$5x = 15$$
$$x = 3$$

*Possible solution 3, which does not check,* ∅

48. $1 - \dfrac{3}{x} = \dfrac{-2}{x^2}$ *LCD* = $x^2$

$$x^2 - 3x = -2$$
$$x^2 - 3x + 2 = 0$$
$$(x - 1)(x - 2) = 0$$
$$x - 1 = 0$$
$$x = 1 \quad \textit{or}$$

$$x - 2 = 0$$
$$x = 2$$

# Chapter 5

## Section 5.1

1 - 15 Odd

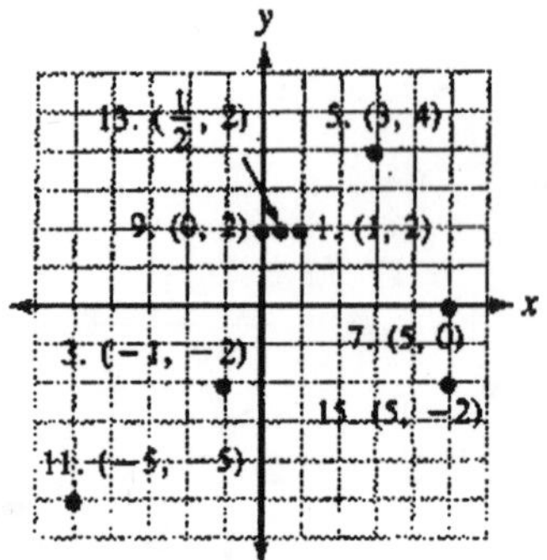


2 - 16 Even

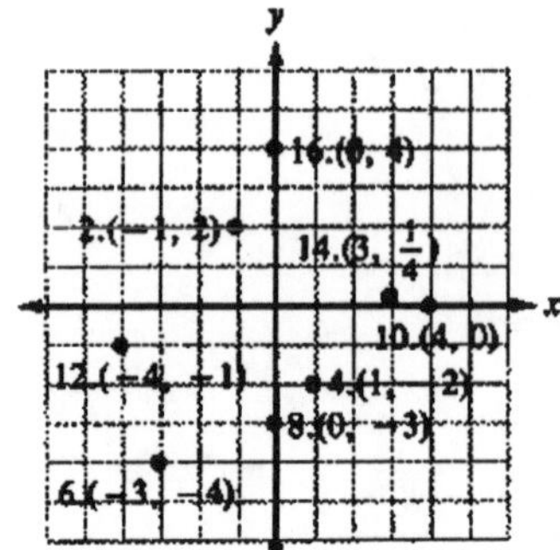


18. (0,5)

19. $\left(-3, \dfrac{5}{2}\right)$

20. (2,2)

22. (4,0)

23. $(-3, -2)$

24. $(1, -2)$

26. $(0, -4)$

27. $(3, -4)$

28. $\left(\frac{9}{2}, -5\right)$

30.

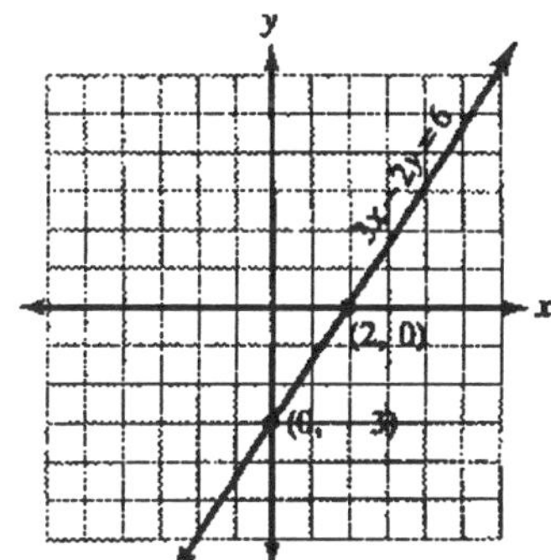


31.

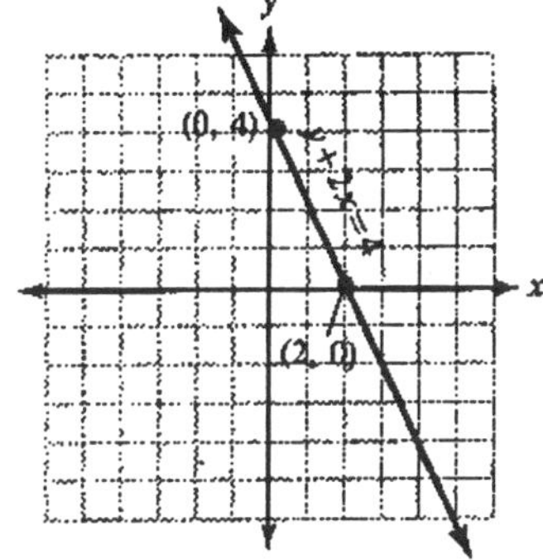


32.

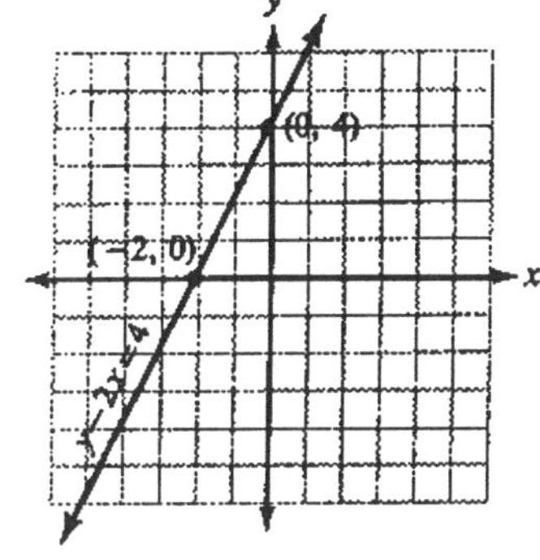


34.

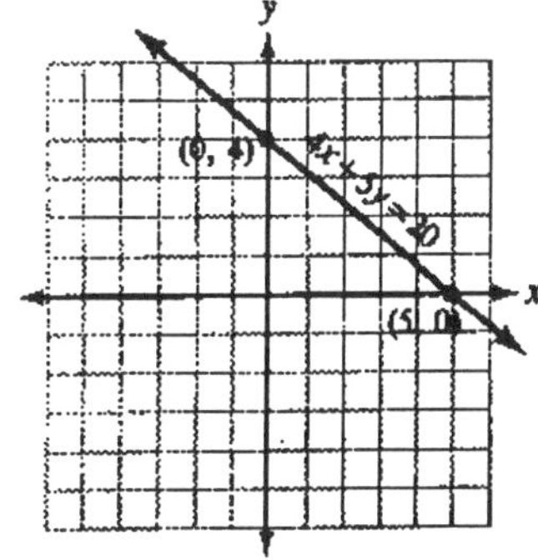


35.

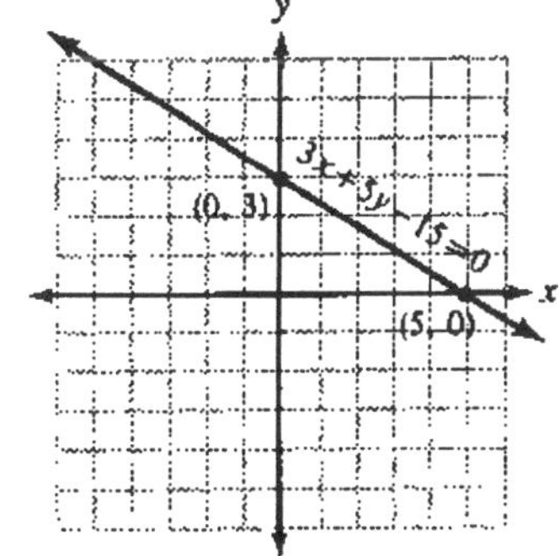


36.

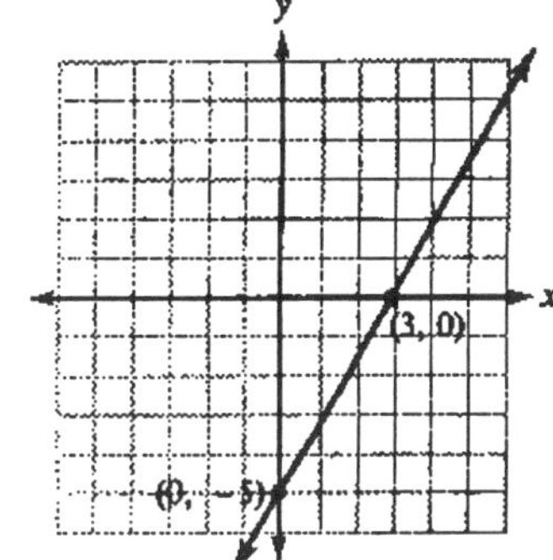


38.

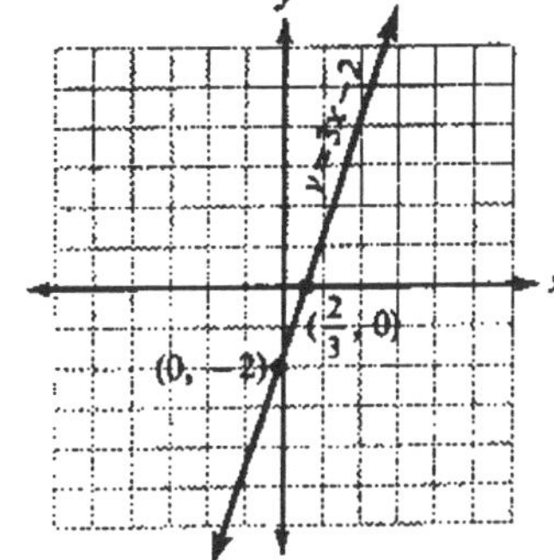

39.

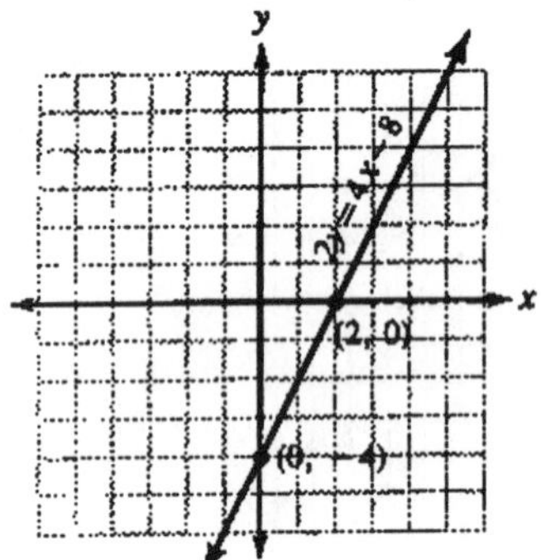


44.

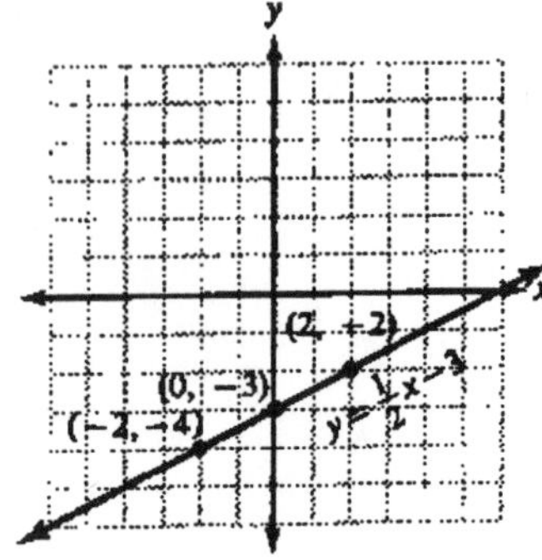


40.

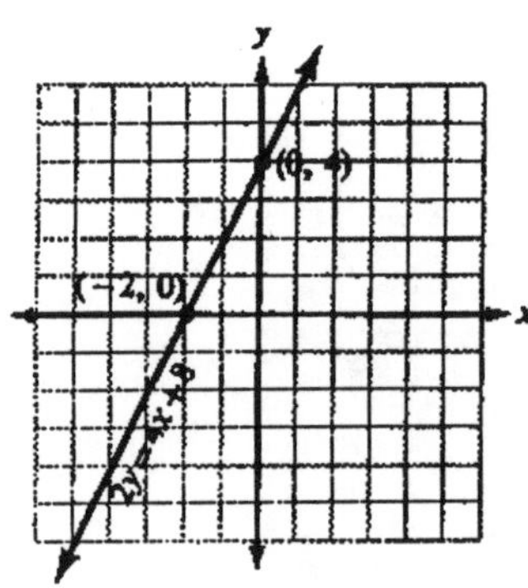


46.

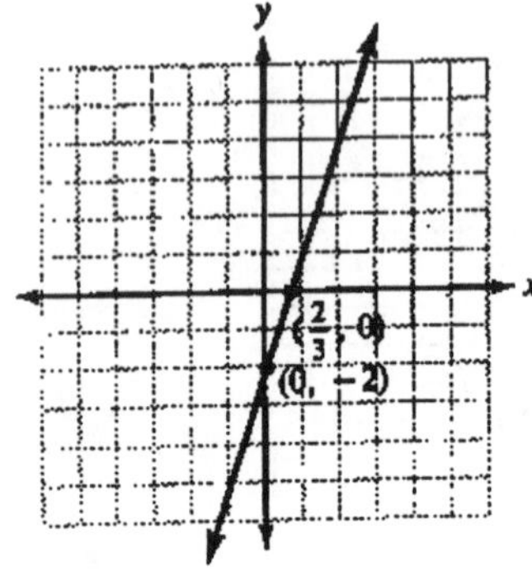


42.

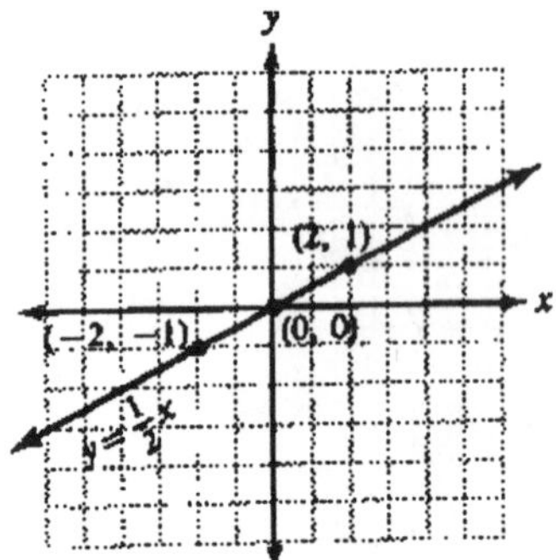


47.

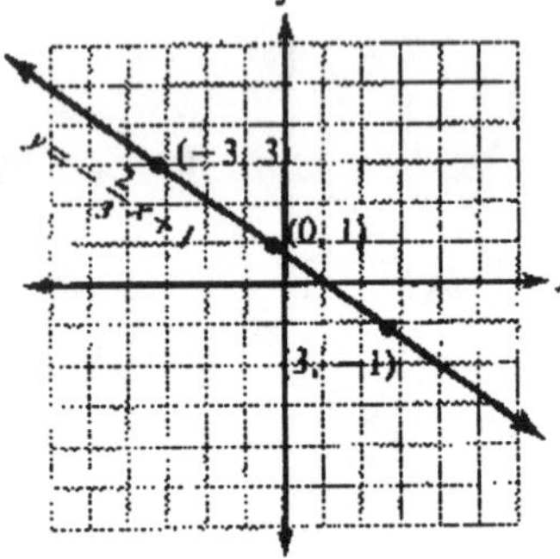


43.

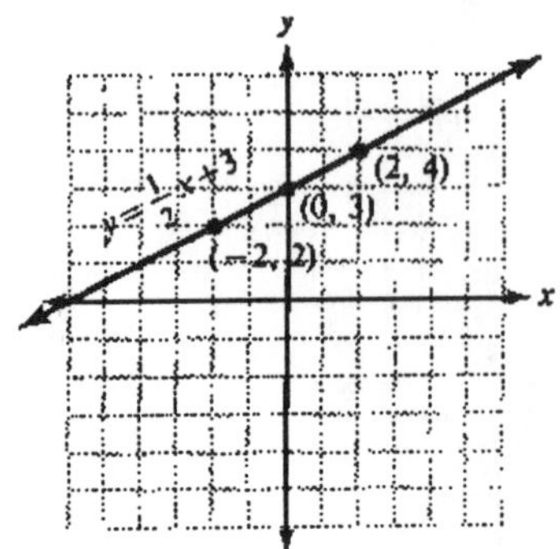


48.

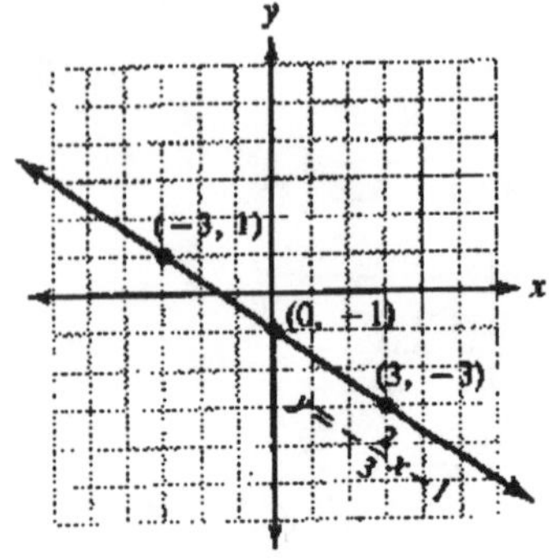

50.

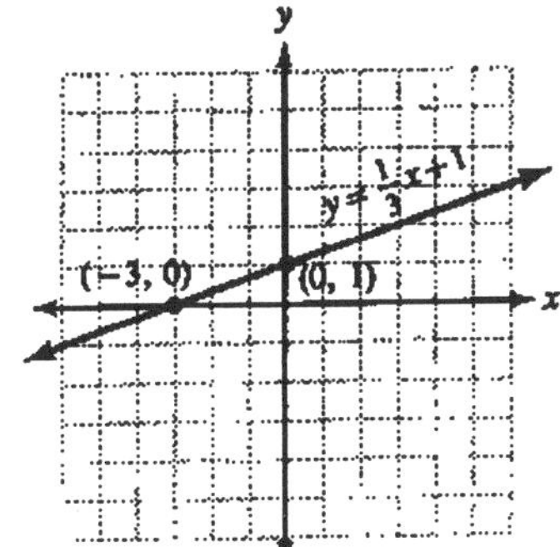


55.

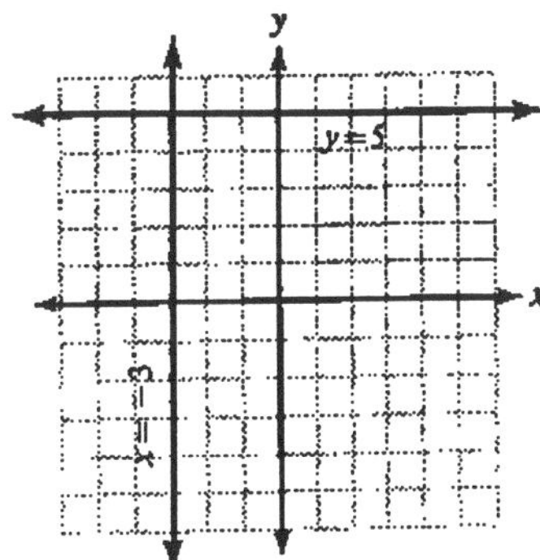


51.

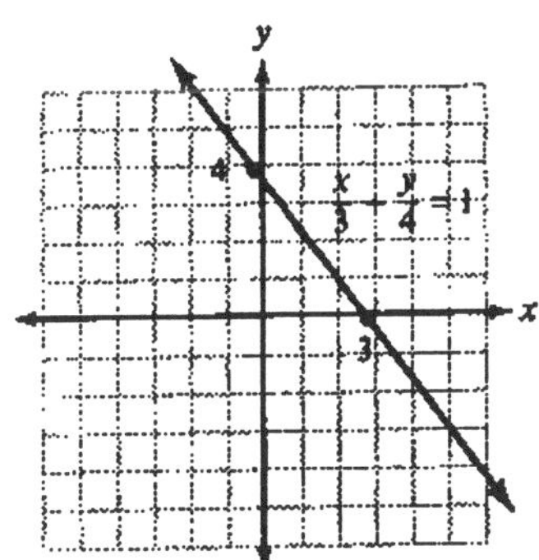


56.

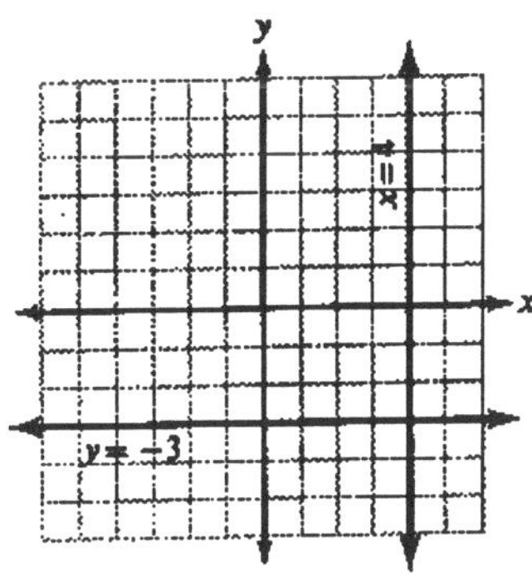


52.

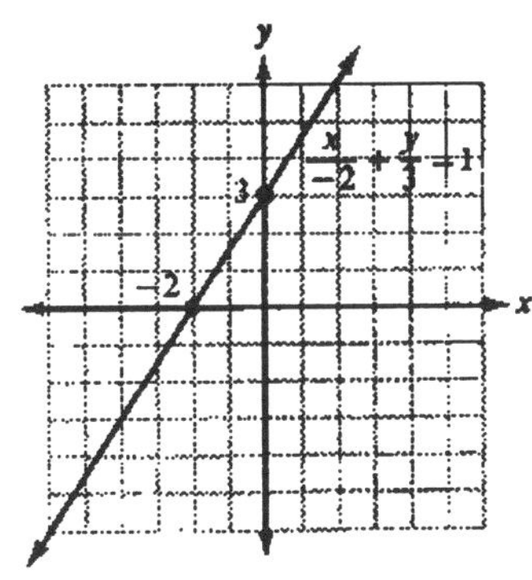


58.

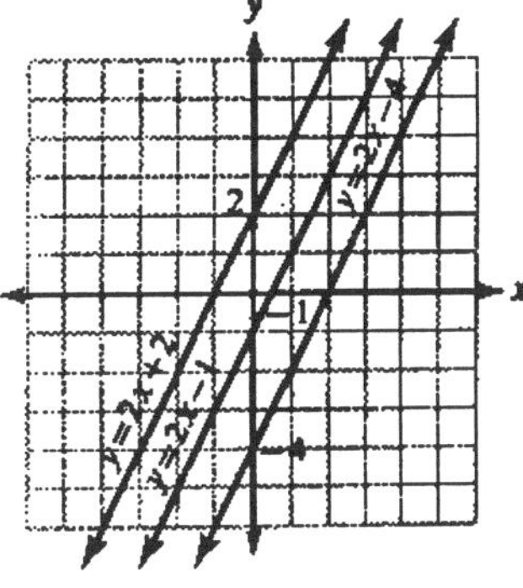


54.

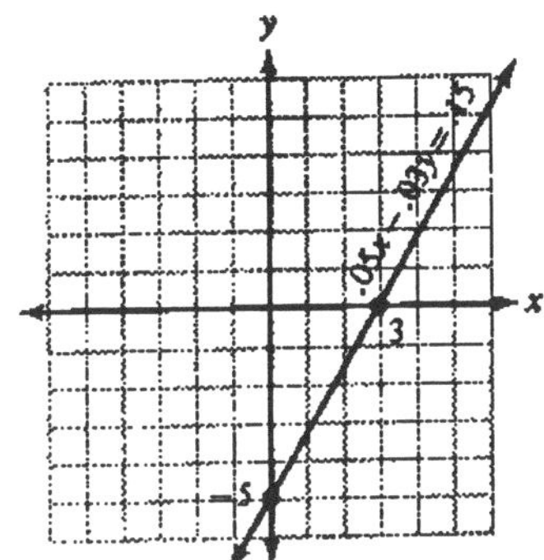


59.

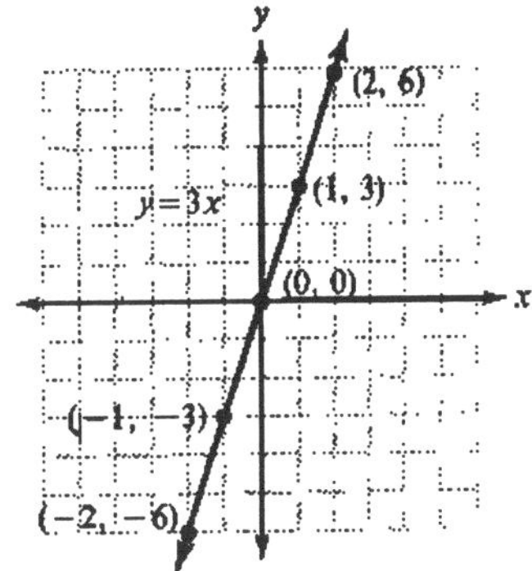

60.

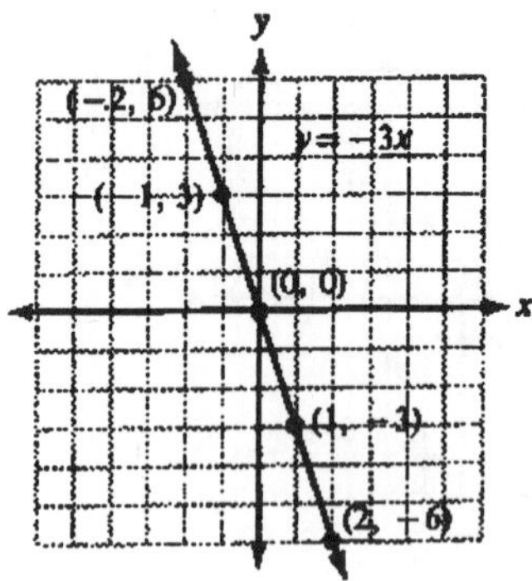


62.

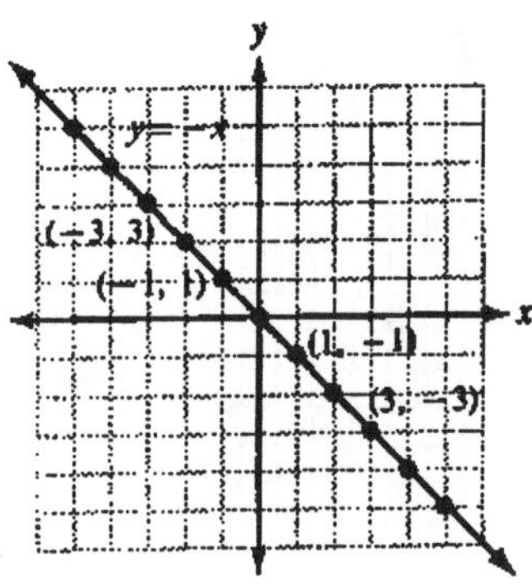


63.

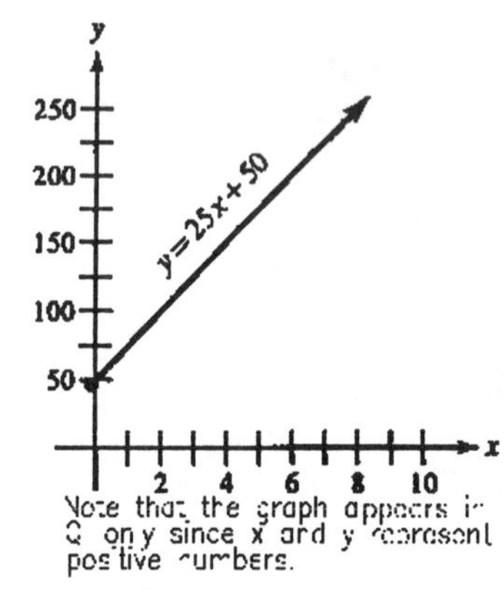


64.

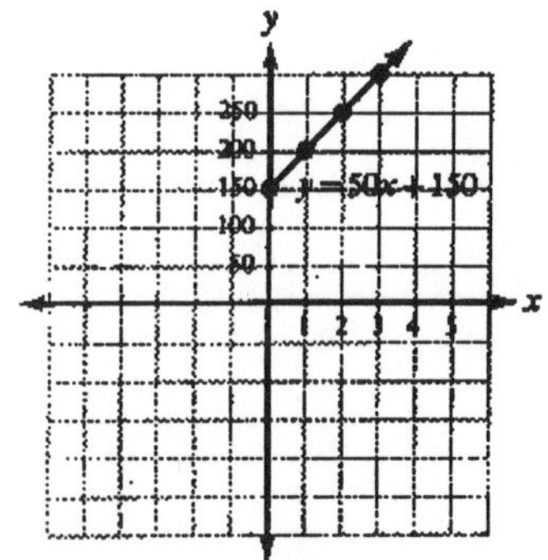


*Note that the graph appears in Q1 only, since x and y represent positive numbers.*

66.

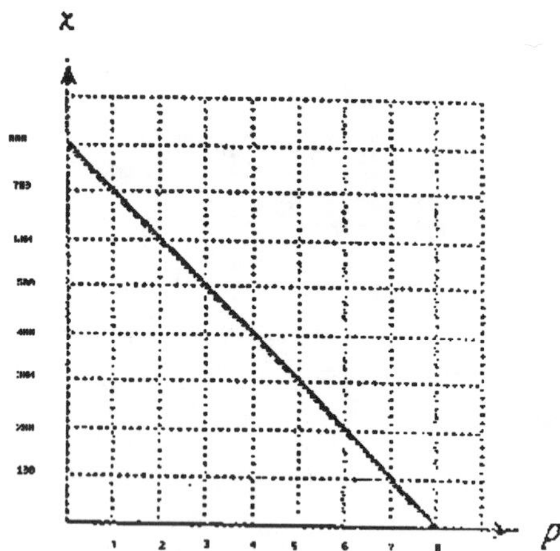


67.

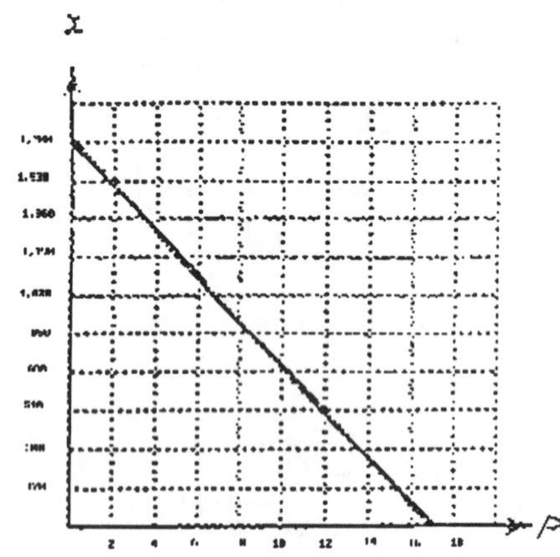


68.

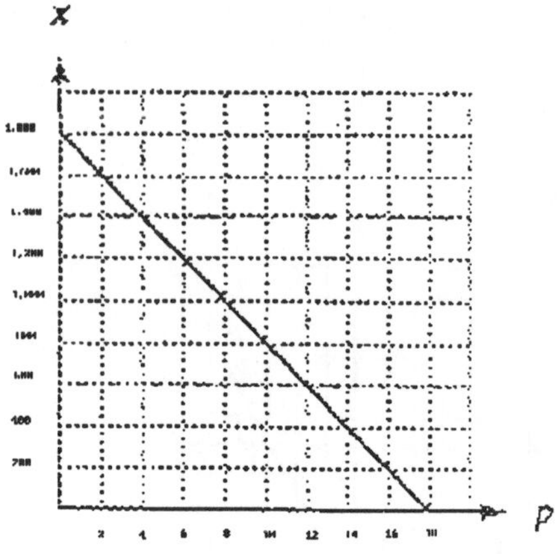

70. $\dfrac{6 - a - a^2}{3 - 2a - a^2} = \dfrac{(3 + a)(2 - a)}{(3 + a)(1 - a)}$

$= \dfrac{2 - a}{1 - a}$ *or*

$= \dfrac{a - 2}{a - 1}$

71. $\dfrac{15x^2y - 20x^4y^2}{5xy} = \dfrac{5x^2y(3 - 4x^2y)}{5xy}$

$= 3x - 4x^3y$

72. $\dfrac{12x^3y^2 - 24x^2y^3}{6xy} = \dfrac{6xy(2x^2y - 4xy^2)}{6xy}$

$= 2x^2y - 4xy^2$

74.
$$
\begin{array}{r}
3x + 7 \\
2x - 5\overline{)\;6x^2 - x - 35} \\
- \quad + \\
\underline{6x^2 - 15x} \\
14x - 35 \\
- \quad + \\
\underline{14x - 35} \\
0
\end{array}
$$

75.
$$
\begin{array}{r}
x^2 + 5x + 25 \\
x - 5\overline{)\;x^3 + 0x^2 + 0x - 125} \\
- \quad + \qquad\qquad \\
\underline{x^3 - 5x^2} \qquad\quad \\
5x^2 + 0x \qquad \\
- \quad + \qquad \\
\underline{5x^2 - 25x} \qquad \\
25x - 125 \\
- \quad + \\
\underline{25x - 125} \\
0
\end{array}
$$

76.
$$
\begin{array}{r}
x^2 - 4x + 16 \\
x + 4\overline{)\;x^3 + 0x^2 + 0x + 64} \\
- \quad - \qquad\qquad \\
\underline{x^3 + 4x^2} \qquad\quad \\
- 4x^2 + 0x \qquad \\
+ \quad + \qquad \\
\underline{- 4x^2 - 16x} \qquad \\
16x + 64 \\
- \quad - \\
\underline{16x + 64} \\
0
\end{array}
$$

## Section 5.2

2. $m = \dfrac{y_2 - y_1}{x_2 - x_1}$

$= \dfrac{-3 - 0}{0 - (-2)}$

$= -\dfrac{3}{2}$

3. $m = \dfrac{y_2 - y_1}{x_2 - x_1}$

$= \dfrac{0 - 1}{-4 - (-4)}$

$= -\dfrac{1}{0}$ *undefined* (*no slope*)

4. $m = \dfrac{y_2 - y_1}{x_2 - x_1}$

$= \dfrac{4 - 4}{0 - 1}$

$= -\dfrac{0}{1}$

$= 0$

6. $$m = \frac{y_2 - y_1}{x_2 - x_1} = \frac{3 - 1}{-2 - 1} = \frac{2}{-3} = -\frac{2}{3}$$

7.

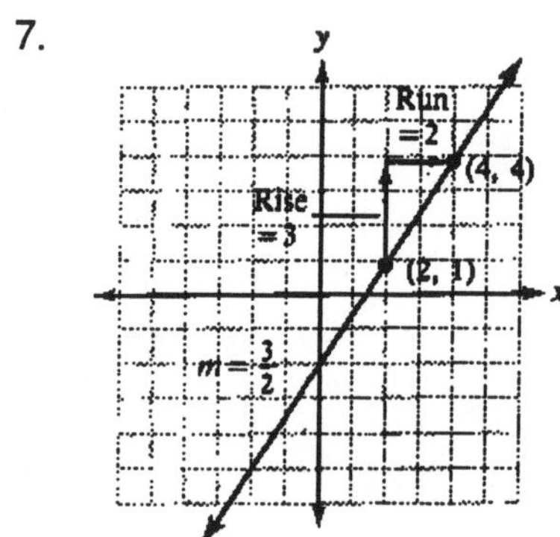


8.

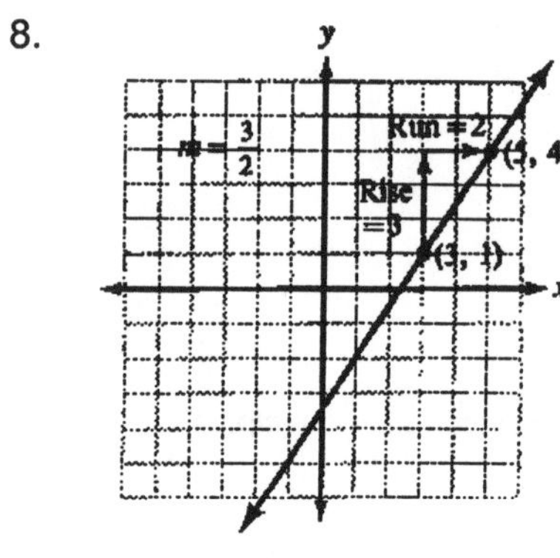


10.

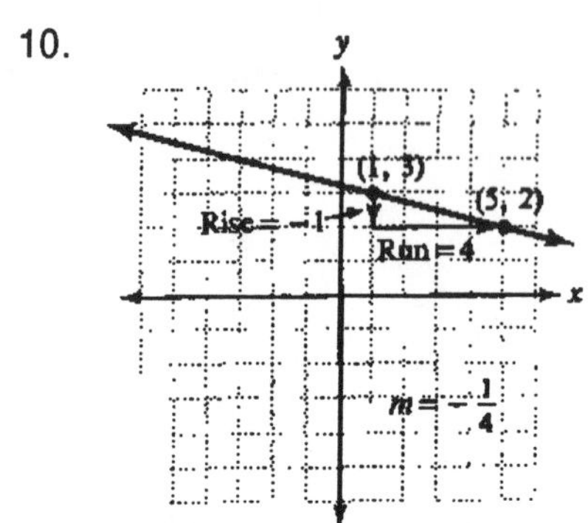


11.

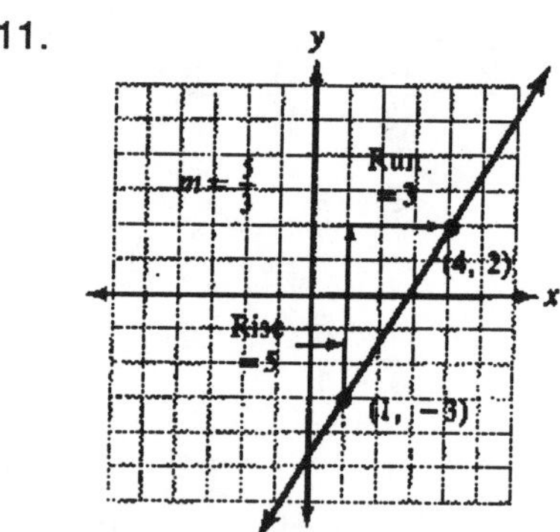


12.

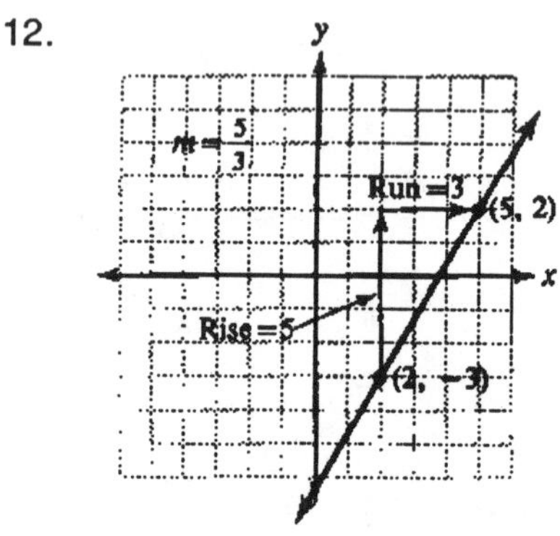


14.

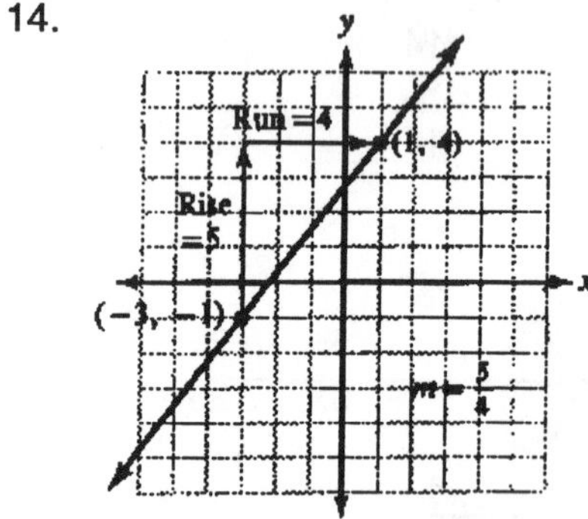


15.

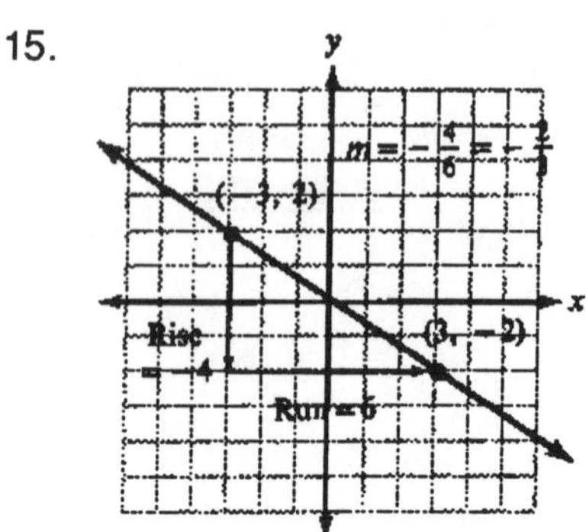

16.

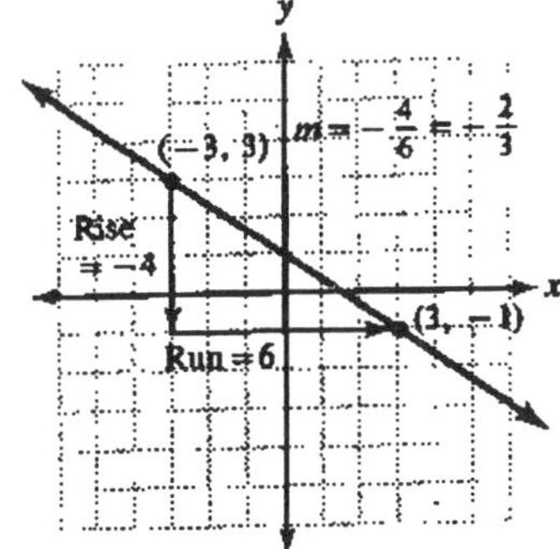


18.

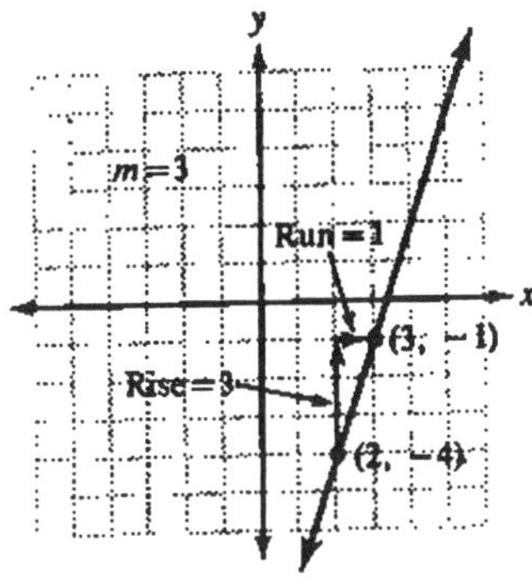


19. $m = \dfrac{y_2 - y_1}{x_2 - x_1}$

$3 = \dfrac{2 - a}{4 - 5}$

$3 = \dfrac{2 - a}{-1}$

$3 = -2 + a$
$5 = a$

20. $m = \dfrac{x_2 - y_1}{x_2 - x_1}$

$-4 = \dfrac{5 - a}{1 - 3}$

$-4 = \dfrac{5 - a}{-2}$

$8 = 5 - a$
$3 = -a$
$-3 = a$

22. $m = \dfrac{y_2 - y_1}{x_2 + x_1}$

$3 = \dfrac{y - 9}{-5 - (-4)}$

$3 = \dfrac{y - 9}{-1}$

$3 = -y + 9$
$-6 = -y$
$6 = y$

23. $m = \dfrac{y_2 - y_1}{x_2 - x_1}$

$3 = \dfrac{y - y^2}{5 - 7}$

$-6 = y - y^2$
$y^2 - y - 6 = 0$
$(y + 2)(y - 3) = 0$
$y + 2 = 0$
$y = -2$ *or*

$y - 3 = 0$
$y = 3$

24. $m = \dfrac{y_2 - y_1}{x_2 - x_1}$

$-5 = \dfrac{y - y^2}{8 - 4}$

$-5 = \dfrac{y - y^2}{4}$

$-20 = y - y^2$
$y^2 - y - 20 = 0$
$(y + 4)(y - 5) = 0$
$y + 4 = 0$
$y = -4$ *or*

$y - 5 = 0$
$y = 5$

26. $m = \dfrac{y_2 - y^1}{x_2 - x_1}$

$-1 = \dfrac{4b - b^2}{2 - 5}$

$3 = 4b - b^2$
$b^2 - 4b + 3 = 0$
$(b - 1)(b - 3) = 0$
$b - 1 = 0$
$b = 1$ *or*

$b - 3 = 0$
$b = 3$

27.

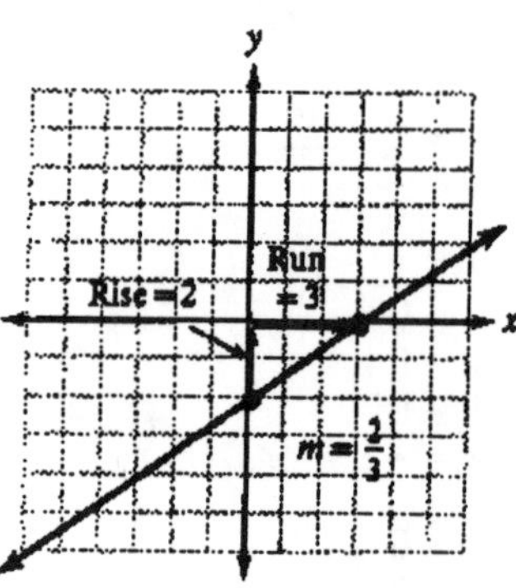


28.

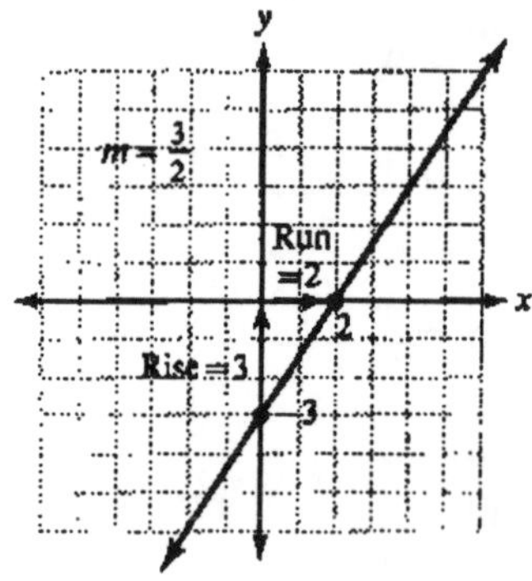


30.

y
x
$m = -\frac{2}{4} = -\frac{1}{2}$
Run = 4
-4
Rise = -2
-2

31. $\dfrac{1 - 3}{-8 - 2} = \dfrac{-2}{-10} = \dfrac{1}{5}$

*To be parallel the slope*

*must equal* $\dfrac{1}{5}$.

32. $\dfrac{-3 - 5}{5 - 2} = \dfrac{-8}{3}$

*To be parallel the slope*

*must equal* $-\dfrac{8}{3}$.

34. $\dfrac{1 - 4}{-3 - 3} = \dfrac{-3}{-6} = \dfrac{1}{2}$

*A line perpendicular to line* 1

*would be a slope of* $-\dfrac{2}{1} = -2$.

35. $\dfrac{2}{3} = \dfrac{c}{12}$

$c = 8$

36. $\dfrac{4}{5} = \dfrac{8}{c}$

$c = 10$

38. *Given* $(7, y^2)$, $(3, 6y)$ *and* $m = -2$,

*we have*

$$m = \frac{y_2 - y_1}{x_2 - x_1}$$

$$= \frac{6y - y^2}{3 - 7}$$

$$= \frac{6y - y^2}{-4}$$

*A parallel line with slope* $-2$

$$-2 = \frac{6y - y^2}{-4}$$

$$8 = 6y - y^2$$
$$y^2 - 6y + 8 = 0$$
$$(y - 2)(y - 4) = 0$$
$$y - 2 = 0$$
$$y = 2 \quad \textit{or}$$

$$y - 4 = 0$$
$$y - 4 = 0$$
$$y = 4$$

39. $8 \div 2 = 4$, *and* $4(3)$ *is* 12 (*radius*).

*The diameter is* 24 *feet*.

40. $\frac{1}{2}$ *of base* $= \frac{1}{2}(750) = 375$

$$\frac{13}{10} = \frac{h}{375}$$

$$10h = 4875$$
$$h = 487.5 \textit{ feet}$$

42. $3x + 2y = 6$
$$2y = -3x + 6$$

$$y = -\frac{3}{2}x + 3$$

43. $2x - 3y = 5$
$$-3y = -2x + 5$$

$$y = \frac{2}{3}x - \frac{5}{3}$$

44. $3x - 2y = 5$
$$-2y = -3x + 5$$

$$y = \frac{3}{2}x - \frac{5}{2}$$

46. $\dfrac{25x^2}{5y^4} \cdot \dfrac{30y^3}{2x^5}$

$$= \frac{750x^2y^3}{10x^5y^4}$$

$$= \frac{75}{x^3y}$$

47. $\dfrac{12x^2 - 4a - 5}{2a + 1} \cdot \dfrac{7a + 3}{42a^2 - 17a - 15}$

$$= \frac{(2a + 1)(6a - 5)}{2a + 1} \cdot \frac{7a + 3}{(7a + 3)(6a - 5)}$$

$= 1$

48. $\dfrac{20a^2 - 7a - 3}{4a + 1} \cdot \dfrac{25a^2 - 5a - 6}{5a + 2}$

$$= \frac{(5a - 3)(4a + 1)}{4a + 1} \cdot \frac{(5a + 2)(5a - 3)}{5a + 2}$$

$= (5a - 3)^2$

50. $\dfrac{27x^3 + 8}{8x^3 + 1} \div \dfrac{6x^2 + x - 2}{4x^2 - 1}$

$$= \frac{(3x + 2)(9x^2 - 6x + 4)}{(2x + 1)(4x^2 - 2x + 1)} \cdot \frac{(2x + 1)(2x - 1)}{(3x + 2)(2x - 1)}$$

$$= \frac{9x^2 - 6x + 4}{4x^2 - 2x + 1}$$

**Section 5.3**

2. $y = -4x + 2$

3. $y = 1x - 5$
   $y = x - 5$

4. $y = -5x - 3$

6. $y = \frac{2}{3}x + \frac{5}{6}$

7. $y = 0x + 4$
   $y = 4$

8. $y = 0x - 2$
   $y = -2$

10.

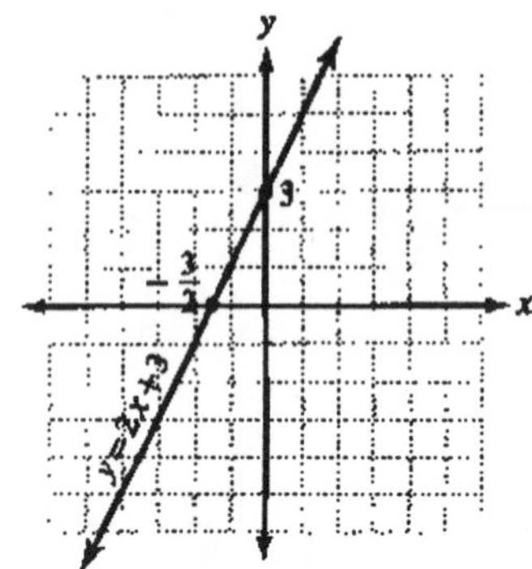


***Slope*** **= 2**

***y-intercept*** **= 3**

***Perpendicular slope*** **=** $-\frac{1}{2}$

11.

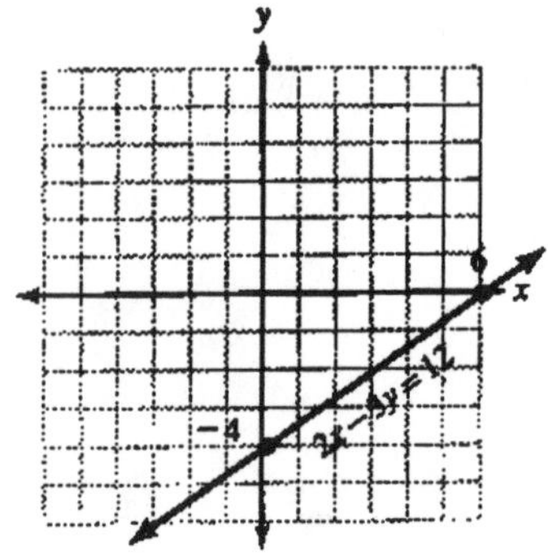


*Slope* = $\frac{2}{3}$

*y-slope* = -4

*Perpendicular slope* = $-\frac{3}{2}$

12.

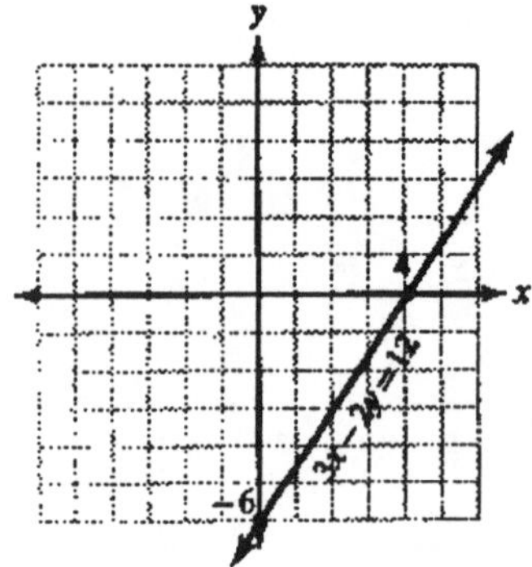


***Slope*** **=** $\frac{3}{2}$

***y-intercept*** **= -6**

***Perpendicular slope*** **=** $-\frac{2}{3}$

14.

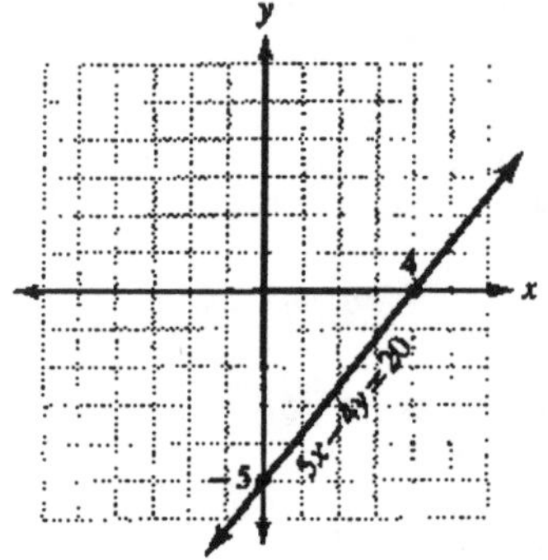


***Slope*** **=** $\frac{5}{4}$

***y-intercept*** **= -5**

***Perpendicular slope*** **=** $-\frac{4}{5}$

15. $-2x + y = 4$
$y = 2x + 4$

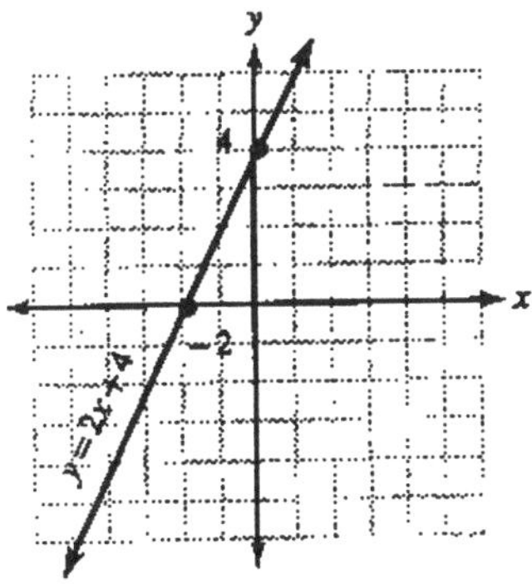


16. $-2x + y = 2$
$y = 2x + 2$

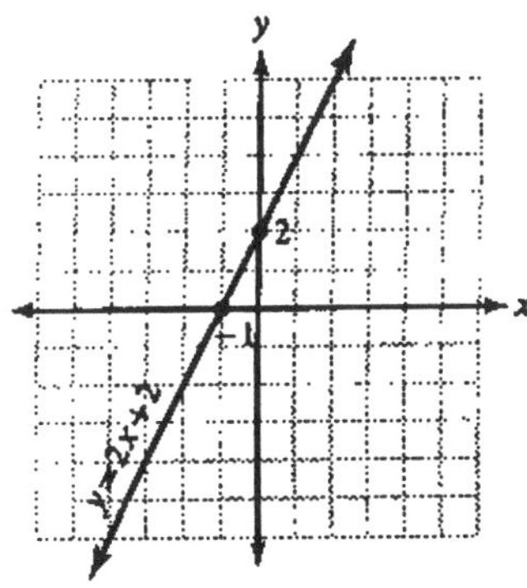


18. $3x + y = 6$
$y = -3x + 6$

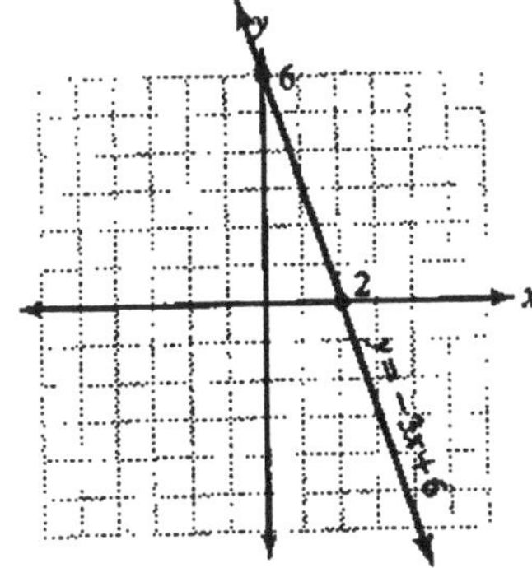


19. $-2x - 5y = 10$
$-5y = 2x + 10$

$$y = -\frac{2}{5}x - 2$$

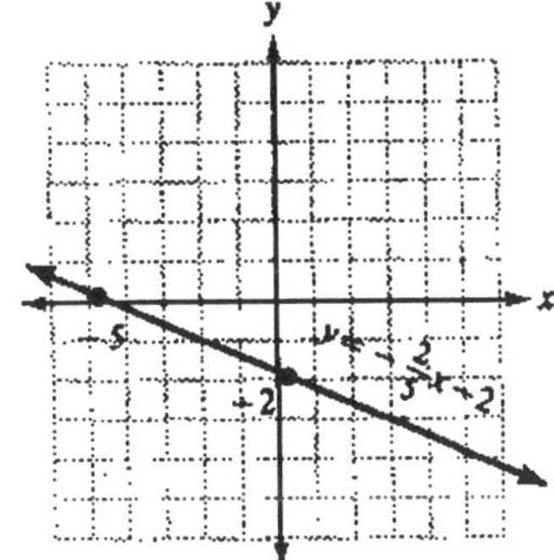


20. $-4x + 5y = 20$
$5y = 4x + 20$

$$y = \frac{4}{5}x + 4$$

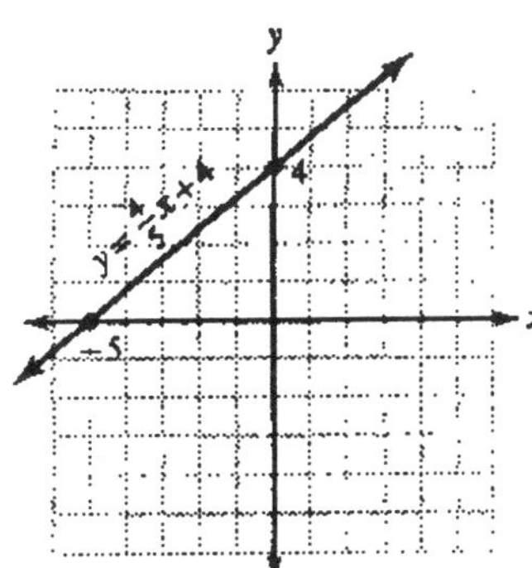


22.
$$\begin{aligned} y - y_1 &= m(x - x_1) \\ y - (-5) &= 2[x - (-1)] \\ y + 5 &= 2x + 2 \\ y &= 2x - 3 \end{aligned}$$

23.
$$y - y_1 = m(x - x_1)$$

$$y - 1 = -\frac{1}{2}[x - (-4)]$$

$$y - 1 = -\frac{1}{2}x - 2$$

$$y = -\frac{1}{2}x - 1$$

24. $y - y_1 = m(x - x_1)$

$y - 1 = -\frac{1}{2}[x - (-2)]$

$y - 1 = -\frac{1}{2}x - 1$

$y = -\frac{1}{2}x$

26. $y - y_1 = m(x - x_1)$

$y - (-4) = \frac{4}{3}(x - 3)$

$y + 4 = \frac{4}{3}x - 4$

$y = \frac{4}{3}x - 8$

27. $y - y_1 = m(x - x_1)$

$y - 2 = -3\left[x - \left(-\frac{1}{3}\right)\right]$

$y - 2 = -3x - 1$
$y = -3x + 1$

28. $y - y_1 = m(x - x_1)$

$y - 5 = -3\left[x - \left(-\frac{2}{3}\right)\right]$

$y - 5 = -3x - 2$
$y = -3x + 3$

30. $y - y_1 = m(x - x_1)$

$y - \frac{1}{7} = -1\left(x - \frac{3}{4}\right)$

$y - \frac{1}{7} = -x + \frac{3}{4}$

$y = -x + \frac{25}{28}$

31. $y = \frac{-1 - (-4)}{1 - (-2)} = \frac{3}{3} = 1$

$y - y_1 = m(x - x_1)$
$y - (-4) = 1[x - (-2)]$
$y + 4 = x + 2$
$x - y = 2$

32. $y = \frac{-1 - 4}{-3 - 2} = \frac{-5}{-5} = 1$

$y - y_1 = m(x - x_1)$
$y - 4 = 1(x - 2)$
$y - 4 = x - 2$
$x - y = -2$

34. $y = \frac{2 - 6}{1 - (-1)} = \frac{-4}{2} = -2$

$y - y_1 = m(x - x_1)$
$y - 2 = -2(x - 1)$
$y - 2 = -2x + 2$
$2x + y = 4$

35. $y = \frac{6 - (-2)}{3 - (-3)} = \frac{8}{6} = \frac{4}{3}$

$y - y_1 = m(x - x_1)$

$y - 6 = \frac{4}{3}(x - 3)$

$3y - 18 = 4x - 12$
$4x - 3y = -6$

36. $y = \frac{-2 - 6}{3 - (-3)} = \frac{-8}{6} = -\frac{4}{3}$

$y - y_1 = m(x - x_1)$

$y - 6 = -\frac{4}{3}[x - (-3)]$

$y - 6 = -\frac{4}{3}x - 4$

$3y - 18 = -4x - 12$
$4x + 3y = 6$

38. $$y = \frac{\frac{1}{10} - \left(-\frac{1}{2}\right)}{\frac{1}{2} - \left(-\frac{1}{2}\right)} = \frac{\frac{3}{5}}{1} = \frac{3}{5}$$

$$y - y_1 = m(x - x_1)$$

$$y - \left(-\frac{1}{2}\right) = \frac{3}{5}\left[x - \left(-\frac{1}{2}\right)\right]$$

$$y + \frac{1}{2} = \frac{3}{5}x + \frac{3}{10}$$

$$10y + 5 = 6x + 3$$
$$6x - 10y = 2$$
$$3x - 5y = 1$$

39. $$m = \frac{-\frac{1}{4} - \frac{1}{8}}{\frac{1}{3} - \left(-\frac{2}{3}\right)} = -\frac{\frac{3}{8}}{1} = -\frac{3}{8}$$

$$y - y_1 = m(x - x_1)$$

$$y - \frac{1}{8} = -\frac{3}{8}\left[x - \left(-\frac{2}{3}\right)\right]$$

$$y - \frac{1}{8} = -\frac{3}{8}x - \frac{1}{4}$$

$$8y - 1 = -3x - 2$$
$$3x + 8y = -1$$

40. $$m = \frac{\frac{1}{6} - \left(-\frac{1}{3}\right)}{\frac{1}{2} - \frac{1}{4}} = \frac{\frac{1}{2}}{\frac{1}{4}} = 2$$

$$y - y_1 = m(x - x_1)$$

$$y - \frac{1}{6} = 2\left(x - \frac{1}{2}\right)$$

$$y - \frac{1}{6} = 2x - 1$$
$$6y - 1 = 12x - 6$$
$$12x - 6y = 5$$

42.

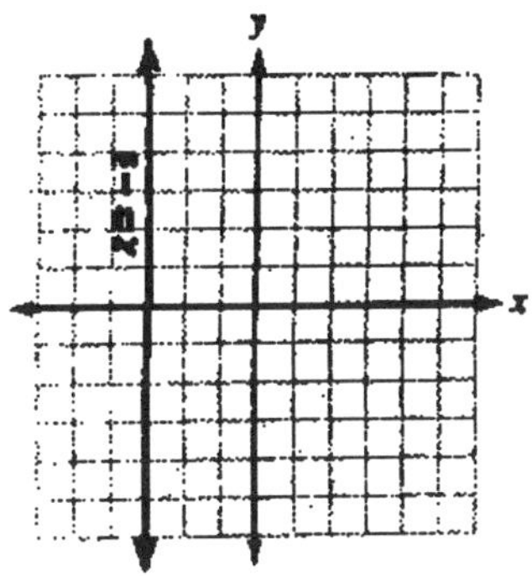


***No slope***

***x-intercept*** = $-3$

***No y-intercept***

43. $$3x - y = 5$$
$$-y = -3x + 5$$
$$y = 3x - 5$$
$$m = 3 \quad (-1, 4)$$
$$y - y_1 = m(x - x_1)$$
$$y - 4 = 3[x - (-1)]$$
$$y - 4 = 3x + 3$$
$$y = 3x + 7$$

44. $$2x - 4y = 5$$
$$-4y = -2x + 4$$

$$y = \frac{1}{2}x - \frac{5}{4}$$

$$m = \frac{1}{2} \quad (0, 3)$$

$$y - y_1 = m(x - x_1)$$

$$y - 3 = \frac{1}{2}(x - 0)$$

$$y = \frac{1}{2}x + 3$$

46.
$$-3x - 5y = 2$$
$$-5y = 3x + 2$$
$$y = -\frac{3}{5}x - \frac{2}{5}$$
$$m = \frac{5}{3} \quad (2, -6)$$
$$y - y_1 = m(x - x_1)$$
$$y - (-6) = \frac{5}{3}(x - 2)$$
$$y + 6 = \frac{5}{3}x - \frac{10}{3}$$
$$y = \frac{5}{3}x - \frac{28}{3}$$

47.
$$y = -4x + 2$$
$$m = \frac{1}{4}(-1, 0)$$
$$y - y_1 = m(x - x_1)$$
$$y - 0 = \frac{1}{4}[x - (-1)]$$
$$y = \frac{1}{4}x + \frac{1}{4}$$

48.
$$7x - 2y = 14$$
$$-2y = -7x + 14$$
$$y = \frac{7}{2}x - 7$$
$$m = \frac{7}{2} \quad (5, 0)$$
$$y - y_1 = m(x - x_1)$$
$$y - 0 = \frac{7}{2}(x - 5)$$
$$y = \frac{7}{2}x - \frac{35}{2}$$

50.
$$(2, 0)(0, 3)$$
$$y = \frac{3 - 0}{0 - 2} = -\frac{3}{2}$$
$$y - y_1 = m(x - x_1)$$
$$y - 0 = -\frac{3}{2}(x - 2)$$
$$y = -\frac{3}{2}x + 3$$
$$y - y_1 = m(x - x_1)$$
$$y - 3 = -\frac{3}{2}(x - 0)$$
$$y = -\frac{3}{2}x + 3$$

51.
$$\left(\frac{1}{2}, 0\right)\left(0, -\frac{1}{4}\right)$$
$$m = \frac{-\frac{1}{4} - 0}{0 - \frac{1}{2}} = \frac{1}{2}$$
$$y - y_1 = m(x - x_1)$$
$$y - 0 = \frac{1}{2}\left(x - \frac{1}{2}\right)$$
$$y = \frac{1}{2}x - \frac{1}{4}$$
$$y - y_1 = m(x - x_1)$$
$$y - \left(-\frac{1}{4}\right) = \frac{1}{2}(x - 0)$$
$$y = \frac{1}{2}x - \frac{1}{4}$$

52. $\left(-\frac{1}{3},0\right)\left(0,\frac{1}{6}\right)$

$$m = \frac{\frac{1}{6} - 0}{0 - \left(-\frac{1}{3}\right)} = \frac{1}{2}$$

$$y - y_1 = m(x - x_1)$$

$$y - 0 = \frac{1}{2}\left[x - \left(-\frac{1}{3}\right)\right]$$

$$y = \frac{1}{2}x + \frac{1}{6}$$

$$y - y_1 = m(x - x_1)$$

$$y - \frac{1}{6} = \frac{1}{2}(x - 0)$$

$$y = \frac{1}{2}x + \frac{1}{6}$$

54. $\frac{2a - 3}{a - 2} - \frac{a - 1}{a - 2}$

$$= \frac{2a - 3 - a + 1}{a - 2}$$

$$= \frac{a - 2}{a - 2}$$

$$= 1$$

55. $3 + \frac{4}{3 - t}$

$$= \frac{9 - 3t + 4}{3 - t}$$

$$= \frac{13 - 3t}{3 - t}$$

56. $6 + \frac{2}{5 - t}$

$$= \frac{30 - 6t}{5 - t} + \frac{2}{5 - t}$$

$$= \frac{32 - 6t}{5 - t}$$

58. $\frac{2}{4x - 5} + \frac{9}{8x^2 - 38x + 35}$

$$= \frac{2}{4x - 5} + \frac{9}{(4x - 5)(2x - 7)}$$

$$= \frac{4x - 14 + 9}{(4x - 5)(2x - 7)}$$

$$= \frac{4x - 5}{(4x - 5)(2x - 7)}$$

$$= \frac{1}{2x - 7}$$

59. $\frac{1}{x - y} - \frac{3xy}{x^3 - y^3}$

$$= \frac{1}{x - y} - \frac{3xy}{(x - y)(x^2 + xy + y^2)}$$

$$= \frac{x^2 + xy + y^2 - 3xy}{(x - y)(x^2 + xy + y^2)}$$

$$= \frac{x^2 - 2xy + y^2}{(x - y)(x^2 + xy + y^2)}$$

$$= \frac{(x - y)(x - y)}{(x - y)(x^2 + xy + y^2)}$$

$$= \frac{x - y}{x^2 + xy + y^2}$$

60. $\frac{1}{x + y} + \frac{3xy}{x^3 + y^3}$

$$= \frac{1}{x + y} + \frac{3xy}{(x + y)(x^2 - xy + y^2)}$$

$$= \frac{x^2 - xy + y^2 + 3xy}{(x + y)(x^2 - xy + y^2)}$$

$$= \frac{x^2 + 2xy + y^2}{(x + y)(x^2 - xy + y^2)}$$

$$= \frac{(x + y)(x + y)}{(x + y)(x^2 - xy + y^2)}$$

$$= \frac{x + y}{x^2 - xy + y^2}$$

62.

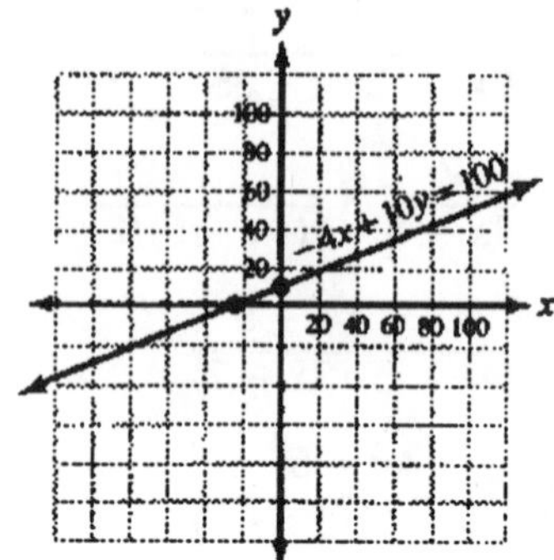


63.

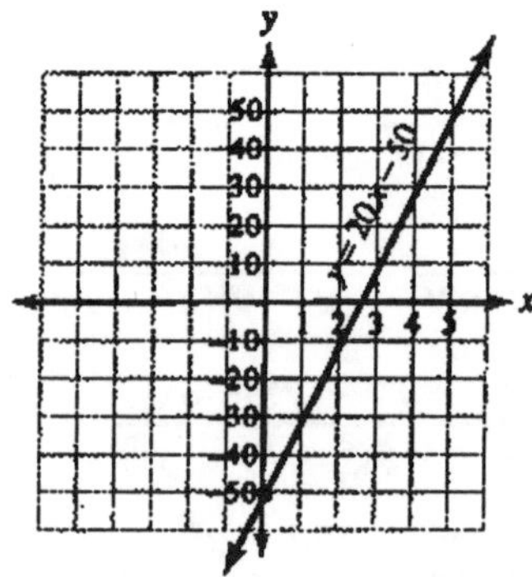


64.

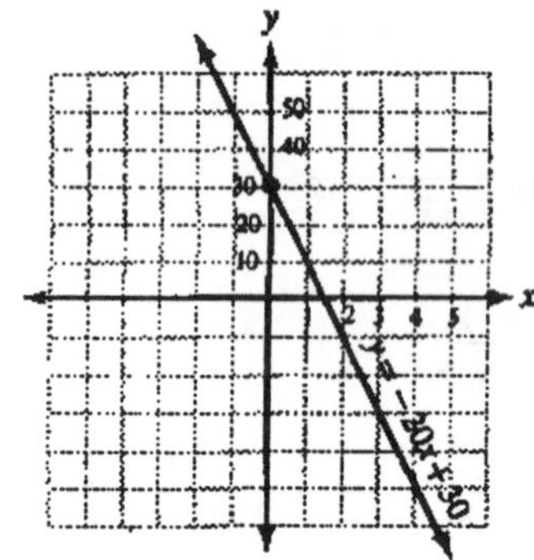


66. $\frac{x}{5} + \frac{y}{4} = 1$

$4x + 5y = 20$
$5y = -4x + 20$

$y = -\frac{4}{5}x + 4$

$Slope = -\frac{4}{5}$

$y\text{-}intercept = 4$
$x\text{-}intercept = 5$

67. $\frac{x}{-2} + \frac{y}{3} = 1$

$-3x + 2y = 6$
$2y = 3x + 6$

$y = \frac{3}{2}x + 3$

$Slope = \frac{3}{2}$

$y\text{-}intercept = 3$

$x\text{-}intercept = -2$

68. $\frac{x}{2} + \frac{y}{-3} = 1$

$-3x + 2y = -6$
$2y = 3x - 6$

$y = \frac{3}{2}x - 3$

$Slope = \frac{3}{2}$

$y\text{-}intercept = -3$
$x\text{-}intercept = 2$

## Section 5.4

2. $x + y \leq -5$
$y \leq -x - 5$

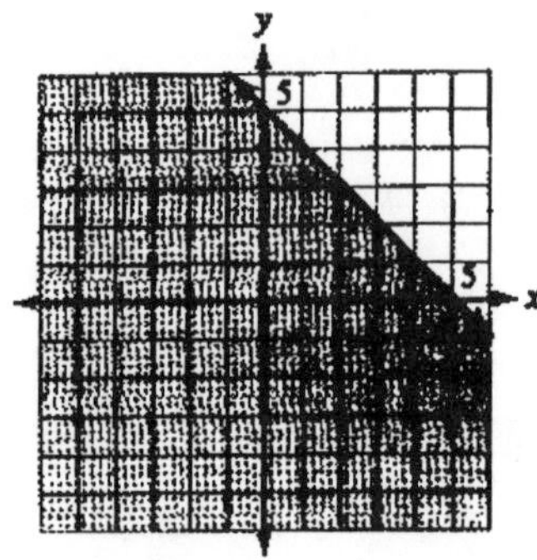

3. $x - y \geq -3$
$y \leq x + 3$

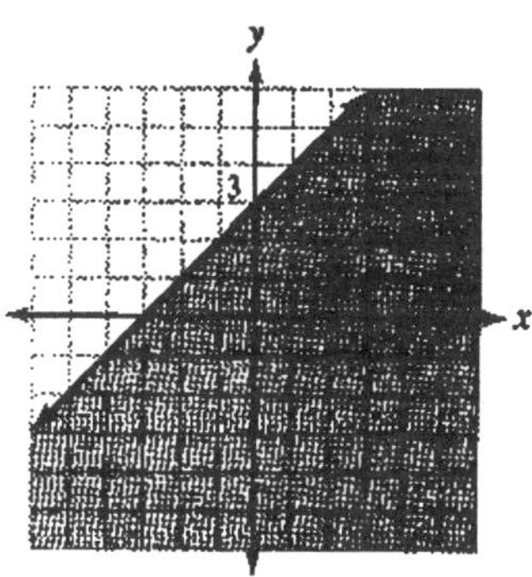


4. $x - y > -3$
$y < x + 3$

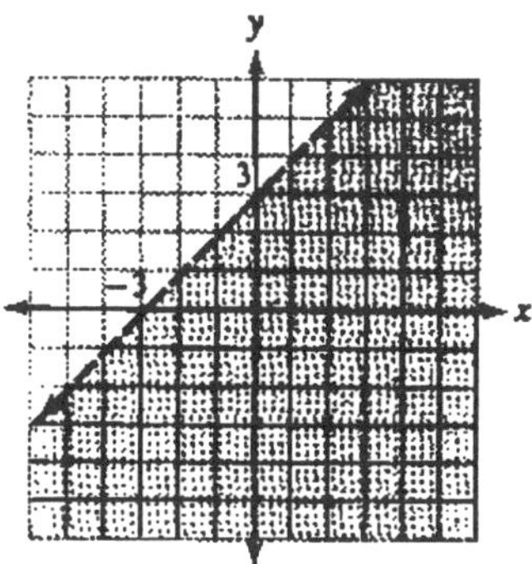


6. $2x - 3y > -6$

$y < \frac{2}{3}x + 2$

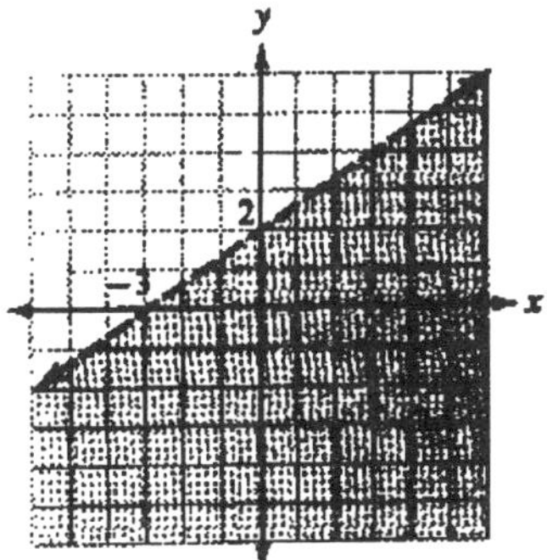


7. $-x + 2y > -4$

$y > \frac{1}{2}x - 2$

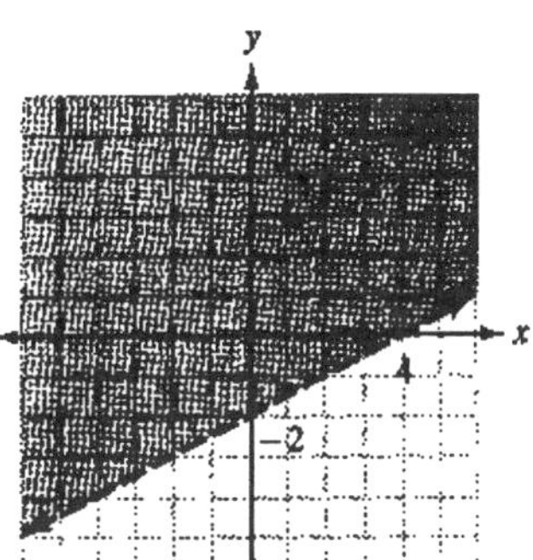


8. $-x - 2y < 4$

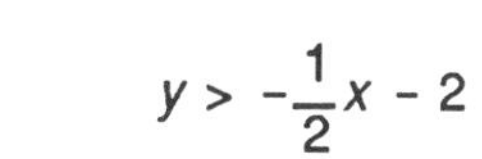
$y > -\frac{1}{2}x - 2$

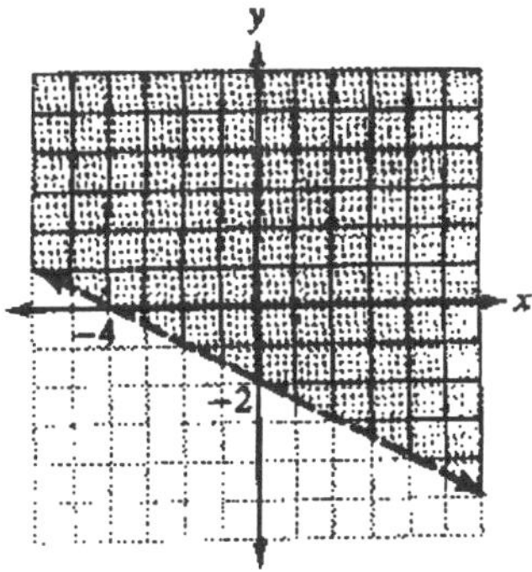


10. $2x + y < -5$
$y < -2x - 5$

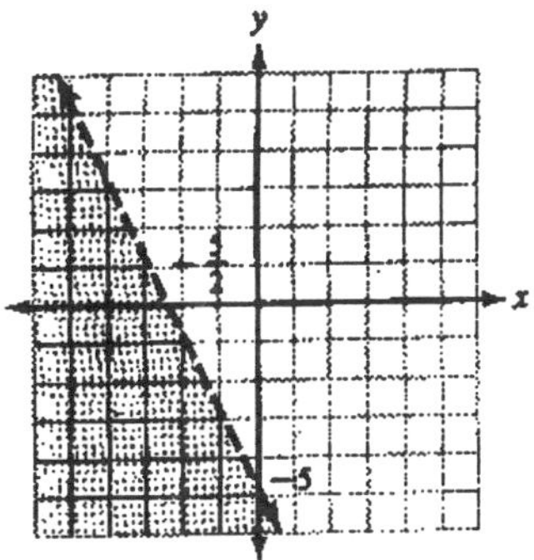

11. $3x + 5y > 7$

$$y > -\frac{3}{5}x + \frac{7}{5}$$

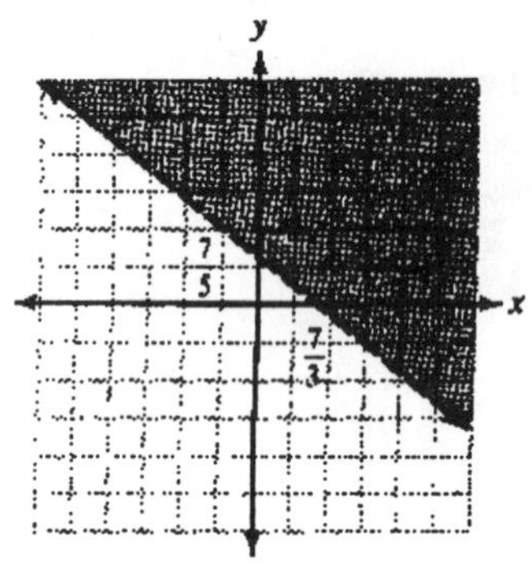


12. $3x - 5y > 7$

$$y < \frac{3}{5}x - \frac{7}{5}$$

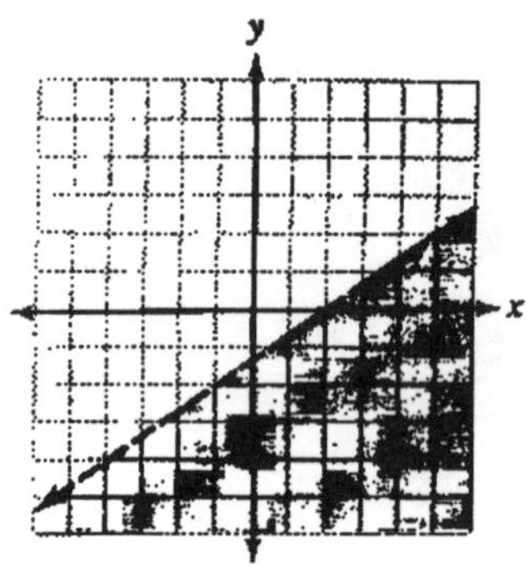


14. $y \geq 2x - 1$

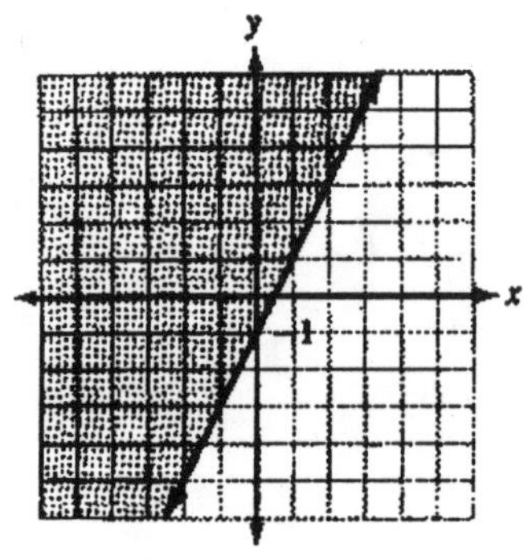


15. $y \geq -3x - 4$

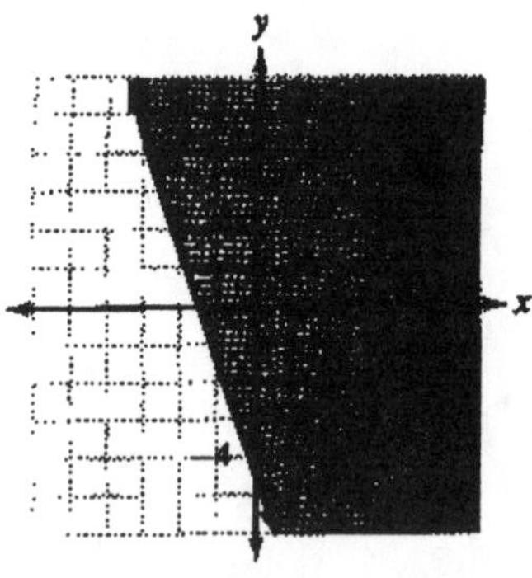


16. $y < -3x + 4$

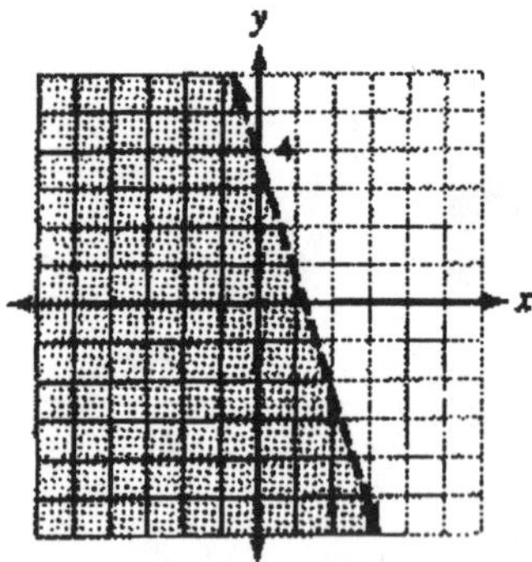


18. $x < -2$

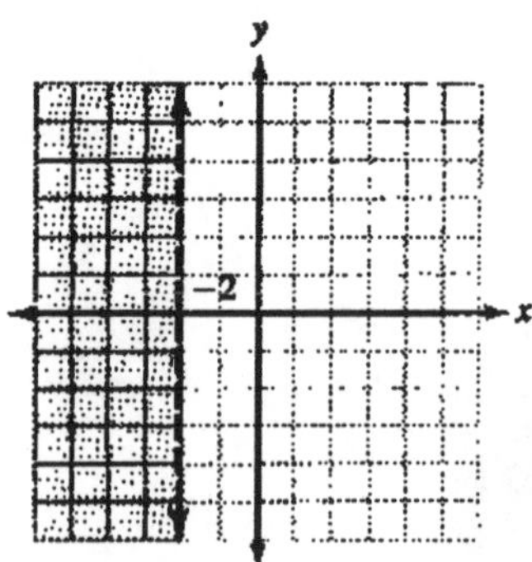

19. $y \le 4$

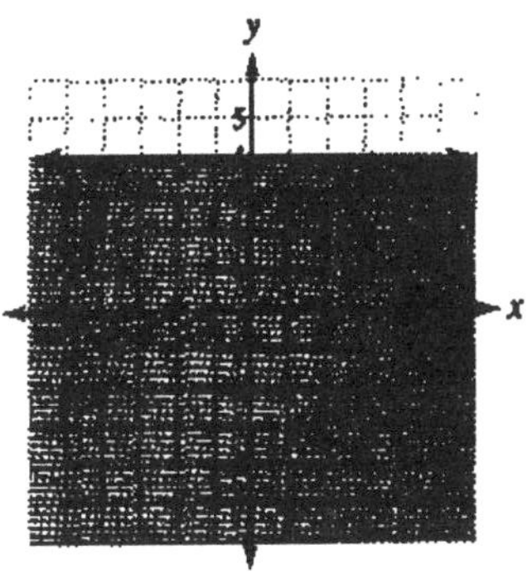


20. $y > -5$

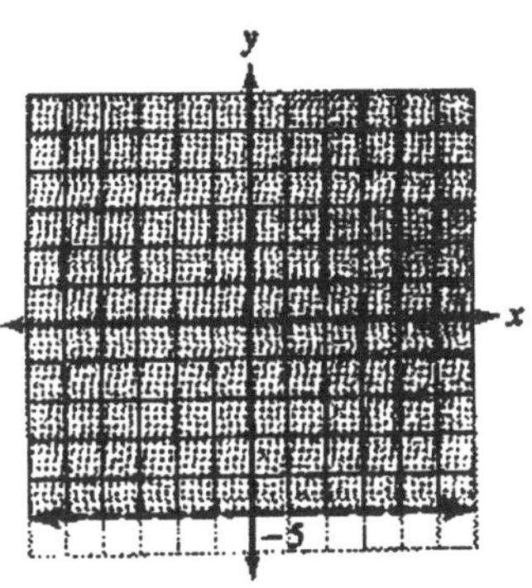


22. $y > -3x$

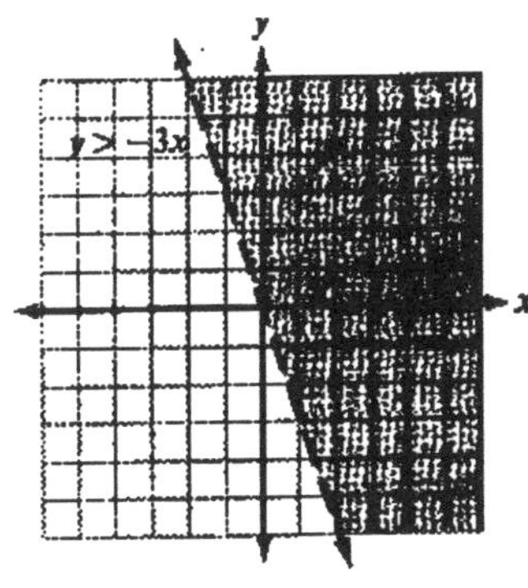


23. $y \ge \frac{1}{2}x$

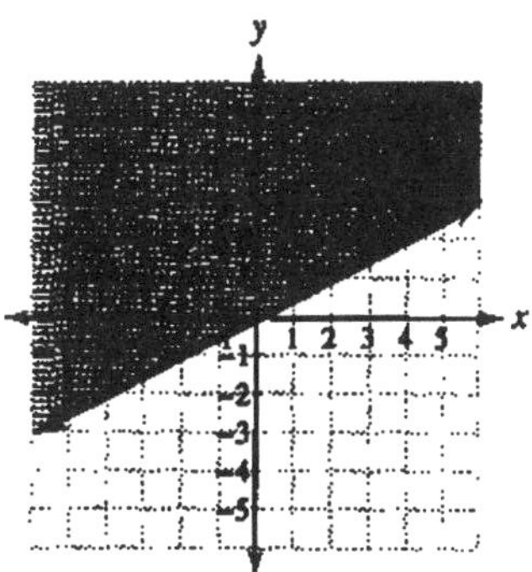


24. $y \le \frac{1}{3}x$

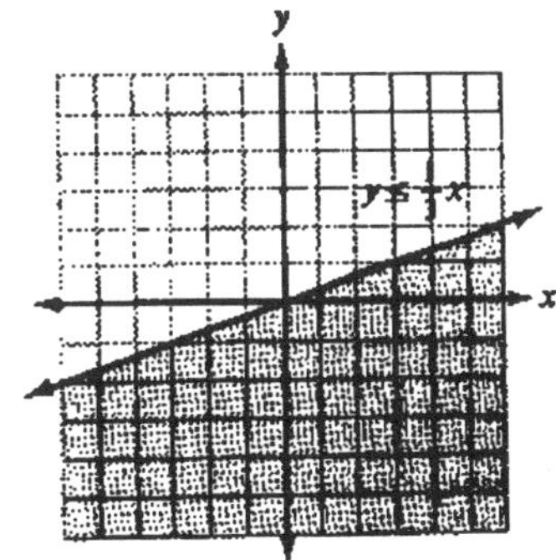


26. $y > -\frac{2}{3}x + 3$

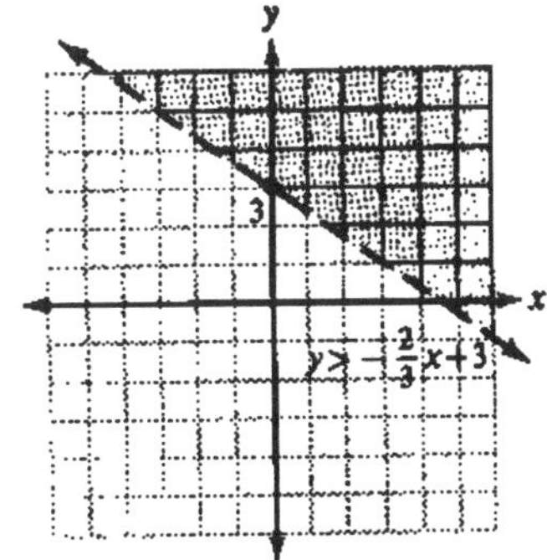

27. $0.03x + 0.02y - 0.06 < 0$

$$3x + 2y - 6 < 0$$

$$y < -\frac{3}{2}x + 3$$

28. $0.05x - 0.03y - 0.15 > 0$

$$5x - 3y - 15 > 0$$

$$y < \frac{5}{3}x - 5$$

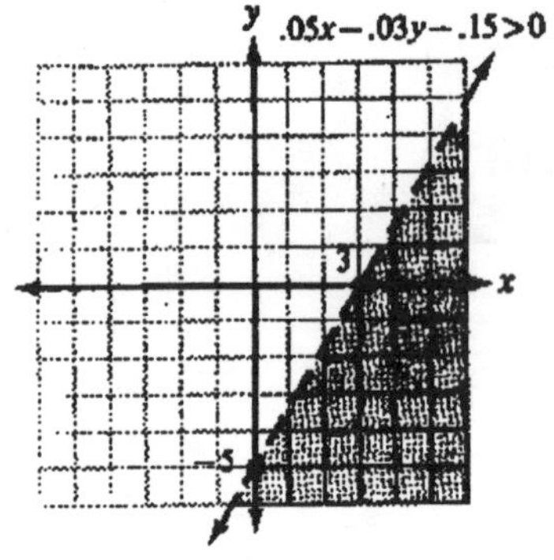


30. $\frac{x}{5} + \frac{y}{4} < 1$

$$4x + 5y < 20$$

$$y < -\frac{4}{5}x + 4$$

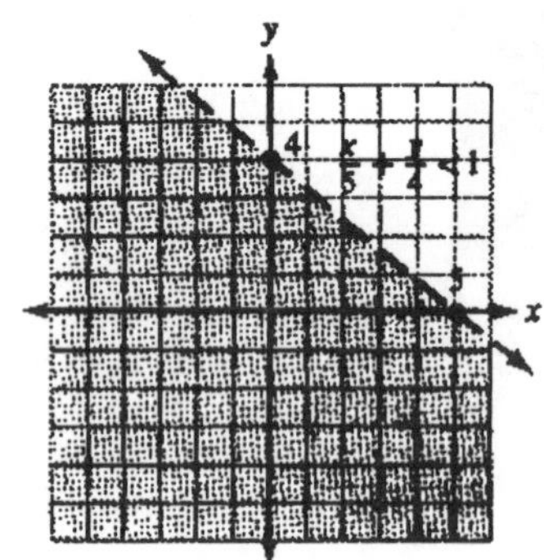


31. $\frac{x}{-3} + \frac{y}{5} \le 1$

$$-5x + 3y \le 15$$

$$y \le \frac{5}{3}x + 5$$

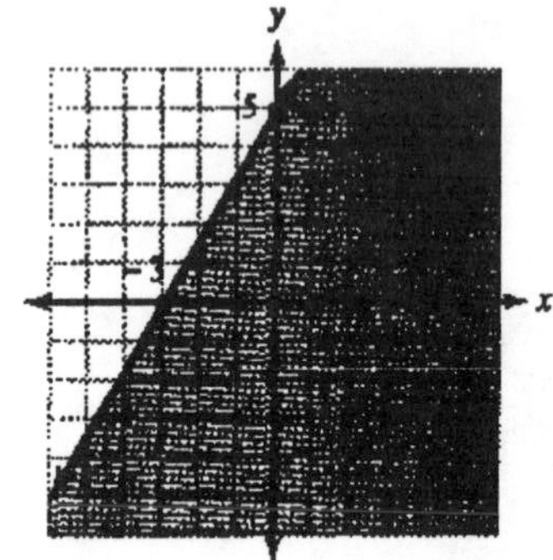

32. $\frac{x}{2} + \frac{y}{-4} \geq 1$

$-2x + y \leq -4$

$y \leq 2x - 4$

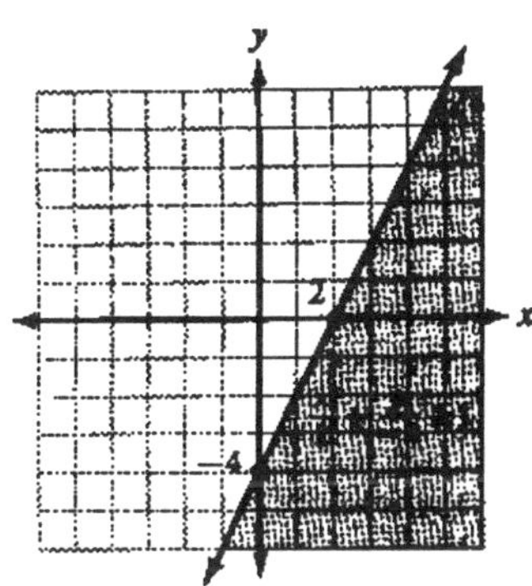


34. $\dfrac{\frac{1}{8} - \frac{1}{3}}{\frac{1}{4} - \frac{1}{3}}$

$= \dfrac{24\left(\frac{1}{8}\right) - 24\left(\frac{1}{3}\right)}{24\left(\frac{1}{4}\right) - 24\left(\frac{1}{3}\right)}$

$= \dfrac{3 - 8}{6 - 8}$

$= \dfrac{5}{2}$

35. $\dfrac{1 - \frac{2}{y}}{1 + \frac{2}{y}}$

$= \dfrac{y(1) - y\left(\frac{2}{y}\right)}{y(1) + y\left(\frac{2}{y}\right)}$

$= \dfrac{y - 2}{y + 2}$

36. $\dfrac{1 + \frac{3}{y}}{1 - \frac{3}{y}}$

$= \dfrac{y(1) + y\left(\frac{3}{y}\right)}{y(1) - y\left(\frac{3}{y}\right)}$

$= \dfrac{y + 3}{y - 3}$

38. $\dfrac{1 - \frac{1}{x} - \frac{6}{x^2}}{1 - \frac{9}{x^2}}$

$= \dfrac{x^2(1) - x^2\left(\frac{1}{x}\right) - x^2\left(\frac{6}{x^2}\right)}{x^2(1) - x^2\left(\frac{9}{x^2}\right)}$

$= \dfrac{x^2 - x - 6}{x^2 - 9}$

$= \dfrac{(x + 2)(x - 3)}{(x + 3)(x - 3)}$

$= \dfrac{x + 2}{x + 3}$

39.

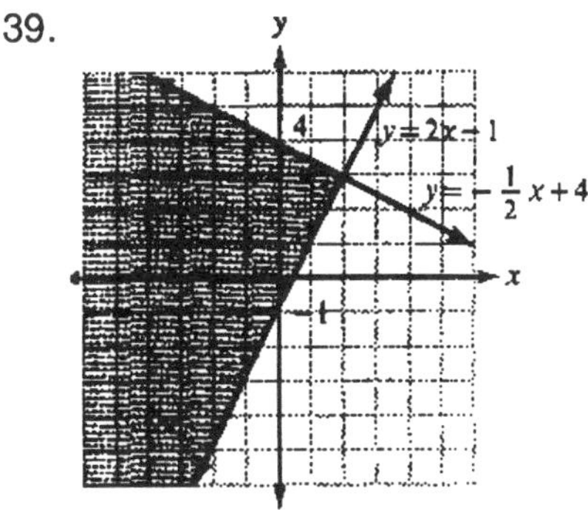

40.

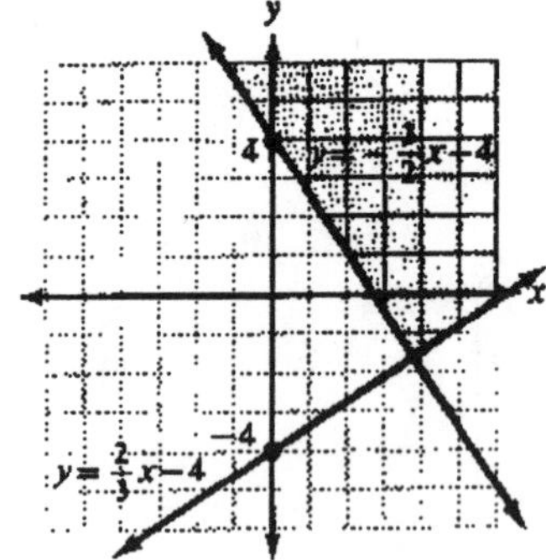


42.

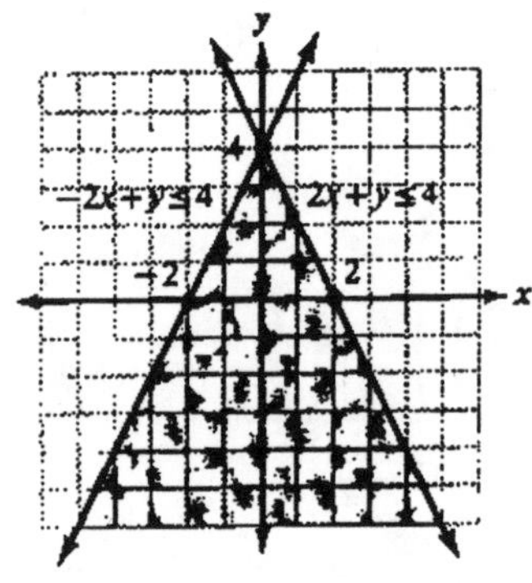


## Section 5.5

2. $y = 20,\ x = 5$
$y = Kx$
$20 = K(5)$
$4 = K$
$y = 4x$ *Letting* $x = 3$
$y = 4(3)$
$y = 12$

3. $y = -32,\ x = 4$
$y = Kx$
$-32 = K(4)$
$-8 = K$
$y = -8x$ *Letting* $y = -40$
$-40 = -8x$
$5 = x$

4. $y = -50,\ x = 5$
$y = Kx$
$-50 = K(5)$
$-10 = K$
$y = -10x$ *Letting* $y = -70$
$-70 = -10x$
$7 = x$

6. $r = -10,\ s = 6$

$$r = \frac{K}{s}$$

$$-10 = \frac{K}{6}$$

$$-60 = K$$

$$r = \frac{-60}{s} \quad \textit{Letting } s = -5$$

$$r = \frac{-60}{-5}$$

$$r = 12$$

7. $r = 8,\ s = 3$

$$r = \frac{K}{s}$$

$$8 = \frac{K}{3}$$

$$24 = K$$

$$r = \frac{24}{s} \quad \textit{Letting } r = 48$$

$$48 = \frac{24}{s}$$

$$s = \frac{1}{2}$$

8. $r = 12,\ s = 5$

$$r = \frac{K}{s}$$

$$12 = \frac{K}{5}$$

$$60 = K$$

$$r = \frac{60}{s} \quad \textit{Letting } r = 30$$

$$30 = \frac{60}{s}$$

$$s = 2$$

10. $d = 12, \ r = 6$
$d = Kr^2$
$12 = K(36)$
$\frac{1}{3} = K$
$d = \frac{1}{3}r^2$ *Letting* $r = 9$
$d = \frac{1}{3}(81)$
$d = 27$

11. $d = 100, \ r = 2$
$d = Kr^2$
$100 = K(4)$
$25 = K$
$d = 25r^2$ *Letting* $r = 3$
$d = 25(9)$
$d = 225$

12. $d = 50, \ r = 5$
$d = Kr^2$
$50 = K(25)$
$2 = K$
$d = 2r^2$ *Letting* $r = 7$
$d = 2(49)$
$d = 98$

14. $y = 12, \ x = 2$
$y = \frac{k}{x^2}$
$12 = \frac{K}{4}$
$48 = K$
$y = \frac{48}{x^2}$ *Letting* $x = 6$
$y = \frac{48}{36}$
$y = \frac{4}{3}$

15. $y = 18, \ x = 3$
$y = \frac{K}{x^2}$
$18 = \frac{K}{9}$
$162 = K$
$y = \frac{162}{x^2}$ *Letting* $y = 2$
$2 = \frac{162}{x^2}$
$x^2 = 81$
$x = \pm 9$

16. $y = 45, \ x = 4$
$y = \frac{K}{x^2}$
$45 = \frac{K}{16}$
$720 = K$
$y = \frac{720}{x^2}$ *Letting* $y = 5$
$5 = \frac{720}{x^2}$
$x^2 = 144$
$x = \pm 12$

18. $z = Kxy^2, \ z = 80, \ x = 5, \ y = 2$
$80 = K(5)(4)$
$4 = K$
$z = 4xy^2, \ x = 2, \ y = 5$
$z = 4(2)(25)$
$z = 200$

19. $z = Kxy^2, \ z = 64, \ x = 1, \ y = 4$
$64 = K(1)(16)$
$4 = K$
$z = 4xy^2, \ z = 32, \ y = 1$
$32 = 4(x)(1)$
$8 = x$

20. $z = Kxy^2$, $z = 27$, $x = 6$, $y = 3$

$27 = K(6)(9)$

$\frac{1}{2} = K$

$z = \frac{1}{2}xy^2$, $z = 50$, $y = 4$

$50 = \frac{1}{2}x(16)$

$\frac{25}{4} = x$

22. Let *w = weight, a = surface area*

$w = Ka$, $w = \frac{1}{2}$, $a = 8$

$\frac{1}{2} = K(8)$

$\frac{1}{16} = K$

$w = \frac{1}{16}a$, $a = 10$

$w = \frac{5}{8}$ *lb.*

23. Let *v = volume, p = pressure*

$v = \frac{K}{p}$, $v = 25$, $p = 36$

$25 = \frac{K}{36}$

$900 = K$

$v = \frac{900}{p}$, $v = 75$

$75 = \frac{900}{p}$

$p = 12$ *lb/sq. in.*

24. Let *F = frequency, L = length*

$F = \frac{K}{L}$, $F = 800$, $L = 200$

$800 = \frac{K}{200}$

$160{,}000 = K$

$K = \frac{160{,}000}{L}$, $L = 500$

$K = \frac{160{,}000}{500}$

$K = 320$ *kilocycles*/sec.

26. Let *c = capacity, h = height, r = radius*

$c = Khr^2$, $r = 169.56$, $h = 6$, $c = 3$

$169.56 = K(6)(9)$

$3.14 = K$

$c = 3.14hr^2$, $r = 4$, $h = 9$

$c = 3.14(9)(16)$

$c = 452.16$ $cm^3$

27. *R = resistance, l = length, d = diameter*

$R = \frac{Kl}{d^2}$, $l = 100$, $d = 0.01$, $R = 10$

$10 = \frac{K(100)}{0.0001}$

$K = 0.00001$

$K = \frac{0.00001l}{d^2}$, $l = 60$, $d = 0.02$

$R = \frac{0.00001(60)}{0.004} = 1.5$ *ohms*

28. *Let v = volume, t = temperature, p = pressure*

$$v = \frac{Kt}{p},\ v = 30,\ t = 300,\ p = 20$$

$$30 = \frac{K(300)}{20}$$

$$2 = K$$

$$v = \frac{2t}{p},\ t = 340,\ p = 30$$

$$v = \frac{2(340)}{30}$$

$$v = \frac{68}{3} \text{ cubic ft.}$$

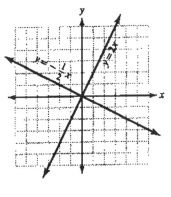

30.

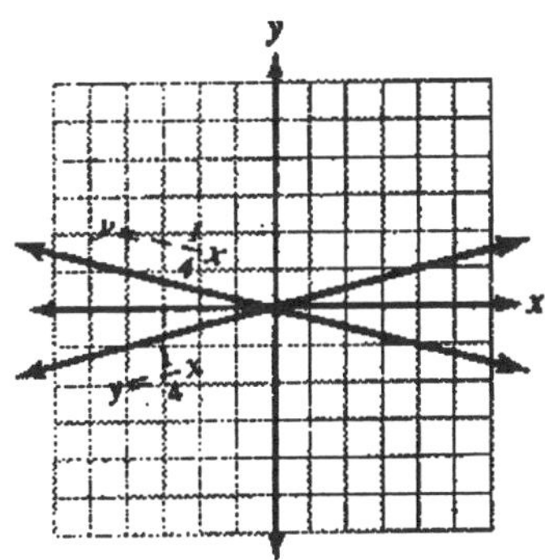


31.

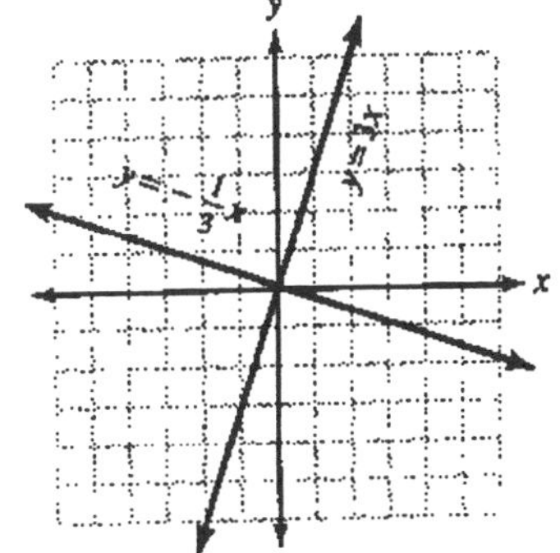


32.

34

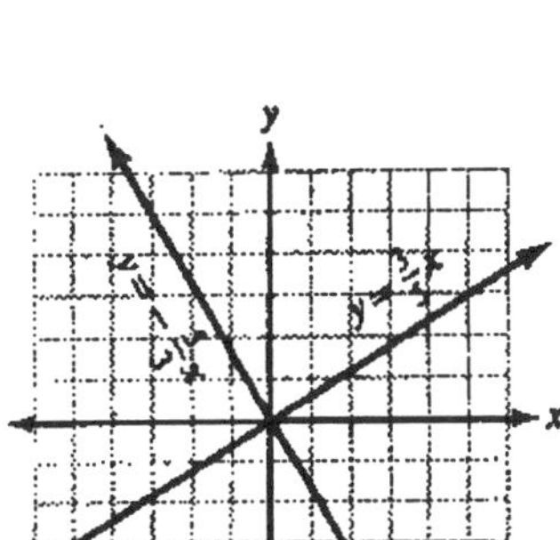


35.

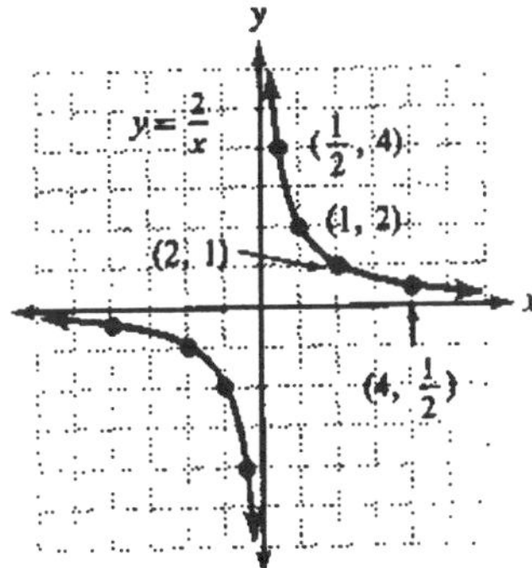


36.

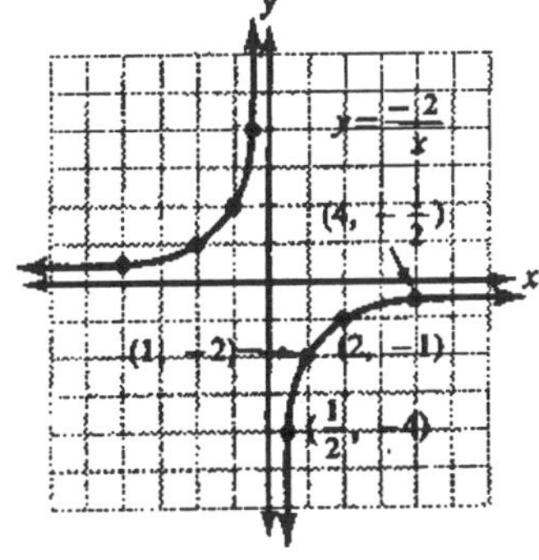

38.

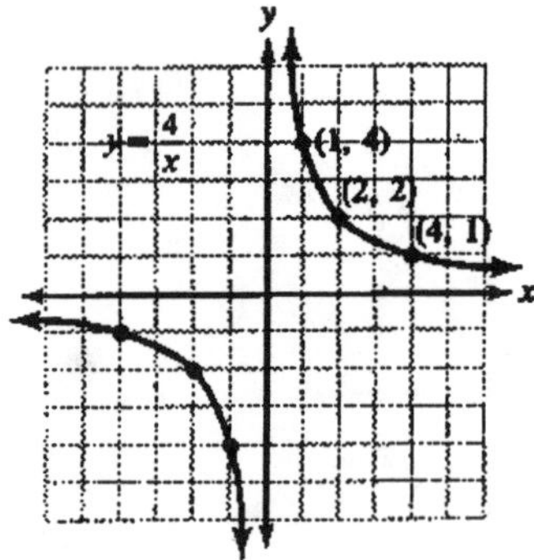


39.

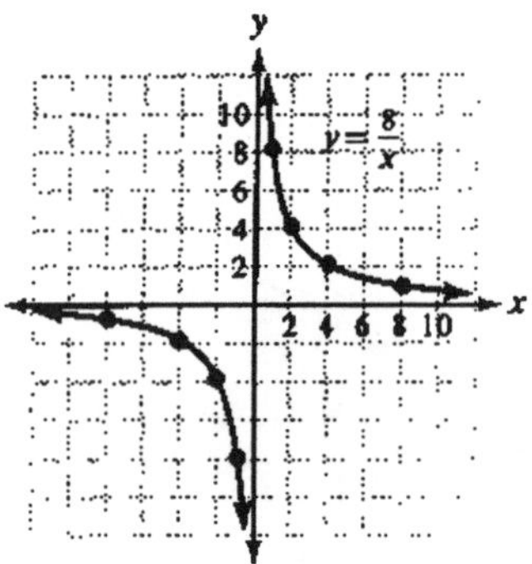


40.

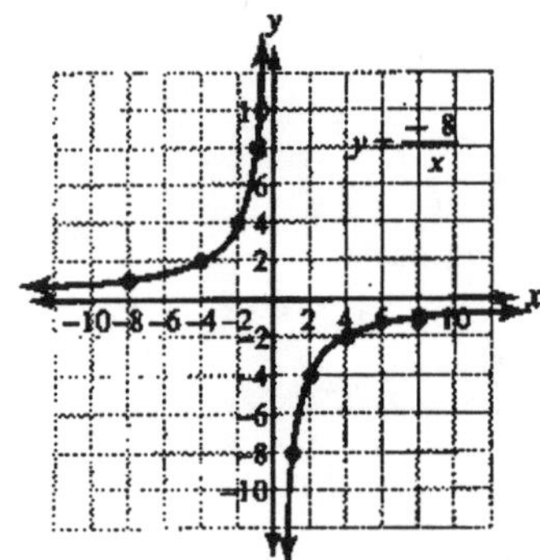


42.

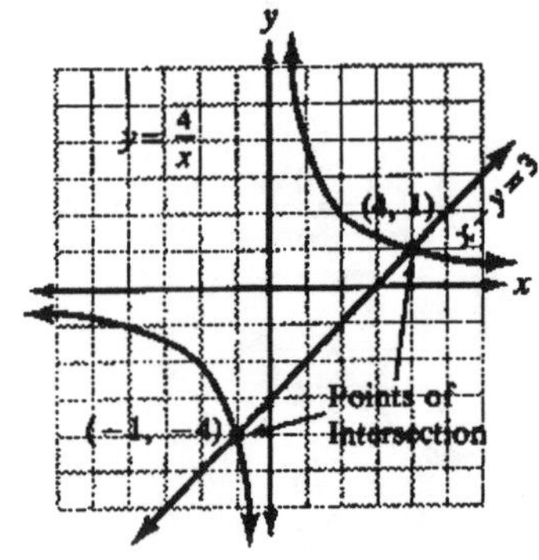


43.

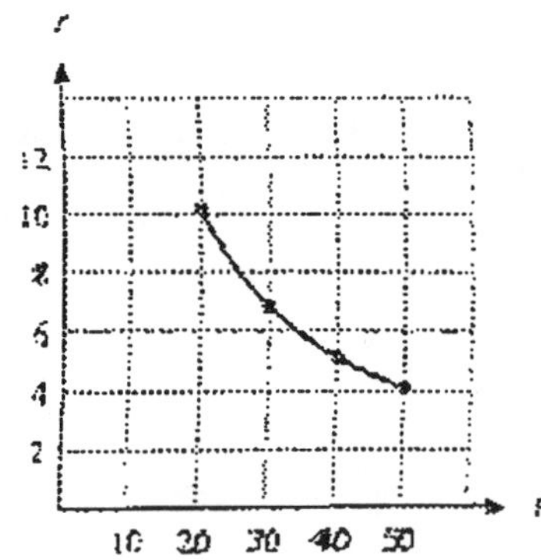


44.

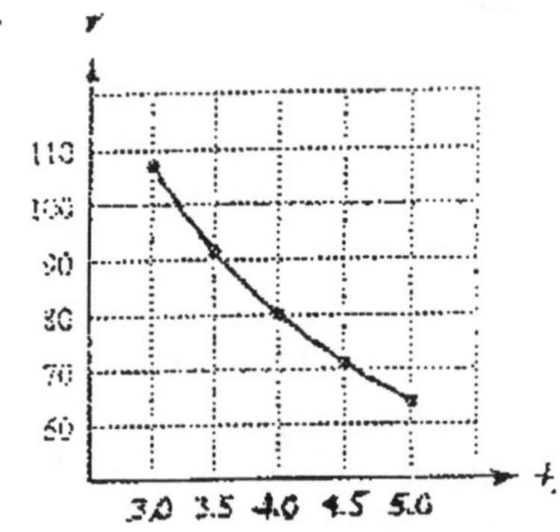


46. $\frac{x}{x-2} + \frac{2}{3} = \frac{2}{x-2}$

$3x + 2x - 4 = 6$

$5x = 10$

$x = 2$

*Possible solution 2, does not check, ∅*

47. $2 + \frac{5}{y} = \frac{3}{y^2}$

$2y^2 + 5y - 3 = 0$

$(y + 3)(2y - 1) = 0$

$y + 3 = 0$

$y = -3$ *or*

$2y - 1 = 0$

$y = \frac{1}{2}$

48. $1 - \frac{1}{y} = \frac{12}{y^2}$

$y^2 - y - 12 = 0$
$(y + 3)(y - 4) = 0$
$y + 3 = 0$
$y = -3$ *or*

$y - 4 = 0$
$y = 4$

50. $\frac{1}{6} - \frac{1}{8} = \frac{1}{x}$

$4x - 3x = 24$
$x = 24$ *hrs.*

# Chapter 6

## Section 6.1

2. $-\sqrt{144} = -12$

3. $\sqrt{-144}$
*Not a real number*

4. $\sqrt{-49}$
*Not a real number*

6. $\sqrt{49} = 7$

7. $\sqrt[3]{-27} = -3$

8. $-\sqrt[3]{27} = -3$

10. $-\sqrt[4]{16} = -2$

11. $\sqrt[4]{-16}$
*Not a real number*

12. $-\sqrt[4]{-16}$
*Not a real number*

14. $\sqrt{0.81} = 0.9$

15. $\sqrt[3]{0.008} = 0.2$

16. $\sqrt[3]{0.125} = 0.5$

18. $\sqrt{49a^{10}} = 7a^5$

19. $\sqrt[3]{27a^{12}} = 3a^4$

20. $\sqrt[3]{8a^{15}} = 2a^5$

22. $\sqrt[3]{x^6y^3} = x^2y$

23. $\sqrt[5]{32x^{10}y^5} = 2x^2y$

24. $\sqrt[5]{32x^5y^{10}} = 2xy^2$

26. $\sqrt[4]{81a^{24}b^8} = 3a^6b^2$

27. $36^{1/2} = 6$

28. $49^{1/2} = 7$

30. $-16^{1/2} = -4$

31. $8^{1/3} = 2$

32. $-8^{1/3} = -2$

34. $-27^{1/3} = -3$

35. $32^{1/5} = 2$

36. $81^{1/4} = 3$

38. $\left(\frac{9}{16}\right)^{1/2} = \frac{3}{4}$

39. $\left(\frac{64}{125}\right)^{1/3} = \frac{4}{5}$

40. $\left(\frac{8}{27}\right)^{1/3} = \frac{2}{3}$

42. $8^{4/3} = 2^4 = 16$

43. $25^{3/2} = 5^3 = 125$

44. $9^{3/2} = 3^3 = 27$

46. $81^{3/4} = 3^3 = 27$

47. $27^{-1/3} = \frac{1}{27^{1/3}} = \frac{1}{3}$

48. $9^{-1/2} = \frac{1}{9^{1/2}} = \frac{1}{3}$

50. $4^{-3/2} = \frac{1}{4^{3/2}} = \frac{1}{2^3} = \frac{1}{8}$

51. $\left(\frac{25}{36}\right)^{-1/2} = \left(\frac{36}{25}\right)^{1/2} = \frac{6}{5}$

52. $\left(\frac{16}{49}\right)^{-1/2} = \left(\frac{49}{16}\right)^{1/2} = \frac{7}{4}$

54. $\left(\frac{27}{8}\right)^{-2/3} = \left(\frac{3}{2}\right)^{-2} = \left(\frac{2}{3}\right)^{2} = \frac{4}{9}$

55. $16^{1/2} + 27^{1/3} = 4 + 3 = 7$

56. $25^{1/2} + 100^{1/2} = 5 + 10 = 15$

58. $49^{-1/2} + 25^{-1/2}$

$$= \frac{1}{49^{1/2}} + \frac{1}{25^{1/2}}$$

$$= \frac{1}{7} + \frac{1}{5}$$

$$= \frac{12}{35}$$

59. $x^{3/5} \cdot x^{1/5} = x^{4/5}$

60. $x^{3/4} \cdot x^{5/4} = x^2$

62. $(a^{2/3})^{3/4} = a^{1/2}$

63. $\frac{x^{1/5}}{x^{3/5}} = \frac{1}{x^{2/5}}$

64. $\frac{x^{2/7}}{x^{5/7}} = \frac{1}{x^{3/7}}$

66. $\dfrac{x^{7/8}}{x^{8/7}} = x^{49/56-64/56}$

$= x^{-15/56}$

$= \dfrac{1}{x^{15/56}}$

67. $(x^{3/5}y^{5/6}z^{1/3})^{3/5}$
$= x^{9/25}y^{15/30}z^{3/15}$
$= x^{9/25}y^{1/2}z^{1/5}$

68. $(x^{3/4}y^{1/8}z^{5/6})^{4/5}$
$= x^{3/5}y^{4/40}z^{20/30}$
$= x^{3/5}y^{1/10}z^{2/3}$

70. $\dfrac{a^{1/3}b^4}{a^{3/5}b^{1/3}}$

$= a^{5/15-9/15}b^{12/3-1/3}$

$= a^{-4/15}b^{11/3}$

$= \dfrac{b^{11/3}}{a^{4/15}}$

71. $\dfrac{(y^{2/3})^{3/4}}{(y^{1/3})^{3/5}}$

$= \dfrac{y^{1/2}}{y^{1/5}}$

$= y^{5/10-2/10}$
$= y^{3/10}$

72. $\dfrac{(y^{5/4})^{2/5}}{(y^{1/4})^{4/3}}$

$= \dfrac{y^{1/2}}{y^{1/3}}$

$= y^{3/6-2/6}$
$= y^{1/6}$

74. $\left(\dfrac{a^{-1/5}}{b^{1/3}}\right)^{15} = \dfrac{a^{-3}}{b^5}$

$= \dfrac{1}{a^3b^5}$

75. $\dfrac{\left(r^{-2}s^{1/3}\right)^6}{r^8s^{3/2}} = \dfrac{r^{-12}s^2}{r^8s^{3/2}}$

$= \dfrac{s^{1/2}}{r^{20}}$

76. $\dfrac{\left(r^{-5}s^{1/2}\right)^4}{r^{12}s^{5/2}} = \dfrac{r^{-20}s^2}{r^{12}s^{5/2}}$

$= \dfrac{1}{r^{32}s^{1/2}}$

78. $\dfrac{(27a^3b^6)^{1/3}}{(81a^8b^{-4})^{1/4}} = \dfrac{3b^2}{3ab^{-1}}$

$= \dfrac{b^3}{a}$

79. $(a^{1/2} + b^{1/2})^2 = a + b \quad a = 9$ *and* $b = 4$
$(9^{1/2} + 4^{1/2})^2 = (9 + 4)$
$(3 + 2)^2 = 13$
$25 = 13$ (*False*)

*Therefore*,
$(a^{1/2} + b^{1/2})^2 \neq a + b$

80. $(a^2 + b^2)^{1/2} = a + b \quad a = 3,\ b = 4$
$(3^2 + 4^2)^{1/2} = 3 + 4$
$25^{1/2} = 7$
$5 = 7$ *false*
*Therefore*,
$(a^2 + b^2) \neq a + b$

82. $\sqrt[3]{\sqrt{a}} = \sqrt[6]{a} \quad (a \geq 0)$
$(a^{1/2})^{1/3} = a^{1/6}$
$a^{1/6} = a^{1/6}$
$\sqrt[6]{a} = \sqrt[6]{a}$

83. $V = \left(\frac{5r}{2}\right)^{1/2}$ $r = 250$

$V = \left(\frac{5(250)}{2}\right)^{1/2}$

$V = \left(\frac{1250}{2}\right)^{1/2}$

$V = (625)^{1/2}$
$V = 25$ *miles/hour*

84. $L = \left(1 - \frac{v^2}{c^2}\right)^{1/2}$ $\frac{v}{c} = \frac{3}{5}$

$L = \left(1 - \frac{9}{25}\right)^{1/2}$

$L = \left(\frac{16}{25}\right)^{1/2}$

$L = \frac{4}{5}$ *ft.*

86. $\frac{2}{a + \sqrt{5}} = 0.618$

87. $\frac{3}{2}, \frac{5}{3}, \frac{8}{5}, \ldots \frac{13}{8}$

*Numerator and denominator are consecutive members of the Fibonacci sequence*

88. $\frac{3}{2} = 1.500$, $\frac{5}{3} = 1.667$, $\frac{13}{8} = 1.625$,

$\frac{21}{13} = 1.615$, $\frac{34}{21} = 1.619$, $\frac{55}{34} = 1.618$

$\frac{89}{55} = 1.618$, $\frac{144}{89} = 1.618$, $\frac{233}{144} = 1.618$

90. $5x^2(2x^3 - x) = 10x^5 - 5x^3$

91. $(x - 3)(x + 5) = x^2 + 2x - 15$

92. $(x - 2)(x + 2) = x^2 - 4$

94. $(x^2 + 5)^2$
$= (x^2)^2 + (2)(5)x^2 + 5^2$
$= x^4 + 10x^2 + 25$

95. $(x - 3)(x^2 + 3x + 9) = x^3 - 27$

96. $(x + 3)(x^2 - 3x + 9) = x^3 + 27$

98. *Let* $x = 0$,
$12(0) - 5y = 15$
$y = -3$
*y-intercept* $-3$

*Let* $y = 0$
$12x - 5(0) = 15$

$x = \frac{15}{12}$

$x = \frac{5}{4}$

*x-intercept* $\frac{5}{4}$

99. *Let* $x = 0$

$y = \frac{2}{3}(0) + 4$

$y = 4$
*y-intercept* 4

*Let* $y = 0$

$0 = \frac{2}{3}x + 4$

$-4 = \frac{2}{3}x$

$-6 = x$
*x-intercept* $-6$

100. *Let* $x = 0$

$$y = \frac{3}{2}(0) - 6$$

$$y = -6$$

*y-intercept* $-6$

*Let* $y = 0$

$$0 = \frac{3}{2}x - 6$$

$$6 = \frac{3}{2}x$$

$$4 = x$$

*x-intercept* 4

## Section 6.2

2. $x^{2/5}(x^{3/5} - x^{8/5})$
$= x^{5/5} - x^{10/5}$
$= x - x^2$

3. $a^{1/2}(a^{3/2} - a^{1/2})$
$= a^{4/2} - a^{2/2}$
$= a^2 - a$

4. $a^{1/4}(a^{3/4} + a^{7/4})$
$= a^{4/4} + a^{8/4}$
$= a + a^2$

6. $5x^{1/2}(4x^{5/2} + 3x^{3/2} + 2x^{1/2})$
$= 20x^{6/2} + 15x^{4/2} + 10x^{2/2}$
$= 20x^3 + 15x^2 + 10x$

7. $4x^{1/2}y^{3/5}(3x^{3/2}y^{-3/5} - 9x^{-1/2}y^{7/5})$
$= 12x^{4/2}y^0 - 36x^0y^{10/5}$
$= 12x^2 - 36y^2$

8. $3x^{4/5}y^{1/3}(4x^{6/5}y^{-1/3} - 12x^{-4/5}y^{5/3})$
$= 12x^{10/5}y^0 - 36x^0y^{6/3}$
$= 12x^2 - 36y^2$

10. $(x^{2/3} - 5)(x^{2/3} + 2)$
$= x^{2/3}x^{2/3} + 2x^{2/3} - 5x^{2/3} - 10$
$= x^{4/3} - 3x^{2/3} - 10$

11. $(a^{1/2} - 3)(a^{1/2} - 7)$
$= a^{1/2}a^{1/2} - 7a^{1/2} - 3a^{1/2} + 21$
$= a - 10a^{1/2} + 21$

12. $(a^{1/2} - 6)(a^{1/2} - 2)$
$= a^{1/2}a^{1/2} - 2a^{1/2} - 6a^{1/2} + 12$
$= a - 8a^{1/2} + 12$

14. $(5y^{1/3} - 2)(4y^{1/3} + 3)$
$= 20y^{2/3} + 3 \cdot 5y^{1/3} - 2 \cdot 4y^{1/3} - 6$
$= 20y^{2/3} + 7y^{1/3} - 6$

15. $(5x^{2/3} + 3y^{1/2})(2x^{2/3} + 3y^{1/2})$
$= 10x^{4/3} + 15x^{2/3}y^{1/2} + 6x^{2/3}y^{1/2} + 9y$
$= 10x^{4/3} + 21x^{2/3}y^{1/2} + 9y$

16. $(4x^{2/3} - 2y^{1/2})(5x^{2/3} - 3y^{1/2})$
$= 20x^{4/3} - 12x^{2/3}y^{1/2} - 10x^{2/3}y^{1/2} + 6y$
$= 20x^{4/3} - 22x^{2/3}y^{1/2} + 6y$

18. $(t^{1/2} - 3)^2$
$= (t^{1/2} - 3)(t^{1/2} - 3)$
$= t - 3t^{1/2} - 3t^{1/2} + 9$
$= t - 6t^{1/2} + 9$

*We can obtain the same result by using the formula for the square of a binomial,*

$(a - b)^2 = a^2 + 2ab + b^2$:
$(t^{1/2} - 3)^2$
$= (t^{1/2})^2 - 2t^{1/2}(3) + 3^2$
$= t - 6t^{1/2} + 9$

19. $(x^{3/2} + 4)^2 = (x^{3/2} + 4)(x^{3/2} + 4)$
$= x^{6/2} + 4x^{3/2} + 4x^{3/2} + 16$
$= x^3 + 8x^{3/2} + 16$

*We can obtain the same result by using the formula for the square of a binomial,*

$(a + b)^2 = a^2 + 2ab + b^2$:
$(x^{3/2} + 4)^2$
$= (x^{3/2})^2 + 2x^{3/2}(4) + 4^2$
$= x^3 + 8x^{3/2} + 16$

20. $(x^{3/2} - 6)^2 = (x^{3/2} - 6)(x^{3/2} - 6)$
$= x^{6/2} - 6x^{3/2} - 6x^{3/2} + 36$
$= x^3 - 12x^{3/2} + 3$

*We can obtain the same result by using the formula for the square of a binomial*

$(a - b)^2 = a^2 - 2ab + b^2$:
$(x^{3/2} - 6)^2$
$= (x^{3/2})^2 - 2x^{3/2} \cdot 6 + 6^2$
$= x^3 - 12x^{3/2} + 36$

22. $(a^{1/2} + b^{1/2})^2$
$= (a^{1/2} + b^{1/2})(a^{1/2} + b^{1/2})$
$= a + a^{1/2}b^{1/2} + a^{1/2}b^{1/2} + b$
$= a + 2a^{1/2}b^{1/2} + b$

*We can obtain the same result by using the formula for the square of a binomial,*

$(a + b)^2 = a^2 + 2ab + b^2$:
$(a^{1/2} + b^{1/2})^2$
$= (a^{1/2})^2 + 2a^{1/2}b^{1/2} + (b^{1/2})^2$
$= a + 2a^{1/2}b^{1/2} + b$

23. $(2x^{1/2} - 3y^{1/2})^2$
$= (2x^{1/2} - 3y^{1/2})(2x^{1/2} - 3y^{1/2})$
$= 4x - 6x^{1/2}y^{1/2} - 6x^{1/2}y^{1/2} + 9y$
$= 4x - 12x^{1/2}y^{1/2} + 9y$

*We can obtain the same result by using the formula for the square of a binomial,*

$(a - b)^2 = a^2 - 2ab + b^2$:
$(2x^{1/2} - 3y^{1/2})^2$
$= (2x^{1/2})^2 - 2(2x^{1/2})(3y^{1/2}) + (3y^{1/2})^2$
$= 4x - 12^{1/2}y^{1/2} + 9y$

24. $(5x^{1/2} + 4y^{1/2})^2$
$= (5x^{1/2} + 4y^{1/2})(5x^{1/2} + 4y^{1/2})$
$= 25x + 20x^{1/2}y^{1/2} + 20x^{1/2}y^{1/2} + 16y$
$= 25x + 40x^{1/2}y^{1/2} + 16y$

*We can obtain the same result by using the formula for the square of a binomial,*

$(a + b)^2 = a^2 + 2ab + b^2$:
$(5x^{1/2} + 4y^{1/2})^2$
$= (5x^{1/2})^2 + 2(5x^{1/2})(4y^{1/2}) + (4y^{1/2})^2$
$= 25x + 40x^{1/2}y^{1/2} + 16y$

26. $(a^{1/2} - 5^{1/2})(a^{1/2} + 5^{1/2})$
$= (a^{1/2})^2 - (5^{1/2})^2$
$= a - 5$

27. $(x^{3/2} + y^{3/2})(x^{3/2} - y^{3/2})$
$= (x^{3/2})^2 - (y^{3/2})^2$
$= x^3 - y^3$

28. $(x^{5/2} + y^{5/2})(x^{5/2} - y^{5/2})$
$= (x^{5/2})^2 - (y^{5/2})^2$
$= x^5 - y^5$

30. $(t^{1/2} - 5^{3/2})(t^{1/2} + 5^{3/2})$
$= (t^{1/2})^2 - (5^{3/2})^2$
$= t - 5^3$
$= t - 125$

31. $(2x^{3/2} + 3^{1/2})(2x^{3/2} - 3^{1/2})$
$= (2x^{3/2})^2 - (3^{1/2})^2$
$= 4x^3 - 3$

32. $(3x^{1/2} + 2^{3/2})(3x^{1/2} - 2^{3/2})$
$= (3x^{1/2})^2 - (2^{3/2})^2$
$= 9x - 2^3$
$= 9x - 8$

34.
$$\begin{array}{r} x^{2/3} + x^{1/3}y^{1/3} + y^{2/3} \\ x^{1/3} - y^{1/3} \\ \hline - x^{2/3}y^{1/3} - x^{1/3}y^{2/3} - y \\ x + x^{2/3}y^{1/3} + x^{1/3}y^{2/3} \qquad\quad \\ \hline x \qquad\qquad\qquad\qquad - y \end{array}$$

The product is x - y.

35.
$$\begin{array}{r} a^{2/3} + 2a^{1/3} + 4 \\ a^{1/3} - 2 \\ \hline - 2a^{2/3} - 4a^{1/3} - 8 \\ a + 2a^{2/3} + 4a^{1/3} \qquad \\ \hline a \qquad\qquad\qquad - 8 \end{array}$$

The product is a - 8.

36.
$$\begin{array}{r} a^{2/3} - 3a^{1/3} + 9 \\ a^{1/3} + 3 \\ \hline 3a^{2/3} - 9a^{1/3} + 27 \\ a - 3a^{2/3} + 9a^{1/3} \qquad \\ \hline a \qquad\qquad\qquad + 27 \end{array}$$

The product is a + 27.

38.
$$\begin{array}{r} 9x^{2/3} + 3x^{1/3} + 1 \\ 3x^{1/3} - 1 \\ \hline - 9x^{2/3} - 3x^{1/3} - 1 \\ 27x + 9x^{2/3} + 3x^{1/3} \qquad \\ \hline 27x \qquad\qquad\qquad - 1 \end{array}$$

39. $(t^{1/4} - 1)(t^{1/4} + 1)(t^{1/2} + 1)$
$= (t^{1/2} - 1)(t^{1/2} + 1)$
$= t - 1$

40. $(t^{1/4} - 2)(t^{1/4} + 2)(t^{1/2} + 4)$
$= (t^{1/2} - 4)(t^{1/2} + 4)$
$= t - 16$

42. $\dfrac{25x^{1/4} + 30x^{3/4}}{5x^{1/4}}$

$= \dfrac{25x^{1/4}}{5x^{1/4}} + \dfrac{30x^{3/4}}{5x^{1/4}}$

$= 5 + 6x^{1/2}$

43. $\dfrac{12x^{2/3}y^{1/3} - 16x^{1/3}y^{2/3}}{4x^{1/3}y^{1/3}}$

$= \dfrac{12x^{2/3}y^{1/3}}{4x^{1/3}y^{1/3}} - \dfrac{16x^{1/3}y^{2/3}}{4x^{1/3}y^{1/3}}$

$= 3x^{1/3} - 4y^{1/3}$

44. $\dfrac{12x^{4/3}y^{1/3} - 18x^{1/3}y^{4/3}}{6x^{1/3}y^{1/3}}$

$= \dfrac{12x^{4/3}y^{1/3}}{6x^{1/3}y^{1/3}} - \dfrac{18x^{1/3}y^{4/3}}{6x^{1/3}y^{1/3}}$

$= 2x - 3y$

46. $\dfrac{24a^{9/5}b^{3/5} - 16a^{4/5}b^{8/5}}{8a^{4/5}b^{3/5}}$

$= \dfrac{24a^{9/5}b^{3/5}}{8a^{4/5}b^{3/5}} - \dfrac{16a^{4/5}b^{8/5}}{8a^{4/5}b^{3/5}}$

$= 3a - 2b$

47. *This solution is similar to factoring out the greatest common factor.*

$12(x - 2)^{3/2} - 9(x - 2)^{1/2}$
$= 3(x - 2)^{1/2}[4(x - 2) - 3]$
$= 3(x - 2)^{1/2}(4x - 11)$

48. *This solution is similar to factoring out the greatest common factor.*

$4(x + 1)^{4/3} + 8(x + 1)^{1/3}$
$= 4(x + 1)^{1/3}[(x + 1) + 2]$
$= 4(x + 1)^{1/3}(x + 3)$

50. *This solution is similar to factoring out the greatest common factor.*

$$\begin{aligned}6(x+3)^{15/7} - 12(x+3)^{8/7} &= 6(x+3)^{1/7}[(x+3)^2 - 2(x+3)]\\ &= 6(x+3)^{1/7}(x^2+6x+9-2x-6)\\ &= 6(x+3)^{1/7}(x^2+4x+3)\\ &= 6(x+3)^{1/7}(x+1)(x+3)\end{aligned}$$

51. *This solution is similar to factoring out the greatest common factor.*

$$\begin{aligned}9x(x+1)^{3/2} + 6(x+1)^{1/2} &= 3(x+1)^{1/2}[3x(x+1)+2]\\ &= 3(x+1)^{1/2}(3x^2+3x+2)\end{aligned}$$

52. *This solution is similar to factoring out the greatest common factor.*

$$\begin{aligned}4x^2(x+1)^{1/2} + 8x(x+1)^{3/2} &= 4(x+1)^{1/2}[x^2+2x(x+1)]\\ &= 4(x+1)^{1/2}(x^2+2x^2+2x)\\ &= 4(x+1)^{1/2}(3x^2+2x)\\ &= 4x(x+1)^{1/2}(3x+2)\end{aligned}$$

54. $x^{2/3} - x^{1/3} - 6$
$= (x^{1/3} - 3)(x^{1/3} + 2)$

55. $a^{2/5} - 2a^{1/5} - 8$
$= (a^{1/5} + 2)(a^{1/5} - 4)$

56. $a^{2/5} + 2a^{1/5} - 8$
$= (a^{1/5} + 4)(a^{1/5} - 2)$

58. $3y^{2/3} + 5y^{1/3} - 2$
$= (3y^{1/3} - 1)(y^{1/3} + 2)$

59. $9t^{2/5} - 25 = (3t^{1/5} + 5)(3t^{1/5} - 5)$

60. $16t^{2/5} - 49 = (4t^{1/5} + 7)(4t^{1/5} - 7)$

62. $25x^{2/7} - 20x^{1/7} + 4$
$= (5x^{1/7} - 2)(5x^{1/7} - 2)$
$= (5x^{1/7} - 2)^2$

63. $$\frac{3}{x^{1/2}} + x^{1/2} = \frac{3}{x^{1/2}} + \frac{x}{x^{1/2}} = \frac{3+x}{x^{1/2}}$$

64. $$\frac{2}{x^{1/2}} - x^{1/2} = \frac{2}{x^{1/2}} - \frac{x}{x^{1/2}} = \frac{2-x}{x^{1/2}}$$

66. $$x^{3/4} - \frac{7}{x^{1/4}} = \frac{x}{x^{1/4}} - \frac{7}{x^{1/4}} = \frac{x-7}{x^{1/4}}$$

67. $$\frac{3x^2}{(x^3+1)^{1/2}} + (x^3+1)^{1/2} = \frac{3x^2}{(x^3+1)^{1/2}} + \frac{(x^3+1)}{(x^3+1)^{1/2}} = \frac{x^3+3x^2+1}{(x^3+1)^{1/2}}$$

68. $$\frac{x^3}{(x^2-1)^{1/2}} + 2x(x^2-1)^{1/2} = \frac{x^3}{(x^2-1)^{1/2}} + \frac{2x(x^2-1)}{(x^2-1)^{1/2}} = \frac{3x^3-2x}{(x^2-1)^{1/2}}$$

70. $\dfrac{x^5}{(x^2-2)^{1/2}} + 4x^3(x^2-2)^{1/2}$

$= \dfrac{x^5}{(x^2-2)^{1/2}} + \dfrac{4x^3(x^2-2)}{(x^2-2)^{1/2}}$

$= \dfrac{5x^5 - 8x^3}{(x^2-2)^{1/2}}$

71. $16^{0.25} = 2$

72. $81^{0.25} = 3$

74. $32^{0.4} = 4$

75. $\left(\dfrac{1}{2}\right)^{1/5} = 0.871$

76. $\left(\dfrac{1}{2}\right)^{1/10} = 0.933$

78. *Using* $A = \$1{,}600$, $P = \$800$ *and* $t = 5$ *in the following formula*:

$r = \left(\dfrac{A}{P}\right)^{1/t} - 1$

$r = \left(\dfrac{1600}{800}\right)^{1/5} - 1$

$r = (2)^{1/5} - 1$

$r = 1.149 - 1$
$r = 14.9\%$

79. *Using* $A = \$80{,}000$, $P = \$60{,}000$ *and* $r = 5$ *in the following formula*:

$r = \left(\dfrac{A}{P}\right)^{1/t} - 1$

$r = \left(\dfrac{80{,}000}{60{,}000}\right)^{1/5} - 1$

$r = \left(\dfrac{4}{3}\right)^{1/5} - 1$

$r = 1.059 - 1$
$r = .059$
$r = 5.9\%$

80. *Using* $A = \$150{,}000$, $P = \$75{,}000$ *and* $r = 10$ *in the following formula*:

$r = \left(\dfrac{A}{P}\right)^{1/t} - 1$

$r = \left(\dfrac{150{,}000}{75{,}000}\right)^{1/10} - 1$

$r = 2^{1/10} - 1$

$r = 1.072 - 1$
$r = 7.2\%$

82. $m = \dfrac{y_2 - y_1}{x_2 - x_1}$

$= \dfrac{1 - (-3)}{-5 - (-2)}$

$= -\dfrac{4}{3}$ *or*

$= \dfrac{-3 - 1}{-2 - (-5)}$

$= -\dfrac{4}{3}$

83. $m = \dfrac{y_2 - y_1}{x_2 - x_1}$

$3 = \dfrac{2 - y}{4 - 5}$

$3 = \dfrac{2 - y}{-1}$

$3 = -2 + y$
$5 = y$

84. $m = \dfrac{y_2 - y_1}{x_2 - x_1}$

$-\dfrac{7}{3} = \dfrac{-2 - 9}{x - 4}$

$-7x + 28 = -6 - 27$
$-7x = -61$

$x = \dfrac{61}{7}$

86. *Slope* $= -\dfrac{3}{2}$

(*Perpendicular lines -- if their slopes are multiplied together, they equal* −1.)

87. (5,0), (0,−2)

$m = \dfrac{-2 - 0}{0 - 5}$

$= \dfrac{2}{5}$

88. (−3,0), (0,6)

$m = \dfrac{6 - 0}{0 - (-3)}$

$= 2$

## Section 6.3

2. $\sqrt{32} = \sqrt{16 \cdot 2}$
$= 4\sqrt{2}$

3. $\sqrt{98} = \sqrt{49 \cdot 2}$
$= 7\sqrt{2}$

4. $\sqrt{75} = \sqrt{25 \cdot 3}$
$= 5\sqrt{3}$

6. $\sqrt{128} = \sqrt{64 \cdot 2}$
$= 8\sqrt{2}$

7. $\sqrt{80} = \sqrt{16 \cdot 5}$
$= 4\sqrt{5}$

8. $\sqrt{200} = \sqrt{100 \cdot 2}$
$= 10\sqrt{2}$

10. $\sqrt{27} = \sqrt{9 \cdot 3}$
$= 3\sqrt{3}$

11. $\sqrt{675} = \sqrt{225 \cdot 3}$
$= 15\sqrt{3}$

12. $\sqrt{972} = \sqrt{324 \cdot 3}$
$= 18\sqrt{3}$

14. $\sqrt[3]{24} = \sqrt[3]{8 \cdot 3}$

$= 2\sqrt[3]{3}$

15. $\sqrt[3]{128} = \sqrt[3]{64 \cdot 2}$

$= 4\sqrt[3]{2}$

16. $\sqrt[3]{162} = \sqrt[3]{27 \cdot 6}$
$= 3\sqrt[3]{6}$

18. $\sqrt[3]{1536} = \sqrt[3]{512 \cdot 3}$
$= 8\sqrt[3]{3}$

19. $\sqrt[5]{64} = \sqrt[5]{32 \cdot 2}$
$= 2\sqrt[5]{2}$

20. $\sqrt[4]{48} = \sqrt[4]{16 \cdot 3}$
$= 2\sqrt[4]{3}$

22. $\sqrt{27x^5} = \sqrt{9x^4 \cdot 3x}$
$= 3x^2\sqrt{3x}$

23. $\sqrt[4]{32y^7} = \sqrt[4]{16y^4 \cdot 2y^3}$
$= 2y\sqrt[4]{2y^3}$

24. $\sqrt[5]{32y^7} = \sqrt[5]{32y^5 \cdot y^2}$
$= 2y\sqrt[5]{y^2}$

26. $\sqrt[3]{128x^6y^2} = \sqrt[3]{64x^6 \cdot 2y^2}$
$= 4x^2\sqrt[3]{2y^2}$

27. $\sqrt{48a^2b^3c^4} = \sqrt{16a^2b^2c^4 \cdot 3b}$
$= 4abc^2\sqrt{3b}$

28. $\sqrt{72a^4b^3c^2} = \sqrt{36a^4b^2c^2 \cdot 2b}$
$= 6a^2bc\sqrt{2b}$

30. $\sqrt[3]{72a^4b^3c^2} = \sqrt[3]{8a^3b^3 \cdot 9ac^2}$
$= 2ab\sqrt[3]{9ac^2}$

31. $\sqrt[5]{64x^8y^{12}} = \sqrt[5]{32x^5y^{10} \cdot 2x^3y^2}$
$= 2xy^2\sqrt[5]{2x^3y^2}$

32. $\sqrt[4]{32x^9y^{10}} = \sqrt[4]{16x^8y^8 \cdot 2xy^2}$
$= 2x^2y^2\sqrt[4]{2xy^2}$

34. $\sqrt[5]{64x^8y^4z^{11}} = \sqrt[5]{32x^5z^{10} \cdot 2x^3y^4z}$
$= 2xz^2\sqrt[5]{2x^3y^4z}$

35. $\sqrt{b^2 - 4ac} = \sqrt{(-6)^2 - 4(2)(3)}$
$= \sqrt{36 - 24}$
$= \sqrt{12}$
$= \sqrt{4 \cdot 3}$
$= 2\sqrt{3}$

36. $\sqrt{b^2 - 4ac} = \sqrt{7^2 - 4(6)(-5)}$
$= \sqrt{49 + 120}$
$= \sqrt{169}$
$= 13$

38. $\sqrt{b^2 - 4ac} = \sqrt{5^2 - 4(2)(3)}$
$= \sqrt{25 - 24}$
$= \sqrt{1}$
$= 1$

39. $\sqrt{b^2 - 4ac} = \sqrt{\left(-\frac{1}{2}\right)^2 - 4\left(\frac{1}{2}\right)\left(-\frac{5}{4}\right)}$

$= \sqrt{\frac{1}{4} + \frac{5}{2}}$

$= \sqrt{\frac{11}{4}}$

$= \frac{\sqrt{11}}{2}$

40. $\sqrt{b^2 - 4ac} = \sqrt{\left(-\frac{3}{4}\right)^2 - 4\left(\frac{7}{4}\right)(-2)}$

$= \sqrt{\frac{9}{16} + 14}$

$= \sqrt{\frac{233}{16}}$

$= \frac{\sqrt{233}}{4}$

42. $\frac{3}{\sqrt{2}} = \frac{3}{\sqrt{2}} \cdot \frac{\sqrt{2}}{\sqrt{2}} = \frac{3\sqrt{2}}{2}$

43. $\frac{5}{\sqrt{6}} = \frac{5}{\sqrt{6}} \cdot \frac{\sqrt{6}}{\sqrt{6}} = \frac{5\sqrt{6}}{6}$

44. $\frac{7}{\sqrt{5}} = \frac{7}{\sqrt{5}} \cdot \frac{\sqrt{5}}{\sqrt{5}} = \frac{7\sqrt{5}}{5}$

46. $\sqrt{\frac{1}{3}} = \frac{\sqrt{1}}{\sqrt{3}} \cdot \frac{\sqrt{3}}{\sqrt{3}} = \frac{\sqrt{3}}{3}$

47. $\sqrt{\frac{1}{5}} = \frac{\sqrt{1}}{\sqrt{5}} \cdot \frac{\sqrt{5}}{\sqrt{5}} = \frac{\sqrt{5}}{5}$

48. $\sqrt{\frac{1}{6}} = \frac{\sqrt{1}}{\sqrt{6}} \cdot \frac{\sqrt{6}}{\sqrt{6}} = \frac{\sqrt{6}}{6}$

50. $\frac{5}{\sqrt[3]{3}} = \frac{5}{\sqrt[3]{3}} \cdot \frac{\sqrt[3]{3^2}}{\sqrt[3]{3^2}} = \frac{5\sqrt[3]{9}}{3}$

51. $\frac{2}{\sqrt[3]{9}} = \frac{2}{\sqrt[3]{9}} \cdot \frac{\sqrt[3]{3}}{\sqrt[3]{3}} = \frac{2\sqrt[3]{3}}{3}$

52. $\frac{3}{\sqrt[3]{4}} = \frac{3}{\sqrt[3]{4}} \cdot \frac{\sqrt[3]{2}}{\sqrt[3]{2}} = \frac{3\sqrt[3]{2}}{2}$

54. $\sqrt[4]{\frac{5}{3x^2}} = \frac{\sqrt[4]{5}}{\sqrt[4]{3x^2}} \cdot \frac{\sqrt[4]{3^3x^2}}{\sqrt[4]{3^3x^2}}$

$= \frac{\sqrt[4]{135x^2}}{3x}$

55. $\sqrt[4]{\frac{8}{y}} = \frac{\sqrt[4]{8}}{\sqrt[4]{y}} \cdot \frac{\sqrt[4]{y^3}}{\sqrt[4]{y^3}}$

$= \frac{\sqrt[4]{8y^3}}{y}$

56. $\sqrt[4]{\frac{27}{y}} = \frac{\sqrt[4]{27}}{\sqrt[4]{y}} \cdot \frac{\sqrt[4]{y^3}}{\sqrt[4]{y^3}}$

$= \frac{\sqrt[4]{27y^3}}{y}$

58. $\sqrt[3]{\dfrac{7x}{6y}} = \dfrac{\sqrt[3]{7x}}{\sqrt[3]{6y}} \cdot \dfrac{\sqrt[3]{6^2y^2}}{\sqrt[3]{6^2y^2}}$

$= \dfrac{\sqrt[3]{252xy^2}}{6y}$

59. $\sqrt[3]{\dfrac{2x}{9y}} = \dfrac{\sqrt[3]{2x}}{\sqrt[3]{9y}} \cdot \dfrac{\sqrt[3]{3y^2}}{\sqrt[3]{3y^2}}$

$= \dfrac{\sqrt[3]{6xy^2}}{3y}$

60. $\sqrt[3]{\dfrac{5x}{4y}} = \dfrac{\sqrt[3]{5x}}{\sqrt[3]{4y}} \cdot \dfrac{\sqrt[3]{2y^2}}{\sqrt[3]{2y^2}}$

$= \dfrac{\sqrt[3]{10xy^2}}{2y}$

62. $\sqrt[4]{\dfrac{8}{9x^3}} = \dfrac{\sqrt[4]{8}}{\sqrt[4]{9x^3}} \cdot \dfrac{\sqrt[4]{9x}}{\sqrt[4]{9x}}$

$= \dfrac{\sqrt[4]{72x}}{3x}$

63. $\sqrt{\dfrac{27x^3}{5y}} = \dfrac{\sqrt{9x^2 \cdot 3x}}{\sqrt{5y}} \cdot \dfrac{\sqrt{5y}}{\sqrt{5y}}$

$= \dfrac{3x\sqrt{15xy}}{5y}$

64. $\sqrt{\dfrac{12x^5}{7y}} = \dfrac{\sqrt{4x^4 \cdot 3x}}{\sqrt{7y}} \cdot \dfrac{\sqrt{7y}}{\sqrt{7y}}$

$= \dfrac{2x^2\sqrt{21xy}}{7y}$

66. $\sqrt{\dfrac{50x^2y^3}{3z}} = \dfrac{\sqrt{25x^2y^2 \cdot 2y}}{\sqrt{3z}} \cdot \dfrac{\sqrt{3z}}{\sqrt{3z}}$

$= \dfrac{5xy\sqrt{6yz}}{3z}$

67. $\sqrt[3]{\dfrac{16a^4b^3}{9c}} = \dfrac{\sqrt{8a^3b^3 \cdot 2a}}{\sqrt[3]{9c}} \cdot \dfrac{\sqrt[3]{3c^2}}{\sqrt[3]{3c^2}}$

$= \dfrac{2ab\sqrt[3]{6ac^2}}{3c}$

68. $\sqrt[3]{\dfrac{54a^5b^4}{25c^2}} = \dfrac{\sqrt[3]{27a^3b^3 \cdot 2a^2b}}{\sqrt[3]{25c^2}} \cdot \dfrac{\sqrt[3]{5c}}{\sqrt[3]{5c}}$

$= \dfrac{3ab\sqrt[3]{10a^2bc}}{5c}$

70. $\sqrt[3]{\dfrac{27x^6y^3}{2z^2}} = \dfrac{3x^2y}{\sqrt[3]{2z^2}} \cdot \dfrac{\sqrt[3]{4z}}{\sqrt[3]{4z}}$

$= \dfrac{3x^2y\sqrt[3]{4z}}{2z}$

71. $\sqrt{25x^2} = 5|x|$

72. $\sqrt{49x^2} = 7|x|$

74. $\sqrt{40x^3y^2} = \sqrt{4x^2y^2} \cdot \sqrt{10x}$

$= 2|xy|\sqrt{10x}$

75. $\sqrt{x^2 - 10x + 25} = \sqrt{(x-5)^2}$

$= |x - 5|$

76. $\sqrt{x^2 - 16x + 64} = \sqrt{(x - 8)^2}$
$= |x - 8|$

78. $\sqrt{16x^2 + 40x + 25} = \sqrt{(4x + 5)^2}$
$= |4x + 5|$

79. $\sqrt{4a^4 + 16a^3 + 16a^2} = \sqrt{4a^2(a^2 + 4a + 4)}$
$= 2\sqrt{a^2(a + 2)^2}$
$= 2|a(a + 2)|$

80. $\sqrt{9a^4 + 18a^3 + 9a^2} = \sqrt{9a^2(a^2 + 2a + 1)}$
$= 3\sqrt{a^2(a + 1)^2}$
$= 3|a(a + 1)|$

82. $\sqrt{18x^3 - 9x^2} = \sqrt{9x^2(2x - 1)}$
$= 3|x|\sqrt{2x - 1}$

83. $\sqrt{9 + 16} = \sqrt{9} + \sqrt{16}$
$\sqrt{25} = 3 + 4$
$5 \neq 7$

84. $a = 0,\ b = 0$
$a = 1,\ b = 0$
$a = 0,\ b = 1$

86. $r = \sqrt[3]{\dfrac{3V}{4\pi}}$

$r = \sqrt[3]{\dfrac{3 \cdot 9}{4\left(\dfrac{22}{7}\right)}}$

$r = \sqrt[3]{27\left(\dfrac{7}{88}\right)}$

$= \dfrac{3\sqrt[3]{7}}{2\sqrt[3]{11}} \cdot \dfrac{\sqrt[3]{11^2}}{\sqrt[3]{11^2}}$

$= \dfrac{3\sqrt[3]{847}}{22}$ *ft.*

90. $\sqrt{4 + 4} = \sqrt{8} = 2\sqrt{2}$
$\sqrt{(\sqrt{4 + 4})^2 + 4} = \sqrt{12} = 2\sqrt{3}$
$\sqrt{(\sqrt{(4 + 4)^2} + 4^2 + 4} = \sqrt{4(3) + 4} = \sqrt{16} = 4$

91.

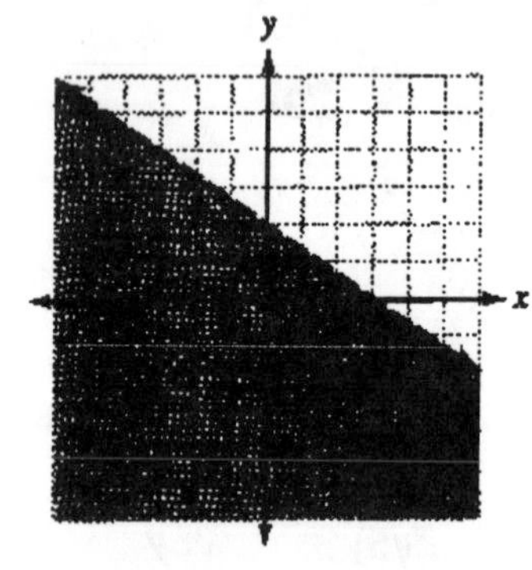


92.

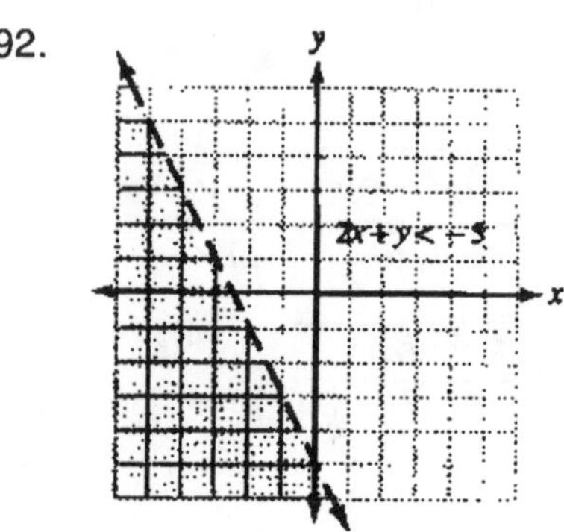

94.

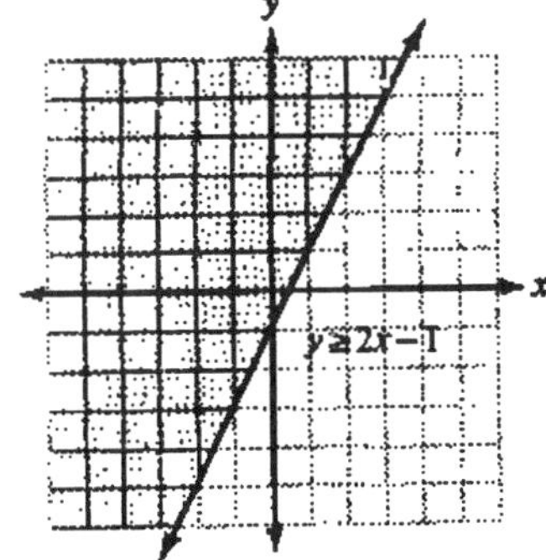


95.

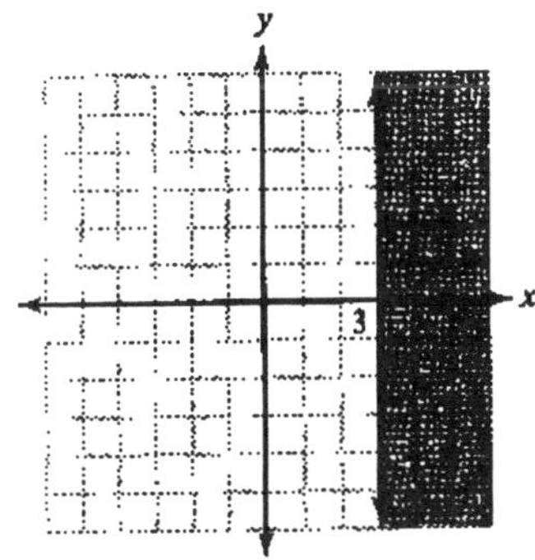


96.

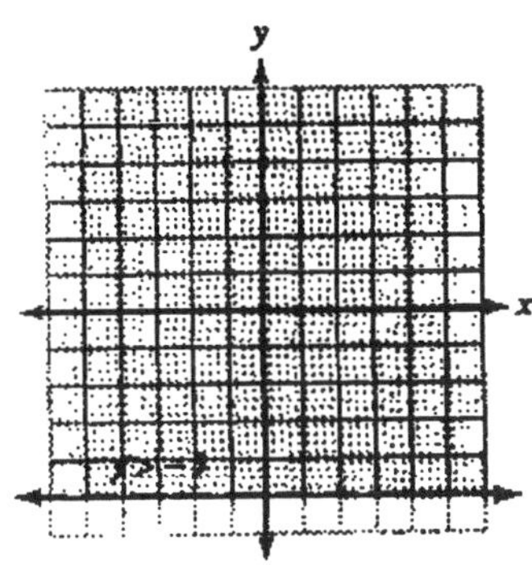


—

98. $\sqrt{8640} = \sqrt{2^6 \cdot 3^3 \cdot 5}$
$= \sqrt{2^6 \cdot 3^2 \cdot 3 \cdot 5}$
$= 24\sqrt{15}$

99. $\sqrt[3]{10{,}584} = \sqrt[3]{2^3 \cdot 3^3 \cdot 7^2}$
$= 6\sqrt[3]{49}$

100. $\sqrt{10{,}584} = \sqrt{2^3 \cdot 3^3 \cdot 7^2}$
$= \sqrt{2^2 \cdot 3^2 \cdot 7^2 \cdot 2 \cdot 3}$
$= 42\sqrt{6}$

102. $\dfrac{1}{\sqrt[12]{a^7}} = \dfrac{1}{\sqrt[12]{a^7}} \cdot \dfrac{\sqrt[12]{a^5}}{\sqrt[12]{a^5}}$
$= \dfrac{\sqrt[12]{a^5}}{a}$

103. $\dfrac{1}{\sqrt[20]{a^{11}}} = \dfrac{1}{\sqrt[20]{a^{11}}} \cdot \dfrac{\sqrt[20]{a^9}}{\sqrt[20]{a^9}}$
$= \dfrac{\sqrt[20]{a^9}}{a}$

104. $\dfrac{1}{\sqrt[15]{a^{13}}} = \dfrac{1}{\sqrt[15]{a^{13}}} \cdot \dfrac{\sqrt[15]{a^2}}{\sqrt[15]{a^2}}$
$= \dfrac{\sqrt[15]{a^2}}{a}$

**Section 6.4**

2. $6\sqrt{3} - 5\sqrt{3} = 1\sqrt{3} = \sqrt{3}$

3. $3x\sqrt{7} - 4x\sqrt{7}$
$= -1x\sqrt{7}$
$= -x\sqrt{7}$

4. $6y\sqrt{a} + 7y\sqrt{a} = 13y\sqrt{a}$

6. $6\sqrt[4]{2} + 9\sqrt[4]{2} = 15\sqrt[4]{2}$

7. $8\sqrt[5]{6} - 2\sqrt[5]{6} + 3\sqrt[5]{6} = 9\sqrt[5]{6}$

8. $7\sqrt[6]{7} - \sqrt[6]{7} + 4\sqrt[6]{7} = 10\sqrt[6]{7}$

10. $5x\sqrt{6} - 3x\sqrt{6} - 2x\sqrt{6} = 0\sqrt{6} = 0$

11. $\sqrt{20} - \sqrt{80} + \sqrt{45}$
$= 2\sqrt{5} - 4\sqrt{5} + 3\sqrt{5}$
$= \sqrt{5}$

12. $\sqrt{8} - \sqrt{32} - \sqrt{18}$
$= 2\sqrt{2} - 4\sqrt{2} - 3\sqrt{2}$
$= -5\sqrt{2}$

14. $\sqrt{48} - 3\sqrt{27} + 2\sqrt{75}$
$= 4\sqrt{3} - 9\sqrt{3} + 10\sqrt{3}$
$= 5\sqrt{3}$

15. $5x\sqrt{8} + 3\sqrt{32x^2} - 5\sqrt{50x^2}$
$= 10x\sqrt{2} + 12x\sqrt{2} - 25x\sqrt{2}$
$= -3x\sqrt{2}$

16. $2\sqrt{50x^2} - 8x\sqrt{18} - 3\sqrt{72x^2}$
$= 10x\sqrt{2} - 24x\sqrt{2} - 18x\sqrt{2}$
$= -32x\sqrt{2}$

18. $\sqrt[3]{81} + 3\sqrt[3]{24}$
$= 3\sqrt[3]{3} + 6\sqrt[3]{3}$
$= 9\sqrt[3]{3}$

19. $\sqrt[3]{x^4y^2} + 7x\sqrt[3]{xy^2}$
$= x\sqrt[3]{xy^2} + 7x\sqrt[3]{xy^2}$
$= 8x\sqrt[3]{xy^2}$

20. $2\sqrt[3]{x^8y^6} - 3y^2\sqrt[3]{8x^8}$
$= 2x^2y^2\sqrt[3]{x^2} - 6x^2y^2\sqrt[3]{x^2}$
$= -4x^2y^2\sqrt[3]{x^2}$

22. $9a\sqrt{20a^3b^2} + 7b\sqrt{45a^5}$
$= 18a^2b\sqrt{5a} + 21a^2b\sqrt{5a}$
$= 39a^2b\sqrt{5a}$

23. $b\sqrt[3]{24a^5b} + 3a\sqrt[3]{81a^2b^4}$
$= 2ab\sqrt[3]{3a^2b} + 9ab\sqrt[3]{3a^2b}$
$= 11ab\sqrt[3]{3a^2b}$

24. $7\sqrt[3]{a^4b^3c^2} - 6ab\sqrt[3]{ac^2}$
$= 7ab\sqrt[3]{ac^2} - 6ab\sqrt[3]{ac^2}$
$= ab\sqrt[3]{ac^2}$

26. $x\sqrt[4]{5xy^8} + y\sqrt[4]{405x^5y^4} + y^2\sqrt[4]{80x^5}$
$= xy^2\sqrt[4]{5x} + 3xy^2\sqrt[4]{5x} + 2xy^2\sqrt[4]{5x}$
$= 6xy^2\sqrt[4]{5x}$

27. $\dfrac{\sqrt{2}}{2} + \dfrac{1}{\sqrt{2}}$
$= \dfrac{\sqrt{2}}{2} + \dfrac{1}{\sqrt{2}} \cdot \dfrac{\sqrt{2}}{\sqrt{2}}$
$= \dfrac{\sqrt{2} + \sqrt{2}}{2}$
$= \dfrac{2\sqrt{2}}{2}$
$= \sqrt{2}$

28. $\dfrac{\sqrt{3}}{3} + \dfrac{1}{\sqrt{3}}$

$= \dfrac{\sqrt{3}}{3} + \dfrac{1}{\sqrt{3}} \cdot \dfrac{\sqrt{3}}{\sqrt{3}}$

$= \dfrac{\sqrt{3} + \sqrt{3}}{3}$

$= \dfrac{2\sqrt{3}}{3}$

30. $\dfrac{\sqrt{6}}{2} + \dfrac{1}{\sqrt{6}}$

$= \dfrac{\sqrt{6}}{2} + \dfrac{1}{\sqrt{6}} \cdot \dfrac{\sqrt{6}}{\sqrt{6}}$

$= \dfrac{3\sqrt{6}}{6} + \dfrac{\sqrt{6}}{6}$

$= \dfrac{4\sqrt{6}}{6}$

$= \dfrac{2\sqrt{6}}{3}$

31. $\sqrt{x} - \dfrac{1}{\sqrt{x}}$

$= \sqrt{x} - \dfrac{1}{\sqrt{x}} \cdot \dfrac{\sqrt{x}}{\sqrt{x}}$

$= \dfrac{x\sqrt{x}}{x} - \dfrac{\sqrt{x}}{x}$

$= \dfrac{(x - 1)\sqrt{x}}{x}$

32. $\sqrt{x} + \dfrac{1}{\sqrt{x}}$

$= \sqrt{x} + \dfrac{1}{\sqrt{x}} \cdot \dfrac{\sqrt{x}}{\sqrt{x}}$

$= \dfrac{x\sqrt{x}}{x} + \dfrac{\sqrt{x}}{x}$

$= \dfrac{(x + 1)\sqrt{x}}{x}$

34. $\dfrac{\sqrt{12}}{6} + \sqrt{\dfrac{1}{3}} + \dfrac{\sqrt{3}}{3}$

$= \dfrac{2\sqrt{3}}{6} + \dfrac{\sqrt{1}}{\sqrt{3}} \cdot \dfrac{\sqrt{3}}{\sqrt{3}} + \dfrac{\sqrt{3}}{3}$

$= \dfrac{\sqrt{3}}{3} + \dfrac{\sqrt{3}}{3} + \dfrac{\sqrt{3}}{3}$

$= \dfrac{3\sqrt{3}}{3}$

$= \sqrt{3}$

35. $\sqrt{6} - \sqrt{\dfrac{2}{3}} + \sqrt{\dfrac{1}{6}}$

$= \dfrac{6\sqrt{6}}{6} - \dfrac{\sqrt{2}}{\sqrt{3}} \cdot \dfrac{\sqrt{3}}{\sqrt{3}} + \dfrac{\sqrt{1}}{\sqrt{6}} \cdot \dfrac{\sqrt{6}}{\sqrt{6}}$

$= \dfrac{6\sqrt{6}}{6} - \dfrac{2\sqrt{6}}{6} + \dfrac{\sqrt{6}}{6}$

$= \dfrac{5\sqrt{6}}{6}$

36. $\sqrt{15} - \sqrt{\frac{3}{5}} + \sqrt{\frac{5}{3}}$

$= \frac{15\sqrt{15}}{15} - \frac{\sqrt{3}}{\sqrt{5}} \cdot \frac{\sqrt{5}}{\sqrt{5}} + \frac{\sqrt{5}}{\sqrt{3}} \cdot \frac{\sqrt{3}}{\sqrt{3}}$

$= \frac{15\sqrt{15}}{15} - \frac{\sqrt{15}}{5} + \frac{\sqrt{15}}{3}$

$= \frac{15\sqrt{15}}{15} - \frac{3\sqrt{15}}{15} + \frac{5\sqrt{15}}{15}$

$= \frac{17\sqrt{15}}{15}$

38. $\sqrt[4]{8} + \frac{1}{\sqrt[4]{2}}$

$= \sqrt[4]{8} + \frac{1}{\sqrt[4]{2}} \cdot \frac{\sqrt[4]{2^3}}{\sqrt[4]{2^3}}$

$= \frac{2\sqrt[4]{8}}{2} + \frac{\sqrt[4]{8}}{2}$

$= \frac{3\sqrt[4]{8}}{2}$

39. $\sqrt{12} \approx 3.464$
$2\sqrt{3} = 2(1.732)$
$\approx 3.464$

40. $\sqrt{50} \approx 7.071$
$5\sqrt{2} = 5(1.414)$
$\approx 7.071$

42. $\sqrt{3} + \sqrt{12} \approx 1.732 + 3.464 = 5.196$
$\sqrt{15} \approx 3.873$
$\sqrt{27} \approx 5.196$

43. $3\sqrt{2x} + 5\sqrt{2x} = 8\sqrt{2x}$

44. $5\sqrt{3} - 7\sqrt{3} = -2\sqrt{3}$

46. $\sqrt{36 + 64} = \sqrt{100} = 10$

54. $y = -3x + 5$

55. $y - y_1 = m(x - x_1)$

$y - 2 = \frac{2}{3}[x - (1 - 6)]$

$y - 2 = \frac{2}{3}x + 4$

$y = \frac{2}{3}x + 6$

56. $y - y_1 = m(x - x_1)$
$y - (-2) = 5(x - 3)$
$y + 2 = 5x - 15$
$y = 5x - 17$

58. $(3,0), (0,-2)$

$m = \frac{-2 - 0}{0 - 3} = \frac{2}{3}$

$y - 0 = \frac{2}{3}(x - 3)$

$y = \frac{2}{3}x - 2$

59. $y - y_1 = m(x - x_1)$

$y - 0 = \frac{3}{4}[(x - (-4)]$

$y = \frac{3}{4}x + 3$

60. $m = -\frac{1}{2}$

$y - 4 = -\frac{1}{2}[x - (-1)]$

$y - 4 = -\frac{1}{2}x - \frac{1}{2}$

$y = -\frac{1}{2}x + \frac{7}{2}$

**Section 6.5**

2. $\sqrt{6}\sqrt{2} = \sqrt{12} = 2\sqrt{3}$

3. $(2\sqrt{3})(5\sqrt{7}) = 10\sqrt{21}$

4. $(3\sqrt{5})(2\sqrt{7}) = 6\sqrt{35}$

6. $(4\sqrt{35})(2\sqrt{21})(5\sqrt{15})$
$= 40\sqrt{11{,}025}$
$= 40 \cdot 105$
$= 4{,}200$

7. $(3\sqrt[3]{3})(6\sqrt[3]{9})$

$= 18\sqrt[3]{27}$
$= 54$

8. $(2\sqrt[3]{2})(6\sqrt[3]{4})$

$= 12\sqrt[3]{8}$
$= 24$

10. $\sqrt{2}(5\sqrt{3} + 4\sqrt{2})$
$= 5\sqrt{6} + 4 \cdot 2$
$= 5\sqrt{6} + 8$

11. $6\sqrt[3]{4}(2\sqrt[3]{2} + 1)$

$= 12\sqrt[3]{8} + 6\sqrt[3]{4}$

$= 24 + 6\sqrt[3]{4}$

12. $7\sqrt[3]{5}(3\sqrt[3]{25} - 2)$

$= 21\sqrt[3]{125} - 14\sqrt[3]{5}$

$= 105 - 14\sqrt[3]{5}$

14. $(\sqrt{5} - \sqrt{2})(3\sqrt{5} + 2\sqrt{2})$
$= 3 \cdot 5 + 2\sqrt{10} - 3\sqrt{10} - 2 \cdot 2$
$= 11 - \sqrt{10}$

15. $(\sqrt{x} + 5)(\sqrt{x} - 3)$
$= x - 3\sqrt{x} + 5\sqrt{x} - 15$
$= x + 2\sqrt{x} - 15$

16. $(\sqrt{x} + 4)(\sqrt{x} + 2)$
$= x + 2\sqrt{x} + 4\sqrt{x} + 8$
$= x + 6\sqrt{x} + 8$

18. $(\sqrt{7} - 3\sqrt{3})(2\sqrt{7} - 4\sqrt{3})$
$= 2 \cdot 7 - 4\sqrt{21} - 6\sqrt{21} - 12 \cdot 3$
$= 50 - 10\sqrt{21}$

19. $(\sqrt{3} + 4)^2$
$= (\sqrt{3})^2 + 2(\sqrt{3})(4) + 4^2$
$= 3 + 8\sqrt{3} + 16$
$= 19 + 8\sqrt{3}$

20. $(\sqrt{5} - 2)^2$
$= (\sqrt{5})^2 - (2)(\sqrt{5})(2) + 2^2$
$= 5 - 4\sqrt{5} + 4$
$= 9 - 4\sqrt{5}$

22. $(\sqrt{x} + 4)^2$
$= (\sqrt{x})^2 + 2(\sqrt{x})(4) + 4^2$
$= x + 8\sqrt{x} + 16$

23. $(2\sqrt{a} - 3\sqrt{b})^2$
$= (2\sqrt{a})^2 - 2(2\sqrt{a})(3\sqrt{b}) + (3\sqrt{b})^2$
$= 4a - 12\sqrt{ab} + 9b$

24. $(5\sqrt{a} - 2\sqrt{b})^2$
$= (5\sqrt{a})^2 + 2(5\sqrt{a})(2\sqrt{b}) + (2\sqrt{b})^2$
$= 25a + 20\sqrt{ab} + 4b$

26. $(\sqrt{x-3} + 2)^2$
$= (\sqrt{x-3})^2 + 2(\sqrt{x-3})(2) + 2^2$
$= x - 3 + 4\sqrt{x-3} + 4$
$= x + 1 + 4\sqrt{x-3}$

27. $(\sqrt{x-5} - 3)^2$
$= (\sqrt{x-5})^2 - 2(\sqrt{x-5})(3) + 3^2$
$= x - 5 - 6\sqrt{x-5} + 9$
$= x + 4 - 6\sqrt{x-5}$

28. $(\sqrt{x-3} - 4)^2$
$= (\sqrt{x-3})^2 - 2(\sqrt{x-3})(4) + 4^2$
$= x - 3 - 8\sqrt{x-3} + 16$
$= x + 13 - 8\sqrt{x-3}$

30. $(\sqrt{5} - \sqrt{2})(\sqrt{5} + \sqrt{2})$
$= (\sqrt{5})^2 - (\sqrt{2})^2$
$= 5 - 2$
$= 3$

31. $(\sqrt{a} + 7)(\sqrt{a} - 7)$
$= (\sqrt{a})^2 - 7^2$
$= a - 49$

32. $(\sqrt{a} + 5)(\sqrt{a} - 5)$
$= (\sqrt{a})^2 - 5^2$
$= a - 25$

34. $(3 - \sqrt{x})(3 + \sqrt{x})$
$= 3^2 - (\sqrt{x})^2$
$= 9 - x$

35. $(\sqrt{x-4} + 2)(\sqrt{x-4} - 2)$
$= (\sqrt{x-4})^2 - 2^2$
$= x - 4 - 4$
$= x - 8$

36. $(\sqrt{x+3} + 5)(\sqrt{x+3} - 5)$
$= (\sqrt{x+3})^2 - 5^2$
$= x + 3 - 25$
$= x - 22$

38. $(\sqrt{5} - 2)^3$
$= (\sqrt{5} - 2)(\sqrt{5} - 2)^2$
$= (\sqrt{5} - 2)(5 - 4\sqrt{5} + 4)$
$= (\sqrt{5} - 2)(-4\sqrt{5} + 9)$
$= -20 + 9\sqrt{5} + 8\sqrt{5} - 18$
$= -38 + 17\sqrt{5}$

39. $\dfrac{\sqrt{2}}{\sqrt{6} - \sqrt{2}}$

$= \dfrac{\sqrt{2}}{\sqrt{6} - \sqrt{2}} \cdot \dfrac{\sqrt{6} + \sqrt{2}}{\sqrt{6} + \sqrt{2}}$

$= \dfrac{\sqrt{12} + 2}{6 - 2}$

$= \dfrac{2\sqrt{3} + 2}{4}$

$= \dfrac{\sqrt{3} + 1}{2}$

40. $\dfrac{\sqrt{5}}{\sqrt{5}+\sqrt{3}}$

$= \dfrac{\sqrt{5}}{\sqrt{5}+\sqrt{3}} \cdot \dfrac{\sqrt{5}-\sqrt{3}}{\sqrt{5}-\sqrt{3}}$

$= \dfrac{5-\sqrt{15}}{5-3}$

$= \dfrac{5-\sqrt{15}}{2}$

42. $\dfrac{\sqrt{7}}{\sqrt{7}-1}$

$= \dfrac{\sqrt{7}}{\sqrt{7}-1} \cdot \dfrac{\sqrt{7}+1}{\sqrt{7}+1}$

$= \dfrac{7+\sqrt{7}}{7-1}$

$= \dfrac{7+\sqrt{7}}{6}$

43. $\dfrac{\sqrt{x}}{\sqrt{x}-3}$

$= \dfrac{\sqrt{x}}{\sqrt{x}-3} \cdot \dfrac{\sqrt{x}+3}{\sqrt{x}+3}$

$= \dfrac{x+3\sqrt{x}}{x-9}$

44. $\dfrac{\sqrt{x}}{\sqrt{x}+2}$

$= \dfrac{\sqrt{x}}{\sqrt{x}+2} \cdot \dfrac{\sqrt{x}-2}{\sqrt{x}-2}$

$= \dfrac{x-2\sqrt{x}}{x-4}$

46. $\dfrac{\sqrt{7}}{3\sqrt{7}-2}$

$= \dfrac{\sqrt{7}}{3\sqrt{7}-2} \cdot \dfrac{3\sqrt{7}+2}{3\sqrt{7}+2}$

$= \dfrac{21+2\sqrt{7}}{63-4}$

$= \dfrac{21+2\sqrt{7}}{59}$

47. $\dfrac{3}{\sqrt{x}-\sqrt{y}}$

$= \dfrac{3}{\sqrt{x}-\sqrt{y}} \cdot \dfrac{\sqrt{x}+\sqrt{y}}{\sqrt{x}+\sqrt{y}}$

$= \dfrac{3\sqrt{x}+3\sqrt{y}}{x-y}$

48. $\dfrac{2}{\sqrt{x}+\sqrt{y}}$

$= \dfrac{2}{\sqrt{x}+\sqrt{y}} \cdot \dfrac{\sqrt{x}-\sqrt{y}}{\sqrt{x}-\sqrt{y}}$

$= \dfrac{2\sqrt{x}-2\sqrt{y}}{x-y}$

50. $\dfrac{\sqrt{5}-\sqrt{3}}{\sqrt{5}+\sqrt{3}}$

$= \dfrac{\sqrt{5}-\sqrt{3}}{\sqrt{5}+\sqrt{3}} \cdot \dfrac{\sqrt{5}-\sqrt{3}}{\sqrt{5}-\sqrt{3}}$

$= \dfrac{5-2\sqrt{15}+3}{5-3}$

$= \dfrac{8-2\sqrt{15}}{2}$

$= 4-\sqrt{15}$

51. $\dfrac{\sqrt{7} - 2}{\sqrt{7} + 2}$

$= \dfrac{\sqrt{7} - 2}{\sqrt{7} + 2} \cdot \dfrac{\sqrt{7} - 2}{\sqrt{7} - 2}$

$= \dfrac{7 - 4\sqrt{7} + 4}{7 - 4}$

$= \dfrac{11 - 4\sqrt{7}}{3}$

52. $\dfrac{\sqrt{11} + 3}{\sqrt{11} - 3}$

$= \dfrac{\sqrt{11} + 3}{\sqrt{11} - 3} \cdot \dfrac{\sqrt{11} + 3}{\sqrt{11} + 3}$

$= \dfrac{11 + 6\sqrt{11} + 9}{11 - 9}$

$= \dfrac{20 + 6\sqrt{11}}{2}$

$= 10 + 3\sqrt{11}$

54. $\dfrac{\sqrt{a} - \sqrt{b}}{\sqrt{a} + \sqrt{b}}$

$= \dfrac{\sqrt{a} - \sqrt{b}}{\sqrt{a} + \sqrt{b}} \cdot \dfrac{\sqrt{a} - \sqrt{b}}{\sqrt{a} - \sqrt{b}}$

$= \dfrac{a - 2\sqrt{ab} + b}{a - b}$

55. $\dfrac{\sqrt{x} + 2}{\sqrt{x} - 2}$

$= \dfrac{\sqrt{x} + 2}{\sqrt{x} - 2} \cdot \dfrac{\sqrt{x} + 2}{\sqrt{x} + 2}$

$= \dfrac{x + 4\sqrt{x} + 4}{x - 4}$

56. $\dfrac{\sqrt{x} - 3}{\sqrt{x} + 3}$

$= \dfrac{\sqrt{x} - 3}{\sqrt{x} + 3} \cdot \dfrac{\sqrt{x} - 3}{\sqrt{x} - 3}$

$= \dfrac{x - 6\sqrt{x} + 9}{x - 9}$

58. $\dfrac{5\sqrt{6} + 2\sqrt{2}}{\sqrt{6} - \sqrt{2}}$

$= \dfrac{5\sqrt{6} + 2\sqrt{2}}{\sqrt{6} - \sqrt{2}} \cdot \dfrac{\sqrt{6} + \sqrt{2}}{\sqrt{6} + \sqrt{2}}$

$= \dfrac{30 + 5\sqrt{12} + 2\sqrt{12} + 4}{6 - 2}$

$= \dfrac{34 + 7\sqrt{12}}{4}$

$= \dfrac{34 + 14\sqrt{3}}{4}$

$= \dfrac{17 + 7\sqrt{3}}{2}$

59. $\dfrac{3\sqrt{x} + 2}{1 + \sqrt{x}}$

$= \dfrac{3\sqrt{x} + 2}{1 + \sqrt{x}} \cdot \dfrac{1 - \sqrt{x}}{1 - \sqrt{x}}$

$= \dfrac{3\sqrt{x} - 3x + 2 - 2\sqrt{x}}{1 - x}$

$= \dfrac{\sqrt{x} - 3x + 2}{1 - x}$

60. $\dfrac{5\sqrt{x} - 1}{2 + \sqrt{x}}$

$= \dfrac{5\sqrt{x} - 1}{2 + \sqrt{x}} \cdot \dfrac{2 - \sqrt{x}}{2 - \sqrt{x}}$

$= \dfrac{10\sqrt{x} - 5x - 2 + \sqrt{x}}{4 - x}$

$= \dfrac{11\sqrt{x} - 5x - 2}{4 - x}$

62.

$$\begin{array}{r} \sqrt[3]{x^2} - 2\sqrt[3]{x} + 4 \\ \sqrt[3]{x} + 2 \\ \hline 2\sqrt[3]{x^2} - 4\sqrt[3]{x} + 8 \\ x - 2\sqrt[3]{x^2} + 4\sqrt[3]{x} \qquad \\ \hline x \qquad\qquad\qquad + 8 \end{array}$$

*The product is* $x + 8$.

63. $5(2\sqrt{3}) = 10\sqrt{3}$

64. $3(2\sqrt{x}) = 6\sqrt{x}$

66. $(\sqrt{x} - 7)^2$
$= (\sqrt{x})^2 - 2(\sqrt{x})(7) + 49$
$= x - 14\sqrt{x} + 49$

67. $(5\sqrt{3})^2 = 25 \cdot 3 = 75$

68. $(3\sqrt{5})^2 = 9 \cdot 5 = 45$

70. *If* $t = 1.25$ *seconds*

*Then* $t = \dfrac{\sqrt{100 - h}}{4}$

*Becomes* $1.25 = \dfrac{\sqrt{100 - h}}{4}$

$$\begin{aligned} 5 &= \sqrt{100 - h} \\ 25 &= 100 - h \\ -75 &= -h \\ 75 \textit{ ft.} &= h \end{aligned}$$

75.

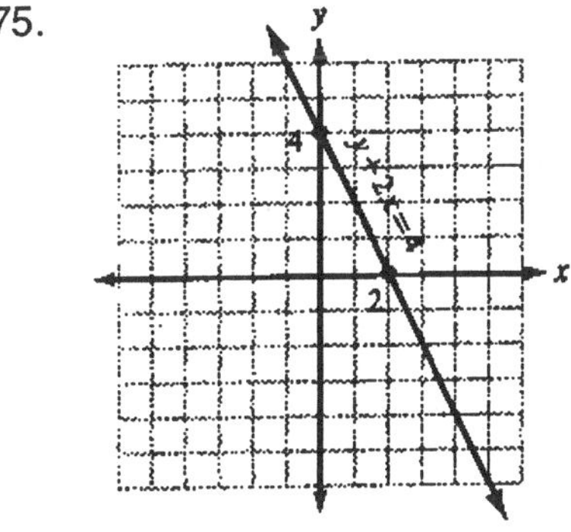


76.

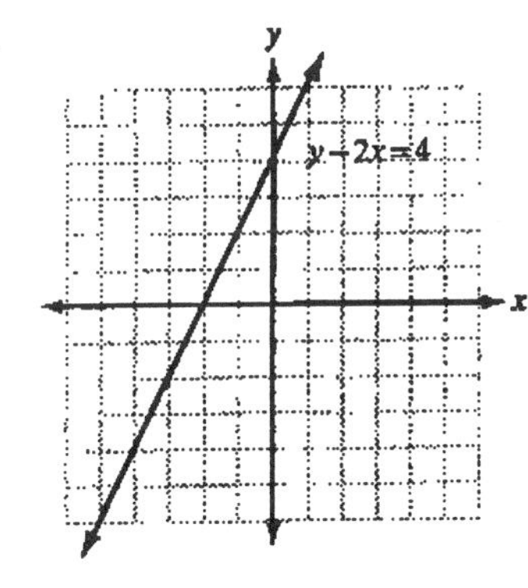


78.

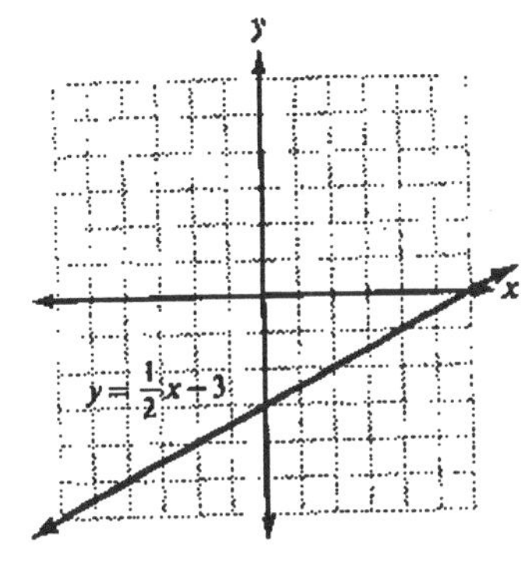

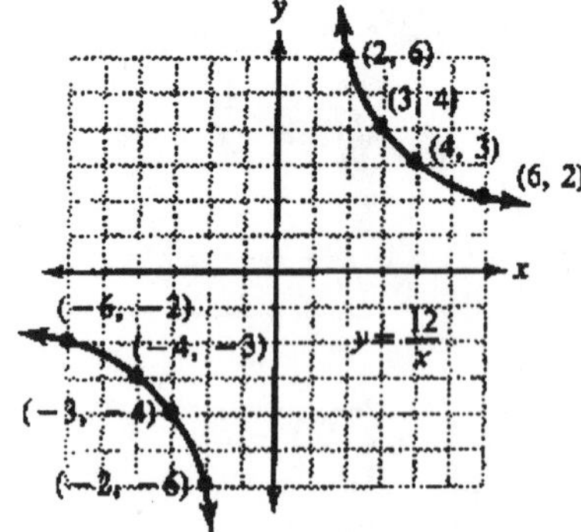


80.

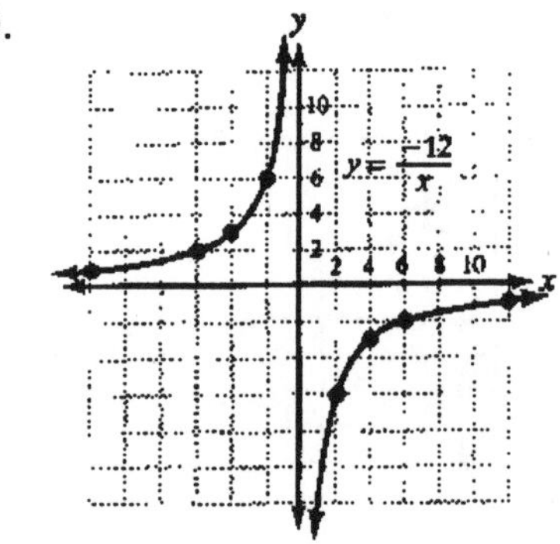


## Section 6.6

2. $\sqrt{3x + 1} = 4$
$(\sqrt{3x + 1})^2 = 4^2$
$3x + 1 = 16$
$3x = 15$
$x = 5$

3. $\sqrt{4x + 1} = -5$
$(\sqrt{4x + 1})^2 = (-5)^2$
$4x + 1 = 25$
$4x = 24$
$x = 6$

*6 does not solve the original equation, ∅*

4. $\sqrt{6x + 1} = -5$
$(\sqrt{6x + 1})^2 = (-5)^2$
$5x + 1 = 25$
$5x = 24$
$x = 4$

*4 does not solve the original equation, ∅*

6. $\sqrt{3y - 1} = 2$
$(\sqrt{3y - 1})^2 = 2^2$
$3y - 1 = 4$
$3y = 5$
$y = \frac{5}{3}$

7. $\sqrt{5x - 7} = -1$
$(\sqrt{5x - 7})^2 = (-1)^2$
$5x - 7 = 1$
$5x = 8$
$x = \frac{8}{5}$

$\frac{8}{5}$ *does not solve the original equation, ∅.*

8. $\sqrt{8x + 3} = -6$
$(\sqrt{8x + 3})^2 = (-6)^2$
$8x + 3 = 36$
$8x = 33$
$x = \frac{33}{8}$

$\frac{33}{8}$ *does not solve the original equation, ∅.*

10. $\sqrt{3x + 1} - 4 = 1$
$\sqrt{3x + 1} = 5$
$(\sqrt{3x + 1})^2 = 5^2$
$3x + 1 = 25$
$3x = 24$
$x = 8$

11. $\sqrt{4a+1} + 3 = 2$
$\sqrt{4a+1} = -1$
$(\sqrt{4a+1})^2 = (-1)^2$
$4a + 1 = 1$
$4a = 0$
$a = 0$

0 *does not solve the original equation,* $\varnothing$

12. $\sqrt{5a-3} + 6 = 2$
$\sqrt{5a-3} = -4$
$(\sqrt{5a-3})^2 = (-4)^2$
$5a - 3 = 16$
$5a = 19$
$a = \frac{19}{5}$

$\frac{19}{5}$ *does not solve the original equation,* $\varnothing$.

14. $\sqrt[4]{4x+1} = 3$
$(\sqrt[4]{4x+1})^4 = 3^4$
$4x + 1 = 81$
$4x = 80$
$x = 20$

15. $\sqrt[3]{2x-5} = 1$
$(\sqrt[3]{2x-5})^3 = 1^3$
$2x - 5 = 1$
$2x = 6$
$x = 3$

16. $\sqrt[3]{5x+7} = 2$
$(\sqrt[3]{5x+7})^3 = 2^3$
$5x + 7 = 8$
$5x = 1$
$x = \frac{1}{5}$

18. $\sqrt[3]{2a+7} = -2$
$(\sqrt[3]{2a+7})^3 = (-2)^3$
$2a + 7 = -8$
$2a = -15$
$a = -\frac{15}{2}$

19. $\sqrt{y-3} = y - 3$
$(\sqrt{y-3})^2 = (y-3)^2$
$y - 3 = y^2 - 6y + 9$
$0 = y^2 - 7y + 12$
$0 = (y-3)(y-4)$
$y - 3 = 0$
$y = 3$ *or*
$y - 4 = 0$
$y = 4$

20. $\sqrt{y+3} = y - 3$
$(\sqrt{y+3})^2 = (y-3)^2$
$y + 3 = y^2 - 6y + 9$
$0 = y^2 - 7y + 6$
$0 = (y-1)(y-6)$
$y - 1 = 0$
$y = 1$ *or*
$y - 6 = 0$
$y = 6$

*Possible solutions* 1 *and* 6; *only* 6 *checks*

22. $\sqrt{a+10} = a - 2$
$(\sqrt{a+10})^2 = (a-2)^2$
$a + 10 = a^2 - 4a + 4$
$0 = a^2 - 5a - 6$
$0 = (a+1)(a-6)$
$a + 1 = 0$
$a = -1$ *or*
$a - 6 = 0$
$a = 6$

*Possible solutions* −1 *and* 6; *only* 6 *checks*

23.
$$\begin{aligned} \sqrt{2x+4} &= \sqrt{1-x} \\ (\sqrt{2x+4})^2 &= (\sqrt{1-x})^2 \\ 2x+4 &= 1-x \\ 3x &= -3 \\ x &= -1 \end{aligned}$$

24.
$$\begin{aligned} \sqrt{3x+4} &= -\sqrt{2x+3} \\ (\sqrt{3x+4})^2 &= (-\sqrt{2x+3})^2 \\ 3x+4 &= 2x+3 \\ x &= -1 \end{aligned}$$

*−1 does not solve the original equation,* ∅

26.
$$\begin{aligned} \sqrt{7a-1} &= \sqrt{2a+4} \\ (\sqrt{7a-1})^2 &= (\sqrt{2a+4})^2 \\ 7a-1 &= 2a+4 \\ 5a &= 5 \\ a &= 1 \end{aligned}$$

27.
$$\begin{aligned} \sqrt[4]{5x-8} &= \sqrt[4]{4x-1} \\ (\sqrt[4]{5x-8})^4 &= (\sqrt[4]{4x-1})^4 \\ 5x-8 &= 4x-1 \\ x &= 7 \end{aligned}$$

28.
$$\begin{aligned} \sqrt[4]{6x+7} &= \sqrt[4]{x+2} \\ (\sqrt[4]{6x+7})^4 &= (\sqrt[4]{x+2})^4 \\ 6x+7 &= x+2 \\ 5x &= -5 \\ x &= -1 \end{aligned}$$

30.
$$\begin{aligned} x-1 &= \sqrt{6x+1} \\ (x-1)^2 &= (\sqrt{6x+1})^2 \\ x^2-2x+1 &= 6x+1 \\ x^2-8x &= 0 \\ x(x-8) &= 0 \\ x &= 0 \quad \text{or} \\ x-8 &= 0 \\ x &= 8 \end{aligned}$$

*Possible solutions* 0 *and* 8, *only* 8 *checks*

31.
$$\begin{aligned} t+5 &= \sqrt{2t+9} \\ (t+5)^2 &= (\sqrt{2t+9})^2 \\ t^2+10t+25 &= 2t+9 \\ t^2+8t+16 &= 0 \\ (t+4)^2 &= 0 \\ t+4 &= 0 \\ t &= -4 \end{aligned}$$

32.
$$\begin{aligned} t+7 &= \sqrt{2t+13} \\ (t+7)^2 &= (\sqrt{2t+13})^2 \\ t^2+14t+49 &= 2t+13 \\ t^2+12t+36 &= 0 \\ (t+6)^2 &= 0 \\ t+6 &= 0 \\ t &= -6 \end{aligned}$$

34.
$$\begin{aligned} \sqrt{2y+5} &= \sqrt{5y+2} \\ (\sqrt{2y+5})^2 &= (\sqrt{5y+2})^2 \\ 2y+5 &= 5y+2 \\ 3 &= 3y \\ 1 &= y \end{aligned}$$

35.
$$\begin{aligned} \sqrt[3]{3x+5} &= \sqrt[3]{5-2x} \\ (\sqrt[3]{3x+5})^3 &= (\sqrt[3]{5-2x})^3 \\ 3x+5 &= 5-2x \\ 5x &= 0 \\ x &= 0 \end{aligned}$$

36.
$$\begin{aligned} \sqrt[3]{4x+9} &= \sqrt[3]{3-2x} \\ (\sqrt[3]{4x+9})^3 &= (\sqrt[3]{3-2x})^3 \\ 4x+9 &= 3-2x \\ 6x &= -6 \\ x &= -1 \end{aligned}$$

38.
$$\begin{aligned} \sqrt{x+3} &= \sqrt{x}-3 \\ (\sqrt{x+3})^2 &= (\sqrt{x}-3)^2 \\ x+3 &= x-6\sqrt{x}+9 \\ -6 &= -6\sqrt{x} \\ 1 &= \sqrt{x} \\ 1 &= x \end{aligned}$$

*Possible solution* 1, *which does not check,* ∅

39.
$$\begin{aligned}\sqrt{x+1} &= \sqrt{x}+1\\ (\sqrt{x+1})^2 &= (\sqrt{x}+1)^2\\ x+1 &= x+2\sqrt{x}+1\\ 0 &= 2\sqrt{x}\\ 0 &= x\end{aligned}$$

40.
$$\begin{aligned}\sqrt{x-1} &= \sqrt{x}-1\\ (\sqrt{x-1})^2 &= (\sqrt{x}-1)^2\\ x-1 &= x-2\sqrt{x}+1\\ -2 &= -2\sqrt{x}\\ 1 &= \sqrt{x}\\ 1 &= x\end{aligned}$$

42.
$$\begin{aligned}\sqrt{x+5} &= \sqrt{x-3}+2\\ (\sqrt{x+5})^2 &= (\sqrt{x-3}+2)^2\\ x+5 &= x-3+4\sqrt{x-3}+4\\ 4 &= 4\sqrt{x-3}\\ 1 &= \sqrt{x-3}\\ 1 &= x-3\\ 4 &= x\end{aligned}$$

43.
$$\begin{aligned}\sqrt{x-5}-3 &= \sqrt{x-8}\\ (\sqrt{x-5}-3)^2 &= (\sqrt{x-8})^2\\ x-5-6\sqrt{x-5}+9 &= x-8\\ -6\sqrt{x-5} &= -12\\ \sqrt{x-5} &= 2\\ x-5 &= 4\\ x &= 9\end{aligned}$$

*Possible solution 9, which does not check, ∅*

44.
$$\begin{aligned}\sqrt{x-3}-4 &= \sqrt{x-3}\\ (\sqrt{x-3}-4)^2 &= (\sqrt{x-3})^2\\ x-3-8\sqrt{x-3}+16 &= x-3\\ -8\sqrt{x-3} &= -16\\ \sqrt{x-3} &= 2\\ x-3 &= 4\\ x &= 7\end{aligned}$$

*Possible solution 7, which does not check, ∅*

46.
$$\begin{aligned}\sqrt{5x+1} &= 1+\sqrt{5x}\\ (\sqrt{5x+1})^2 &= (1+\sqrt{5x})^2\\ 5x+1 &= 1+2\sqrt{5x}+5x\\ 0 &= 2\sqrt{5x}\\ 0 &= \sqrt{5x}\\ 0 &= x\end{aligned}$$

47.
$$\begin{aligned}\sqrt{2x+4} &= \sqrt{x+3}+1\\ (\sqrt{2x+4})^2 &= (\sqrt{x+3}+1)^2\\ 2x+4 &= x+3+2\sqrt{x+3}+1\\ x &= 2\sqrt{x+3}\\ x^2 &= 4x+12\\ x^2-4x-12 &= 0\\ (x+2)(x-6) &= 0\\ x+2 &= 0\\ x &= -2 \quad \textit{or}\\ x-6 &= 0\\ x &= 6\end{aligned}$$

*Possible solutions −2 and 6; only 6 checks*

48.
$$\begin{aligned}\sqrt{2x-1} &= \sqrt{x-4}+2\\ (\sqrt{2x-1})^2 &= (\sqrt{x-4}+2)^2\\ 2x-1 &= x-4+4\sqrt{x-4}+4\\ (x-1)^2 &= (4\sqrt{x-4})^2\\ x^2-2x+1 &= 16x-64\\ x^2-18x+65 &= 0\\ (x-5)(x-13) &= 0\\ x-5 &= 0\\ x &= 5 \quad \textit{or}\\ x-13 &= 0\\ x &= 13\end{aligned}$$

50.
$$\begin{aligned}t &= \sqrt{\frac{2h-40t}{g}}\\ t^2 &= \frac{2h-40t}{g}\\ gt^2 &= 2h-40t\\ gt^2+40t &= 2h\\ \frac{gt^2+40t}{2} &= h\end{aligned}$$

51. $T = 2\pi\sqrt{\frac{L}{32}}, \quad T = 2$

$$2 = 2\left(\frac{22}{7}\right)\sqrt{\frac{L}{32}}$$

$$\frac{7}{22} = \sqrt{\frac{L}{32}}$$

$$\frac{49}{484} = \frac{L}{32}$$

$$\frac{49 \cdot 32}{484} = L$$

$$\frac{392}{121} = L$$

$$3.24 \text{ ft.} \approx L$$

52. $T = 2\pi\sqrt{\frac{L}{32}}$

$$\frac{T}{2\pi} = \sqrt{\frac{L}{32}}$$

$$\frac{T^2}{4\pi^2} = \frac{L}{32}$$

$$\frac{32T^2}{4\pi^2} = L$$

$$\frac{8T^2}{\pi^2} = L$$

54.

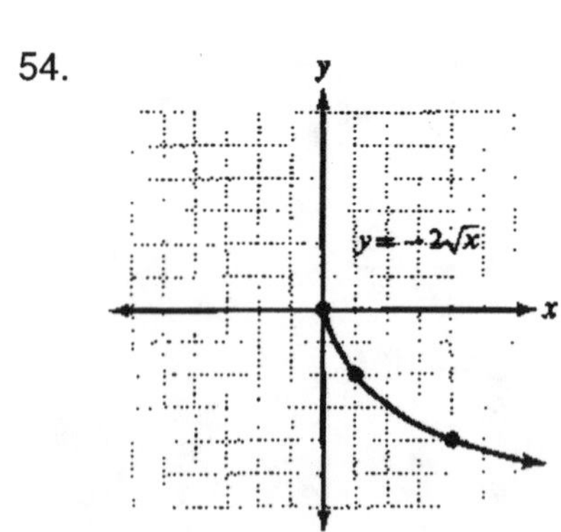


55.

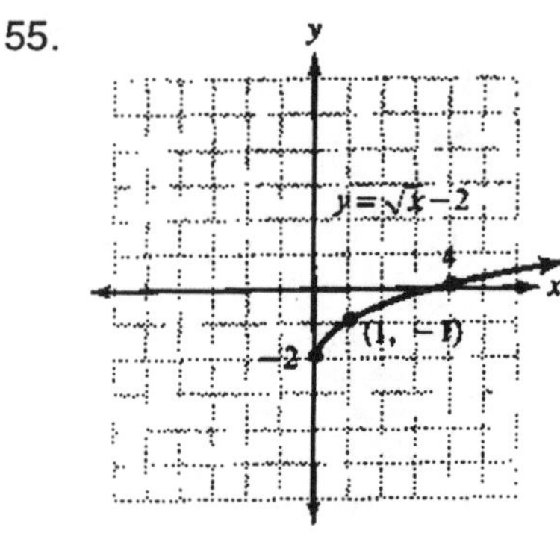


56.

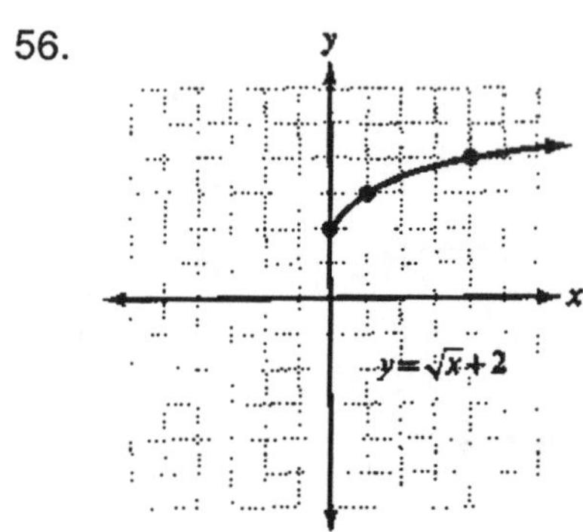


58.

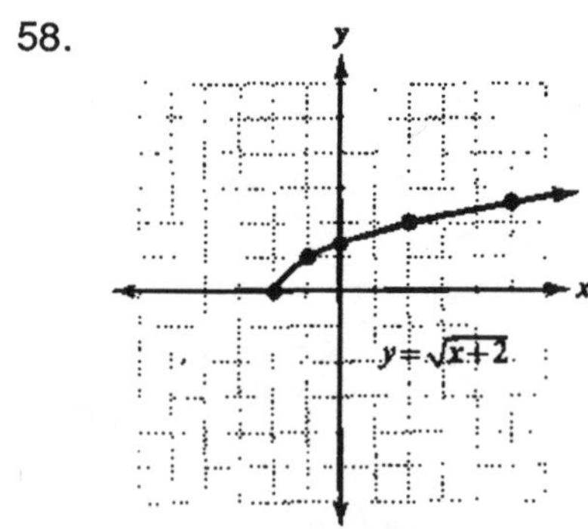


59.

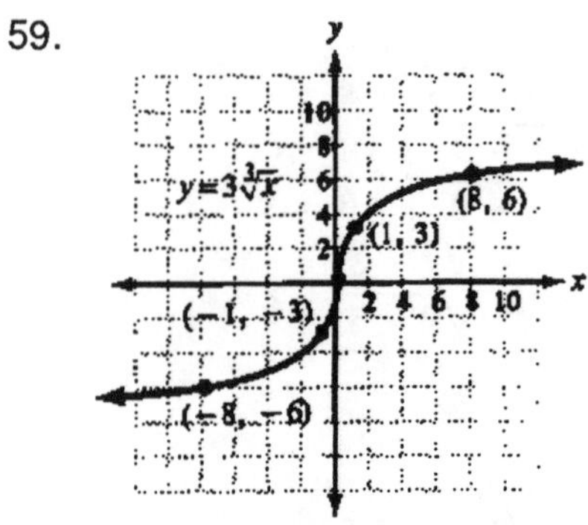

60.

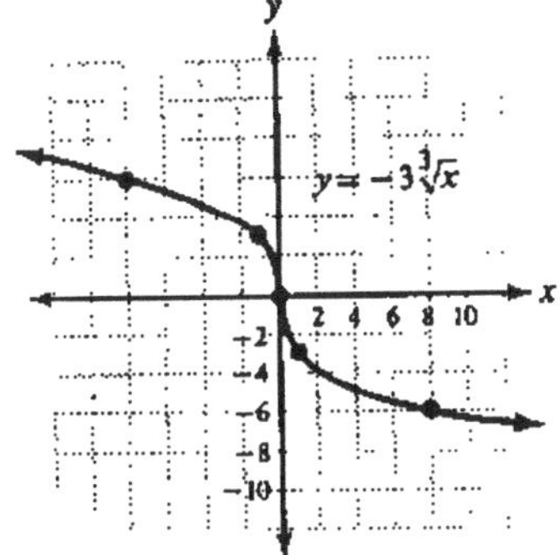


62.

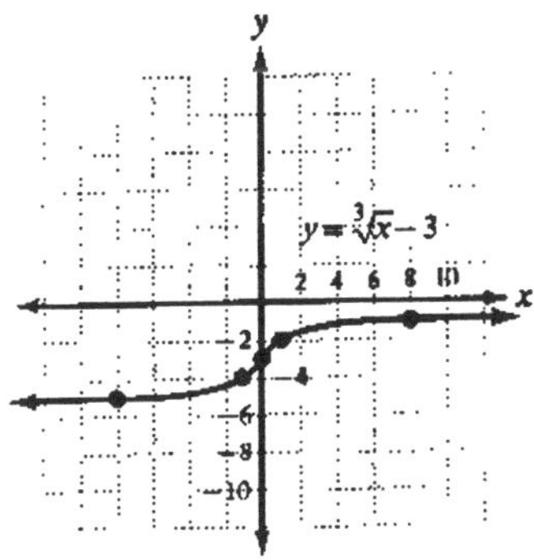


63.

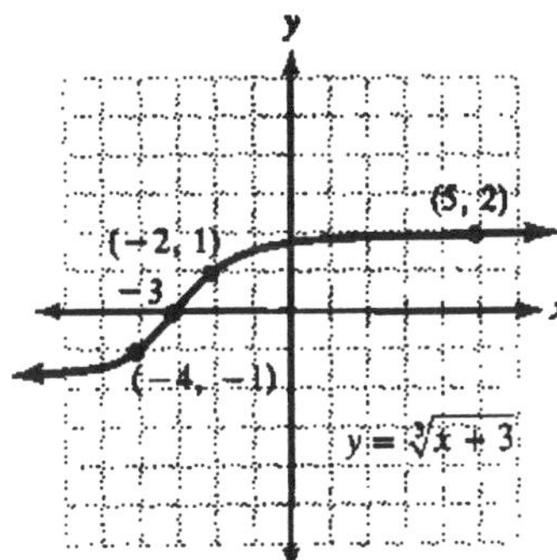


64.

66. $(\sqrt{x} - 4)(\sqrt{x} + 5)$

$= x + 5\sqrt{x} - 4\sqrt{x} - 20$

$= x + \sqrt{x} - 20$

67. $(\sqrt{x} + 5)^2 = (\sqrt{x})^2 + 2(\sqrt{5})(5) + 5^2$

$= x + 10\sqrt{5} + 25$

68. $(\sqrt{5} + \sqrt{3})(\sqrt{5} - \sqrt{3}) = 5 - 3 = 2$

70. $\dfrac{\sqrt{5} - \sqrt{3}}{\sqrt{5} + \sqrt{3}}$

$= \dfrac{\sqrt{5} - \sqrt{3}}{\sqrt{5} + \sqrt{3}} \cdot \dfrac{\sqrt{5} - \sqrt{3}}{\sqrt{5} - \sqrt{3}}$

$= \dfrac{5 - 2\sqrt{15} + 3}{5 - 3}$

$= \dfrac{8 - 2\sqrt{15}}{2}$

$= 4 - \sqrt{15}$

71. $\dfrac{x}{3\sqrt{2x - 3}} - \dfrac{1}{\sqrt{2x - 3}} = \dfrac{1}{3}$

$$x - 3 = \sqrt{2x - 3}$$
$$x^2 - 6x + 9 = 2x - 3$$
$$x^2 - 8x + 12 = 0$$
$$(x - 2)(x - 6) = 0$$
$$x - 2 = 0$$
$$x = 2 \quad \textit{or}$$

$$x - 6 = 0$$
$$x = 6$$

*Possible solution 2 and 6, only 6 checks*

72. $\dfrac{x}{5\sqrt{2x+10}} + \dfrac{1}{\sqrt{2x+10}} = \dfrac{1}{5}$

$$\begin{aligned} x + 5 &= \sqrt{2x+10} \\ x^2 + 10x + 25 &= 2x + 10 \\ x^2 + 8x + 15 &= 0 \\ (x+3)(x+5) &= 0 \\ x + 3 &= 0 \\ x &= -3 \quad \text{or} \\ x + 5 &= 0 \\ x &= -5 \end{aligned}$$

*Possible solution -3 and -5; only -3 checks*

74. $x - 1 = \sqrt[3]{4x-4}$

$$\begin{aligned} (x-1)^3 &= (\sqrt[3]{4x-4}\,)^3 \\ x^3 - 3x^2 + 3x - 1 &= 4x - 4 \\ x^3 - 3x^2 - x + 3 &= 0 \\ x^2(x-3) - 1(x-3) &= 0 \\ (x^2-1)(x-3) &= 0 \\ (x+1)(x-1)(x-3) &= 0 \\ x + 1 &= 0 \\ x &= -1 \quad \text{or} \\ x - 1 &= 0 \\ x &= 1 \quad \text{or} \\ x - 3 &= 0 \\ x &= 3 \end{aligned}$$

75. $y + 2 = \sqrt{x^2 + (y-2)^2}$

$$\begin{aligned} (y+2)^2 &= \left(\sqrt{x^2 + (y-2)^2}\right)^2 \\ y^2 + 4y + 4 &= x^2 + y^2 - 4y + 4 \\ 8y &= x^2 \\ y &= \frac{1}{8}x^2 \end{aligned}$$

76. $y + \dfrac{1}{2} = \sqrt{x^2 + \left(y - \dfrac{1}{2}\right)^2}$

$$\begin{aligned} \left(y + \frac{1}{2}\right)^2 &= \left(\sqrt{x^2 + \left(y - \frac{1}{2}\right)^2}\right)^2 \\ y^2 + y + \frac{1}{4} &= x^2 + y^2 - y + \frac{1}{4} \\ 2y &= x^2 \\ y &= \frac{1}{2}x^2 \end{aligned}$$

## Section 6.7

2. $\sqrt{-49} = \sqrt{49}\sqrt{-1} = 7i$

3. $-\sqrt{-25} = -\sqrt{25}\sqrt{-1} = -5i$

4. $-\sqrt{-81} = -\sqrt{81}\sqrt{-1} = -9i$

6. $\sqrt{-48} = \sqrt{16 \cdot 3}\sqrt{-1} = 4i\sqrt{3}$

7. $-\sqrt{-12} = -\sqrt{4 \cdot 3}\sqrt{-1} = -2i\sqrt{3}$

8. $-\sqrt{-75} = -\sqrt{25 \cdot 3}\sqrt{-1} = -5i\sqrt{3}$

10. $$\begin{aligned} i^{31} &= (i^2)^{15} \cdot i \\ &= (-1)^{15} \cdot i \\ &= (-1)i \\ &= -i \end{aligned}$$

11. $i^{26} = (i^2)^{13} = (-1)^{13} = -1$

12. $$\begin{aligned} i^{37} &= (i^2)^{18} \cdot i \\ &= (-1)^{18} \cdot i \\ &= 1i \\ &= i \end{aligned}$$

14. $i^{42} = (i^2)^{21} = (-1)^{21} = -1$

15. $2x + 3yi = 6 - 3i$
$2x = 6 \quad 3y = -3$
$x = 3 \quad y = -1$

16. $4x - 2yi = 4 + 8i$
$4x = 4 \quad -2y = 8$
$x = 1 \quad y = -4$

18. $4 + 7i = 6x - 14yi$
$4 = 6x \quad 7 = -14y$
$\frac{2}{3} = x \quad -\frac{1}{2} = y$

19. $2x + 10i = -16 - 2yi$
$2x = -16 \quad 10 = -2y$
$x = -8 \quad -5 = y$

20. $4x - 5i = -2 + 3yi$
$4x = -2 \quad -5 = 3y$
$x = -\frac{1}{2} \quad -\frac{5}{3} = y$

22. $(4x - 3) - 2i = 8 + yi$
$4x - 3 = 8 \quad -2 = y$
$4x = 11$
$x = \frac{11}{4}$

23. $(7x - 1) + 4i = 2 + (5y + 2)i$
$7x - 1 = 2 \quad 4 = 5y + 2$
$7x = 3 \quad 2 = 5y$
$x = \frac{3}{7} \quad \frac{2}{5} = y$

24. $(5x + 2) - 7i = 4 + (2y + 1)i$
$5x + 2 = 4 \quad -7 = 2y + 1$
$5x = 2 \quad -8 = 2y$
$x = \frac{2}{5} \quad -4 = y$

26. $(4 + i) + (3 + 2i) = 7 + 3i$

27. $(3 - 5i) + (2 + 4i) = 5 - i$

28. $(7 + 2i) + (3 - 4i) = 10 - 2i$

30. $(6 + 7i) - (4 + i) = 2 + 6i$

31. $(3 - 5i) - (2 + i) = 1 - 6i$

32. $(7 - 3i) - (4 + 10i) = 3 - 13i$

34. $[(4 - 5i) - (2 + i)] + (2 + 5i)$
$= (2 - 6i) + (2 + 5i)$
$= 4 - i$

35. $[(7 - i) - (2 + 4i)] - (6 + 2i)$
$= (5 - 5i) - (6 + 2i)$
$= -1 - 7i$

36. $[(3 - i) - (4 + 7i)] - (3 - 4i)$
$= (-1 - 8i) - (3 - 4i)$
$= -4 - 4i$

38. $(7 - 4i) - [(-2 + i) - (3 + 7i)]$
$= (7 - 4i) - (-5 - 6i)$
$= 12 + 2i$

39. $(4 - 9i) + [(2 - 7i) - (4 + 8i)]$
$= (4 - 9i) + (-2 - 15i)$
$= 2 - 24i$

40. $(10 - 2i) - [(2 + i) - (3 - i)]$
$= (10 - 2i) - (-1 + 2i)$
$= 11 - 4i$

42. $2i(3 + 4i) = 6i + 8i^2$
$= -8 + 6i$

43. $6i(4 - 3i) = 24i - 18i^2$
$= 18 + 24i$

44. $11i(2 - i) = 22i - 11i^2$
$= 11 + 22i$

46. $(2 - 4i)(3 + i)$
$= 6 - 10i - 4i^2$
$= 6 - 10i + 4$
$= 10 - 10i$

47. $(4 + 9i)(3 - i)$
$= 12 + 23i - 9i^2$
$= 12 + 23i + 9$
$= 21 + 23i$

48. $(5 - 2i)(1 + i)$
$= 5 + 3i - 2i^2$
$= 5 + 3i + 2$
$= 7 + 3i$

50. $(1 - i)^3$
$= (1 - i)^2(1 - i)$
$= (1 - 2i + i^2)(1 - i)$
$= (1 - 2i - 1)(1 - i)$
$= (-2i)(1 - i)$
$= -2i + 2i^2$
$= -2 - 2i$

51. $(2 - i)^3$
$= (2 - i)^3(2 - i)$
$= (4 - 4i + i^2)(2 - i)$
$= (4 - 4i - 1)(2 - i)$
$= (3 - 4i)(2 - i)$
$= 6 - 11i + 4i^2$
$= 6 - 11i - 4$
$= 2 - 11i$

52. $(2 + i)^3$
$= (2 + i)^2(2 + i)$
$= (4 + 4i + i^2)(2 + i)$
$= (4 + 4i - 1)(2 + i)$
$= (3 + 4i)(2 + i)$
$= (6 + 11i + 4i^2)$
$= 6 + 11i - 4$
$= 2 + 11i$

54. $(3 + 2i)^2$
$= 9 + 12i + 4i^2$
$= 9 + 12i - 4$
$= 5 + 12i$

55. $(1 - i^2)$
$= 1 - 2i + i^2$
$= 1 - 2i - 1$
$= -2i$

56. $(1 + i)^2$
$= 1 + 2i + i^2$
$= 1 + 2i - 1$
$= 2i$

58. $(6 - 5i)^2$
$= 36 - 60i + 25i^2$
$= 36 - 60i - 25$
$= 11 - 60i$

59. $(2 + i)(2 - i)$
$= 4 - i^2$
$= 4 + 1$
$= 5$

60. $(3 + i)(3 - i)$
$= 9 - i^2$
$= 9 + 1$
$= 10$

62. $(5 + 4i)(5 - 4i)$
$= 25 - 16i^2$
$= 25 + 16$
$= 41$

63. $(2 + 3i)(2 - 3i)$
$= 4 - 9i^2$
$= 4 + 9$
$= 13$

64. $(2 - 7i)(2 + 7i)$
$= 4 - 49i^2$
$= 4 + 49$
$= 53$

66. $(11 - 7i)(11 + 7i)$
$= 121 - 49i^2$
$= 121 + 49$
$= 170$

67. $\dfrac{2-3i}{i} = \dfrac{2-3i}{i} \cdot \dfrac{i}{i}$

$= \dfrac{2i - 3i^2}{i^2}$

$= \dfrac{3+2i}{-1}$

$= -3 - 2i$

68. $\dfrac{3+4i}{i} = \dfrac{3+4i}{i} \cdot \dfrac{i}{i}$

$= \dfrac{3i + 4i^2}{i^2}$

$= \dfrac{-4+3i}{-1}$

$= 4 - 3i$

70. $\dfrac{4-3i}{-i} = \dfrac{4-3i}{-i} \cdot \dfrac{i}{i}$

$= \dfrac{4i - 3i^2}{-i^2}$

$= \dfrac{3+4i}{1}$

$= 3 + 4i$

71. $\dfrac{4}{2-3i} = \dfrac{4}{2-3i} \cdot \dfrac{2+3i}{2+3i}$

$= \dfrac{8+12i}{4-9i^2}$

$= \dfrac{8+12i}{13}$

$= \dfrac{8}{13} + \dfrac{12}{13}i$

72. $\dfrac{3}{4-5i} = \dfrac{3}{4-5i} \cdot \dfrac{4+5i}{4+5i}$

$= \dfrac{12+15i}{16-25i^2}$

$= \dfrac{12+15i}{41}$

$= \dfrac{12}{41} + \dfrac{15}{41}i$

74. $\dfrac{-1}{-2-5i} = \dfrac{-1}{-2-5i} \cdot \dfrac{-2+5i}{-2+5i}$

$= \dfrac{2-5i}{4-25i^2}$

$= \dfrac{2-5i}{29}$

$= \dfrac{2}{29} - \dfrac{5}{29}i$

75. $\dfrac{2+3i}{2-3i} = \dfrac{2+3i}{2-3i} \cdot \dfrac{2+3i}{2+3i}$

$= \dfrac{4+12i+9i^2}{4-9i^2}$

$= \dfrac{-5+12i}{13}$

$= -\dfrac{5}{13} + \dfrac{12}{13}i$

76. $\dfrac{4-7i}{4+7i} = \dfrac{4-7i}{4+7i} \cdot \dfrac{4-7i}{4-7i}$

$= \dfrac{16-56i+49i^2}{16-49i^2}$

$= \dfrac{-33-56i}{65}$

$= -\dfrac{33}{65} - \dfrac{56}{65}i$

78. $\dfrac{2+i}{5-6i} = \dfrac{2+i}{5-6i} \cdot \dfrac{5+6i}{5+6i}$

$= \dfrac{10+17i+6i^2}{25-36i^2}$

$= \dfrac{4+17i}{61}$

$= \dfrac{4}{61} + \dfrac{17}{61}i$

79. $\dfrac{3-7i}{9-5i} = \dfrac{3-7i}{9-5i} \cdot \dfrac{9+5i}{9+5i}$

$= \dfrac{27-48i-35i^2}{81-25i^2}$

$= \dfrac{62-48i}{106}$

$= \dfrac{62}{106} - \dfrac{48}{106}i$

$= \dfrac{31}{53} - \dfrac{24}{53}i$

80. $\dfrac{4+10i}{3+6i} = \dfrac{4+10i}{3+6i} \cdot \dfrac{3-6i}{3-6i}$

$= \dfrac{12+6i-60i^2}{9-36i^2}$

$= \dfrac{72+6i}{45}$

$= \dfrac{72}{45} - \dfrac{6}{45}i$

$= \dfrac{8}{5} - \dfrac{2}{15}i$

82. $y = \sqrt[3]{x}K \quad y = 14,\ x = 8$

$14 = \sqrt[3]{8}K$
$14 = 2K$
$7 = K$

$y = \sqrt[3]{x}K \quad y = 21$

$21 = \sqrt[3]{x}(7)$

$3 = \sqrt[3]{x}$
$27 = x$

83. $y = \dfrac{K}{\sqrt{x}} \quad y = 10,\ x = 25$

$10 = \dfrac{K}{\sqrt{25}}$

$10 = \dfrac{K}{5}$

$50 = K$

$y = \dfrac{K}{\sqrt{x}} \quad y = 5$

$5 = \dfrac{50}{\sqrt{x}}$

$\sqrt{x} = 10$
$x = 100$

84. $y = \dfrac{K}{x^3} \quad y = 2,\ x = 2$

$2 = \dfrac{K}{2^3}$

$16 = K$

$y = \dfrac{K}{x^3} \quad x = 4$

$y = \dfrac{16}{64}$

$y = \dfrac{1}{4}$

86. $z = x\sqrt[3]{y}K \quad z = 48,\ x = 3,\ y = 8$

$$48 = 3 \cdot \sqrt[3]{8}K$$
$$48 = 6K$$
$$8 = K$$

$$z = x\sqrt[3]{y}K \quad x = 4,\ y = \frac{1}{8}$$

$$z = 4\sqrt[3]{\frac{1}{8}}\ (8)$$

$$z = 4\left(\frac{1}{2}\right)(8)$$

$$z = 16$$

# Chapter 7

## Section 7.1

2. $x^2 = 16$
$$x = \pm\sqrt{16}$$
$$x = \pm 4$$

3. $a^2 = -9$
$$a = \pm\sqrt{-9}$$
$$a = \pm 3i$$

4. $a^2 = -49$
$$a = \pm\sqrt{-49}$$
$$a = \pm 7i$$

6. $y^2 = \frac{5}{9}$

$$y = \pm\sqrt{\frac{5}{9}}$$

$$y = \frac{\pm\sqrt{5}}{3}$$

7. $x^2 + 12 = 0$
$$x^2 = -12$$
$$x = \pm\sqrt{-12}$$
$$x = \pm 2i\sqrt{3}$$

8. $x^2 + 8 = 0$
$$x^2 = -8$$
$$x = \pm\sqrt{-8}$$
$$x = \pm 2i\sqrt{2}$$

10. $9a^2 - 20 = 0$
$$9a^2 = 20$$

$$a^2 = \frac{20}{9}$$

$$a = \pm\sqrt{\frac{20}{9}}$$

$$a = \pm\frac{2\sqrt{5}}{3}$$

11. $(2y - 1)^2 = 25$
$$2y - 1 = \pm\sqrt{25}$$
$$2y - 1 = \pm 5$$
$$2y = 1 \pm 5$$

$$y = \frac{1 \pm 5}{2}$$

$$y = \frac{1 + 5}{2} \quad \textit{or} \quad y = \frac{1 - 5}{2}$$

$$y = 3 \qquad\qquad y = -2$$

12. $(3y + 7)^2 = 1$
$$3y + 7 = \pm\sqrt{1}$$
$$3y = -7 \pm 1$$
$$y = \frac{-7 \pm 1}{3}$$
$$y = \frac{-7 + 1}{3} \quad or \quad y = \frac{-7 - 1}{3}$$
$$y = -2 \qquad y = -\frac{8}{3}$$

14. $(3a - 5)^2 = -49$
$$3a - 5 = \pm\sqrt{49}$$
$$3a - 5 = \pm 7i$$
$$3a = 5 \pm 7i$$
$$a = \frac{5 \pm 7i}{3}$$

15. $(5x + 2)^2 = -8$
$$5x + 2 = \pm\sqrt{-8}$$
$$5x + 2 = \pm 2i\sqrt{2}$$
$$5x = -2 \pm 2i\sqrt{2}$$
$$x = \frac{-2 \pm 2i\sqrt{2}}{5}$$

16. $(6x - 7)^2 = -75$
$$6x - 7 = \pm\sqrt{-75}$$
$$6x - 7 = \pm 5i\sqrt{3}$$
$$6x = 7 \pm 5i\sqrt{3}$$
$$x = \frac{7 \pm 5i\sqrt{3}}{6}$$

17. $x^2 + 8x + 16 = -27$
$$(x + 4)^2 = -27$$
$$x + 4 = \pm\sqrt{-27}$$
$$x + 4 = \pm 3i\sqrt{3}$$
$$x = -4 \pm 3i\sqrt{3}$$

18. $x^2 - 12x + 36 = -8$
$$(x - 6)^2 = -8$$
$$x - 6 = \pm\sqrt{-8}$$
$$x - 6 = \pm 2i\sqrt{2}$$
$$x = 6 \pm 2i\sqrt{2}$$

19. $4a^2 - 12a + 9 = -4$
$$(2a - 3)^2 = -4$$
$$2a - 3 = \pm\sqrt{-4}$$
$$2a - 3 = \pm 2i$$
$$2a = 3 \pm 2i$$
$$a = \frac{3 + 2i}{2}$$

20. $9a^2 - 12a + 4 = -9$
$$(3a - 2)^2 = -9$$
$$3a - 2 = \pm\sqrt{-9}$$
$$3a - 2 = \pm 3i$$
$$3a = 2 \pm 3i$$
$$a = \frac{2 \pm 3i}{3}$$

22. $(2x + 1)^2 + (2x - 1)^2 = 10$
$$4x^2 + 4x + 1 + 4x^2 - 4x + 1 = 10$$
$$8x^2 + 2 = 10$$
$$8x^2 = 8$$
$$x^2 = 1$$
$$x = \pm\sqrt{1}$$
$$x = \pm 1$$

23. $(2x + 3)^2 + (2x - 3)^2 = 26$
$$4x^2 + 12x + 9 + 4x^2 - 12x + 9 = 26$$
$$8x^2 + 18 = 26$$
$$8x^2 = 8$$
$$x^2 = 1$$
$$x = \pm\sqrt{1}$$
$$x = \pm 1$$

24. $(3x + 2)^2 + (3x - 2)^2 = 26$
$$9x^2 + 12 + 4 + 9x^2 - 12 + 4 = 26$$
$$18x^2 + 8 = 26$$
$$18x^2 = 18$$
$$x^2 = 1$$
$$x = \pm\sqrt{1}$$
$$x = \pm 1$$

26. $(3x + 4)(3x - 4) - (x + 2)(x - 2) = -4$
$$9x^2 - 16 - x^2 + 4 = -4$$
$$8x^2 - 12 = -4$$
$$8x^2 = 8$$
$$x^2 = 1$$
$$x = \pm\sqrt{1}$$
$$x = \pm 1$$

27. $x^2 + 12x + \underline{\ 36\ } = (x + \underline{\ 6\ })^2$

28. $x^2 + 6x + \underline{\ 9\ } = (x + \underline{\ 3\ })^2$

30. $x^2 - 2x + \underline{\ 1\ } = (x + \underline{\ 1\ })^2$

31. $a^2 - 10a + \underline{\ 25\ } = (a - \underline{\ 5\ })^2$

32. $a^2 - 8a + \underline{\ 16\ } = (a - \underline{\ 4\ })^2$

34. $x^2 + 3x + \underline{\frac{9}{4}} = (x + \underline{\frac{3}{2}})^2$

35. $y^2 - 7y + \underline{\frac{49}{4}} = (y - \underline{\frac{7}{2}})^2$

36. $y^2 - y + \underline{\frac{1}{4}} = (y - \underline{\frac{1}{2}})^2$

38.
$$x^2 - 2x = 8$$
$$x^2 - 2x + 1 = 8 + 1$$
$$(x - 1)^2 = 9$$
$$x - 1 = \pm\sqrt{9}$$
$$x - 1 = \pm 3$$
$$x = 1 \pm 3$$

$x = 1 + 3$ *or* $x = 1 - 3$
$x = 4$ $\quad x = -2$

39.
$$x^2 + 12x = -27$$
$$x^2 + 12x + 36 = -27 + 36$$
$$(x + 6)^2 = 9$$
$$x + 6 = \pm\sqrt{9}$$
$$x + 6 = \pm 3$$
$$x = -6 \pm 3$$

$x = -6 + 3$ *or* $x = -6 - 3$
$x = -3$ $\quad x = -9$

40.
$$x^2 - 6x = 16$$
$$x^2 - 6x + 9 = 16 + 9$$
$$(x - 3)^2 = 25$$
$$x - 3 = \pm\sqrt{25}$$
$$x - 3 = \pm 5$$
$$x = 3 \pm 5$$

$x = 3 + 5$ *or* $x = 3 - 5$
$x = 8$ $\quad x = -2$

42.
$$a^2 + 10a + 22 = 0$$
$$a^2 + 10a + 25 = -22 + 25$$
$$(a + 5)^2 = 3$$
$$a + 5 = \pm\sqrt{3}$$
$$a = -5 \pm \sqrt{3}$$

43.
$$y^2 - 8y + 1 = 0$$
$$y^2 - 8y + 16 = -1 + 16$$
$$(y - 4)^2 = 15$$
$$y - 4 = \pm\sqrt{15}$$
$$y = 4 \pm \sqrt{15}$$

44.
$$y^2 - 6y - 1 = 0$$
$$y^2 - 6y = 1$$
$$y^2 - 6y + 9 = 1 + 9$$
$$(y - 3)^2 = 10$$
$$y - 3 = \pm\sqrt{10}$$
$$y = 3 \pm \sqrt{10}$$

46.
$$x^2 - 5x - 2 = 0$$
$$x^2 - 5x + \frac{25}{4} = 2 + \frac{25}{4}$$
$$\left(x - \frac{5}{2}\right)^2 = \frac{33}{4}$$
$$x - \frac{5}{2} = \pm\sqrt{\frac{33}{4}}$$
$$x - \frac{5}{2} = \pm\frac{\sqrt{33}}{2}$$
$$x = \frac{5 \pm \sqrt{33}}{2}$$

47.
$$2x^2 - 4x - 8 = 0$$
$$x^2 - 2x - 4 = 0$$
$$x^2 - 2x + 1 = 4 + 1$$
$$(x - 1)^2 = 5$$
$$x - 1 = \pm\sqrt{5}$$
$$x = 1 \pm \sqrt{5}$$

48. $3x^2 - 9x - 12 = 0$
$x^2 - 3x - 4 = 0$

$$x^2 - 3x + \frac{9}{4} = 4 + \frac{9}{4}$$

$$\left(x - \frac{3}{2}\right)^2 = \frac{25}{4}$$

$$x - \frac{3}{2} = \pm\sqrt{\frac{25}{4}}$$

$$x - \frac{3}{2} = \pm\frac{5}{2}$$

$$x = \frac{3}{2} \pm \frac{5}{2}$$

$x = \frac{3}{2} + \frac{5}{2}$ *or* $x = \frac{3}{2} - \frac{5}{2}$

$x = 4$ $\quad$ $x = -1$

50. $5t^2 + 12t - 1 = 0$

$$t^2 + \frac{12}{5}t = \frac{1}{5}$$

$$t^2 + \frac{12}{5}t + \frac{36}{25} = \frac{1}{5} + \frac{36}{25}$$

$$\left(t + \frac{6}{5}\right)^2 = \frac{41}{25}$$

$$t + \frac{6}{5} = \pm\sqrt{\frac{41}{25}}$$

$$t + \frac{6}{5} = \pm\frac{\sqrt{41}}{5}$$

$$t = \frac{-6 \pm \sqrt{41}}{5}$$

51. $4x^2 - 3x + 5 = 0$

$$x^2 - \frac{3}{4}x = -\frac{5}{4}$$

$$x - \frac{3}{4}x + \frac{9}{64} = -\frac{5}{4} + \frac{9}{64}$$

$$\left(x - \frac{3}{8}\right)^2 = \frac{-71}{64}$$

$$x - \frac{3}{8} = \pm\sqrt{\frac{-71}{64}}$$

$$x = \frac{3 \pm i\sqrt{71}}{8}$$

52. $7x^2 - 5x + 2 = 0$

$$x^2 - \frac{5}{7}x + \frac{25}{196} = -\frac{2}{7} + \frac{25}{196}$$

$$\left(x - \frac{5}{14}\right)^2 = \frac{-56}{196} + \frac{25}{196}$$

$$x - \frac{5}{14} = \pm\sqrt{\frac{-31}{196}}$$

$$x - \frac{5}{14} = \pm\frac{i\sqrt{31}}{14}$$

$$x = \frac{5 \pm i\sqrt{31}}{14}$$

54. $x^2 + \left(\frac{1}{2}\right)^2 = 1^2$

$$x^2 = \frac{3}{4}$$

$x = \frac{\sqrt{3}}{2}$ *inches, 1 inch*

55. $x^2 + 3^2 = 6^2$
$x^2 = 27$
$x = \pm 3\sqrt{3}$ *feet, 6 feet*

56. $A^2 + x^2 = (2x)^2$
$A^2 = 3x^2$
$A = x\sqrt{3},\ 2x$

58. $3^2 + 3^2 = x^2$
$18 = x^2$
$x = 3\sqrt{2}$ *inches*

59. $x^2 + x^2 = 1^2$
$2x^2 = 1$
$x^2 = \frac{1}{2}$
$x = \frac{\sqrt{2}}{2}$ *inches*

60. $x^2 + x^2 = 2^2$
$2x^2 = 4$
$x^2 = 2$
$x = \sqrt{2}$ *feet*

62. $a^2 + a^2 = x^2$
$2a^2 = x^2$
$a^2 = \frac{x^2}{2}$
$a = \frac{x\sqrt{2}}{2}$

63. $790^2 = 120^2 + x^2$
$624{,}100 = 14{,}400 + x^2$
$609{,}700 = x^2$
$x = 781$ *feet*

64. $4{,}100^2 = 480^2 + x^2$
$16{,}810{,}000 = 230{,}400 + x^2$
$16{,}579{,}600 = x^2$
$x = 4{,}072$ *feet*

66. $\frac{710}{4{,}838} = 0.15$
*to the nearest hundredth*

67. $\sqrt{45} = \sqrt{9 \cdot 5} = 3\sqrt{5}$

68. $\sqrt{24} = \sqrt{4 \cdot 6} = 2\sqrt{6}$

70. $\sqrt{8y^3} = \sqrt{4y^2 \cdot 2y} = 2y\sqrt{2y}$

71. $\sqrt[3]{54x^6y^5}$
$= \sqrt[3]{27x^6y^3 \cdot 2y^2}$
$= 3x^2y\sqrt[3]{2y^2}$

72. $\sqrt[3]{16x^9y^4}$
$= \sqrt[3]{8x^9y^6 \cdot 2y}$
$= 2x^3y^2\sqrt[3]{2y}$

74. $\sqrt{b^2 - 4ac}$, $a = 2$, $b = -6$, $c = 3$
$= \sqrt{(-6)^2 - 4(2)(3)}$
$= \sqrt{36 - 24}$
$= \sqrt{12}$
$= 2\sqrt{3}$

75. $\frac{3}{\sqrt{2}} = \frac{3}{\sqrt{2}} \cdot \frac{\sqrt{2}}{\sqrt{2}} = \frac{3\sqrt{2}}{2}$

76. $\frac{5}{\sqrt{3}} = \frac{5}{\sqrt{3}} \cdot \frac{\sqrt{3}}{\sqrt{3}} = \frac{5\sqrt{3}}{3}$

78. $\frac{3}{\sqrt[3]{2}} = \frac{3}{\sqrt[3]{2}} \cdot \frac{\sqrt[3]{4}}{\sqrt[3]{4}}$
$= \frac{3\sqrt[3]{4}}{\sqrt[3]{8}}$
$= \frac{3\sqrt[3]{4}}{2}$

**Section 7.2**

2. $x^2 + 5x - 6 = 0$
$(x + 2)(x - 1) = 0$
$x + 6 = 0$
$x = -6$ *or*

$x - 1 = 0$
$x = 1$

3. $a^2 - 4a + 1 = 0$

$$x = \frac{-(-4) \pm \sqrt{(-4)^2 - 4(1)(1)}}{2(1)}$$

$$x = \frac{4 \pm \sqrt{16 - 4}}{2}$$

$$x = \frac{4 \pm \sqrt{12}}{2}$$

$$x = \frac{4 \pm 2\sqrt{3}}{2}$$

$$x = 2 \pm \sqrt{3}$$

4. $a^2 + 4a + 1 = 0$

$$x = \frac{-4 \pm \sqrt{4^2 - 4(1)(1)}}{2(1)}$$

$$x = \frac{-4 \pm \sqrt{16 - 4}}{2}$$

$$x = \frac{-4 \pm \sqrt{12}}{2}$$

$$x = \frac{-4 \pm 2\sqrt{3}}{2}$$

$$x = -2 \pm \sqrt{3}$$

6. $\frac{1}{4}x^2 + \frac{1}{4}x - \frac{1}{2} = 0$

$$x^2 - x - 2 = 0$$
$$(x + 2)(x - 1) = 0$$

$x + 2 = 0$ *or* $x - 1 = 0$
$x = -2$ $\quad x = 1$

7. $\frac{x^2}{2} + 1 = \frac{2x}{3}$

$$3x^2 - 4x + 6 = 0$$

$$x = \frac{-(-4) \pm \sqrt{(-4)^2 - 4(3)(6)}}{2(3)}$$

$$x = \frac{4 \pm \sqrt{16 - 72}}{6}$$

$$x = \frac{4 \pm \sqrt{-56}}{6}$$

$$x = \frac{4 \pm 2i\sqrt{14}}{6}$$

$$x = \frac{2 \pm i\sqrt{14}}{3}$$

8. $\frac{x^2}{2} + \frac{2}{3} = -\frac{2x}{3}$

$$3x^2 + 4x + 4 = 0$$

$$x = \frac{-4 \pm \sqrt{4^2 - 4(3)(4)}}{2(3)}$$

$$x = \frac{-4 \pm \sqrt{16 - 48}}{6}$$

$$x = \frac{-4 \pm \sqrt{-32}}{6}$$

$$x = \frac{-4 \pm 4i\sqrt{2}}{6}$$

$$x = \frac{-2 + 2i\sqrt{2}}{3}$$

10. $2y^2 + 10y = 0$
$2y(y + 5) = 0$
$2y = 0$ *or* $y + 5 = 0$
$y = 0$ $\quad y = -5$

11. $30x^2 + 40x = 0$
$10x(3x + 4) = 0$
$10x = 0$ *or* $3x + 4 = 0$
$x = 0$ $\quad 3x = -4$

$$x = -\frac{4}{3}$$

12. $50x^2 - 20x = 0$
$10x(5x - 2) = 0$

$10x = 0$ *or* $5x - 2 = 0$
$x = 0$ $\quad 5x = 2$

$$x = \frac{2}{5}$$

14. $$\frac{t^2}{3} - \frac{t}{2} = -\frac{3}{2}$$

$2t^2 - 3t + 9 = 0$

$$x = \frac{-(-3) \pm \sqrt{(-3)^2 - 4(2)(9)}}{2(2)}$$

$$x = \frac{3 \pm \sqrt{9 - 72}}{4}$$

$$x = \frac{3 \pm \sqrt{-63}}{4}$$

$$x = \frac{3 \pm 3i\sqrt{7}}{4}$$

15. $0.01x^2 + 0.06x - 0.08 = 0$
$x^2 + 6x - 8 = 0$

$$x = \frac{-6 \pm \sqrt{6^2 - 4(1)(-8)}}{2(1)}$$

$$x = \frac{-6 \pm \sqrt{36 + 32}}{2}$$

$$x = \frac{-6 \pm \sqrt{68}}{2}$$

$$x = \frac{-6 \pm 2\sqrt{17}}{2}$$

$$x = -3 \pm \sqrt{17}$$

16. $0.02x^2 - 0.03x + 0.05 = 0$

$$2x^2 - 3x + 5 = 0$$

$$x = \frac{-(-3) \pm \sqrt{9^2 - 4(2)(5)}}{2(2)}$$

$$x = \frac{3 \pm \sqrt{9 - 40}}{4}$$

$$x = \frac{3 \pm \sqrt{-31}}{4}$$

$$x = \frac{3 \pm i\sqrt{31}}{4}$$

18. $2x - 3 = 3x^2$

$$3x^2 - 2x + 3 = 0$$

$$x = \frac{-(-2) \pm \sqrt{(-2)^2 - 4(3)(3)}}{2(3)}$$

$$x = \frac{2 \pm \sqrt{4 - 36}}{6}$$

$$x = \frac{2 \pm \sqrt{-32}}{6}$$

$$x = \frac{2 \pm 4i\sqrt{2}}{6}$$

$$x = \frac{1 \pm 2i\sqrt{2}}{3}$$

19. $100x^2 - 200x + 100 = 0$

$$x^2 - 2x + 1 = 0$$
$$(x - 1)(x - 1) = 0$$
$$x - 1 = 0$$
$$x = 1$$

20. $100x^2 - 600x + 900 = 0$

$$x^2 - 6x + 9 = 0$$
$$(x - 3)(x - 3) = 0$$
$$x - 3 = 0$$
$$x = 3$$

22. $$\frac{1}{4}r^2 = \frac{2}{5}r + \frac{1}{10}$$

$$5r^2 - 8r - 2 = 0$$

$$x = \frac{-(-8) \pm \sqrt{(-8)^2 - 4(5)(-2)}}{2(5)}$$

$$x = \frac{8 \pm \sqrt{64 + 40}}{10}$$

$$x = \frac{8 \pm \sqrt{104}}{10}$$

$$x = \frac{8 \pm 2\sqrt{26}}{10}$$

$$x = \frac{4 \pm \sqrt{26}}{5}$$

23. $$(x - 3)(x - 5) = 1$$
$$x^2 - 8x + 15 - 1 = 0$$
$$x^2 - 8x + 14 = 0$$

$$x = \frac{-(-8) \pm \sqrt{(-8)^2 - 4(1)(14)}}{2(1)}$$

$$x = \frac{8 \pm \sqrt{64 - 56}}{2}$$

$$x = \frac{8 \pm \sqrt{8}}{2}$$

$$x = \frac{8 \pm 2\sqrt{2}}{2}$$

$$x = 4 \pm \sqrt{2}$$

24. $$(x - 3)(x + 1) = -6$$
$$x^2 - 2x - 3 + 6 = 0$$
$$x^2 - 2x + 3 = 0$$

$$x = \frac{-(-2) \pm \sqrt{(-2)^2 - 4(1)(3)}}{2(1)}$$

$$x = \frac{2 \pm \sqrt{4 - 12}}{2}$$

$$x = \frac{2 \pm 2i\sqrt{2}}{2}$$

$$x = 1 \pm i\sqrt{2}$$

26. $$(x - 4)^2 + (x + 2)(x + 1) = 9$$
$$x^2 - 8x + 16 + x^2 + 3x + 2 = 9$$
$$2x^2 - 5x + 9 = 0$$

$$x = \frac{-(-5) \pm \sqrt{(-5)^2 - 4(2)(9)}}{2(2)}$$

$$x = \frac{5 \pm \sqrt{25 - 72}}{4}$$

$$x = \frac{5 \pm \sqrt{-47}}{4}$$

$$x = \frac{5 \pm i\sqrt{47}}{4}$$

27. $$\frac{x^2}{3} - \frac{5x}{6} = \frac{1}{2}$$

$$2x^2 - 5x - 3 = 0$$
$$(2x + 1)(x - 3) = 0$$
$$2x + 1 = 0 \quad or \quad x - 3 = 0$$

$$x = -\frac{1}{2} \qquad x = 3$$

28. $$\frac{x^2}{6} + \frac{5}{6} = -\frac{x}{3}$$

$$x^2 + 2x + 5 = 0$$

$$x = \frac{-2 \pm \sqrt{2^2 - 4(1)(5)}}{2(1)}$$

$$x = \frac{-2 \pm \sqrt{4 - 20}}{2}$$

$$x = \frac{-2 \pm \sqrt{-16}}{2}$$

$$x = \frac{-2 \pm 4i}{2}$$

$$x = -1 \pm 2i$$

30. $\dfrac{1}{x+1} + \dfrac{1}{x} = \dfrac{1}{3}$

$$3x + 3(x+1) = x(x+1)$$
$$3x + 3x + 3 = x^2 + x$$
$$0 = x^2 - 5x - 3$$

$$x = \frac{-(-5) \pm \sqrt{(-5)^2 - 4(1)(-3)}}{2(1)}$$

$$x = \frac{5 \pm \sqrt{25 + 12}}{2}$$

$$x = \frac{5 \pm \sqrt{37}}{2}$$

34. $\dfrac{1}{x+3} + \dfrac{1}{x+4} = 1$

$$x + 4 + x + 3 = (x+3)(x+4)$$
$$2x + 7 = x^2 + 7x + 12$$
$$0 = x^2 + 5x + 5$$

$$x = \frac{-5 \pm \sqrt{5^2 - 4(1)(5)}}{2(1)}$$

$$x = \frac{-5 \pm \sqrt{25 - 20}}{2}$$

$$x = \frac{-5 \pm \sqrt{5}}{2}$$

31. $\dfrac{1}{y-1} + \dfrac{1}{y+1} = 1$

$$y + 1 + y - 1 = (y-1)(y+1)$$
$$2y = y^2 - 1$$
$$0 = y^2 - 2y - 1$$

$$x = \frac{-(-2) \pm \sqrt{(-2)^2 - 4(1)(-1)}}{2(1)}$$

$$x = \frac{2 \pm \sqrt{4 + 4}}{2}$$

$$x = \frac{2 \pm 2\sqrt{2}}{2}$$

$$x = 1 \pm \sqrt{2}$$

32. $\dfrac{2}{y+2} + \dfrac{3}{y-2} = 1$

$$2(y-2) + 3(y+2) = (y+2)(y-2)$$
$$2y - 4 + 3y + 6 = y^2 - 4$$
$$0 = y^2 - 5y - 6$$
$$0 = (y+1)(y-6)$$

$y + 1 = 0$ *or* $y - 6 = 0$

$y = -1$ $\quad y = 6$

35. $\dfrac{6}{r^2 - 1} - \dfrac{1}{2} = \dfrac{1}{r+1}$

$$12 - (r^2 - 1) = 2(r - 1)$$
$$12 - r^2 + 1 = 2r - 2$$
$$0 = r^2 + 2r - 15$$
$$0 = (r+5)(r-3)$$

$r + 5 = 0$ *or* $r - 3 = 0$

$r = -5$ $\quad r = 3$

36. $2 + \dfrac{5}{r-1} = \dfrac{12}{(r-1)^2}$

$$2(r-1)^2 + 5(r-1) = 12$$
$$2r^2 - 4r + 2 + 5r - 5 - 12 = 0$$
$$2r^2 + r - 15 = 0$$
$$(2x+5)(r-3) = 0$$
$$2x + 5 = 0$$

$x = \dfrac{5}{2}$ *or* $x + 3 = 0$

$$x = -3$$

38. $x^3 - 27 = 0$

$$(x-3)(x^2 - 3x + 9) = 0$$
$$x - 3 = 0$$

$x = 3$ *or* $x = \dfrac{-(-3) \pm \sqrt{(-3)^2 - 4(1)(9)}}{2(1)}$

$$x = \frac{3 \pm \sqrt{9 - 36}}{2}$$

$$x = \frac{3 \pm \sqrt{-27}}{2}$$

$$x = \frac{3 \pm 3i\sqrt{3}}{2}$$

39.
$$8a^3 + 27 = 0$$
$$(2a + 3)(4a^2 + 6a + 9) = 0$$
$$2a + 3 = 0$$
$$a = -\frac{3}{2} \quad or \quad x = \frac{-6 \pm \sqrt{6^2 - 4(4)(9)}}{2(4)}$$
$$x = \frac{-6 \pm \sqrt{36 - 144}}{8}$$
$$x = \frac{-6 =- \sqrt{-108}}{8}$$
$$x = \frac{-6 \pm 6i\sqrt{3}}{3}$$
$$x = \frac{-3 \pm 3i\sqrt{3}}{4}$$

40.
$$27a^3 + 8 = 0$$
$$(3a + 2)(9a^2 + 6a + 4) = 0$$
$$3a + 2 = 0$$
$$a = -\frac{2}{3} \quad or \quad a = \frac{-6 \pm \sqrt{6^2 - 4(9)(4)}}{2(9)}$$
$$a = \frac{-6 \pm \sqrt{36 - 144}}{18}$$
$$a = \frac{-6 \pm \sqrt{-108}}{18}$$
$$a = \frac{-6 \pm 6i\sqrt{3}}{18}$$
$$a = \frac{-1 \pm i\sqrt{3}}{3}$$

42.
$$64t^3 + 1 = 0$$
$$(4t + 1)(16t^2 - 4t + 1) = 0$$
$$4t + 1 = 0$$
$$t = -\frac{1}{4} \quad or \quad t = \frac{-(-4) \pm \sqrt{(-4)^2 - 4(16)(1)}}{2(16)}$$
$$t = \frac{4 \pm \sqrt{16 - 64}}{32}$$
$$t = \frac{4 \pm \sqrt{-48}}{32}$$
$$t = \frac{4 \pm 4i\sqrt{3}}{32}$$
$$t = \frac{1 \pm i\sqrt{3}}{8}$$

43.
$$2x^3 + 2x^2 + 3x = 0$$
$$x(2x^2 + 2x + 3) = 0$$
$$2x^2 + 2x + 3 = 0$$
$$x = 0 \quad or \quad x = \frac{-2 \pm \sqrt{2^2 - 4(2)(3)}}{2(2)}$$
$$x = \frac{-2 \pm \sqrt{4 - 24}}{4}$$
$$x = \frac{-2 \pm \sqrt{-20}}{4}$$
$$x = \frac{-2 \pm -2i\sqrt{5}}{4}$$
$$x = \frac{-1 \pm i\sqrt{5}}{2}$$

44. $6x^3 - 4x^2 + 6x = 0$

$x(6x^2 - 4x + 6) = 0$

$x = 0 \quad or \quad x = \dfrac{-(-4) \pm \sqrt{(-4)^2 - 4(6)(6)}}{2}$

$x = \dfrac{4 \pm \sqrt{16 - 144}}{12}$

$x = \dfrac{4 \pm \sqrt{-128}}{12}$

$x = \dfrac{4 \pm 8i\sqrt{2}}{12}$

$x = \dfrac{1 \pm 2i\sqrt{2}}{3}$

46. $4y^4 = 16y^3 - 20y^2$

$4y^4 - 16y^3 + 20y^2 = 0$

$4y^2(y^2 - 4y + 5) = 0$

$4y^2 = 0$

$y^2 = 0$

$y = 0 \quad or$

$y = \dfrac{-(-4) \pm \sqrt{(-4)^2 - 4(1)(5)}}{2(1)}$

$y = \dfrac{4 \pm \sqrt{16 - 20}}{2}$

$y = \dfrac{4 \pm \sqrt{-4}}{2}$

$y = \dfrac{4 \pm 2i}{2}$

$y = 2 \pm i$

47. $6t^5 + 4t^4 = -2t^3$

$6t^5 + 4t^4 + 2t^3 = 0$

$2t^3(3t^2 + 2t + 1) = 0$

$2t^3 = 0$

$t^3 = 0$

$t = 0 \quad or$

$t = 0 \quad or \quad t = \dfrac{-2 \pm \sqrt{2^2 - 4(3)(1)}}{2(3)}$

$t = \dfrac{-2 \pm \sqrt{4 - 12}}{6}$

$t = \dfrac{-2 \pm \sqrt{-8}}{6}$

$t = \dfrac{-2 \pm 2i\sqrt{2}}{6}$

$t = \dfrac{-1 \pm i\sqrt{2}}{3}$

48. $8t^5 + 2t^4 = -10t^3$

$8t^5 + 2t^4 + 10t^3 = 0$

$2t^3(4t^2 + t + 5) = 0$

$2t^3 = 0$

$t^3 = 0$

$t = 0 \quad or \quad t = \dfrac{-1 \pm \sqrt{1^2 - 4(4)(5)}}{2(4)}$

$t = \dfrac{-1 \pm \sqrt{1 - 80}}{8}$

$t = \dfrac{-1 \pm \sqrt{-79}}{8}$

$t = \dfrac{-1 \pm i\sqrt{79}}{8}$

50. $\dfrac{-2 - 3i\sqrt{2}}{5}$

51. $s = 5t + 16t^2$

$74 = 5t + 16t^2$

$0 = 16t^2 + 5t - 74$

$0 = (t - 2)(16t + 37)$

$t - 2 = 0$

$t = 2$ sec $\quad or \quad 16t + 37 = 0$

$t = -\dfrac{37}{16}$

*No solution*

52.

$$s = 16t^2$$
$$100 = 16t^2$$
$$0 = 16t^2 - 100$$
$$0 = 4(4t^2 - 25)$$
$$0 = (2t + 5)(2t - 5)$$
$$2t + 5 = 0$$
$$t = -\frac{5}{2} \quad or \quad 2t - 5 = 0$$

*No solution* $\qquad t = \frac{5}{2}$ sec.

54.

$$h = 16 + 32t - 16t^2$$
$$32 = 16 + 32t - 16t^2$$
$$16t^2 - 32t + 16 = 0$$
$$16(t^2 - 2t + 1) = 0$$
$$(t - 1)(t - 1) = 0$$
$$t - 1 = 0$$
$$t = 1 \text{ sec.}$$

55.

$$P = R - C \quad P = \$300,\ R = 100x - .5x^2,\ C = 60x + 300$$
$$300 = 100x - .5x^2 - (60x + 300)$$
$$300 = 100x - .5x^2 - 60x - 300$$
$$.5x^2 - 40x + 600 = 0$$

$$x = \frac{-(-40) \pm \sqrt{(-40)^2 - 4(.5)(600)}}{2(.5)}$$

$$x = \frac{40 \pm \sqrt{1600 - 1200}}{1}$$

$$x = 40 \pm \sqrt{400}$$
$$x = 40 \pm 20$$
$$x = 20 \quad or \quad x = 60$$

56.

$$P = R - C \quad P = \$2150,\ R = 300x - .5x^2,\ C = 200x + 1600$$
$$2150 = 300x - .5x^2 - (200x + 16)))$$
$$2150 = 300x - .5x^2 - 200x - 1600$$
$$.5x^2 - 100x + 3750 = 0$$

$$x = \frac{-(-100) \pm \sqrt{(-100)^2 - 4(.5)(3750)}}{2(.5)}$$

$$x = \frac{100 \pm \sqrt{10,000 - 7500}}{1}$$

$$x = 100 \pm \sqrt{2500}$$

$$x = 100 \pm 50$$
$$x = 150 \text{ items} \quad or \quad x = 50 \text{ items}$$

58.

$$P = R - C \quad P = \$2300,\ R = 9x - 0.002x^2,\ C = 1200 - 3.5x$$

$$2300 = 9x - 0.002x^2 - (1200 + 3.5x)$$

$$2300 = 9x - 0.002x^2 - 1200 - 3.5x$$

$$0.002x^2 - 5.5x + 3500 = 0$$

$$x = \frac{-(-5.5) \pm \sqrt{(-5.5)^2 - 4(.002)(3500)}}{2(0.002)}$$

$$x = \frac{5.5 \pm \sqrt{30.25 - 28}}{0.004}$$

$$x = \frac{5.5 \pm \sqrt{2.25}}{0.004}$$

$$x = \frac{5.5 \pm 1.5}{0.004}$$

$x = 1000$ *frames* or $x = 1750$ *frames*

59.

$$4y + 1 + \frac{-2}{2y - 7}$$

$2y - 7\,)\ 8y^2 - 26y - 9$

$\quad - \quad +$

$\quad \underline{8y^2 - 28y}$

$\quad\quad 2y - 9$

$\quad\quad - \quad +$

$\quad\quad \underline{2y - 7}$

$\quad\quad\quad -2$

60.

$$2y + 5 + \frac{2}{3y - 4}$$

$3y - 4\,)\ 6y^2 - 7y - 18$

$\quad - \quad +$

$\quad \underline{6y^2 - 8y}$

$\quad\quad 15y - 18$

$\quad\quad - \quad +$

$\quad\quad \underline{15y - 20}$

$\quad\quad\quad 2$

62.

$$x^2 + 3x + 2$$

$x + 3\,)\ x^3 + 6x^2 + 11x + 6$

$\quad - \quad -$

$\quad \underline{x^3 + 3x^2}$

$\quad\quad 3x^2 + 11x$

$\quad\quad - \quad -$

$\quad\quad \underline{3x^2 + 9x}$

$\quad\quad\quad 2x + 6$

$\quad\quad\quad - \quad -$

$\quad\quad\quad \underline{2x + 6}$

$\quad\quad\quad\quad 0$

63. $25^{1/2} = 5$

64. $8^{1/3} = 2$

66. $\left(\frac{16}{81}\right)^{3/4} = \left[\left(\frac{16}{81}\right)^{1/4}\right]^3 = \left(\frac{2}{3}\right)^3 = \frac{8}{27}$

67. $8^{-2/3} = \frac{1}{8^{2/3}} = \frac{1}{2^2} = \frac{1}{4}$

68. $4^{-3/2} = \frac{1}{4^{3/2}} = \frac{1}{2^3} = \frac{1}{8}$

70. $\frac{(x^{-2}y^{1/3})^6}{x^{-10}y^{3/2}} = \frac{x^{-12}y^2}{x^{-10}y^{3/2}} = \frac{y^{1/2}}{x^2}$

71. $x^2 + \sqrt{3}x - 6 = 0$

$$x = \frac{-\sqrt{3} \pm \sqrt{(\sqrt{3})^2 - 4(1)(-6)}}{2(1)}$$

$$x = \frac{-\sqrt{3} \pm \sqrt{3 + 24}}{2}$$

$$x = \frac{-\sqrt{3} \pm 3\sqrt{3}}{2}$$

$x = \frac{2\sqrt{3}}{2}$ *or* $x = \frac{-4\sqrt{3}}{2}$

$x = \sqrt{3} \qquad x = -2\sqrt{3}$

72. $x^2 - \sqrt{5}x - 5 = 0$

$$x = \frac{-(-5) \pm \sqrt{(-5\sqrt{5})^2 - 4(1)(-5)}}{2(1)}$$

$$x = \frac{\sqrt{5} \pm \sqrt{5 + 20}}{2}$$

$$x = \frac{\sqrt{5} \pm 5}{2}$$

74. $\sqrt{7}\,x^2 + 2\sqrt{2}x - \sqrt{7} = 0$

$$x = \frac{-2\sqrt{2} \pm \sqrt{2\sqrt{2})^2 - 4(\sqrt{7})(-\sqrt{7})}}{2(\sqrt{7})}$$

$$x = \frac{-2\sqrt{2} \pm \sqrt{8 + 28}}{2\sqrt{7}}$$

$$x = \frac{-2\sqrt{2} \pm 6}{2\sqrt{7}}$$

$$x = \frac{-\sqrt{2} \pm 3}{\sqrt{7}} \cdot \frac{\sqrt{7}}{\sqrt{7}}$$

$$x = \frac{-\sqrt{14} \pm 3\sqrt{7}}{7}$$

75. $x^2 + ix + 2 = 0$

$$x = \frac{-i \pm \sqrt{i^2 - 4(1)(2)}}{2(1)}$$

$$x = \frac{-i \pm \sqrt{-1 - 8}}{2}$$

$$x = \frac{-i \pm 3i}{2}$$

$x = -2i$ or $x = i$

76. $x^2 + 3ix - 2 = 0$

$$x = \frac{-3i \pm \sqrt{(3i)^2 - 4(1)(-2)}}{2(1)}$$

$$x = \frac{-3i \pm \sqrt{9i^2 + 8}}{2}$$

$$x = \frac{-3i \pm \sqrt{-1}}{2}$$

$$x = \frac{-3i \pm i}{2}$$

$x = -i$ *or* $x = -2i$

78. $4ix^2 + 5x + 9i = 0$

$$x = \frac{-5 \pm \sqrt{5^2 - 4(4i)(9i)}}{2(4i)}$$

$$x = \frac{-5 \pm \sqrt{25 - 144i^2}}{8i}$$

$$x = \frac{-5 \pm \sqrt{169}}{8i}$$

$$x = \frac{-5 \pm 13}{8i}$$

$x = \frac{8}{8i} \cdot \frac{i}{3}$ *or* $x = \frac{-18}{8i} \cdot \frac{i}{i}$

$x = \frac{8i}{-18}$ $\quad x = \frac{-18i}{-8}$

$x = -i$ $\quad x = \frac{9}{4}i$

## Section 7.3

2. $x^2 - x - 12 = 0$
$a = 1$
$b = -1$
$c = 12$

$(-1)^2 - 4(1)(-12) = 1 + 48$
$= 49$

*The discriminant is a perfect square. Therefore, the equation has two rational solutions.*

3. $4x^2 - 4x = -1$
$4x^2 - 4x + 1 = 0$
$a = 4$
$b = -4$
$c = 1$

$(-4)^2 - 4(4)(1) = 16 - 16$
$= 0$

*The discriminant is zero. Therefore, the equation has one rational solution.*

4. $9x^2 + 12x = -4$
$9x^2 + 12x + 4 = 0$
$a = 9$
$b = 12$
$c = 4$

$(12)^2 - 4(9)(4) = 144 - 144$
$= 0$

*The discriminant is zero. Therefore, the equation has one rational solution.*

6. $x^2 - 2x + 3 = 0$
$a = 1$
$b = -2$
$c = 3$

$(-2)^2 - 4(1)(3) = 4 - 12$
$= -8$

*The discriminant is zero. Therefore, the equation has two complex solutions containing i.*

7. $\frac{1}{3}y^2 = \frac{1}{2}y + \frac{1}{6}$

$2y^2 - 3y - 1 = 0$
$a = 2$
$b = -3$
$c = -1$

$(-3)^2 - 4(2)(-1) = 9 + 8$
$= 17$

*The discriminant is a positive number, but not a perfect square. Therefore, the equation will have two irrational solutions.*

8. $$\frac{1}{2}y^2 = \frac{2}{3}y - \frac{1}{3}$$

$$3y^2 - 4y + 2 = 0$$
$$a = 3$$
$$b = -4$$
$$c = 2$$

$$(-4)^2 - 4(3)(2) = 16 - 24 = -8$$

*The discriminant is a negative number. Therefore, the equation will have two complex solutions containing i.*

10. $$.04x^2 - .81 = 0$$
$$4x^2 - 81 = 0$$
$$a = 4$$
$$b = 0$$
$$c = -81$$

$$(0)^2 - 4(4)(-81) = 1296$$

*The discriminant is a perfect square. Therefore, the equation will have two rational solutions.*

11. $$50a^2 - 40a = 50$$
$$5a^2 - 4a - 5 = 0$$

$$(-4)^2 - 4(5)(-5) = 116$$

*The discriminant is a positive number that is not a perfect square. Therefore, the equation will have two irrational solutions.*

12. $$30a = 40a^2 - 50$$
$$4a^2 - 3a - 5 = 0$$
$$a = 4$$
$$b = -3$$
$$c = -5$$

$$(-3)^2 - 4(4)(-5) = 89$$

*The discriminant is a positive number that is not a perfect square. Therefore, the equation will have two irrational solutions.*

14. $$x^2 + kx + 25 = 0$$
$$a = 1$$
$$b = k$$
$$c = 25$$

$$k^2 - 4(1)(25) = k^2 - 100$$
$$k^2 - 100 = 0$$
$$k^2 = 100$$
$$k = \pm 10$$

15. $$x^2 = kx - 36$$
$$x^2 - kx + 36 = 0$$
$$a = 1$$
$$b = -k$$
$$c = 36$$

$$(-k)^2 - 4(1)(36) = k^2 - 144 = 0$$
$$k^2 - 144 = 0$$
$$k^2 = 144$$
$$k = \pm 12$$

16. $$x^2 = kx - 49$$
$$x^2 - kx + 49 = 0$$
$$a = 1$$
$$b = -k$$
$$c = 49$$

$$(-k)^2 - 4(1)(49) = k^2 - 196$$
$$k^2 - 196 = 0$$
$$k^2 = 196$$
$$k = \pm 14$$

18. $$9x^2 + 30x + k = 0$$
$$a = 9$$
$$b = 30$$
$$c = k$$

$$30^2 - 4(9)(k) = 900 - 36k$$
$$900 - 36k = 0$$
$$900 = 36k$$
$$25 = k$$

19. $$kx^2 - 40x = 25$$
$$kx^2 - 40x - 25 = 0$$
$$a = k$$
$$b = -40$$
$$c = -25$$

$$(-40)^2 - 4(k)(-25) = 1600 - 100k$$
$$1600 + 100k = 0$$
$$1600 = -100k$$
$$-16 = k$$

20. $kx^2 - 2x = -1$
$kx^2 - 2x + 1 = 0$
$a = k$
$b = -2$
$c = 1$
$(-2)^2 - 4(k)(1) = 4 - 4k$
$4 - 4k = 0$
$4 = 4k$
$1 = k$

22. $5x^2 + kx + 1 = 0$
$a = 5$
$b = k$
$c = 1$

$k^2 - 4(5)1 = k^2 - 20$
$k^2 - 20 = 0$
$k^2 = 20$
$k = \pm\sqrt{20}$
$k = \pm 2\sqrt{5}$

23. $x = 5 \qquad x = 2$
$x - 5 = 0 \quad x - 2 = 0$
$(x - 5)(x - 2) = 0$
$x^2 - 7x + 10 = 0$

24. $x = -5 \qquad x = -2$
$x + 5 = 0 \quad x + 2 = 0$
$(x + 5)(x + 2) = 0$
$x^2 + 7x + 10 = 0$

26. $t = -4 \qquad t = 2$
$t + 4 = 0 \quad t - 2 = 0$
$(t + 4)(t - 2) = 0$
$t^2 - 2t - 8 = 0$

27. $y = 2 \qquad y = -2 \qquad y = 4$
$y - 2 = 0 \quad y + 2 = 0 \quad y - 4 = 0$
$(y - 2)(y + 2)(y - 4) = 0$
$y^3 - 4y^2 - 4y + 16 = 0$

28. $y = 1 \qquad y = -1 \qquad y = 3$
$y - 1 = 0 \quad y + 1 = 0 \quad y - 3 = 0$
$(y - 1)(y + 1)(y - 3) = 0$
$y^3 - 3y^2 - y + 3 = 0$

30. $x = \frac{1}{3} \qquad x = 5$

$3x - 1 = 0 \quad x - 5 = 0$
$(3x - 1)(x - 5) = 0$
$3x^2 - 16x + 5 = 0$

31. $t = -\frac{3}{4} \qquad t = 3$

$4t + 3 = 0 \quad t - 3 = 0$
$(4t + 3)(t - 3) = 0$
$4t^2 - 9t - 9 = 0$

32. $t = -\frac{4}{5} \qquad t = 2$

$5t + 4 = 0 \quad t - 2 = 0$
$(5t + 4)(t - 2) = 0$
$5t^2 - 6t - 8 = 0$

34. $x = 5 \qquad x = -5 \qquad x = \frac{2}{3}$

$x - 5 = 0 \quad x + 5 = 0 \quad 3x - 2 = 0$
$(x - 5)(x + 5)(3x - 2) = 0$
$3x^3 - 2x^2 - 75x + 50 = 0$

35. $a = -\frac{1}{2} \qquad a = \frac{3}{5}$

$2a + 1 = 0 \quad 5a - 3 = 0$
$(2a + 1)(5a - 3) = 0$
$10a^2 - a - 3 = 0$

36. $a = -\frac{1}{3} \qquad a = \frac{4}{7}$

$3a + 1 = 0 \quad 7a - 4 = 0$
$(3a + 1)(7a - 4) = 0$
$21a^2 - 5a - 4 = 0$

38. $x = -\frac{4}{5} \qquad x = \frac{4}{5} \qquad x = -1$

$5x + 4 = 0 \quad 5x - 4 = 0 \quad x + 1 = 0$
$(5x + 4)(5x - 4)(x + 1) = 0$
$25x^3 + 25x^2 - 16x - 16 = 0$

39. $x = 2 \qquad x = -2 \qquad x = 3 \qquad x = -3$
$x - 2 = 0 \quad x + 2 = 0 \quad x - 3 = 0 \quad x + 3 = 0$
$(x - 2)(x + 2)(x - 3)(x + 3) = 0$
$x^4 - 13x^2 + 36 = 0$

40. $x = 1 \qquad x = -1 \qquad x = 5 \qquad x = -5$
$x - 1 = 0 \quad x + 1 = 0 \quad x - 5 = 0 \quad x + 5 = 0$
$(x - 1)(x + 1)(x - 5)(x + 5) = 0$
$x^2 - 26x^2 + 25 = 0$

42. $(a^{1/2} - 5)(a^{1/2} + 3) = a - 2a^{1/2} - 15$

43. $(x^{3/2} - 3)^2$
$= (x^{3/2})^2 - 2(x^{3/2})(3) + (-3)^2$
$= x^3 - 6x^{3/2} + 9$

44. $(x^{1/2} - 8)(x^{1/2} + 8) = x - 64$

46. $\dfrac{45x^{5/3}y^{7/3} - 36x^{8/3}y^{4/3}}{9x^{2/3}y^{1/3}}$

$= \dfrac{45x^{5/3}y^{7/3}}{9x^{2/3}y^{1/3}} - \dfrac{36x^{8/3}y^{4/3}}{9x^{2/3}y^{1/3}}$

$= 5xy^2 - 4x^2y$

47. $\dfrac{10(x - 3)^{3/2} - 15(x - 3)^{1/2}}{5(x - 3)^{1/2}}$

$= \dfrac{10(x - 3)^{3/2}}{5(x - 3)^{1/2}} - \dfrac{15(x - 3)^{1/2}}{5(x - 3)^{1/2}}$

$= 2(x - 3) - 3$
$= 2x - 9$
$5(x - 3)^{1/2}(2x - 9)$

48. $\dfrac{8(x + 1)^{4/3} - 2(x + 1)^{1/3}}{2(x + 1)^{1/3}}$

$= \dfrac{8(x + 1)^{4/3}}{2(x + 1)^{1/3}} - \dfrac{2(x + 1)^{1/3}}{2(x + 1)^{1/3}}$

$= 4(x + 1) - 1$
$= 4x + 3$
$2(x + 1)^{1/3}(4x + 3)$

50. $9x^{2/3} + 12x^{1/3} + 4$
$= (3x^{1/3} + 2)^2$

## Section 7.4

2. $(x + 4)^2 - (x + 4) - 6 = 0$
$y^2 - y - 6 = 0 \quad y = x + 4$
$(y - 3)(y + 2) = 0$
$y - 3 = 0$ *or* $y + 2 = 0$
$y = 3 \qquad y = -2$
*Now we replace y with x + 4 and solve for x:*

$x + 4 = 3$ *or* $x + 4 = -2$
$x = -1 \qquad x = -6$

*Another method of solving the equation is by expanding which gives us the following:*

$(x + 4)^2 - (x + 4) - 6 = 0$
$x^2 + 8x + 16 - x - 4 - 6 = 0$
$x^2 + 7x + 6 = 0$
$(x + 1)(x + 6) = 0$
$x + 1 = 0$ *or* $x + 6 = 0$
$x = -1 \qquad x = -6$

3. $2(x + 4)^2 + 5(x + 4) - 12 = 0$
$2x^2 + 16x + 32 + 5x + 20 - 12 = 0$
$2x^2 + 21x + 40 = 0$
$(2x + 5)(x + 8) = 0$
$2x + 5 = 0$ *or* $x + 8 = 0$

$x = -\dfrac{5}{2} \qquad x = -8$

4. $3(x - 5)^2 + 14(x - 5) - 5 = 0$
$3x^2 - 30x + 75 + 14x - 70 - 5 = 0$
$3x^2 - 16x = 0$
$x(3x - 16) = 0$
$x = 0$ *or* $3x - 16 = 0$

$x = \dfrac{16}{3}$

6. $x^4 - 2x^2 - 8 = 0$
$(x^2 + 4)(x^2 - 2) = 0$
$x^2 + 4 = 0$ *or* $x^2 - 2 = 0$
$x^2 = -4 \qquad x^2 = 2$
$x = \pm 2i \qquad x = \pm\sqrt{2}$

7. $x^4 + 9x^2 = -20$
$x^4 + 9x^2 + 20 = 0$
$(x^2 + 5)(x^2 + 4) = 0$
$x^2 + 5 = 0$ *or* $x^2 + 4 = 0$
$x^2 = -5 \qquad x^2 = -4$
$x = \pm i\sqrt{5} \qquad x = \pm 2i$

8. $x^4 - 11x^2 = -30$
$x^4 - 11x^2 + 30 = 0$
$(x^2 - 5)(x^2 - 6) = 0$
$x^2 - 5 = 0$ *or* $x^2 - 6 = 0$
$x^2 = 5 \qquad x^2 = 6$
$x = \pm\sqrt{5} \qquad x = \pm\sqrt{6}$

10. $(3a - 2)^2 + 2(3a - 2) = 3$

$$x^2 + 2x - 3 = 0 \quad x = 3a - 2$$
$$(x + 3)(x - 1) = 0$$
$$x + 3 = 0 \quad \textit{or} \quad x - 1 = 0$$
$$x = -3 \qquad x = 1$$

*Now we replace x with 3a - 2 and solve for a:*

$$3a - 2 = -3 \quad \textit{or} \quad 3a - 2 = 1$$
$$a = -\frac{1}{3} \qquad a = 1$$

*By the expanding method, we have*

$$(3a - 2)^2 + 2(3a - 2) = 3$$
$$9a^2 - 12a + 4 + 6a - 4 - 3 = 0$$
$$9a^2 - 6a - 3 = 0$$
$$3(3a^2 - 2a - 1) = 0$$
$$(a - 1)(3a + 1) = 0$$
$$a - 1 = 0 \quad \textit{or} \quad 3a + 1 = 0$$
$$a = 1 \qquad a = -\frac{1}{3}$$

11. $2(4a + 2)^2 = 3(4a + 2) + 20$

$$2x^2 - 3x - 20 = 0 \quad x = 4a + 2$$
$$(2x + 5)(x - 4) = 0$$
$$2x + 5 = 0 \quad \textit{or} \quad x - 4 = 0$$
$$x = -\frac{5}{2} \qquad x = 4$$

*Now we replace x with 4a + 2 and solve for a:*

$$4a + 2 = -\frac{5}{2} \quad \textit{or} \quad 4a + 2 = 4$$
$$4a = -\frac{9}{2} \qquad 4a = 2$$
$$a = -\frac{9}{8} \qquad a = \frac{1}{2}$$

*By the expanding method, we have*

$$2(4a + 2)^2 = 3(4a + 2) + 20$$
$$32a^2 + 32a + 8 = 12a + 6 + 20$$
$$32a^2 + 20a - 18 = 0$$
$$2(16a^2 + 10a - 9) = 0$$
$$(8a + 9)(2a - 1) = 0$$
$$8a + 9 = 0 \quad \textit{or} \quad 2a - 1 = 0$$
$$a = -\frac{9}{8} \qquad a = \frac{1}{2}$$

12.
$$6(2a + 4)^2 = (2a + 4) + 2$$
$$6x^2 - x - 2 = 0 \quad x = 2a + 4$$
$$(2x + 1)(3x - 2) = 0$$
$$2x + 1 = 0 \quad or \quad 3x - 2 = 0$$
$$x = -\frac{1}{2} \qquad x = \frac{2}{3}$$

*Now we replace x with 2a + 4 and solve for a:*

$$2a + 4 = -\frac{1}{2} \quad or \quad 2a + 4 = \frac{2}{3}$$
$$2a = -\frac{9}{2} \qquad 2a = -\frac{10}{3}$$
$$a = -\frac{9}{4} \qquad a = -\frac{5}{3}$$

*By the expanding method, we have*

$$6(2a + 4)^2 = (2a + 4) + 2$$
$$24a^2 + 96a + 96 - 2a - 6 = 0$$
$$24a^2 + 94a + 90 = 0$$
$$2(12a^2 + 47a + 45) = 0$$
$$(4a + 9)(3a + 5) = 0$$
$$4a + 9 = 0 \quad or \quad 3a + 5 = 0$$
$$a = -\frac{9}{4} \qquad a = \frac{5}{3}$$

14.
$$3t^4 = -2t^2 + 8$$
$$3x^2 + 2x - 8 = 0 \quad x = t^2$$
$$(x + 2)(3x - 4) = 0$$
$$x + 2 = 0 \quad or \quad 3x - 4 = 0$$
$$x = -2 \qquad x = \frac{4}{3}$$

*Now we replace x with $t^2$ and solve for t:*

$$t^2 = -2 \quad or \quad t^2 = \frac{4}{3}$$
$$t = \pm i\sqrt{2} \qquad t = \pm\sqrt{\frac{4}{3}} \cdot \sqrt{\frac{3}{3}}$$
$$t = \pm\frac{2\sqrt{3}}{3}$$

15.
$$9x^4 - 49 = 0$$
$$9t^2 - 49 = 0 \quad t = x^2$$
$$(3t + 7)(3t - 7) = 0$$
$$3t + 7 = 0 \quad or \quad 3t - 7 = 0$$
$$t = -\frac{7}{3} \qquad t = \frac{7}{3}$$

*Now we replace t with $x^2$ and solve for x:*

$$x^2 = -\frac{7}{3} \quad or \quad x^2 = \frac{7}{3}$$
$$x = \pm i\sqrt{\frac{7}{3}} \cdot \sqrt{\frac{3}{3}} \qquad x = \pm\sqrt{\frac{7}{3}} \cdot \sqrt{\frac{3}{3}}$$
$$x = \pm\frac{i\sqrt{21}}{3} \qquad x = \pm\frac{\sqrt{21}}{3}$$

16.
$$25x^4 - 9 = 0$$
$$25t^2 - 9 = 0 \quad t = x^2$$
$$(5t + 3)(5t - 3) = 0$$
$$5t + 3 = 0 \quad or \quad 5t - 3 = 0$$
$$t = -\frac{3}{5} \qquad t = \frac{3}{5}$$

*Now we replace t with $x^2$ and solve for x:*

$$x^2 = -\frac{3}{5} \quad or \quad x^2 = \frac{3}{5}$$
$$x = \pm\sqrt{\frac{3}{5}} \cdot \sqrt{\frac{5}{5}} \qquad x = \pm\sqrt{\frac{3}{5}} \cdot \sqrt{\frac{5}{5}}$$
$$x = \pm\frac{i\sqrt{15}}{5} \qquad x = \pm\frac{\sqrt{15}}{5}$$

18.
$$x - 6\sqrt{x} + 8 = 0$$
$$a^2 - 6a + 8 = 0 \quad a = \sqrt{x}$$
$$(a - 2)(a - 4) = 0$$
$$a - 2 = 0 \quad or \quad a - 4 = 0$$
$$a = 2 \qquad a = 4$$

*Now we replace a with $\sqrt{x}$ and solve for x:*

$$\sqrt{x} = 2 \quad or \quad \sqrt{x} = 4$$
$$x = 4 \qquad x = 16$$

*Both solutions {4,16} check.*

19. $t - 2\sqrt{t} - 15 = 0$

$x^2 - 2x - 15 = 0 \quad x = \sqrt{t}$

$(x + 3)(x - 5) = 0$

$x + 3 = 0$ *or* $x - 5 = 0$

$x = -3 \qquad x = 5$

*Now we replace x with* $\sqrt{t}$ *and solve for t:*

$\sqrt{t} = -3$ *or* $\sqrt{x} = 5$

$t = 9 \qquad x = 25$

*Possible solutions* 9 ∧ 25, *only* 25 *checks.*

20. $t - 3\sqrt{t} - 10 = 0$

$x^2 - 3x - 10 = 0 \quad x = \sqrt{t}$

$(x + 2)(x - 5) = 0$

$x + 2 = 0$ *or* $x - 5 = 0$

$x = -2 \qquad x = 5$

*Now we replace x with* $\sqrt{t}$ *and solve for t:*

$\sqrt{t} = -2$ *or* $\sqrt{t} = 5$

$t = 4 \qquad t = 25$

*Possible solution* 25 *and* 4, *only* 25 *checks.*

22. $2x + \sqrt{x} = 15$

$2t^2 + 5 - 15 = 0 \quad t = \sqrt{x}$

$(2t - 5)(t + 3) = 0$

$2t - 5 = 0$ *or* $t + 3 = 0$

$t = \frac{5}{2} \qquad t = -3$

*Now we replace t with* $\sqrt{x}$ *and solve for x:*

$\sqrt{x} = \frac{5}{2}$ *or* $\sqrt{3} = -3$

$x = \frac{25}{4} \qquad x = 9$

*Possible solutions* $\frac{25}{4}$ *and* 9,

*only* $\frac{25}{4}$ *checks.*

23. $(a - 2) - 11\sqrt{a - 2} + 30 = 0$

$x^2 - 11x + 30 = 0 \quad x = a - 2$

$(x - 5)(x - 6) = 0$

$x - 5 = 0$ *or* $x - 6 = 0$

$x = 5 \qquad x = 6$

*Now we replace x with* $\sqrt{a - 2}$ *and solve for a:*

$\sqrt{a - 2} = 5$ *or* $\sqrt{a - 2} = 6$

$a - 2 = 25 \qquad a - 2 = 36$

$a = 27 \qquad a = 38$

*Both solutions* {27,38} *check.*

24. $(a - 3) - 9\sqrt{a - 3} + 20 = 0$

$x^2 - 9x + 20 = 0 \quad x = \sqrt{a - 3}$

$(x - 4)(x - 5) = 0$

$x - 4 = 0$ *or* $x - 5 = 0$

$x = 4 \qquad x = 5$

*Now we replace x with* $\sqrt{a - 3}$ *and solve for a:*

$\sqrt{a - 3} = 4$ *or* $\sqrt{a - 3} = 5$

$a - 3 = 16 \qquad a - 3 = 25$

$a = 19 \qquad a = 28$

*Both solutions* {19,28} *check.*

26. $(2x - 3) - 7\sqrt{2x - 3} + 12 = 0$

$y^2 - 7y + 12 = 0 \quad y = \sqrt{2x - 3}$

$(y - 3)(y - 4) = 0$

$y - 3 = 0$ *or* $y - 4 = 0$

$y = 3 \qquad y = 4$

*Now we replace y with* $\sqrt{2x - 3}$ *and solve for x:*

$\sqrt{2x - 3} = 3$ *or* $\sqrt{2x - 3} = 4$

$2x - 3 = 9 \qquad 2x - 3 = 16$

$2x = 12 \qquad 2x = 19$

$x = 6 \qquad x = \frac{19}{2}$

*Both solutions* $\{6, \frac{19}{2}\}$ *check.*

27. $16t^2 - 8t - h = 0$

$$t = \frac{-(-8) \pm \sqrt{(-8)^2 - 4(16)(-h)}}{2(16)}$$

$$= \frac{8 \pm \sqrt{64 + 64h}}{32}$$

$$= \frac{8 \pm 8\sqrt{1 + h}}{32}$$

$$= \frac{1 \pm \sqrt{1 + h}}{4}$$

28. $16t^2 - 6t - h = 0$

$$t = \frac{-(-6) \pm \sqrt{(-6)^2 - 4(16)(-h)}}{2(16)}$$

$$= \frac{6 \pm \sqrt{36 + 64h}}{32}$$

$$= \frac{6 \pm 2\sqrt{9 + 16h}}{32}$$

$$= \frac{3 \pm \sqrt{9 + 16h}}{16}$$

30. $16t^2 - vt - 40 = 0$

$$t = \frac{-(-v) \pm \sqrt{(-v)^2 - 4(16)(-40)}}{2(16)}$$

$$= \frac{v \pm \sqrt{v^2 - 2{,}560}}{32}$$

35. $5\sqrt{7} - 2\sqrt{7} = 3\sqrt{7}$

36. $6\sqrt{2} - 9\sqrt{3} = -3\sqrt{2}$

38. $\sqrt{50} + \sqrt{72} - \sqrt{8}$
$= 5\sqrt{2} + 6\sqrt{2} - 2\sqrt{2}$
$= 9\sqrt{2}$

39. $9x\sqrt{20x^3y^2} + 7y\sqrt{45x^5}$
$= 18x^2y\sqrt{5x} + 21x^2y\sqrt{5x}$
$= 39x^2y\sqrt{5x}$

40. $5x^2 \sqrt{27xy^3} - 6y\sqrt{12x^5y}$
$= 15x^2y\sqrt{3xy} - 12x^2y\sqrt{3xy}$
$= 3x^2y\sqrt{3xy}$

42. $(2\sqrt{3} - 7)(2\sqrt{3} + 7)$
$= 12 - 49$
$= -37$

43. $(\sqrt{x} + 2)^2$
$= (\sqrt{x})^2 + 2(2\sqrt{x}) + 2^2$
$= x + 4\sqrt{x} + 4$

44. $(3 - \sqrt{x})(3 + \sqrt{x}) = 9 - x$

46. $\dfrac{\sqrt{5} - \sqrt{2}}{\sqrt{5} + \sqrt{2}} = \dfrac{\sqrt{5} - \sqrt{2}}{\sqrt{5} + \sqrt{2}} \cdot \dfrac{\sqrt{5} - \sqrt{2}}{\sqrt{5} - \sqrt{2}}$

$= \dfrac{5 - 2\sqrt{10} + 2}{5 - 2}$

$= \dfrac{7 - 2\sqrt{10}}{3}$

47. *Let* $y = 0$
$y = x^3 - 4x$
$0 = x^3 - 4x$
$0 = x(x^2 - 4)$
$0 = x(x + 2)(x - 2)$
$x = 0$ *or* $x + 2 = 0$ *or* $x - 2 = 0$
$x = -2$ $x = 2$

*The x-intercepts are* 0,2,−2.

*Let* $x = 0$
$y = x^3 - 4x$
$y = 0^3 - 4(0)$
$y = 0$

*The y-intercept is* 0.

48. *Let* $y = 0$
$0 = x^4 - 10x^2 + 9$
$0 = (x^2 - 1)(x^2 - 9)$
$0 = (x + 1)(x - 1)(x + 3)(x - 3)$
$x + 1 = 0$ *or* $x - 1 = 0$ *or* $x + 3 = 0$ *or* $x - 3 = 0$
$x = -1$ $x = 1$ $x = -3$ $x = 3$
*The x-intercepts are* 1,−1,3,−3

*Let* $x = 0$
$y = 0^4 - 10 \cdot 0^2 + 9$
$y = 9$

*The y-intercept is* 9.

50. *Let* $y = 0$

$$y = 2x^3 + x^2 - 8x - 4$$
$$0 = 2x^3 + x^2 - 8x - 4$$
$$0 = x^2(2x + 1) - 4(2x + 1)$$
$$0 = (2x + 1)(x + 2)(x - 2)$$

$2x + 1 = 0$ *or* $x + 2 = 0$ *or* $x - 2 = 0$

$x = -\frac{1}{2}$ $\quad x = -2$ $\quad x = 2$

*The x-intercepts are* $-\frac{1}{2}, -2, 2$.

*Let* $x = 0$

$$y = 2 \cdot 0^3 + 0^2 - 8 \cdot 0 - 4$$
$$y = -4$$

*The y-intercept is* $-4$.

51. *Let* $y = 0$

$$y = 2x^3 - 7x^2 - 5x + 4$$
$$0 = (x - 4)(x + 1)(2x - 1)$$

$x - 4 = 0$ *or* $x + 1 = 0$ *or* $2x - 1 = 0$

$x = 4$ $\quad x = -1$ $\quad 2x = 1$

$x = \frac{1}{2}$

*The other x-intercepts are* $-1, \frac{1}{2}$.

52. *Let* $y = 0$

$$0 = 6x^3 + x^2 - 12x + 5$$
$$0 = (x - 1)(6x^2 + 7x - 5)$$
$$0 = (x - 1)(3x + 5)(2x - 1)$$

$x - 1 = 0$ *or* $3x + 5 = 0$ *or* $2x - 1 = 0$

$x = 1$ $\quad x = -\frac{5}{3}$ $\quad x = \frac{1}{2}$

*The other x-intercepts are* $-\frac{5}{3}, \frac{1}{2}$.

**Section 7.5**

2. $x^2 + x - 6 < 0$

$(x + 3)(x - 2) < 0$

3 $\quad$ 2

3. $x^2 - x - 12 \leq 0$

$(x + 3)(x - 4) \leq 0$

-3 $\quad$ 4

4. $x^2 - x - 12 \geq 0$

$(x + 3)(x - 4) \geq 0$

-3 $\quad$ 4

6. $x^2 - 5x > 6$
$x^2 - 5x - 6 > 0$
$(x + 1)(x - 6) > 0$

7. $\frac{2}{5}x^2 < \frac{1}{3}x - \frac{1}{15}$

$6x^2 - 5x + 1 < 0$
$(2x - 1)(3x - 1) < 0$

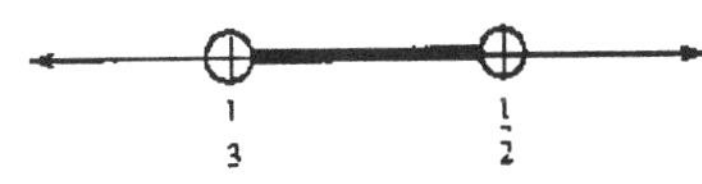


8. $\frac{1}{3}x^2 \geq -\frac{5}{12}x + \frac{1}{2}$

$4x^2 + 5x - 6 \geq 0$
$(x + 2)(4x - 3) \geq 0$

10. $x^2 - 16 \geq 0$
$(x + 4)(x - 4) \geq 0$

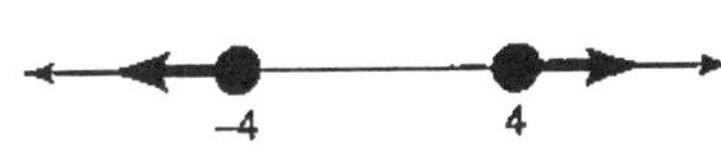


11. $.04x^2 - .09 \geq 0$
$4x^2 - 9 \geq 0$
$(2x + 3)(2x - 3) \geq 0$

12. $.09x^2 - .04 < 0$
$9x^2 - 4 < 0$
$(3x + 2)(3x - 2) < 0$

14. $300x^2 + 100x - 1000 \geq 0$
$3x^2 + x - 10 \geq 0$
$(x + 2)(3x - 5) \geq 0$

15. $x^2 - 4x + 4 \geq 0$
$(x - 2)(x - 2) \geq 0$

*All are real numbers.*

16. $x^2 - 4x + 4 < 0$
$(x - 2)(x - 2) < 0$

*This is a special case in which both factors are the same. Since $(x - 2)^2$ is always negative, there is no real solution.*

18. $x^2 - 10x + 25 > 0$
$(x - 5)(x - 5) > 0$

*All real numbers except* 5.

19. $(x - 2)(x - 3)(x - 4) > 0$

20. $(x - 2)(x - 3)(x - 4) < 0$

22. $(x + 1)(x + 2)(x + 3) \leq 0$

23. $y = x^2 - 25$
$y = (x + 5)(x - 5)$

*Positive for $x < -5$ or $x > 5$, negative for $-5 < x < 5$.*

24. $y = x^2 - 36$
$y = (x + 6)(x - 6)$

*Positive for $x < -6$ or $x > 6$; negative for $-6 < x < 6$.*

26. $y = x^2 - 2x - 3$
$y = (x + 1)(x - 3)$

*Positive for $x < -1$ or $x > 3$; negative for $-1 < x < 3$.*

27. $y = x^2 + 4$

*Always positive.*

28. $y = x^2 + 49$

*Always positive.*

30. *Let* $x$ = *width*
*let* $3x - 5$ = *length*
*and area* = 12

$$A \le 12$$
$$L \times W \le 12$$
$$(3x - 5)x \le 12$$
$$3x^2 - 5x - 12 \le 0$$
$$3x + 4 \le 0 \quad \text{or} \quad x - 3 \le 0$$
$$x \le -\frac{4}{3} \qquad x \le 3$$

*The width is less than or equal to 3 inches.*

31.
$$R = 1300p - 100p^2 \quad R = \$4000$$
$$4000 = 1300p - 100p^2$$
$$100p^2 - 1300p + 4000 = 0$$
$$p^2 - 13p + 40 = 0$$
$$(p - 5)(p - 8) = 0$$
$$p - 5 = 0$$
$$p = 5 \quad \text{or}$$
$$p - 8 = 0$$
$$p = 8$$
$$5 \le p \le 8$$

*She should charge at least* \$5 *but no more than* \$8 *for each radio.*

32.
$$R = 1700p - 100p^2 \quad R = \$7000$$
$$7000 = 1700p - 100p^2$$
$$100p^2 - 1700p + 7000 = 0$$
$$p^2 - 17p + 70 = 0$$
$$(p - 7)(p - 10) = 0$$
$$p - 7 = 0$$
$$p = 7 \quad \text{or}$$
$$p - 10 = 0$$
$$p = 10$$
$$7 \le p \le 10$$

*Charge at least* \$7 *but no more than* \$10 *for each calculator.*

34. *Let* $y = 0$

$$-2x + 4y = 6$$
$$-2x + 4(0) = 6$$
$$-2x = 6$$
$$x = -3$$

*The x-intercept is* $-3$.

*Let* $x = 0$

$$-2x + 4y = 6$$
$$-2(0) + 4y = 6$$
$$y = \frac{3}{2}$$

*The y-intercept is* $\frac{3}{2}$.

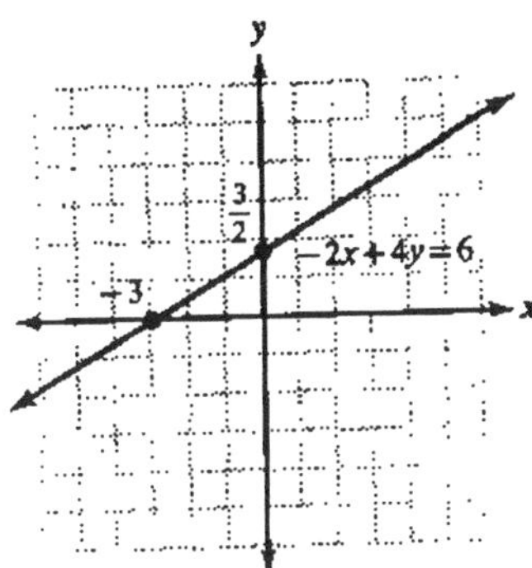


35. *Let* $y = 0$

$$\frac{1}{2}x + \frac{1}{3}y = 1$$
$$\frac{1}{2}x + \frac{1}{3}(0) = 1$$
$$x = 2$$

*The x-intercept is* 2.

*Let* $x = 0$

$$\frac{1}{2}x + \frac{1}{3}y = 1$$
$$\frac{1}{2}(0) + \frac{1}{3}y = 1$$
$$y = 3$$

*The y-intercept is* 3.

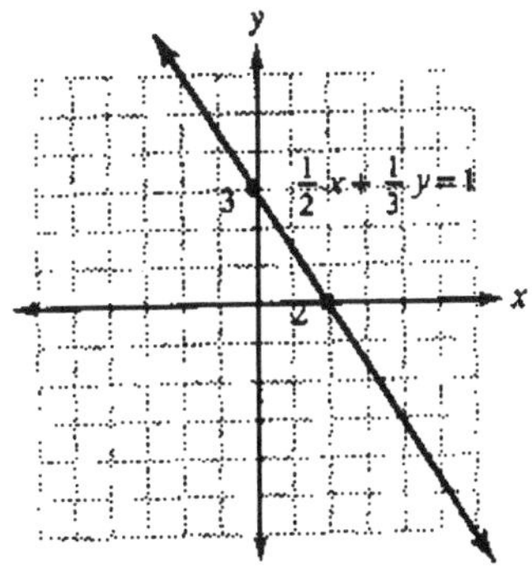


36. *Let* $y = 0$

$$\frac{2}{3}x - \frac{4}{3}y = 4$$
$$\frac{2}{3}x - \frac{4}{3}(0) = 4$$
$$x = 6$$

*The x-intercept is* 6.

*Let* $x = 0$

$$\frac{2}{3}x - \frac{4}{3}y = 4$$
$$\frac{2}{3}(0) - \frac{4}{3}y = 4$$
$$y = -3$$

*The y-intercept is* $-3$.

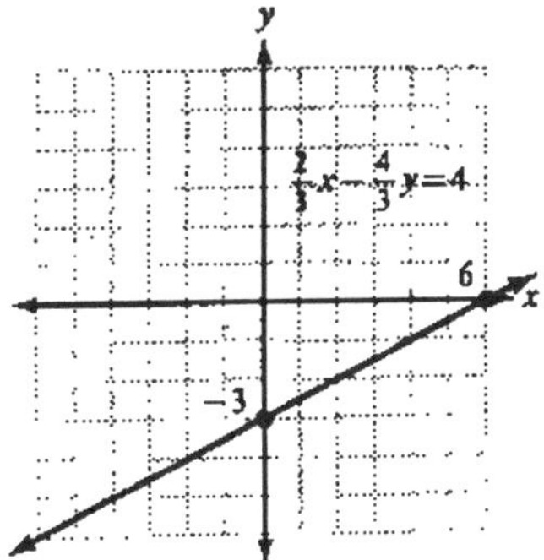

38. $\sqrt{4t + 5} + 7 = 3$

$\sqrt{4t + 5} = -4$

$4t + 5 = 16$

$4t = 11$

$t = \dfrac{11}{4}$

*Possible solution* $\dfrac{11}{4}$,

*which does not check;* $\varnothing$.

39. $\sqrt{x + 3} = x - 3$

$x + 3 = (x - 3)^2$

$x + 3 = x^2 - 6x + 9$

$0 = x^2 - 7x + 6$

$0 = (x - 1)(x - 6)$

$x - 1 = 0$

$x = 1$ *or*

$x - 6 = 0$

$x = 6$

*Possible solutions* 1 *and* 6; *only* 6 *checks.*

40. $\sqrt{x + 3} = \sqrt{x} - 3$

$x + 3 = (\sqrt{x} - 3)^2$

$x + 3 = x - 6\sqrt{x} + 9$

$-6 = -6\sqrt{x}$

$1 = \sqrt{x}$

$1 = x$

*Possible solution* 1, *which does not check;* $\varnothing$

42. *Let* $x = -8$

$y = \sqrt[3]{-8} - 1$

$y = -2 - 1$

$y = -3$

*Let* $x = -1$

$y = \sqrt[3]{-1} - 1$

$y = -1 - 1$

$y = -2$

*Let* $x = 0$

$y = \sqrt[3]{0} - 1$

$y = -1$

*Let* $x = 1$

$y = \sqrt[3]{1} - 1$

$y = 0$

*Let* $x = 8$

$y = \sqrt[3]{8} - 1$

$y = 2 - 1$

$y = 1$

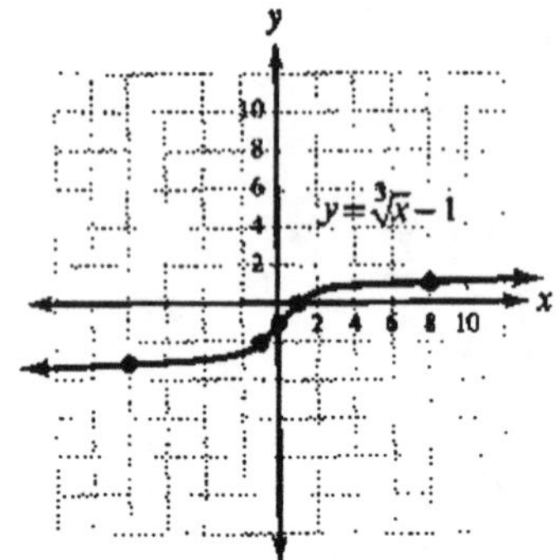

43. $x^2 - 2x - 1 < 0$

$$x = \frac{-(-2) \pm \sqrt{(-2)^2 - 4(1)(-1)}}{2(1)}$$

$$= \frac{2 \pm \sqrt{4 + 4}}{2}$$

$$= \frac{2 \pm 2\sqrt{2}}{2}$$

$$= 2 \pm \sqrt{2}$$

$1-\sqrt{2}$ $1+\sqrt{2}$

44. $x^2 - 6x + 7 < 0$

$$x = \frac{-(-6) \pm \sqrt{(-6)^2 - 4(1)(7)}}{2(1)}$$

$$= \frac{6 \pm \sqrt{36 - 28}}{2}$$

$$= \frac{6 \pm 2\sqrt{2}}{2}$$

$$= 3 \pm \sqrt{2}$$

$3-\sqrt{2}$ $3+\sqrt{2}$

46. $x^2 - 10x + 18 > 0$

$$x = \frac{-(-10) \pm \sqrt{(-10)^2 - 4(1)(18)}}{2(1)}$$

$$= \frac{10 \pm \sqrt{100 - 72}}{2}$$

$$= \frac{10 \pm 2\sqrt{7}}{2}$$

$$= 5 \pm \sqrt{7}$$

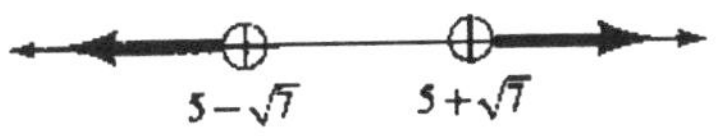

$5-\sqrt{7}$ $5+\sqrt{7}$

**Section 7.6**

All graphs asked for in Section 7.6 can be found in the instructor's textbook.

2. $y = x^2 - 2x - 3 \quad y = 0$
$0 = x^2 - 2x - 3$
$0 = (x + 1)(x - 3)$
$x = -1$ *or* $x = 3$

*The x-intercepts are* $-1$ *and* $3$

$$x = \frac{-b}{2a} = \frac{-(-2)}{2(1)} = 1$$

$$y = 1^2 - 2(1) - 3 = -4$$

*The vertex is* $(1,-4)$.

3. $y = -x^2 - 4x + 5 \quad y = 0$
$0 = -x^2 - 4x + 4$
$0 = x^2 + 4x - 5$
$0 = (x + 5)(x - 1)$
$x = -5$ *or*

$x = 1$

*The x-intercepts are* $-5$ *and* $1$.

$$x = \frac{-b}{2a} = \frac{-(-4)}{2(-1)} = -2$$

$$y = -(-2)^2 - 4(-2) + 5 = 9$$

*The vertex is* $(-2,9)$.

4. $y = x^2 + 4x - 5 \quad y = 0$
$0 = x^2 + 4x - 5$
$0 = (x + 5)(x - 1)$
$x = -5$ *or* $x = 1$

*The x-intercepts are* $-5$ *and* $1$.

$$x = \frac{-b}{2a} = \frac{-4}{2(1)} = -2$$

$$y = (-2)^2 + 4(-2) - 5 = -9$$

*The vertex is* $(-2,9)$.

6. $y = x^2 - 4 \quad y = 0$
$0 = x^2 - 4$
$0 = (x + 2)(x - 2)$
$x = -2$ *or*

$x = 2$

*The x-intercepts are* −2 *and* 2.

$$x = \frac{-b}{21} = \frac{-0}{2(1)} = 0$$

$y = 0^2 - 4 = -4$

*The vertex is* (0,4).

7. $y = -x^2 + 9 \quad y = 0$
$0 = -x^2 + 9$
$0 = x^2 - 9$
$0 = (x + 3)(x - 3)$
$x = -3$ *or*

$x = 3$

*The x-intercepts are* −3 *and* 3.

$$x = \frac{-b}{2a} = \frac{-0}{2(-1)} = 0$$

$y = -0^2 + 9 = 9$

*The vertex is* (0,9).

8. $y = -x^2 + 1 \quad y = 0$
$0 = -x^2 + 1$
$0 = x^2 - 1$
$0 = (x + 1)(x - 1)$
$x = -1$ *or*

$x = 1$

*The x-intercepts are* −1 *and* 1.

$$x = \frac{-1b}{2a} = \frac{-0}{2(1)} = 0$$

$y = -0^2 + 1 = 1$

*The vertex is* (0,1).

10. $y = 2x^2 + 4x - 6 \quad y = 0$
$0 = 2x^2 + 4x - 6$
$0 = x^2 + 2x - 3$
$0 = (x + 3)(x - 1)$
$x = -3$ *or*

$x = 1$

*The x-intercepts are* −3 *and* 1.

$$x = \frac{-b}{2a} = \frac{-4}{2(2)} = -1$$

$y = 2(-1)^2 + 4(-1) - 6 = -8$

*The vertex is* (−1,−8).

11. $y = x^2 - 2x - 4 \quad y = 0$
$0 = x^2 - 2x - 4$

$$x = \frac{-(-2) \pm \sqrt{(-2)^2 - 4(1)(-4)}}{2(1)}$$

$$= \frac{2 \pm \sqrt{4 + 16}}{2}$$

$$= \frac{2 \pm 2\sqrt{5}}{2}$$

$$= 1 \pm \sqrt{5}$$

*The x-intercepts are* $1 + \sqrt{5}$ *and* $1 - \sqrt{5}$

$$x = \frac{-(-2)}{2(1)} = 1$$

$y = 1^2 - 2(1) - 4 = -5$

*The vertex is* (1,−5).

12. $y = x^2 - 2x - 2 \quad y = 0$
$0 = x^2 - 2x - 2$

$$x = \frac{-(-2) \pm \sqrt{(-2)^2 - 4(1)(-2)}}{2(1)}$$

$$= \frac{2 \pm \sqrt{12}}{2}$$

$$= \frac{2 \pm 2\sqrt{3}}{2}$$

$$= 1 \pm \sqrt{3}$$

*The x-intercepts are* $1 + \sqrt{3}$ *and* $1 - \sqrt{3}$

$$x = \frac{-b}{2a}$$

$$= \frac{-(-2)}{2(1)} = 1$$

$y = 1^2 - 2(1) - 2 = -3$

*The vertex is* $1 + (1,-3)$.

14. $y = x^2 - 2x + 3$

$$x = \frac{-(-2)}{2(1)} = 1$$

$y = 1^2 - 2(1) + 3 = 2$

$y = (x^2 - 2x) + 3$
$y = (x^2 - 2x + 4) + 3 - 4$
$y = (x - 2)^2 - 1$

*In either case the vertex is* (1,2).

*Let's let* $x = 0$ *and* $x = 2$, *since each point is the same distance* $x = 1$ *and on either side:*

*When* $x = 0$
$y = 0^2 - 2(0) + 3$
$y = 3$

*When* $x = 2$
$y = 2^2 - 2(2) + 3$
$y = 3$

*The two additional points on the graph are* (0,3) *and* (2,3).

15. $y = -x^2 + 2x - 5$

$$x = \frac{-2}{2(-1)} = 1$$

$y = -(1)^2 + 2(1) - 5 = -4$

*The vertex is* (1,−4).

*Let's let* $x = 0$ *and* $x = 2$, *since each point is the same distance* $x = 1$, *and on either side:*

*When* $x = 0$
$y = -0^2 + 2(0) - 5$
$y = -5$

*When* $x = 2$
$y = -2^2 + 2(2) - 5$
$y = -5$

*The two additional points on the graph are* (0,−4) *and* (4,−4).

16. $y = -x^2 + 4x - 2$

$$x = \frac{-(4)}{2(-1)} = 2$$

$y = -2^2 + 4(2) - 2 = 2$

*The vertes is* (2,2).

*Let's let* $x = 0$ *and* $x = 4$, *since each point is the same distance* $x = 2$, *and on either side:*

*When* $x = 0$
$y = -0^2 + 4(0) - 2$
$y = -2$

*When* $x = 4$
$y = -4^2 + 4(4) - 2$
$y = -2$

*The two additional points on the graph are* (0,−2) *and* (4,−2).

18. $y = x^2 + 4$

$$x = \frac{-0}{2(1)} = 0$$

$y = 0^2 + 4 = 4$

$y = (x^2 + \quad) + 4$
$y = (x^2 + 0) + 4 - 0$
$y = (x + 0)^2 + 4$

*In either case, the vertex is* (0,4).

*Let's let* $x = -1$ *and* $x = 1$, *since each point is the same distance from* $x = 0$, *and on either side:*

*When* $x = -1$
$y = (-1)^2 + 4$
$y = 5$

*When* $x = 1$
$y = 1^2 + 4$
$y = 5$

*The two additional points on the graph are* (−1,5) *and* (1,5).

19. $y = -x^2 - 3$

$$x = \frac{-0}{2(-1)} = 0$$

$y = -0^2 - 3 = -3$

*The vertex is* (0,−3).

*Let's let* $x = -1$ *and* $x = 1$, *since each point is the same distance from* $x = 0$, *and on either side.*

*When* $x = -1$
$y = (-1)^2 - 3$
$y = -2$

*When* $x = 1$
$y = 1^2 - 3$
$y = -2$

*The two additional points on the graph are* (−1,−2) *and* (1,−2).

20. $y = -x^2 - 2$

$$x = \frac{-0}{2(-1)} = 0$$

$y = -0^2 - 2 = -2$

*The vertex is* (0,−2).

*Let's let* $x = -2$ *and* $x = 2$, *since each point is the same distance from* $x = 0$, *and on either side.*

*When* $x = -2$
$y = -(-2)^2 - 2$
$y = -6$

*When* $x = 2$
$y = -2^2 - 2$
$y = -6$

*The two additional points on the graph are* (−2,−6) *and* (2,−6).

22. $y = 2x^2 + 4x + 3$

$$x = \frac{-4}{2(2)} = -1$$

$y = 2(-1)^2 + 4(-1) + 3 = 1$

$y = 2(x^2 + 2x \quad) + 3$
$y = 2(x^2 + 2x + 1) + 3 - 2$
$y = 2(x + 1)^2 + 1$

*In either case, the vertex is* (−1,1).

*Let's let* $x = -2$ *and* $x = 0$.

*When* $x = -2$
$y = 2(-2)^2 + 4(-2) + 3$
$y = 3$

*When* $x = 0$
$y = 2(0)^2 + 4(0) + 3$
$y = 3$

23. $y = x^2 - 6x + 5$

$$x = \frac{-(-6)}{2(1)} = 3$$

$y = 3^2 - 6(3) + 5 = -4$

$y = (x^2 - 6x \quad) + 5$
$y = (x^2 - 6x + 9) + 5 - 9$
$y = (x - 3)^2 - 4$

*In either case, the vertex is* (3,−4).

*The graph will be concave up because* $x$ *is positive. This means the vertex* (3,−4) *is the lowest point.*

24. $y = -x^2 + 6x - 5$

$$x = \frac{-6}{2(-1)} = 3$$

$y = -3^2 + 6(3) - 5 = 4$

$y = -1(x^2 - 6x \quad ) - 5$
$y = -1(x^2 - 6x + 9) - 5 + 9$
$y = -1(x - 3)^2 + 4$

*In either case, the vertex is* (3,4).

*The graph will be concave down because x is negative. This means the vertex* (3,4) *is the highest point.*

26. $y = x^2 - 2x - 8$

$$x = \frac{-(-2)}{2(1)} = 1$$

$y = (-1)^2 - 2(-1) - 8 = -9$

$y = (x^2 - 2x \quad ) - 8$
$y = (x^2 - 2x + 1) - 8 - 1$
$y = (x - 1)^2 - 9$

*The vertex is* (1,−9).

*The graph will be concave up because x is positive. This means the vertex* (1,−9) *is the lowest point.*

27. $y = 12 + 4x - x^2$
$y = -x^2 + 4x + 12$

$$x = \frac{-4}{2(-1)} = 2$$

$y = -2^2 + 4(2) + 12 = 16$

$y = -1(x^2 - 4x \quad ) + 12$
$y = -1(x^2 - 4x + 4) + 12 + 4$
$y = -1(x - 2)^2 + 16$

*The vertex is* (2,16).

*The graph will be concave down because x is negative. This means the vertex* (2,16) *is the highest point.*

28. $y = -12 - 4x + x^2$
$y = x^2 - 4x - 12$

$$x = \frac{-(-4)}{2(1)} = 2$$

$y = 2^2 - 4(2) - 12 = -16$

$y = (x^2 - 4x \quad ) - 12$
$y = (x^2 - 4x + 4) - 12 - 4$
$y = (x - 2)^2 - 16$

*The vertex is* (2,−16).

*The graph will be concave up because x is positive. This means the vertex* (2,−16) *is the lowest point.*

30. $y = x^2 + 8x$

$$x = \frac{-8}{2(1)} = -4$$

$y = (-4)^2 + 8(-4) = -16$

$y = (x^2 + 8x + \quad ) + 0$
$y = (x^2 + 8x + 16) + 0 - 16$
$y = (x + 4) - 16$

*The vertex is* (−4,−16).

*The graph will be concave up because x is positive. This means the vertex* (−4,−16) *is the lowest point.*

31. $P = -0.5x^2 + 40x - 300$

$$x = \frac{-(40)}{2(-0.5)} = 40 \text{ items to sell each week}$$

$P = 0.5(40)^2 + 40(40) - 300$
$= -800 + 1600 - 300$
$= \$500$ *maximum weekly profit*

32. $P = -0.5x^2 + 100x - 1600$

$$x = \frac{-100}{2(-0.5)} = 100 \text{ items to sell each week}$$

$P = -0.5(100)^2 + 100(100) - 1600$
$= -5000 + 10{,}000 - 1600$
$= \$3{,}400$ *maximum weekly profit*

34. $P = -0.002x^2 + 5.5x - 1200$

$x = \dfrac{-5.5}{2(-0.002)}$ = 1,375 *picture frames to sell each month*

$P = -0.002(1{,}375)^2 + 5.5(1{,}375) - 1200$
$= -0.002(1{,}890{,}625) + 7{,}562.5 - 1200$
$= -3{,}781.25 + 7{,}562.5 - 1200$
= \$2,581.25 *maximum weekly profit*

35. $h = 128t - 16t^2$
$y = -16t^2 + 128t$

$t = \dfrac{-128}{2(-16)} = 4$

$y = -16(4)^2 + 128(4)$
$= -256 + 512$
= 256 *feet maximum height*

36. $h = 32t - 16t^2$
$y = -16t^2 + 32t$

$t = \dfrac{-32}{2(-16)} = 1$

$y = -16(1)^2 + 32(1)$
= 16 *feet maximum height*

38. $R = (800 - 100p)p$
$R = 800p - 100p^2$
$R = -100p^2 + 800p$

$p = \dfrac{-b}{2a} = \dfrac{-800}{2(-100)}$ = \$4.00

$R = -100(4)^2 + 800(4)$
$R = -1{,}600 + 3{,}200$
$R$ = \$1,600 *maximum*

*See the graph in the instructor's textbook.*

39. $R = (1{,}700 - 100p)p$
$R = 1{,}700p - 100p^2$
$R = -100p^2 + 1{,}700p$

$p = \dfrac{-b}{2a} = \dfrac{-1{,}700}{2(-100)}$ = \$8.50

$R = -100(8.50)^2 + 1{,}700(8.50)$
$R = -7{,}225 + 14{,}450$
$R$ = \$7,225 *maximum*

*See the graph in the instructor's textbook.*

40. $R = (1{,}800 - 100p)p$
$R = 1{,}800p - 100p^2$
$R = -100p^2 + 1{,}800p$

$p = \dfrac{-b}{2a} = \dfrac{-1{,}800}{2(-100)}$ = \$9.50

$R = -100(9)^2 + 1{,}800(9)$
$R = -8{,}100 + 16{,}200$
$R$ = \$8,100 *maximum*

*See the graph in the instructor's textbook.*

42. $2i(5 - 6i) = 10i - 12i^2$
$= 12 + 10i$

43. $(3 + 2i)(7 - 3i)$
$= 21 + 5i - 6i^2$
$= 27 + 5i$

44. $(4 + 5i)^2 = (4 + 5i)(4 + 5i)$
$= 16 + 40i + 25i^2$
$= -9 + 40i$

46. $\dfrac{2 + 3i}{2 - 3i} = \dfrac{2 + 3i}{2 - 3i} \cdot \dfrac{2 + 3i}{2 + 3i}$

$= \dfrac{4 + 12i + 9i^2}{4 - 9i^2}$

$= \dfrac{-5 + 12i}{13}$

$= -\dfrac{5}{13} + \dfrac{12}{13}i$

**Section 7.7**

(See the graphs in the instructor's textbook.)

2. $x = y^2 - 26 - 3$

*x-intercept:* when $y = 0,\ x = -3$
*y-intercept:* when $x = 0$

$0 = y^2 - 2y - 3$
$0 = (x + 1)(x - 3)$
$x + 1 = 0$
$x = -1$ *or*

$x - 3 = 0$
$x = 3$

*Vertex:* $y = \dfrac{-b}{2a} = \dfrac{-(-2)}{2(1)} = 1$

$x = 1^2 - 2(1) - 3$
$y = -4$

*The vertex is* (-4,1).

3. $x = -y^2 - 4y + 5$

*x-intercept:* when $y = 0,\ x = 5$
*y-intercept:* when $x = 0$

$0 = -y^2 - 4y + 5$
$0 = y^2 + 4y - 5$
$0 = (y + 5)(y - 1)$
$y + 5 = 0$
$y = -5$ *or*

$y - 1 = 0$
$y = 1$

*Vertex:* $y = \dfrac{-b}{2a} = \dfrac{-(-4)}{2(-1)} = -2$

$x = -(-2)^2 - 4(-2) + 5$
$x = 9$

*The vertex is* (9,-2).

4. $x = y^2 + 4y - 5$

*x-intercept:* when $y = 0,\ x = -5$
*y-intercept:* when $x = 0$

$0 = y^2 + 4y - 5$
$0 = (y + 5)(y - 1)$
$y + 5 = 0$
$y = -5$ *or*

$y - 1 = 0$
$y = 1$

*Vertex:* $y = \dfrac{-b}{2a} = \dfrac{-4}{2(1)} = -2$

$x = (-2)^2 + 4(-2) - 5$
$x = -9$

*The vertex is* (-9,-2).

6. $x = y^2 - 4$

*x-intercept:* when $y = 0,\ x = -4$
*y-intercept:* when $x = 0$

$0 = y^2 - 4$
$(y + 2)(y - 2) = 0$
$y + 2 = 0$
$y = -2$ *or*

$y - 2 = 0$
$y = 2$

*Vertex:* $y = \dfrac{-b}{2a} = \dfrac{-0}{2(1)} = 0$

$x = 0^2 - 4$
$x = -4$

*The vertex is* (-4,0).

7. $x = -y^2 + 9$

*x-intercept:* when $y = 0,\ x = 9$
*y-intercept:* when $x = 0$

$0 = -y^2 + 9$
$y^2 = 9$
$y = \pm 3$

*Vertex:* $y = \dfrac{-b}{2a} = \dfrac{-0}{2(-1)} = 0$

$x = -(0)^2 + 9$
$x = 9$

*The vertex is* (9,0).

8. $x = -y^2 + 1$

*x-intercept:* when $y = 0$, $x = 1$
*y-intercept:* when $x = 0$

$$0 = -y^2 + 1$$
$$y^2 = 1$$
$$y = \pm 1$$

*Vertex:* $y = \dfrac{-b}{2a} = \dfrac{-0}{2(-1)} = 0$

$$x = -(0)^2 + 1$$
$$x = 1$$

*The vertex is* (1,0).

10. $x = 2y^2 + 4y - 6$

*x-intercept:* when $y = 0$, $s = -6$
*y-intercept:* when $x = 0$

$$0 = 2y^2 + 4y - 6$$
$$0 = y^2 + 2y - 3$$
$$0 = (y + 3)(y - 1)$$
$$y + 3 = 0$$
$$y = -3 \quad or$$

$$y - 1 = 0$$
$$y = 1$$

*Vertex:* $y = \dfrac{-b}{2a} = \dfrac{-4}{2(2)} = -1$

$$x = 2(-1)^2 + 4(-1) - 6$$
$$x = -8$$

*The vertex is* (-8,1).

11. $x = y^2 - 2y - 4$

*x-intercept:* when $y = 0$, $s = -4$
*y-intercept:* when $x = 0$

$$0 = y^2 - 2y - 4$$

$$y = \frac{-(-2) \pm \sqrt{(-2)^2 - 4(1)(-4)}}{2(1)}$$

$$y = \frac{2 \pm \sqrt{20}}{2}$$

$$y = \frac{2 \pm 2\sqrt{5}}{2}$$

$$y = 1 \pm \sqrt{5}$$

*Vertex:* $y = \dfrac{-b}{2a} = \dfrac{-(-2)}{2(1)} = 1$

$$x = 1^2 - 2(1) - 5$$
$$x = -5$$

*The vertex is* (-5,1).

12. $x = y^2 - 2y + 3$

*x-intercept:* when $y = 0$, $x = 3$
*y-intercept:* when $x = 0$

$$0 = y^2 - 2y + 3$$

$$y = \frac{-(-2) \pm \sqrt{(-2)^2 - 4(1)(3)}}{2(1)}$$

$$y = \frac{2 \pm \sqrt{-8}}{2}$$

$$y = \frac{2 \pm 2i\sqrt{2}}{2}$$

$$y = 1 \pm i\sqrt{2}$$

*The parabola does not intercept the y-axis.*

*Vertex:* $y = \dfrac{-b}{2a} = \dfrac{-(-2)}{2(1)} = 1$

$$x = 1^2 - 2(1) + 3$$
$$x = 2$$

*The vertex is* (2,1).

14. $-\sqrt{-20} = -2i\sqrt{5}$

15. $i^{20} = 1$

16. $i^{22} = -1$

18. $\dfrac{-3 + 4i}{i} \cdot \dfrac{i}{i} = \dfrac{-3i + 4i^2}{a^2}$

$= \dfrac{-4 - 3i}{-1}$

$= 4 + 3i$

# Chapter 8

**Section 8.1** (See graphs in the instructor's textbook.)

2. (4,5)

3. (−5,−6)

4. (−2,−3)

6. (6,4)

7. *Lines are parallel; there is no solution.*

8. *Lines coincide; any solution to one of the equations is a solution to the other.*

10. *Lines are parallel; there is no solution.*

11. $\begin{aligned} x + y &= 5 \\ \underline{3x - y} &\underline{= 3} \\ 4x &= 8 \\ x &= 2 \end{aligned}$ $\quad$ $\begin{aligned} 2 + y &= 5 \\ y &= 3 \end{aligned}$

*The solution to the system is* (2,3).

12. $\begin{aligned} x - y &= 4 \\ \underline{-x + 2y} &\underline{= -3} \\ y &= 1 \end{aligned}$ $\quad$ $\begin{aligned} x - 1 &= 4 \\ x &= 5 \end{aligned}$

*The solution to the system is* (5,1).

14. $6x - 2y = -10$ *Multiply* $-1 \rightarrow$ $6x - 2y = -10$
$6x + 3y = -15$ *Multiply* $-1 \rightarrow$ $\underline{-6x - 3y = 15}$
$-5y = 5$
$y = -1$

$6x - 2(-1) = -10$
$x = -2$

*The solution to the system is* (−2,−1).

15. $3x - 2y = 6$ *Multiply* $-2 \rightarrow$ $-6x + 4y = -12$
$6x - 4y = 12$ *Multiply* $+1 \rightarrow$ $\underline{6x - 4y = 12}$
$0 = 0$

*Lines coincide*: $\{(x,y) \mid 3x - 2y = 6\}$

16.
$$\begin{aligned} 4x + 5y &= -3 \quad \textit{Multiply } 2 \rightarrow \\ -8x - 10y &= 3 \quad \textit{Multiply } +1 \rightarrow \end{aligned} \qquad \begin{array}{r} 8x + 10y = -6 \\ \underline{-8x - 10y = \;\;3} \\ 0 = -3 \end{array}$$

*Parallel lines:* ∅

18.
$$\begin{aligned} x + 3y &= 3 \quad \textit{Multiply } -2 \rightarrow \\ 2x - 9y &= 1 \quad \textit{Multiply } +1 \rightarrow \end{aligned} \qquad \begin{array}{r} -2x - 6y = -6 \\ \underline{2x - 9y = \;\;1} \\ -15y = -5 \\ y = \dfrac{1}{3} \end{array}$$

$$x + 3\left(\frac{1}{3}\right) = 3$$

$$x = 2$$

*The solution to the system is* $\left(2, \frac{1}{3}\right)$.

19.
$$\begin{aligned} 2x - 5y &= 16 \quad \textit{Multiply } -2 \rightarrow \\ 4x - 3y &= 11 \quad \textit{Multiply } +1 \rightarrow \end{aligned} \qquad \begin{array}{r} -4x + 10y = -32 \\ \underline{4x - 3y = \;\;11} \\ 7y = -21 \\ y = -\;3 \end{array}$$

$$2x - 5(-3) = 16$$

$$x = \frac{1}{2}$$

*The solution to the system is* $\left(\frac{1}{2}, -3\right)$.

20.
$$\begin{aligned} 5x - 3y &= -11 \quad \textit{Multiply } 2 \rightarrow \\ 7x + 6y &= -12 \quad \textit{Multiply } 1 \rightarrow \end{aligned} \qquad \begin{array}{r} 10x - 6y = -22 \\ \underline{7x + 6y = -12} \\ 17x = -34 \\ x = -\;2 \end{array}$$

$$5(-2) - 3y = -11$$

$$y = \frac{1}{3}$$

*The solution to the system is* $\left(-2, \frac{1}{3}\right)$.

22. $5x + 4y = -1$ *Multiply* $3 \rightarrow$ $15x + 12y = -3$
$7x + 6y = -2$ *Multiply* $-2 \rightarrow$ $-14x - 12y = 4$

$$x = 1$$

$5(1) + 4y = -1$

$$y = -\frac{3}{2}$$

*The solution to the system is* $\left(1, -\frac{3}{2}\right)$.

23. $4x + 3y = 14$ *Multiply* $2 \rightarrow$ $8x + 6y = 28$
$9x - 2y = 14$ *Multiply* $3 \rightarrow$ $27x - 6y = 42$

$$35x = 70$$
$$x = 2$$

$4(2) + 3y = 14$
$y = 2$

*The solution to the system is* (2,2).

24. $7x - 6y = 13$ *Multiply* $5 \rightarrow$ $35x - 30y = 65$
$6x - 5y = 11$ *Multiply* $-6 \rightarrow$ $-36x + 30y = -66$

$$x = 1$$

$7(1) - 6y = 13$
$y = -1$

*The solution to the system is* (1,−1).

26. $3x - 2y = 1$ *Multiply* $2 \rightarrow$ $6x - 4y = 2$
$-6x + 4y = -2$ *Multiply* $1 \rightarrow$ $-6x + 4y = -2$

$$0 = 0$$

*The result is the true statement* 0 = 0, *which indicates all real numbers solve the system. If we were to graph the two lines, we would find they coincide.*

*The solution is* $\{x,y \mid 3x - 26 = 1\}$.

27. $\frac{1}{4}x - \frac{1}{6}y = -2$ *Multiply* 60 → $15x - 10y = -120$

$-\frac{1}{6}x + \frac{1}{5}y = 4$ *Multiply* 90 → $-15x + 18y = 360$

$8y = 240$
$y = 30$

$\frac{1}{4}x - \frac{1}{6}(30) = -2$

$\frac{1}{4}x = 3$

$x = 12$

*The solution to the system is* {12,30}.

28. $-\frac{1}{3}x + \frac{1}{4}y = 0$ *Multiply* 12 → $-4x + 3y = 0$

$\frac{1}{5}x - \frac{1}{10}y = 1$ *Multiply* 20 → $4x - 2y = 20$

$y = 20$

$-\frac{1}{3}x + \frac{1}{4}(20) = 0$

$x = 15$

*The solution to the system is* (15,20).

30. $\frac{1}{2}x + \frac{1}{3}y = \frac{2}{3}$ *Multiply* 60 → $30x + 20y = 40$

$\frac{2}{3}x + \frac{2}{5}y = \frac{14}{15}$ *Multiply* -45 → $-30x - 18y = -42$

$2y = -2$
$y = -1$

$\frac{1}{2}x + \frac{1}{3}(-1) = \frac{2}{3}$

$\frac{1}{2}x = 1$

$x = 2$

*The solution to the system is* (2,−1).

31. $\frac{2}{3}x + \frac{2}{5}y = 4$ *Multiply* 15 → $10x + 6y = 60$

$\frac{1}{3}x - \frac{1}{2}y = -\frac{1}{3}$ *Multiply* −30 → $\underline{-10x + 15y = 10}$

$21y = 70$

$y = \frac{10}{3}$

$\frac{2}{3}x + \frac{2}{5}\left(\frac{10}{3}\right) = 4$

$\frac{2}{3}x = \frac{8}{3}$

$x = 4$

*The solution to the system is* $\left(4, \frac{10}{3}\right)$.

32. $\frac{1}{2}x - \frac{1}{3}y = \frac{5}{6}$ *Multiply* 24 → $12x - 8y = 20$

$-\frac{2}{5}x + \frac{1}{2}y = -\frac{9}{10}$ *Multiply* 30 → $\underline{-12x + 15y = -27}$

$7y = -7$

$y = -1$

$\frac{1}{2}x - \frac{1}{3}(-1) = \frac{5}{6}$

$\frac{1}{2}x = \frac{1}{2}$

$x = 1$

*The solution to the system is* $(1, -1)$.

34. $3x - y = -8 \quad y = 6x + 3$

$3x - (6x + 3) = -8$

$3x - 6x - 3 = -8$

$-3x = -5$

$x = \frac{5}{3}$

$y = 6\left(\frac{5}{3}\right) + 3$

$y = 13$

*The solution to the system is* $\left(\frac{5}{3}, 13\right)$.

35. $6x - y = 10 \quad y = -\frac{3}{4}x - 1$

$$6x - \left(-\frac{3}{4}x - 1\right) = 10$$

$$\frac{27}{4}x + 1 = 10$$

$$\frac{27}{4}x = 9$$

$$x = \frac{4}{3}$$

$$y = -\frac{3}{4}\left(\frac{4}{3}\right) - 1$$

$$y = -2$$

*The solution to the system is* $\left(\frac{4}{3}, -2\right)$.

36. $2x - y = 6 \quad y = -\frac{4}{3}x + 1$

$$2x - \left(-\frac{4}{3}x + 1\right) = 6$$

$$\frac{10}{3}x - 1 = 6$$

$$\frac{10}{3}x = 7$$

$$x = \frac{21}{10}$$

$$y = -\frac{4}{3}\left(\frac{21}{10}\right) + 1$$

$$y = -\frac{9}{5}$$

*The solution to the system is* $\left(\frac{21}{10}, -\frac{9}{5}\right)$

38.
$$x + y = 3$$
$$x = -y + 3$$

$$2x + 3y = -4$$
$$2(-y + 3) + 3y = -4$$
$$y = -10$$

$$x = -(-10) + 3$$
$$x = 13$$

*The solution to the system is* (13,−10).

39.
$$y = 3x - 2$$
$$4x - 4 = 3x - 2$$
$$x = 2$$

$$y = 4x - 4$$
$$y = 4(2) - 4$$
$$y = 4$$

*The solution to the system is* (2,4).

40.
$$y = 5x - 2$$
$$-2x + 5 = 5x - 2$$
$$7 = 7x$$
$$x = 1$$

$$y = -2x + 5$$
$$y = -2(1) + 5$$
$$y = 3$$

*The solution to the system is* (1,3).

42.
$$-10x + 8y = -6 \quad y = \frac{5}{4}x$$

$$-10x + 8\left(\frac{5}{4}x\right) = -6$$

$$-10x + 10x = -6$$
$$0 = -6$$

*The lines are parallel,* ∅.

43.
$$\frac{1}{3}x - \frac{1}{2}y = 0 \quad x = \frac{3}{2}y$$

$$\frac{1}{3}\left(\frac{3}{2}y\right) - \frac{1}{2}y = 0$$

$$\frac{1}{2}y - \frac{1}{2}y = 0$$

$$0 = 0$$

*The lines coincide,* $\left\{(x,y)\,|\,x = \frac{3}{2}y\right\}$.

44.
$$\frac{2}{5}x - \frac{2}{3}y = 0 \quad y = \frac{3}{5}x$$

$$\frac{2}{5}x - \frac{2}{3}\left(\frac{3}{5}x\right) = 0$$

$$\frac{2}{5}x - \frac{2}{5}x = 0$$

$$0 = 0$$

*The lines coincide,* $\left\{(x,y)\,|\,y = \frac{3}{5}x\right\}$.

46.
$$\begin{array}{lll} 3x - 4y = 7 & \textit{Multiply } -2 & -6x + 8y = -14 \\ 6x - 3y = 5 & \textit{Multiply } +1 & \underline{\;6x - 3y = -\;5} \\ & & 5y = -\;9 \end{array}$$

$$y = -\;\frac{9}{5}$$

$$\begin{array}{lll} 3x - 4y = 7 & \textit{Multiply } 3 & 9x - 12y = \;21 \\ 6x - 3y = 5 & \textit{Multiply } -4 & \underline{-24x + 12y = -20} \\ & & -15x \quad = \;1 \end{array}$$

$$x = -\frac{1}{15}$$

*The solution set is* $\left(-\frac{1}{15}, -\frac{9}{5}\right)$.

47.
$$\begin{array}{lll} 9x - 8y = 4 & \textit{Multiply } 2 & 18x - 16y = \;8 \\ 2x + 3y = 6 & \textit{Multiply } -9 & \underline{-18x - 27y = -54} \\ & & 43y = -46 \end{array}$$

$$y = -\frac{46}{43}$$

$$\begin{array}{llr} 9x - 8y = 4 & \textit{Multiply } 3 & 27x - 24y = 12 \\ 2x + 3y = 6 & \textit{Multiply } 8 & \underline{16x + 24y = 48} \\ & & 43x \quad = 60 \\ & & x \quad = \dfrac{60}{43} \end{array}$$

*The solution set is* $\left(\frac{60}{43}, -\frac{46}{43}\right)$.

48. $$\begin{array}{llr} 4x - 7y = \ \ 10 & \textit{Multiply } 3 & 12x - 21y = \ \ 30 \\ -3x + 2y = -\ 9 & \textit{Multiply } 4 & \underline{-12x + \ \ 8y = -36} \\ & & -\ 13y = -\ 6 \\ & & y = \dfrac{6}{13} \end{array}$$

$$\begin{array}{llr} 4x - 7y = \ \ 10 & \textit{Multiply } 2 & 8x - 14y = \ \ 20 \\ -3x + 2y = -\ 9 & \textit{Multiply } 7 & \underline{-21x + 14y = -63} \\ & & -13x \quad = -43 \\ & & x \quad = \dfrac{43}{13} \end{array}$$

*The solution set is* $\left(\frac{43}{13}, \frac{6}{13}\right)$.

50. $$\begin{array}{llr} 4x - 3y = -1 & \textit{Multiply } \ 5 & 20x - 15y = -\ 5 \\ 5x + 8y = \ \ 2 & \textit{Multiply } -4 & \underline{20x - 32y = -\ 8} \\ & & -\ 47y = \ \ 13 \\ & & y = \dfrac{13}{47} \end{array}$$

$$\begin{array}{llr} 4x - 3y = -1 & \textit{Multiply } 8 & 32x - 24y = -\ 8 \\ 5x + 8y = \ \ 2 & \textit{Multiply } 3 & \underline{15x + 24y = \ \ \ 6} \\ & & 47x \quad = -\ 2 \\ & & x \quad = -\dfrac{2}{47} \end{array}$$

*The solution set is* $\left(-\frac{2}{47}, \frac{13}{47}\right)$.

51.
$$\begin{array}{rl} x + y = 10{,}000 & \textit{Multiply } -6 \\ .06x + .05y = 560 & \textit{Multiply } 100 \end{array} \qquad \begin{array}{r} -6x - 6y = -60{,}000 \\ \underline{6x + 5y = 56{,}000} \\ -y = -4{,}000 \\ y = 4{,}000 \end{array}$$

$$\begin{aligned} x + 4{,}000 &= 10{,}000 \\ x &= 6{,}000 \end{aligned}$$

*The solution set is* (6,000, 4,000).

52.
$$\begin{array}{rl} x + y = 12 & \textit{Multiply } -2 \\ .20x + .50y = .30(12) & \textit{Multiply } 10 \end{array} \qquad \begin{array}{r} -2x - 2y = -24 \\ \underline{2x + 5y = 36} \\ 3y = 12 \\ y = 4 \end{array}$$

$$\begin{aligned} x + 4 &= 12 \\ x &= 8 \end{aligned}$$

*The solution set is* (8,4).

54.
$$\begin{array}{rl} 5x - 7y = C & -15x + 21y = 9 \\ 1(5x - 7y) = C & -3(5x - 7y) = -3(-3) \\ C = -3 & \end{array}$$

55. *a.)*
$$\begin{aligned} y &= 32x + 41 \quad x = 9 \\ y &= 32(9) + 41 \\ y &= \$3.29 \end{aligned}$$

*b.)* $y = 30x + 45$

*c.)*
$$\begin{aligned} 32x + 41 &= 30x + 45 \\ 2x &= 4 \\ x &= 2 \textit{ minutes} \end{aligned}$$

56. *a.)*
$$y = 10x + 75 \quad 9\frac{6}{7} = \frac{69}{7}$$

$$y = 10(69) + 75 \quad x = 69$$

$$y = \$7.65$$

*b.)* $y = 15x + 50$

*c.)*
$$\begin{aligned} 10x + 75 &= 15x + 50 \\ 25 &= 5x \\ 5 &= x \end{aligned}$$

$$\frac{5}{7} + \frac{1}{7} = \frac{6}{7} \textit{ of a mile.}$$

58. $(3x + 5)^2 = -12$

$$3x + 5 = \pm 2i\sqrt{3}$$

$$x = \frac{-5 \pm 2i\sqrt{3}}{3}$$

59. $x^2 - 10x + 25$ (*add* 25)

60. $x^2 - 5x + \frac{25}{4}$ $\left(add\ \frac{25}{4}\right)$

62. $x^2 - 5x + 4 = 0$

$$x^2 - 5x = -4$$

$$x^2 - 5x + \frac{25}{4} = -4 + \frac{25}{4}$$

$$\left(x - \frac{5}{2}\right)^2 = \frac{9}{4}$$

$$x - \frac{5}{2} = \pm\frac{3}{2}$$

$$x = \frac{5}{2} \pm \frac{3}{2}$$

$$x = 4 \quad or \quad x = 1$$

63. $3x^2 - 6x + 6 = 0$

$$x^2 - 2x = -2$$

$$x^2 - 2x + 1 = -2 + 1$$

$$(x - 1)^2 = -1$$

$$x - 1 = \pm i$$

$$x = 1 \pm i$$

64. $4x^2 - 16x - 8 = 0$

$$x^2 - 4x = 2$$

$$x^2 - 4x + 4 = 2 + 4$$

$$(x - 2)^2 = 6$$

$$x - 2 = \pm\sqrt{6}$$

$$x = 2 \pm \sqrt{6}$$

66. $ax + by = 2 \quad (2,2),(6,7)$

$a(2) + b(2) = 2$ *becomes* $2a + 2b = 2$
$a(6) + b(7) = 2$ *becomes* $6a + 7b = 2$

*To solve for a and b, we*

$2a + 2b = 2$ *Multiply* $-3$ $\quad -6a - 6b = -6$
$6a + 7b = 2$ *Multiply* $+1$ $\quad 6a + 7b = 2$

$$b = -4$$

$$2a + 2(-4) = 2$$

$$2a = 10$$

$$a = 5$$

67. $y = ax^2 + bx \quad (-1,3),(3,3)$

$$3 = a(-1)^2 + b(-1)$$

$$3 = a - b$$

$$3 = a(3)^2 + b(3)$$

$$3 = 9a + 3b$$

*To solve for a and b, we*

$a - b = 3$ *Multiply* $3$ $\quad 3a - 3b = 9$
$9a + 3b = 3$ *Multiply* $+1$ $\quad 9a + 3b = 3$

$$12a = 12$$

$$a = 1$$

$$1 - b = 3$$

$$b = -2$$

$$y = (1)x^2 + (-2)x$$

$$y = x^2 - 2x$$

*Vertex is* $(1,-1)$.

68. $y = ax^2 + bx \quad (1,3),(-3,3)$

$$3 = a(1)^2 + b(1)$$
$$3 = a + b$$

$$3 = a(-3)^2 + b(-3)$$
$$3 = 9a - 3b$$

*To solve for a and b, we*

$a + b = 3$ *Multiply* 3 $\quad 3a + 3b = 9$
$9a - 3b = 3$ *Multiply* +1 $\quad 9a - 3b = 3$

$$12a = 12$$
$$a = 1$$

$$a + b = 3$$
$$b = 2$$

$$y = (1)x^2 + (2)x$$
$$y = x^2 + 2x$$

*Vertex* (−1,−1).

## Section 8.2

2. $x - y - 2z = -1 \quad (1)$
$x + y + z = 6 \quad (2)$
$x + y - z = 4 \quad (3)$

$$x - y - 2z = -1 \quad (1)$$
$$x + y + z = 6 \quad (2)$$
$$2x - z = 5 \quad (4)$$

$$x - y - 2z = -1 \quad (1)$$
$$x + y - z = 4 \quad (3)$$
$$2x - 3z = 3 \quad (5)$$

$2x - z = 5$ *Multiply* 1 $\quad 2x - z = 5$
$2x - 3z = 3$ *Multiply* −1 $\quad -2x + 3z = -3$

$$2z = 2$$
$$z = 1$$

$$2x - 1 = 5$$
$$x = 3$$

$$3 - y - 2(1) = -1$$
$$y = 2$$

*The solution set for the system is the ordered triple* (3,2,1).

3. $x + y + z = 6 \quad (1)$
$x - y + 2z = 7 \quad (2)$
$2x - y - 4z = -9 \quad (3)$

$$x + y + z = 6 \quad (1)$$
$$x - y + 2z = 7 \quad (2)$$
$$2x + 3z = 13 \quad (4)$$

$$x + y + z = 6 \quad (1)$$
$$2x - y - 4z = -9 \quad (3)$$
$$3x - 3z = -3 \quad (5)$$

$$2x + 3z = 13$$
$$3x - 3z = -3$$
$$5x = 10$$
$$x = 2$$

$$2(2) + 3z = 13$$
$$3z = 9$$
$$z = 3$$

$$2 + y + 3 = 6$$
$$y = 1$$

*The solution set for the system is the ordered triple* (2,1,3).

4. $x + y + z = 0 \quad (1)$
$x + y - z = 6 \quad (2)$
$x - y + 2z = -7 \quad (3)$

$$x + y + z = 0 \quad (1)$$
$$x - y + 2z = -7 \quad (3)$$
$$2x + 3z = -7 \quad (4)$$

$$x + y - z = 6 \quad (2)$$
$$x - y + 2z = -7 \quad (3)$$
$$2x + z = -1 \quad (5)$$

$2x + 3z = -7$ *Multiply* 1 $\quad 2x + 3z = -7$
$2x + z = -1$ *Multiply* −1 $\quad -2x - z = 1$

$$2z = -6$$
$$z = -3$$

$$2x + (-3) = -1$$
$$2x = 2$$
$$x = 1$$

$$1 + y + (-3) = 0$$
$$y = 2$$

*The solution set for the system is the ordered triple* (1,2,−3).

6.

$$\begin{aligned} 2+ \quad y - 3z &= -14 \quad (1)\\ x - 3y + 4z &= 22 \quad (2)\\ 3x + 2y + z &= 0 \quad (3) \end{aligned}$$

$$\begin{aligned} 2x + y - 3z &= -14 \quad (1)\\ -2x + 6y - 8z &= -44 \quad (2)\ \textit{by}\ -2\\ \hline 7y - 11z &= -58 \quad (4) \end{aligned}$$

$$\begin{aligned} -3x + 9y - 12z &= -66 \quad (2)\ \textit{by}\ -3\\ 3x + 2y + z &= 0 \quad (3)\\ \hline 11y - 11z &= -66 \quad (5) \end{aligned}$$

$$\begin{aligned} 7y - 11z &= -58 \quad \textit{Multiply}\ -1 \qquad 7y + 11z = 58\\ 11y - 11z &= -66 \quad \textit{Multiply}\ \ 1 \qquad 11y - 11z = -66\\ &\qquad\qquad\qquad\qquad\qquad 4y = -8\\ &\qquad\qquad\qquad\qquad\qquad y = -2 \end{aligned}$$

$$\begin{aligned} 7(-2) - 11z &= -58\\ -11z &= -44\\ z &= 4 \end{aligned}$$

$$\begin{aligned} 2x + (-2) - 3(4) &= -14\\ 2x &= 0\\ x &= 0 \end{aligned}$$

*The solution for the system is the ordered triple* (0,−2,4).

7.

$$\begin{aligned} 2x + 3y - 2z &= 4 \quad (1)\\ x + 3y - 3z &= 4 \quad (2)\\ 3x - 6y + z &= -3 \quad (3) \end{aligned}$$

$$\begin{aligned} 2x + 3y - 2x &= 4 \quad (1)\\ -x - 3y + 3z &= -4 \quad (2)\ \textit{by}\ -1\\ \hline x \qquad + z &= 0 \quad (4) \end{aligned}$$

$$\begin{aligned} 2x + 6y - 6z &= 8 \quad (2)\ \textit{by}\ 2\\ 3x - 6y + z &= -3 \quad (3)\\ \hline 5x \qquad + 5z &= 5 \quad (5) \end{aligned}$$

$$\begin{aligned} x + z &= 0 \quad \textit{Multiply}\ 5 \qquad 5x + 5z = 0\\ 5x - 5z &= 5 \quad \textit{Multiply}\ 1 \qquad 5x - 5z = 5\\ &\qquad\qquad\qquad\qquad 10x = 5\\ &\qquad\qquad\qquad\qquad x = \frac{1}{2} \end{aligned}$$

$$\frac{1}{2} + z = 0$$

$$z = -\frac{1}{2}$$

$$2\left(\frac{1}{2}\right) + 3y - 2\left(-\frac{1}{2}\right) = 4$$

$$3y = 2$$

$$y = \frac{2}{3}$$

*The solution set for the system is*

*the ordered triple* $\left(\frac{1}{2}, \frac{2}{3}, -\frac{1}{2}\right)$.

8. $4x + y - 2z = 0$ (1)
$2x - 3y + 3z = 9$ (2)
$-6x - 2y + z = 0$ (3)

$$\begin{array}{rl} 4x + y - 2z = 0 & (1) \\ \underline{-4x + 6y - 6z = -18} & (2)\ \textit{by}\ -2 \\ 7y - 8z = -18 & \end{array}$$

$$\begin{array}{rl} 6x - 9y + 9z = 27 & (2)\ \textit{by}\ 3 \\ \underline{-6x - 2y + z = 0} & (3) \\ -11y + 10z = 27 & (5) \end{array}$$

$$\begin{array}{rlr} 7y - 8z = -18 & \textit{Multiply}\ 11 & 77y - 88z = -198 \\ -11y + 10z = 27 & \textit{Multiply}\ 7 & \underline{-77y + 70z = 189} \\ & & -18z = -9 \\ & & z = \frac{1}{2} \end{array}$$

$$7y - 8\left(\frac{1}{2}\right) = -18$$

$$7y = -14$$

$$y = -2$$

$$4x + (-2) - 2\left(\frac{1}{2}\right) = 0$$

$$4x = 3$$

$$x = \frac{3}{4}$$

*The solution set for the system is*

*the ordered triple* $\left(\frac{3}{4}, -2, \frac{1}{2}\right)$.

10. $4x + 6y - 8z = 1$ (1)
$-6x - 9y + 12z = 0$ (2)
$x - 2y - 2z = 3$ (3)

$$\begin{array}{rl} 4x + 6y - 8z = 1 & (1) \\ \underline{-4x + 8y + 8z = -12} & (3)\ \textit{by}\ -4 \\ 14y = -11 & \end{array}$$

$$\begin{array}{rl} -6x - 9y + 12z = 0 & (2) \\ 6x - 12y - 12z = 18 & (3)\ \textit{by}\ 6 \\ -21y = 18 & \end{array}$$

*No solution, inconsistent system.*

11. $\frac{1}{2}x - y + z = 0$ (1)

$2x + \frac{1}{3}y + z = 2$ (2)

$x + y + z = -4$ (3)

$\frac{1}{2}x - y + z = 0$ (1)

$-2x - \frac{1}{3}y - z = -2$ (2) *by* −1

$-\frac{3}{2}x - \frac{4}{3}y = -2$ (4)

$2x + \frac{1}{3}y + z = 2$ (2)

$-x - y - z = 4$ (3) *by* −1

$x - \frac{2}{3}y = 6$ (5)

$-\frac{3}{2}x - \frac{4}{3}y = -2$ (4)

$-2x + \frac{4}{3}y = -12$ (5) *by* −2

$-\frac{7}{2}x = -14$

$x = 4$

$4 - \frac{2}{3}y = 6$

$-\frac{2}{3}y = 2$

$y = -3$

$4 + (-3) + z = -4$
$z = -5$

*The solution set for the system is the ordered triple* (4, −3, −5).

12. $\frac{1}{3}x + \frac{1}{2}y + z = -1$ (1)

$x - y + \frac{1}{5}z = 1$ (2)

$x + y + z = 5$ (3)

$x - y + \frac{1}{5}z = 1$ (2)

$x + y + z = 5$ (3)

$2x + \quad + \frac{6}{5}z = 6$ (4)

$-\frac{2}{3}x - y - 2z = 2$ (1) *by* −2

$x + y + z = 5$ (3)

$\frac{1}{3}x \quad - z = 7$ (5)

$2x + \frac{6}{5}z = 6$ (4)

$-2x + 6z = -42$ (5) *by* −6

$\frac{36}{5}z = -36$

$z = -5$

$-2x + 6(-5) = -42$
$x = 6$

$6 + y + (-5) = 5$
$y = 4$

*The solution set for the system is the ordered triple* (6,4,−5).

14. $3x + 2y + z = 3$ (1)
$x - 3y + z = 4$ (2)
$-6x - 4y - 2z = 1$ (3)

$6x + 4y + 2z = 6$ (1) *by* 2
$-6x - 4y - 2z = 1$
$0 = 7$

*No solution, inconsistent system.*

15.
$$\begin{aligned} 2x - y + 3z &= 4 \quad (1)\\ x + 2y - z &= -3 \quad (2)\\ 4x + 3y + 2z &= -5 \quad (3) \end{aligned}$$

$$\begin{aligned} 4x - 2y + 6z &= 8 \quad (1)\ by\ 2\\ x + 2y - z &= -3 \quad (2)\\ \hline 5x + 5z &= 5 \quad (4) \end{aligned}$$

$$\begin{aligned} 6x - 3y + 9z &= 12 \quad (1)\ by\ 3\\ 4x + 3y + 2z &= -5 \quad (3)\\ \hline 10x + 11z &= 7 \end{aligned}$$

$$\begin{aligned} -10x - 10z &= -10 \quad (4)\ by\ -2\\ 10x + 11z &= 7\\ \hline z &= -3 \end{aligned}$$

$$\begin{aligned} 5x + 5(-3) &= 5\\ x &= 4 \end{aligned}$$

$$\begin{aligned} 4 + 2y - (-3) &= -3\\ y &= -5 \end{aligned}$$

*The solution set for the system is the ordered triple* (4,−5,−3).

16.
$$\begin{aligned} 6x - 2y + z &= 5 \quad (1)\\ 3x + y + 3z &= 7 \quad (2)\\ x + 4y - z &= 4 \quad (3) \end{aligned}$$

$$\begin{aligned} 6x - 2y + z &= 5 \quad (1)\\ x + 4y - z &= 4 \quad (3)\\ \hline 7x + 2y &= 9 \quad (4) \end{aligned}$$

$$\begin{aligned} 3x + y + 3z &= 7 \quad (2)\\ 3x + 12y - 3z &= 12 \quad (3)\ by\ 3\\ \hline 6x + 13y &= 19 \quad (5) \end{aligned}$$

$$\begin{aligned} 42x + 12y &= 54 \quad (4)\ by\ 6\\ -42x - 91y &= -133 \quad (5)\ by\ -7\\ \hline -79y &= -79\\ y &= 1 \end{aligned}$$

$$\begin{aligned} 7x + 2(1) &= 9\\ 7x &= 7\\ x &= 1 \end{aligned}$$

$$\begin{aligned} 6(1) - 2(1) + z &= 5\\ z &= 1 \end{aligned}$$

*The solution set for the system is the ordered triple* (1,1,1).

18.
$$\begin{aligned} x - y &= -3 \quad (1)\\ x + z &= 2 \quad (2)\\ y - z &= 7 \quad (3) \end{aligned}$$

$$\begin{aligned} x + z &= 2 \quad (2)\\ y - z &= 7 \quad (3)\\ \hline x + y &= 9 \quad (4) \end{aligned}$$

$$\begin{aligned} x - y &= -3 \quad (1)\\ x + y &= 9 \quad (4)\\ \hline 2x &= 6\\ x &= 3 \end{aligned}$$

$$\begin{aligned} 3 + y &= 9\\ y &= 6 \end{aligned}$$

$$\begin{aligned} 3 + z &= 2\\ z &= -1 \end{aligned}$$

*The solution set for the system is the ordered triple* (3,6,−1).

19.
$$\begin{aligned} 2x + y &= 2 \quad (1)\\ y + z &= 3 \quad (2)\\ 4x - z &= 0 \quad (3) \end{aligned}$$

$$\begin{aligned} y + z &= 3 \quad (2)\\ 4x - z &= 0 \quad (3)\\ \hline 4x + y &= 3 \quad (4) \end{aligned}$$

$$\begin{aligned} 2x + y &= 2 \quad (1)\\ -4x - y &= -3 \quad (4)\ by\ -1\\ \hline -2x &= -1\\ x &= \frac{1}{2} \end{aligned}$$

$$\begin{aligned} 2\left(\frac{1}{2}\right) + y &= 2\\ y &= 1 \end{aligned}$$

$$\begin{aligned} 1 + z &= 3\\ z &= 2 \end{aligned}$$

*The solution set for the system is the ordered triple* $\left(\frac{1}{2},1,2\right)$.

20. $\begin{aligned} 2x + y &= 6 & (1) \\ 3y - 2z &= -8 & (2) \\ x + z &= 5 & (3) \end{aligned}$

$$\begin{array}{rl} 2x + y \qquad = 6 & (1) \\ \underline{-2x \qquad - 2z = -10} & (3)\ by\ -2 \\ y - 2z = -4 & (4) \end{array}$$

$$\begin{array}{rl} 3y - 2z = -8 & (2) \\ \underline{-y + 2z = 4} & (4)\ by\ -1 \\ 2y \qquad = -4 & \\ y \qquad = -2 & \end{array}$$

$$\begin{aligned} -2 - 2z &= -4 \\ -2z &= -2 \\ z &= 1 \end{aligned}$$

$$\begin{aligned} x + 1 &= 5 \\ x &= 4 \end{aligned}$$

*The solution set for the system is the ordered triple* (4,-2,1).

22. $\begin{aligned} 3x + 2y &= 3 & (1) \\ y + 2z &= 2 & (2) \\ 6x - 4z &= 1 & (3) \end{aligned}$

$$\begin{array}{rl} 3x + 2y \qquad = 3 & (1) \\ \underline{- 2y - 4z = -4} & (2)\ by\ -2 \\ 3x \qquad - 4z = -1 & (4) \end{array}$$

$$\begin{array}{rl} 6x - 4z = 1 & (3) \\ \underline{-6x + 8z = 3} & (4)\ by\ -2 \\ 4z = 3 & \\ z = \frac{3}{4} & \end{array}$$

$$3x - 4\left(\frac{3}{4}\right) = -1$$

$$\begin{aligned} 3x - 3 &= -1 \\ 3x &= 2 \\ x &= \frac{2}{3} \end{aligned}$$

$$3\left(\frac{2}{3}\right) + 2y = 3$$

$$\begin{aligned} 2y &= 1 \\ y &= \frac{1}{2} \end{aligned}$$

*The solution set for the system is the ordered triple* $\left(\frac{2}{3}, \frac{1}{2}, \frac{3}{4}\right)$.

23. $\begin{aligned} \frac{1}{2}x + \frac{2}{3}y &= \frac{5}{2} & (1) \\ \frac{1}{5}x - \frac{1}{2}z &= -\frac{3}{10} & (2) \\ \frac{1}{3}y - \frac{1}{4}z &= \frac{3}{4} & (3) \end{aligned}$

$$\begin{array}{rl} 3x + 4y = 15 & (1)\ by\ 6 \\ 2x - 5z = -3 & (2)\ by\ 10 \\ 4y - 3z = 9 & (3)\ by\ 12 \end{array}$$

$$\begin{array}{rl} 3x + 4y \qquad = 15 & (1) \\ \underline{- 4y + 3z = -9} & (3)\ by\ -1 \\ 3x \qquad + 3z = 6 & (4) \end{array}$$

$$\begin{array}{rl} 6x + 6z = 12 & (4)\ by\ 2 \\ \underline{-6x + 15z = 9} & (2)\ by\ -3 \\ 21z = 21 & \\ z = 1 & \end{array}$$

$$\begin{aligned} 3x + 3(1) &= 6 \\ 3x &= 3 \\ x &= 1 \end{aligned}$$

$$\begin{aligned} 3(1) + 4y &= 15 \\ 4y &= 12 \\ y &= 3 \end{aligned}$$

*The solution set for the system is the ordered triple* (1,3,1).

24. $\frac{1}{2}x - \frac{1}{3}y = \frac{1}{6}$ (1)

$\frac{1}{3}y - \frac{1}{3}z = 1$ (2)

$\frac{1}{5}x - \frac{1}{2}z = -\frac{4}{5}$ (3)

$3x - 2y = 1$ (1) *by* 6
$z - z = 3$ (2) *by* 3
$2x - 5z = -8$ (3) *by* 10

$3x - 2y \quad = 1$ (1)
$\underline{\quad 2y - 2z = 6}$ (2) *by* 2
$3x \quad - 2z = 7$ (4)

$6x - 4z = 14$ (4) *by* 2
$\underline{-6x + 15z = 24}$ (3) *by* -3
$11z = 38$

$$z = \frac{38}{11}$$

$4x - 10z = -16$ (3) *by* 2
$-15x + 10x = -35$ (4) *by* -5
$-11x = -51$

$$x = \frac{51}{11}$$

$$y - \frac{38}{11} = 3$$

$$y = \frac{71}{11}$$

*The solution set for the system is the ordered triple* $\left(\frac{51}{11}, \frac{38}{11}, \frac{71}{11}\right)$.

26. $\frac{1}{2}x + \frac{1}{2}y + z = \frac{1}{2}$ (1)
$\frac{1}{2}x - \frac{1}{4}y - \frac{1}{4}z = 0$ (2)
$\frac{1}{4}x + \frac{1}{12}y + \frac{1}{6}z = \frac{1}{6}$ (3)

$x + y + 2z = 1$ (1) *by* 2
$2x - y - z = 0$ (2) *by* 4
$3x + y + 2x = 2$ (3) *by* 12

$x + y + 2z = 1$ (1)
$\underline{2x - y - z = 0}$ (2)
$3x \quad + z = 1$ (4)

$2x - y - z = 0$ (2)
$\underline{3x + y + 2z = 2}$ (3)
$5x \quad + z = 2$

$3x + z = 1$ (2)
$\underline{-5x - z = -2}$ (3) *by* -1
$-2x \quad = -1$
$x \quad = \frac{1}{2}$

$$3\left(\frac{1}{2}\right) + z = 1$$

$$z = -\frac{1}{2}$$

$$\frac{1}{2} + y + 2\left(-\frac{1}{2}\right) = 1$$

$$y = \frac{3}{2}$$

*The solution set for the system is the ordered triple* $\left(\frac{1}{2}, \frac{3}{2}, -\frac{1}{2}\right)$.

27. $x - y - z = 0$ (1)
$5x + 20y \quad = 80$ (2)
$20y - 10z = 50$ (3)

$5x + 20y \quad = 80$ (2)
$\underline{- 20y + 10z = -50}$ (3) *by* -1
$5x + \quad + 10z = 30$ (4)

$20x - 20y - 20z = 0$ (1) *by* 20
$\underline{5x + 20y \quad = 80}$ (2)
$25x \quad - 20z = 80$ (5)

$10x + 20z = 60$ (4) *by* 2
$\underline{25x - 20z = 80}$
$35x \quad = 140$
$x \quad = 4$ *amp*

$5(4) + 10z = 30$
$10z = 10$
$z = 1$ *amp*

$4 - y - 1 = 0$
$y = 3$ *amp*

28. a.) $z = 10(2) + .08(200)$
$z = 20 + 16$
$z = \$36$

b.) $z = 12x + .06y$

c.) $z = 10x + .08y$ (1) $x = 2$
$z = 12x + .06y$ (2)

$z = 20 + .08y$ (1)
$z = 24 + .06y$ (2)

$z = 20 + .08y$ (1)
$-z = -24 - .06y$ (2) *by* $-1$

$0 = -4 + .02y$
$y = 200$ *miles*

30. $3x + 2y = 6$
$2y = -3x + 6$

$$y = -\frac{3}{2}x + 3$$

31. $2x - 3y = 5$
$-3y = -2x + 5$

$$y = \frac{2}{3}x - \frac{5}{3}$$

32. $3x - 2y = 5$
$-2y = -3x + 5$

$$y = \frac{3}{2}x - \frac{5}{2}$$

34. $3x^2 + 4x - 2 = 0$

$$x = \frac{-4 \pm \sqrt{4^2 - 4(3)(-2)}}{2(3)}$$

$$x = \frac{-4 \pm \sqrt{40}}{6}$$

$$x = \frac{-4 \pm 2\sqrt{10}}{6}$$

$$x = \frac{-2 \pm \sqrt{10}}{3}$$

35. $(2y - 3)(2y - 1) = -4$
$4y^2 - 8y + 7 = 0$

$$x = \frac{-(-8) \pm \sqrt{(-8)^2 - 4(4)(7)}}{2(4)}$$

$$x = \frac{8 \pm \sqrt{-48}}{8}$$

$$x = \frac{8 \pm 4i\sqrt{3}}{8}$$

$$x = \frac{2 \pm i\sqrt{3}}{2}$$

36. $(y - 1)(3y - 3) = 10$
$3y^2 - 6y - 7 = 0$

$$x = \frac{-(-6) \pm \sqrt{(-6)^2 - 4(3)(-7)}}{2(3)}$$

$$x = \frac{6 \pm \sqrt{120}}{6}$$

$$x = \frac{6 \pm 2\sqrt{30}}{6}$$

$$x = \frac{3 \pm \sqrt{30}}{3}$$

38. $8t^3 + 1 = 0$
$(2t + 1)(4t^2 + 2t + 1) = 0$

$2t + 1 = 0$

$$t = -\frac{1}{2} \quad \text{or} \quad t = \frac{-2 \pm \sqrt{2^2 - 4(4)(1)}}{2(4)}$$

$$t = \frac{-2 \pm \sqrt{-12}}{8}$$

$$t = \frac{-2 \pm 2i\sqrt{3}}{8}$$

$$t = \frac{-1 \pm i\sqrt{3}}{4}$$

39.
$$4x^5 - 16x^4 = 20x^3$$
$$4x^5 - 16x^4 - 20x^3 = 0$$
$$4x^3(x^2 - 4x - 5) = 0$$
$$4x^3(x + 1)(x - 5) = 0$$
$$4x^3 = 0$$

$x = 0$ *or* $x + 1 = 0$ *or* $x - 5 = 0$

$x = -1$ $\quad$ $x = 5$

40.
$$3x^4 + 6x^2 = 6x^3$$
$$3x^4 - 6x^3 + 6x^2 = 0$$
$$3x^2(x^2 - 2x + 2) = 0$$
$$3x^2 = 0$$

$x = 0$ *or* $x = \dfrac{-(-2) \pm \sqrt{(-2)^2 - 4(1)(2)}}{2(1)}$

$$x = \frac{2 =- \sqrt{-4}}{2}$$

$$x = \frac{2 \pm 2i}{2}$$

$$x = 1 \pm i$$

42. $\dfrac{1}{x + 3} + \dfrac{1}{x - 2} = 1$

$$x - 2 + x + 3 = (x - 2)(x + 3)$$
$$2x + 1 = x^2 + x - 6$$
$$0 = x^2 - x - 7$$

*Substituting* $a = 1$, $b = -1$ *and* $c = -7$ *into the quadratic formula gives us*

$$x = \frac{1 \pm \sqrt{29}}{2}$$

43.
$y = ax^2 + bx + 3$
$0 = a + b + c$ (1) (1,0)
$-4 = 9a + 3b + c$ (2) (3,−4)
$0 = 25a + 5b + c$ (3) (5,0)

$0 = a + b + c$ (1)
$4 = -9a - 3b - c$ (2) *by* −1
$4 = -8a - 2b$

$0 = a + b + c$ (1)
$0 = -25a - 5b - c$ (3) *by* −1
$0 = -24a - 4b$ (5)

$-8 = 16a + 4b$ (4) *by* −2
$0 = -24a - 4b$ (5)
$-8 = -8a$
$1 = a$

$4 = -8(1) - 2b$
$-6 = b$
$0 = 1 + (-6) + c$
$5 = c$

44.
$y = ax^2 + bx + 3$
$3 = 0a + 0b + c$ (1) (0,3)
$0 = a + b + c$ (2) (1,0)
$4 = a - b + c$ (3) (−1,4)

$0 = a + b + c$ (2)
$4 = a - b + c$ (3)
$4 = 2a + 2c$

$c = 3$

$4 = 2a + 2(3)$
$-1 = a$

$4 = -1 - b + 3$
$-2 = b$

46.
$$\begin{array}{ll} x + y + z - w = 16 & (1) \\ x - y + 2z - w = 1 & (2) \\ x + 3y - z - w = -2 & (3) \\ x - 3y - 2z + 2w = -4 & (4) \end{array}$$

$$\begin{array}{ll} x + y + z + w = 16 & (1) \\ \underline{x + 3y - z - w = -2} & (3) \\ 2x + 4y = 14 & (5) \end{array}$$

$$\begin{array}{ll} x - y + 2z - w = 1 & (2) \\ \underline{x - 3y - 2z + 2w = -4} & (4) \\ 2x - 4y + w = -3 & (6) \end{array}$$

$$\begin{array}{ll} x - y + 2z - w = 1 & (2) \\ \underline{2x + 6y - 2z - 2w = -4} & (3) \textit{ by } 2 \\ 3x + 5y - 3w = -3 & (7) \end{array}$$

$$\begin{array}{ll} 6x - 12y + 3w = -9 & (6) \textit{ by } 3 \\ \underline{3x + 5y - 3w = -3} & (8) \\ 9x - 7y = -12 & (9) \end{array}$$

$$\begin{array}{ll} 14x + 28y = 98 & (5) \textit{ by } 7 \\ \underline{3yx - 28y = -48} & (9) \textit{ by } 4 \\ 50x = 50 & \\ x = 1 & \end{array}$$

$$\begin{array}{ll} 2(1) + 4y = 14 & (5) \\ 4y = 12 & \\ y = 3 & \end{array}$$

$$\begin{array}{ll} 2(1) - 4(3) + w = -3 & (7) \\ -10 + w = -3 & \\ w = 7 & \end{array}$$

$$\begin{array}{ll} 1 + 3 + 2 + 7 = 16 & (1) \\ 2 + 11 = 16 & \\ z = 5 & \end{array}$$

*The solution set is* (1,3,5,7).

## Section 8.3

2. $\begin{vmatrix} 5 & 4 \\ 3 & 2 \end{vmatrix} = 5(2) - 3(4) = -2$

3. $\begin{vmatrix} 2 & 1 \\ 3 & 4 \end{vmatrix} = 2(4) - 3(1) = 5$

4. $\begin{vmatrix} 4 & 1 \\ 5 & 2 \end{vmatrix} = 4(2) - 5(1) = 3$

6. $\begin{vmatrix} 1 & 0 \\ 0 & 1 \end{vmatrix} = 1(1) - 0(0) = 1$

7. $\begin{vmatrix} -3 & 2 \\ 6 & -4 \end{vmatrix} = -3(-4) - 6(2) = 0$

8. $\begin{vmatrix} 8 & -3 \\ -2 & 5 \end{vmatrix} = 8(5) - (-2)(-3) = 34$

10. $\begin{vmatrix} 5 & 3 \\ 7 & -6 \end{vmatrix} = 5(6) - 7(3) = -51$

11. $\begin{vmatrix} 2x & 1 \\ x & 3 \end{vmatrix} = 10$

$$\begin{array}{r} 2x(3) - x(1) = 10 \\ 5x = 10 \\ x = 2 \end{array}$$

12. $\begin{vmatrix} 3x & -2 \\ 2x & 3 \end{vmatrix} = 26$

$$\begin{array}{r} 3x(3) - 2x(-2) = 26 \\ 13x = 26 \\ x = 2 \end{array}$$

14. $\begin{vmatrix} -5 & 4x \\ 1 & -x \end{vmatrix} = 27$

$$\begin{array}{r} -5(-x) - 1(4x) = 27 \\ x = 27 \end{array}$$

15. $\begin{vmatrix} 2x & -4 \\ 2 & x \end{vmatrix} = -8x$

$$\begin{aligned} 2x(x) - 2(-4) &= -8x \\ 2x^2 + 8x + 8 &= 0 \\ x^2 + 4x + 4 &= 0 \\ (x + 2)(x + 2) &= 0 \\ x + 2 &= 0 \\ x &= -2 \end{aligned}$$

18. $\begin{vmatrix} x^2 & -2 \\ x & 1 \end{vmatrix} = 35$

$$\begin{aligned} x^2(1) - x(-2) &= 35 \\ x^2 + 2x - 35 &= 0 \\ (x + 7)(x - 5) &= 0 \end{aligned}$$

$x + 7 = 0$ *or* $x - 5 = 0$

$x = -7$ $\quad$ $x = 5$

16. $\begin{vmatrix} 3x & 2 \\ 2 & x \end{vmatrix} = -11x$

$$\begin{aligned} 3x(x) - 2(2) &= -11x \\ 3x^2 + 11x - 4 &= 0 \\ (x + 4)(3x - 1) &= 0 \\ x + 4 &= 0 \end{aligned}$$

$x = -4$ *or* $3x - 1 = 0$

$$x = \frac{1}{3}$$

19. $\left|\begin{array}{ccc|cc} 1 & 2 & 0 & 1 & 2 \\ 0 & 2 & 1 & 0 & 2 \\ 1 & 1 & 1 & 1 & 1 \end{array}\right.$

$= 1(2)1 + 2(1)1 + 0(0)1 - 1(2)0 - 1(1)(1) - 1(0)(2)$

$= 2 + 2 + 0 - 0 - 1 - 0$

$= 3$

20. $\left|\begin{array}{ccc|cc} -1 & 0 & 2 & -1 & 0 \\ 3 & 0 & 1 & 3 & 0 \\ 0 & 1 & 3 & 0 & 1 \end{array}\right.$

$= -1(0)(3) + 0(1)(0) + 2(3)1 - 0(0)(2) - 1(1) - 1 - 3(3)0$

$= 0 + 0 + 6 - 0 + 1 - 0$

$= 7$

22. 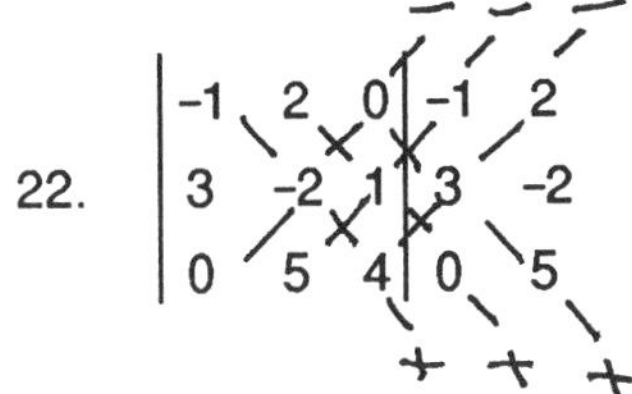

$= -1(-2)(4) + 2(1)(0) + 0(3)(5) - 0(2)0 - 5(1)(-1) - 4(3)2$
$= 8 + 0 + 0 - 0 + 5 - 24$
$= -11$

23. $\begin{vmatrix} 0 & 1 & 2 \\ 1 & 0 & 1 \\ -1 & 2 & 0 \end{vmatrix}$

$= 0\begin{vmatrix} 0 & 1 \\ 2 & 0 \end{vmatrix} - 1\begin{vmatrix} 1 & 1 \\ -1 & 0 \end{vmatrix} + 2\begin{vmatrix} 1 & 0 \\ -1 & 2 \end{vmatrix}$

$= 0[0(0) - 2(1)] - 1[1(0) - (-1)(1)] + 2[1(2) - (-1)0]$
$= 0 - 1 + 4$
$= 3$

24. $\begin{vmatrix} 3 & -2 & 1 \\ 0 & -1 & 0 \\ 2 & 0 & 1 \end{vmatrix}$

$= 3\begin{vmatrix} -1 & 0 \\ 0 & 1 \end{vmatrix} + 2\begin{vmatrix} 0 & 0 \\ 2 & 1 \end{vmatrix} + 1\begin{vmatrix} -1 & 0 \\ 0 & 1 \end{vmatrix}$

$= 3[-1(0) - 0(0)] + 2[0(1) - 2(0)] + 1[-1(1) - 0(0)]$
$= 0 + 0 - 1$
$= -1$

26. $\begin{vmatrix} 1 & 1 & 1 \\ 1 & -1 & 1 \\ 1 & 1 & -1 \end{vmatrix}$

$= 1\begin{vmatrix} -1 & 1 \\ 1 & -1 \end{vmatrix} - 1\begin{vmatrix} 1 & 1 \\ 1 & -1 \end{vmatrix} + 1\begin{vmatrix} 1 & -1 \\ 1 & 1 \end{vmatrix}$

$= 1[-1(-1) - 1(1)] - 1[1(-1) - 1(1)] + 1[1(1) - 1(-1)]$
$= 0 + 2 + 2$
$= 4$

27. $\begin{vmatrix} 2 & -1 & 0 \\ 1 & 0 & -2 \\ 0 & 1 & 2 \end{vmatrix} \begin{matrix} 2 & -1 \\ 1 & 0 \\ 0 & 1 \end{matrix}$

$= 2(0)2 + (-1)(-2)0 + 0(1)1 - 0(0)0 - 1(-2)2 - 2(1)(-1)$
$= 0 + 0 + 0 - 0 + 4 + 2$
$= 6$

28. $\begin{vmatrix} 5 & 0 & -4 \\ 0 & 1 & 3 \\ -1 & 2 & -1 \end{vmatrix} \begin{matrix} 5 & 0 \\ 0 & 1 \\ -1 & 2 \end{matrix}$

$= 5(1)(-1) + 0(3)(-1) + (-4)0(2) - (-1)(1)(-4) - 2(3)(5) - (-1)0(0)$
$= -5 - 0 + 0 - 4 - 30 - 0$
$= -39$

30. $\begin{vmatrix} 2 & 1 & 5 \\ 6 & -3 & 4 \\ 8 & 9 & -2 \end{vmatrix} \begin{matrix} 2 & 1 \\ 6 & -3 \\ 8 & 9 \end{matrix}$

$= 2(-3)(-2) + 1(4)(8) + 5(6)(9) - 8(-3)(5) - 9(4)(2) - (-2)(6)(1)$
$= 12 + 32 + 270 + 120 - 72 + 12$
$= 374$

31. $\begin{vmatrix} y & x \\ m & 1 \end{vmatrix} = b$

$y(1) - m(x) = b$
$y = mx + b$

32. $\begin{vmatrix} C & F & 1 \\ 5 & 41 & 1 \\ -10 & 14 & 1 \end{vmatrix} = 0$

$0 = C\begin{vmatrix} 41 & 1 \\ 14 & 1 \end{vmatrix} - F\begin{vmatrix} 5 & 1 \\ -10 & 1 \end{vmatrix} + 1\begin{vmatrix} 5 & 41 \\ -10 & 14 \end{vmatrix}$

$0 = C(41 - 14) - F(5 + 10) + 1(70 + 410)$
$0 = 27C - 15F + 480$
$15F = 27C + 480$

$F = \frac{9}{5}C + 32$

34. *Using* $a = 4$, $b = -12$ *and* $c = 9$ *in the discriminant, we have*

$b^2 - 4ac = (-12)^2 - 4(4)(9) = 0$

*Since the discriminant is* 0, *we will have one rational solution.*

35.
$$x = -3$$
$$x + 3 = 0$$
$$x = 5$$
$$x - 5 = 0$$
$$(x + 3)(x - 5) = 0$$
$$x^2 - 2x - 15 = 0$$

36.
$$x = 2$$
$$x - 2 = 0$$
$$x = -2$$
$$x + 2 = 0$$
$$x = 1$$
$$x - 1 = 0$$
$$(x - 2)(x + 2)(x - 1) = 0$$
$$(x^2 - 4)(x - 1) = 0$$
$$x^3 - x^2 - 4x + 4 = 0$$

38.
$$y = -\frac{3}{5}$$
$$5y + 3 = 0$$
$$y = 2$$
$$y - 2 = 0$$
$$(5y + 3)(y - 2) = 0$$
$$5y^2 - 7y - 6 = 0$$

39.
$$\begin{array}{r} x^2 - 5x + 6 \\ x - 3\overline{)\ x^3 - 8x^2 + 21x - 18} \\ -\quad + \qquad\qquad\quad \\ \underline{x^3 - 3x^2} \qquad\qquad\quad \\ -5x^2 + 21x \qquad \\ + \quad - \qquad \\ \underline{-5x^2 + 15x} \qquad \\ 6x - 18 \\ - \quad + \\ \underline{6x - 18} \\ 0 \end{array}$$

$$x^3 - 8x^2 + 21x - 18$$
$$= (x - 3)(x^2 - 5x + 6)$$
$$= (x - 3)(x - 2)(x - 3)$$

$x = 2$, $x = 3$ (*multiplicity* 2)

40.
$$\begin{array}{r} 3x^2 + 4x - 2 \\ x - 2\overline{)\ 3x^3 - 2x^2 - 10x + 4} \\ -\quad + \qquad\qquad\quad \\ \underline{3x^3 - 6x^2} \qquad\qquad\quad \\ 4x^2 - 10x \qquad \\ - \quad + \qquad \\ \underline{4x^2 - 8x} \qquad \\ -2x + 4 \\ + \quad - \\ \underline{-2x + 4} \\ 0 \end{array}$$

$$3x^3 - 2x^2 - 10x + 4 = (x - 2)(3x^2 + 4x - 2)$$

$$x - 2 = 0 \quad or \quad x = \frac{-4 \pm \sqrt{4^2 - 4(2)(-2)}}{2(3)}$$

$$x = 2 \qquad x = \frac{-4 \pm \sqrt{40}}{6}$$

$$x = \frac{-4 \pm 2\sqrt{10}}{6}$$

$$x = \frac{-2 \pm \sqrt{10}}{3}$$

42. *The products of the four elements in column 4 with their minors are:*

$$-(-3)\overset{a}{\begin{vmatrix} -1 & 2 & 0 \\ -3 & 0 & 1 \\ 1 & 1 & 0 \end{vmatrix}} + 1\overset{b}{\begin{vmatrix} 2 & 0 & 1 \\ -3 & 0 & 1 \\ 1 & 1 & 0 \end{vmatrix}} - 0\overset{c}{\begin{vmatrix} 2 & 0 & 1 \\ -1 & 2 & 0 \\ 1 & 1 & 0 \end{vmatrix}} + 0\overset{d}{\begin{vmatrix} 2 & 0 & 1 \\ -1 & 2 & 0 \\ -3 & 0 & 1 \end{vmatrix}}$$

*The products of the three elements of* ***a*** *in row 1 with their minors are:*

$$-1\begin{vmatrix} 0 & 1 \\ 1 & 0 \end{vmatrix} - 2\begin{vmatrix} -3 & 1 \\ 1 & 0 \end{vmatrix} + 0\begin{vmatrix} -3 & 0 \\ 1 & 1 \end{vmatrix}$$

$$\begin{aligned} \boldsymbol{a} &= -1(0 - 1) - 2(0 - 1) + 0(-3 - 0) \\ &= 1 + 2 + 0 \\ &= 3 \end{aligned}$$

*The products of the elements of* ***b*** *in row 1 with their minors are:*

$$2\begin{vmatrix} 0 & 1 \\ 1 & 0 \end{vmatrix} - 0\begin{vmatrix} -3 & 1 \\ 1 & 0 \end{vmatrix} + 1\begin{vmatrix} -3 & 0 \\ 1 & 1 \end{vmatrix}$$

$$\begin{aligned} \boldsymbol{b} &= 2(0 - 1) - 0(0 - 1) + 1(-3 - 0) \\ &= -2 - 0 - 3 \\ &= -5 \end{aligned}$$

*The products of the elements of* ***c*** *in row 1 with their minors are:*

$$2\begin{vmatrix} 2 & 0 \\ 1 & 0 \end{vmatrix} - 0\begin{vmatrix} -1 & 0 \\ 1 & 0 \end{vmatrix} + 1\begin{vmatrix} -1 & 2 \\ 1 & 1 \end{vmatrix}$$

$$\begin{aligned} \boldsymbol{c} &= 2(0 - 0) - 0(0 - 0) + 1(-1 - 2) \\ &= 2 \end{aligned}$$

*The products of the elements of* ***d*** *in row 1 with their minors are:*

$$2\begin{vmatrix} 2 & 0 \\ 0 & 1 \end{vmatrix} - 0\begin{vmatrix} -1 & 0 \\ -3 & 1 \end{vmatrix} + 1\begin{vmatrix} -1 & 2 \\ -3 & 0 \end{vmatrix}$$

$$\begin{aligned} \boldsymbol{d} &= 2(2 - 0) - 0(-1 - 0) + 1(0 + 6) \\ &= 4 - 0 + 6 \\ &= 10 \end{aligned}$$

*Substituting into the original product,*

$$\begin{aligned} &3(3) + 1(-5) - 0(2) + 0(10) \\ &\quad = 9 - 5 - 0 + 0 \\ &\quad = 4 \end{aligned}$$

43. *The products of the four elements in column* 3 *with their minors are:*

$$1\overset{a}{\begin{vmatrix} -1 & 2 & 1 \\ -3 & 0 & 0 \\ 1 & 1 & 0 \end{vmatrix}} - 0\overset{b}{\begin{vmatrix} 2 & 0 & -3 \\ -3 & 0 & 0 \\ 1 & 1 & 0 \end{vmatrix}} + 1\overset{c}{\begin{vmatrix} 2 & 0 & -3 \\ -1 & 2 & 1 \\ 1 & 1 & 0 \end{vmatrix}} - 0\overset{d}{\begin{vmatrix} 2 & 0 & -3 \\ -1 & 2 & 1 \\ -3 & 0 & 0 \end{vmatrix}}$$

*The products of the three elements of* **a** *in row* 1 *with their minors are:*

$$-1\begin{vmatrix} 0 & 0 \\ 1 & 0 \end{vmatrix} - 2\begin{vmatrix} -3 & 0 \\ 1 & 0 \end{vmatrix} + 1\begin{vmatrix} -3 & 0 \\ 1 & 1 \end{vmatrix}$$

$$\begin{aligned} \boldsymbol{a} &= -1(0 - 0) - 2(0 - 0) + 1(-3 - 0) \\ &= -3 \end{aligned}$$

*The products of the three elements of* **b** *in row* 1 *with their minors are:*

$$2\begin{vmatrix} 0 & 0 \\ 1 & 0 \end{vmatrix} - 0\begin{vmatrix} -3 & 0 \\ 1 & 0 \end{vmatrix} + (-3)\begin{vmatrix} -3 & 0 \\ 1 & 1 \end{vmatrix}$$

$$\begin{aligned} \boldsymbol{b} &= 2(0 - 0) - 0(0 - 0) - 3(-3 - 0) \\ &= 9 \end{aligned}$$

*The products of the three elements of* **c** *in row* 1 *with their minors are:*

$$2\begin{vmatrix} 2 & 1 \\ 1 & 0 \end{vmatrix} - 0\begin{vmatrix} -1 & 1 \\ 1 & 0 \end{vmatrix} + (-3)\begin{vmatrix} -1 & 2 \\ 1 & 1 \end{vmatrix}$$

$$\begin{aligned} \boldsymbol{c} &= 2(0 - 1) - 1(0 - 1) - 3(-1 - 2) \\ &= -2 - 0 + 9 \\ &= 7 \end{aligned}$$

*The products of the elements of* **d** *in row* 1 *with their minors are:*

$$2\begin{vmatrix} 2 & 1 \\ 0 & 0 \end{vmatrix} - 0\begin{vmatrix} -1 & 1 \\ -3 & 0 \end{vmatrix} + (-3)\begin{vmatrix} -1 & 2 \\ -3 & 0 \end{vmatrix}$$

$$\begin{aligned} \boldsymbol{d} &= 2(0 - 0) - 0(0 + 3) - 3(0 + 6) \\ &= 0 + 0 - 18 \\ &= -18 \end{aligned}$$

*Substituting into the original product,*

$$\begin{aligned} &1(-3) - 0(9) + 1(7) - 0(-18) \\ &\quad = -3 - 0 + 7 - 0 \\ &\quad = 4 \end{aligned}$$

44. *The products of the four elements in row 4 with their minors are:*

$$-1\overset{a}{\begin{vmatrix} 0 & 1 & -3 \\ 2 & 0 & 1 \\ 0 & 1 & 0 \end{vmatrix}} + 1\overset{b}{\begin{vmatrix} 2 & 1 & -3 \\ -1 & 0 & 1 \\ -3 & 1 & 0 \end{vmatrix}} - 0\overset{c}{\begin{vmatrix} 2 & 0 & -3 \\ -1 & 2 & 1 \\ -3 & 0 & 0 \end{vmatrix}} + 0\overset{d}{\begin{vmatrix} 2 & 0 & 1 \\ -1 & 2 & 0 \\ -3 & 0 & 1 \end{vmatrix}}$$

*The products of the three elements of* ***a*** *in row 1 with their minors are:*

$$0\begin{vmatrix} 0 & 1 \\ 1 & 0 \end{vmatrix} - 1\begin{vmatrix} 2 & 1 \\ 0 & 0 \end{vmatrix} + (-3)\begin{vmatrix} 2 & 0 \\ 0 & 1 \end{vmatrix}$$

$$\begin{aligned} \boldsymbol{a} &= 0(0 - 1) - 1(0 - 0) - 3(2 - 0) \\ &= -6 \end{aligned}$$

*The products of the three elements of* ***b*** *in row 1 with their minors are:*

$$2\begin{vmatrix} 0 & 1 \\ 1 & 0 \end{vmatrix} - 1\begin{vmatrix} -1 & 1 \\ -3 & 0 \end{vmatrix} + (-3)\begin{vmatrix} -1 & 0 \\ -3 & 1 \end{vmatrix}$$

$$\begin{aligned} \boldsymbol{b} &= 2(0 - 1) - 1(0 + 3) - 3(-1 - 0) \\ &= -2 - 3 + 3 \\ &= -2 \end{aligned}$$

*The products of the three elements of* ***c*** *in row 1 with their minors are:*

$$2\begin{vmatrix} 2 & 1 \\ 0 & 0 \end{vmatrix} - 0\begin{vmatrix} -1 & 1 \\ -3 & 0 \end{vmatrix} + (-3)\begin{vmatrix} -1 & 2 \\ -3 & 0 \end{vmatrix}$$

$$\begin{aligned} \boldsymbol{c} &= 2(0 - 0) - 0(0 + 3) - 3(0 + 6) \\ &= 0 - 0 - 18 \\ &= -18 \end{aligned}$$

*The products of the elements of* ***d*** *in row 1 with their minors are:*

$$2\begin{vmatrix} 2 & 0 \\ 0 & 1 \end{vmatrix} - 0\begin{vmatrix} -1 & 0 \\ -3 & 1 \end{vmatrix} + 1\begin{vmatrix} -1 & 2 \\ -3 & 0 \end{vmatrix}$$

$$\begin{aligned} \boldsymbol{d} &= 2(2 - 0) - 0(-1 + 0) + 1(0 + 6) \\ &= 4 - 0 + 6 \\ &= 10 \end{aligned}$$

*Substituting into the original product,*

$$-1(-6) + 1(-2) - 0(-18) + 0(10) = 4$$

**Section 8.4**

2. $3x + y = -2$
$-3x + 2y = -4$

$$D = \begin{vmatrix} 3 & 1 \\ -3 & 2 \end{vmatrix}$$

$$= 3(2) - (-3)(1)$$
$$= 9$$

$$D_x = \begin{vmatrix} -2 & 1 \\ -4 & 2 \end{vmatrix}$$

$$= -2(2) - (-4)(1)$$
$$= 0$$

$$D_y = \begin{vmatrix} 3 & -2 \\ -3 & -4 \end{vmatrix}$$

$$= 3(-4) - (-3)(-2)$$
$$= -18$$

$$x = \frac{D_x}{D} = \frac{0}{9} = 0 \quad \textit{and}$$

$$y = \frac{D_y}{D} = \frac{-18}{9} = -2$$

*The solution set for the system is* {(0,−2)}.

3. $5x - 2y = 4$
$-10x + 4y = 1$

$$D = \begin{vmatrix} 5 & -2 \\ -10 & 4 \end{vmatrix}$$

$$= 5(4) - (-10)(-2)$$
$$= 0$$

$$D_x = \begin{vmatrix} 5 & -2 \\ -10 & 4 \end{vmatrix}$$

$$= 5(4) - (-10)(-2)$$
$$= 0$$

$$D_y = \begin{vmatrix} 5 & 4 \\ -10 & 1 \end{vmatrix}$$

$$= 5(1) - (-10)4$$
$$= 45$$

*Lines are parallel,* ∅

4. $-4x + 3y = -11$
$5x + 4y = 6$

$$D = \begin{vmatrix} -4 & 3 \\ 5 & 4 \end{vmatrix}$$

$$= -4(4) - 5(3)$$
$$= -31$$

$$D_x = \begin{vmatrix} -11 & 3 \\ 6 & 4 \end{vmatrix}$$

$$= -11(4) - 6(3)$$
$$= -62$$

$$D_y = \begin{vmatrix} -4 & -11 \\ 5 & 6 \end{vmatrix}$$

$$= -4(6) - 5(-11)$$
$$= 31$$

$$x = \frac{D_x}{D} = \frac{-62}{-31} = 2 \quad \textit{and}$$

$$y = \frac{D_y}{D} = \frac{31}{-31} = -1$$

*The solution set for the system is* {(2,−1)}.

6. $3x - 4y = 7$
$6x - 2y = 5$

$$D = \begin{vmatrix} 3 & -4 \\ 6 & -2 \end{vmatrix}$$
$$= 3(-2) - 6(-4)$$
$$= 18$$

$$D_x = \begin{vmatrix} 7 & -4 \\ 5 & -2 \end{vmatrix}$$
$$= 7(-2) - 5(-4)$$
$$= 6$$

$$D_y = \begin{vmatrix} 3 & 7 \\ 6 & 5 \end{vmatrix}$$
$$= 3(5) - 6(7)$$
$$= -27$$

$$x = \frac{D_x}{D} = \frac{6}{18} = \frac{1}{3} \quad \text{and}$$

$$y = \frac{D_y}{D} = \frac{-27}{18} = -\frac{3}{2}$$

*The solution set for the system is* $\left\{\left(\frac{1}{3}, -\frac{3}{2}\right)\right\}$

7. $9x - 8y = 4$
$2x + 3y = 6$

$$D = \begin{vmatrix} 9 & -8 \\ 2 & 3 \end{vmatrix}$$
$$= 9(3) - 2(-8)$$
$$= 43$$

$$D_x = \begin{vmatrix} 4 & -8 \\ 6 & 3 \end{vmatrix}$$
$$= 4(3) - 6(-8)$$
$$= 60$$

$$D_y = \begin{vmatrix} 9 & 4 \\ 2 & 6 \end{vmatrix}$$
$$= 9(6) - 2(4)$$
$$= 46$$

$$x = \frac{D_x}{D} = \frac{60}{43} \quad \text{and}$$

$$y = \frac{D_y}{D} = \frac{46}{43}$$

*The solution set for the system is* $\left\{\left(\frac{60}{43}, \frac{46}{43}\right)\right\}$

8. $4x - 7y = 10$
$-3x + 2y = -9$

$$D = \begin{vmatrix} 4 & -7 \\ -3 & 2 \end{vmatrix}$$
$$= 4(2) - (-3)(-7)$$
$$= -13$$

$$D_x = \begin{vmatrix} 10 & -7 \\ -9 & 2 \end{vmatrix}$$
$$= 10(2) - (-9)(-7)$$
$$= -43$$

$$D_y = \begin{vmatrix} 4 & 10 \\ -3 & -9 \end{vmatrix}$$
$$= 4(-9) - (-3)(10)$$
$$= -6$$

$$x = \frac{D_x}{D} = \frac{-43}{13} = \frac{43}{13} \quad \text{and}$$

$$y = \frac{D_y}{D} = \frac{-6}{-13} = \frac{6}{13}$$

*The solution set is* $\left\{\left(\frac{43}{13}, \frac{6}{13}\right)\right\}$.

10. $$\begin{aligned} -1x + y + 3z &= 6 \\ x + y + 2z &= 7 \\ 2x + 3y + z &= 4 \end{aligned}$$

$$D = \begin{vmatrix} -1 & 1 & 3 \\ 1 & 1 & 2 \\ 2 & 3 & 1 \end{vmatrix}$$

$$= -1(1)1 + 1(2)2 + 3(1)3 - 2(1)3 - 3(2)(-1) - 1(1)1$$
$$= -1 + 4 + 9 - 6 + 6 - 1$$
$$= 11$$

$$D_x = \begin{vmatrix} 6 & 1 & 3 \\ 7 & 1 & 2 \\ 4 & 3 & 1 \end{vmatrix}$$

$$= 6(1)1 + 1(2)4 + 3(7)3 - 4(1)3 - 3(2)6 - 1(7)1$$
$$= 6 + 8 + 63 - 12 - 36 - 7$$
$$= 22$$

$$D_y = \begin{vmatrix} -1 & 6 & 3 \\ 1 & 7 & 2 \\ 2 & 4 & 1 \end{vmatrix}$$

$$= -1(7)1 + 6(2)2 + 3(1)4 - 2(7)3 - 4(2)(-1) - 1(1)6$$
$$= -7 + 24 + 12 - 42 + 8 - 6$$
$$= -11$$

$$D_z = \begin{vmatrix} -1 & 1 & 6 \\ 1 & 1 & 7 \\ 2 & 3 & 4 \end{vmatrix}$$

$$= -1(1)4 + 1(7)2 + 6(1)3 - 2(1)6 - 3(7)(-1) - 4(1)(1)$$
$$= -4 + 14 + 18 - 12 + 21 - 4$$
$$= 33$$

$$x = \frac{D_x}{D} = \frac{22}{11} = 2$$

$$y = \frac{D_y}{D} = \frac{-11}{11} = -1$$

$$z = \frac{D_z}{D} = \frac{33}{11} = 3$$

*The solution set is* {(2,−1,3)}.

11. $x + y - z = 2$
$-x + y + z = 3$
$x + y + z = 4$

$$D = \begin{vmatrix} 1 & 1 & -1 \\ -1 & 1 & 1 \\ 1 & 1 & 1 \end{vmatrix}$$

$= 1(1)1 + 1(1)1 + -1(-1)(1) - 1(1)(-1) - 1(1)1 - 1(-1)1$
$= 1 + 1 + 1 + 1 - 1 + 1$
$= 4$

$$D_x = \begin{vmatrix} 2 & 1 & -1 \\ 3 & 1 & 1 \\ 4 & 1 & 1 \end{vmatrix}$$

$= 2(1)1 + 1(1)4 + (-1)3(1) - 4(1)(-1) - 1(1)2 - 1(3)1$
$= 2 + 4 - 3 + 4 - 2 - 3$
$= 2$

$$D_y = \begin{vmatrix} 1 & 2 & -1 \\ -1 & 3 & 1 \\ 1 & 4 & 1 \end{vmatrix}$$

$= 1(3)1 + 2(1)1 + (-1)(-1)4 - 1(3)(-1) - 4(1)1 - 1(-1)2$
$= 3 + 2 + 4 + 3 - 4 + 2$
$= 10$

$$D_z = \begin{vmatrix} 1 & 1 & 2 \\ -1 & 1 & 3 \\ 1 & 1 & 4 \end{vmatrix}$$

$= 1(1)4 + 1(3)1 + 2(-1)1 - 1(1)2 - 1(3)1 - 4(-1)1$
$= 4 + 3 - 2 - 2 - 3 + 4$
$= 4$

$$x = \frac{D_x}{D} = \frac{2}{4} = \frac{1}{2}$$

$$y = \frac{D_y}{D} = \frac{10}{4} = \frac{5}{2}$$

$$z = \frac{D_z}{D} = \frac{4}{4} = 1$$

*The solution set is* $\left\{\left(\frac{1}{2}, \frac{5}{2}, 1\right)\right\}$.

12. $-x - y + z = 1$
$x - y + z = 3$
$x + y - z = 4$

$$D = \begin{vmatrix} -1 & -1 & 1 \\ 1 & -1 & 1 \\ 1 & 1 & -1 \end{vmatrix}$$

$= -1(-1)(-1) + (-1)1(1) + 1(1)1 - 1(-1)1 - 1(1)(-1) - (-1)(1)(-1)$
$= -1 - 1 + 1 + 1 + 1 - 1$
$= 0$

$$D_x = \begin{vmatrix} 1 & -1 & 1 \\ 3 & -1 & 1 \\ 4 & 1 & -1 \end{vmatrix}$$

$= 1(-1)(-1) + (-1)1(4) + 1(3)1 - 4(-1)1 - 1(1)1 - (-1)(3)(-1)$
$= 1 - 4 + 3 + 4 - 1 - 3$
$= 0$

$$D_y = \begin{vmatrix} -1 & 1 & 1 \\ 1 & 3 & 1 \\ 1 & 4 & -1 \end{vmatrix}$$

$= -1(3)(-1) + 1(1)1 + 1(1)4 - 1(3)1 - 4(1)(-1) - (-1)1(1)$
$= 3 + 1 + 4 - 3 + 4 + 1$
$= 10$

$$D_z = \begin{vmatrix} -1 & -1 & 1 \\ 1 & -1 & 3 \\ 1 & 1 & 4 \end{vmatrix}$$

$= -1(-1)4 + (-1)3(1) + 1(1)1 - 1(-1)1 - 1(3)(-1) - 4(1)(-1)$
$= 4 - 3 + 1 + 1 + 3 + 4$
$= 10$

*Inconsistent system*; $\varnothing$

14. $2x - 3y + z = 1$
$3x - y - z = 4$
$4x - 6y + 2z = 3$

$$D = \begin{vmatrix} 2 & -3 & 1 \\ 3 & -1 & -1 \\ 4 & -6 & 2 \end{vmatrix}$$

$= 2(-1)2 + (-3)(-1)4 + 1(3)(-6) - 4(-1)1 - (-6)(-1)2 - 2(3)(-3)$
$= -4 + 12 - 18 + 4 - 12 + 18$
$= 0$

$$D_x = \begin{vmatrix} 1 & -3 & 1 \\ 4 & -1 & -1 \\ 3 & -6 & 2 \end{vmatrix}$$

$= 1(-1)2 + (-3)(-1)3 + 1(4)(-6) - 3(-1)1 - (-6)(-1)1 + 2(4)(-3)$
$= -2 + 9 - 24 + 3 + 6 - 24$
$= -32$

$$D_y = \begin{vmatrix} 2 & 1 & 1 \\ 3 & 4 & -1 \\ 4 & 3 & 2 \end{vmatrix}$$

$= 2(4)2 + 1(-1)4 + 1(3)(3) - 4(4)1 - 3(-1)2 - 2(3)1$
$= 16 - 4 + 9 - 16 + 6 - 6$
$= 5$

$$D_z = \begin{vmatrix} 2 & -3 & 1 \\ 3 & -1 & 4 \\ 4 & -6 & 3 \end{vmatrix}$$

$= 2(-1)(3) + (-3)4(4) + 1(3)(-6) - 4(-1)1 - (-6)(4)2 - 3(3)(-3)$
$= -6 - 48 - 18 + 4 + 48 + 27$
$= 7$

*Inconsistent system*; ∅

15. $2x - y + 3z = 4$
$x - 5y - 2z = 1$
$-4x - 2y + z = 3$

$$D = \begin{vmatrix} 2 & -1 & 3 \\ 1 & -5 & -2 \\ -4 & -2 & 1 \end{vmatrix}$$

$= 2(-5)1 + (-1)(-2)(-4) + 3(1)(-2) - (-4)(-5)3 - (-2)(-2)2 - 1(1)(-1)$
$= -10 - 8 - 6 - 60 - 8 + 1$
$= -91$

$$D_x = \begin{vmatrix} 4 & -1 & 3 \\ 1 & -5 & -2 \\ 3 & -2 & 1 \end{vmatrix}$$

$= 4(-5)(1) + (-1)(-2)3 + 3(1)(-2) - 3(-5)3 - (-2)(-2)4 - 1(1)(-1)$
$= -20 + 6 - 6 + 45 - 16 + 1$
$= 10$

$$D_y = \begin{vmatrix} 2 & 4 & 3 \\ 1 & 1 & -2 \\ -4 & 3 & 1 \end{vmatrix}$$

$= 2(1)(1) + 4(-2)(-4) + 3(1)(3) - (-4)1(3) - 3(-2)2 - 1(1)4$
$= 2 + 32 + 9 + 12 + 12 - 4$
$= 63$

$$D_z = \begin{vmatrix} 2 & -1 & 4 \\ 1 & -5 & 1 \\ -4 & 2 & 3 \end{vmatrix}$$

$= 2(-5)3 + (-1)1(-4) + 4(1)(-2) - (-4)(-5)4 - (-2)(1)(2) - 3(1)(-1)$
$= -30 + 4 - 8 - 80 + 4 - 3$
$= -107$

$$x = \frac{D_x}{D} = \frac{10}{-91} = -\frac{10}{91}$$

$$y = \frac{D_y}{D} = \frac{63}{-91} = -\frac{9}{13}$$

$$z = \frac{D_z}{D} = \frac{-107}{-91} = \frac{107}{91}$$

*The solution set is* $\left\{\left(-\frac{10}{91}, -\frac{9}{13}, \frac{107}{91}\right)\right\}$.

16. $4x - y + 5z = 1$
$2x + 3y + 4z = 5$
$x + y + 3z = 2$

$$D = \begin{vmatrix} 4 & -1 & 5 \\ 2 & 3 & 4 \\ 1 & 1 & 3 \end{vmatrix}$$

$= 4(3)(3) + (-1)(4)1 + 5(2)1 - 1(3)5 - 1(4)4 - 3(2)(-1)$
$= 36 - 4 + 10 - 15 - 16 + 6$
$= 17$

$$D_x = \begin{vmatrix} 1 & -1 & 5 \\ 5 & 3 & 4 \\ 2 & 1 & 3 \end{vmatrix}$$

$= 1(3)3 + (-1)4(2) + 5(5)1 - 2(3)5 - 1(4)1 - 3(5)(-1)$
$= 9 - 8 + 25 - 30 - 4 + 15$
$= 7$

$$D_y = \begin{vmatrix} 4 & 1 & 5 \\ 2 & 5 & 4 \\ 1 & 2 & 3 \end{vmatrix}$$

$= 4(5)3 + 1(4)(1) + 5(2)2 - 1(5)5 - 2(4)4 - 3(2)1$
$+ 60 + 4 + 20 - 25 - 32 - 6$
$= 21$

$$D_z = \begin{vmatrix} 4 & -1 & 1 \\ 2 & 3 & 5 \\ 1 & 1 & 2 \end{vmatrix}$$

$= 4(3)2 + (-1)(5)1 + 1(2)1 - 1(3)1 - 1(5)4 - 2(2)(-1)$
$= 24 - 5 + 2 - 3 - 20 + 4$
$= 2$

$$x = \frac{D_x}{D} = \frac{7}{17}$$

$$y = \frac{D_y}{D} = \frac{21}{17}$$

$$z = \frac{2}{17}$$

*The solution set is* $\left\{\left(\frac{7}{17}, \frac{21}{17}, \frac{2}{17}\right)\right\}$.

18. $x + y + 0z = 2$
$-x + 0y + 3z = 0$
$0x + 2y + z = 3$

$$D = \begin{vmatrix} 1 & 1 & 0 \\ -1 & 0 & 3 \\ 0 & 2 & 1 \end{vmatrix}$$

$= 1(0)1 + 1(3)0 + 0(-1)2 - 0(0)0 - 2(3)(1) - 1(-1)1$
$= 0 + 0 + 0 - 0 - 6 + 1$
$= -5$

$$D_x = \begin{vmatrix} 2 & 1 & 0 \\ 0 & 0 & 3 \\ 3 & 2 & 1 \end{vmatrix}$$

$= 2(0)1 + 1(3)(3) + 0(0)2 - 3(0)0 - 2(3)2 - 1(0)1$
$= 0 + 9 + 0 - 0 - 12 - 1$
$= -3$

$$D_y = \begin{vmatrix} 1 & 2 & 0 \\ -1 & 0 & 3 \\ 0 & 3 & 1 \end{vmatrix}$$

$= 1(0)1 + 2(3)0 + 0(-1)3 - 0(0)0 - 3(3)1 - 1(-1)2$
$= 0 + 0 + 0 - 0 - 9 + 2$
$= -7$

$$D_z = \begin{vmatrix} 1 & 1 & 2 \\ -1 & 0 & 0 \\ 0 & 2 & 3 \end{vmatrix}$$

$= 1(0)3 + 1(0)0 + 2(-1)2 - 0(0)2 - 2(0)1 - 3(-1)1$
$= 0 + 0 - 4 - 0 - 0 + 3$
$= -1$

$$x = \frac{D_x}{D} = \frac{-3}{-5} = \frac{3}{5}$$

$$y = \frac{D_y}{D} = \frac{-7}{-5} = \frac{7}{5}$$

$$z = \frac{D_z}{D} = \frac{-1}{-5} = \frac{1}{5}$$

*The solution set is* $\left\{\left(\frac{3}{5}, \frac{7}{5}, \frac{1}{5}\right)\right\}$.

19. $x - y + 0z = 2$
$3x + 0y + z = 11$
$0x + y - 2z = -3$

$$D = \begin{vmatrix} 1 & -1 & 0 \\ 3 & 0 & 1 \\ 0 & 1 & -2 \end{vmatrix}$$

$= 1(0)(-2) + (-1)(1)(0) + 0(3)1 - 0(0)0 - 1(1)1 - (-2)(3)(-1)$
$= 0 + 0 + 0 - 0 - 1 - 6$
$= -7$

$$D_x = \begin{vmatrix} 2 & -1 & 0 \\ 11 & 0 & 1 \\ -3 & 1 & -2 \end{vmatrix}$$

$= 2(0)(-2) + (-1)1(-3) + 0(11)1 - (-3)0(0) - 1(1)2 - (-2)(11)(-1)$
$= 0 + 3 + 0 - 0 - 2 - 22$
$= -21$

$$D_y = \begin{vmatrix} 1 & 2 & 0 \\ 3 & 11 & 1 \\ 0 & -3 & -2 \end{vmatrix}$$

$= 1(11)(-2) + 2(1)0 + 0(3)(-3) - 0(11)0 - (-3)(1)(1) - (-2)(3)(2)$
$= -22 + 0 + 0 - 0 + 3 + 12$
$= -7$

$$D_z = \begin{vmatrix} 1 & -1 & 2 \\ 3 & 0 & 11 \\ 0 & 1 & -3 \end{vmatrix}$$

$= 1(0)(-3) + (-1)(11)0 + 2(3)1 - 0(0)2 - 1(11)1 - (-3)(3)(-1)$
$= 0 + 0 + 6 - 0 - 11 - 9$
$= -14$

$$x = \frac{D_x}{D} = \frac{-21}{-7} = 3$$

$$y = \frac{D_y}{D} = \frac{-7}{-7} = 1$$

$$z = \frac{D_z}{D} = \frac{-14}{-7} = 2$$

*The solution set is* {(3,1,2)}.

20. $4x + 5y + 0z = -1$
$0x + 2y + 3z = -5$
$x + 0y + 2z = -1$

$$D = \begin{vmatrix} 4 & 5 & 0 \\ 0 & 2 & 3 \\ 1 & 0 & 2 \end{vmatrix}$$

$= 4(2)2 + 5(3)1 + 0(0)0 - 1(2)0 - 0(3)4 - 2(0)5$
$= 16 + 15 + 0 - 0 - 0 - 0$
$= 31$

$$D_x = \begin{vmatrix} -1 & 5 & 0 \\ -5 & 2 & 3 \\ -1 & 0 & 2 \end{vmatrix}$$

$= -1(2)2 + 5(3)(-1) + 0(-5)0 - (-1)(2)0 - 0(3)1 - 2(-5)5$
$= -4 - 15 + 0 - 0 - 0 + 50$
$= 31$

$$D_y = \begin{vmatrix} 4 & -1 & 0 \\ 0 & -5 & 3 \\ 1 & -1 & 2 \end{vmatrix}$$

$= 4(-5)2 + (-1)3(1) + 0(0)(-1) - 1(-5)0 - (-1)3(4) - 2(0)(-1)$
$= -40 - 3 + 0 - 0 + 12 - 0$
$= -31$

$$D_z = \begin{vmatrix} 4 & 5 & -1 \\ 0 & 2 & -5 \\ 1 & 0 & -1 \end{vmatrix}$$

$= 4(2)(-1) + 5(-5)1 + (-1)0(0) - 1(2)(-1) - 0(-5)(4) - (-1)(0)(5)$
$= -8 - 25 + 0 + 2 - 0 - 0$
$= -31$

$$x = \frac{D_x}{D} = \frac{31}{31} = 1$$

$$y = \frac{D_y}{D} = \frac{-31}{31} = -1$$

$$z = \frac{D_z}{D} = \frac{-31}{31} = -1$$

*The solution set is* $\{(1,-1,-1)\}$.

22\. *a)* $y = 20x + 200$

*b)* $y = 25x$

*c)* $-20x + y = 200$
$-25x + y = 0$

$$D = \begin{vmatrix} -20 & 1 \\ -25 & 1 \end{vmatrix} = -20(1) - (-25)1 = 5$$

$$D_x = \begin{vmatrix} 200 & 1 \\ 0 & 1 \end{vmatrix} = 200(1) - 0(1) = 200$$

$$x = \frac{D_x}{D} = \frac{200}{5} = 40 \text{ items}$$

23\.
$$x^4 - 2x^2 - 8 = 0$$
$$(x^2 + 2)(x^2 - 4) = 0$$
$$x^2 + 2 = 0$$

$x^2 = -2$ or $x^2 - 4 = 0$
$x = \pm i\sqrt{2}$ $x^2 = 4$
$x = \pm 2$

24\.
$$x^4 - 8x^2 - 9 = 0$$
$$(x^2 + 1)(x^2 - 9) = 0$$
$$x^2 + 1 = 0$$

$x^2 = -1$ or $x^2 - 9 = 0$
$x = \pm 1$ $x^2 = 9$
$x = \pm 3$

26\. $x^{2/3} - 3x^{1/3} + 2 = 0$ $y = x^{1/3}$
$$y^2 - 3y + 2 = 0$$
$$(y - 1)(y - 2) = 0$$
$y - 1 = 0$ or $y - 2 = 0$
$y = 1$ $y = 2$

*Now we replace y with* $x^{1/3}$
*and solve for x*:

$x^{1/3} = 1$ or $x^{1/3} = 2$
$x = 1$ $x = 8$

27\. $2x - 5\sqrt{x} + 3 = 0$ $y = \sqrt{x}$
$$2y^2 - 5y + 3 = 0$$
$$(2y - 3)(y - 1) = 0$$
$$2y - 3 = 0$$
$2y = 3$ or $y - 1 = 0$

$y = \frac{3}{2}$ $y = 0$

*Now we replace y with* $\sqrt{x}$

*and solve for x*:

$\sqrt{x} = \frac{3}{2}$ or $\sqrt{x} = 1$

$x = \frac{9}{4}$ $x = 1$

28\. $3x - 8\sqrt{x} + 4 = 0$ $y = \sqrt{x}$
$$3y^2 - 8y + 4 = 0$$
$$(3y - 2)(y - 2) = 0$$
$3y - 2 = 0$ or $y - 2 = 0$

$y = \frac{2}{3}$ $y = 2$

*Now we replace y with* $\sqrt{x}$

*and solve for x*:

$\sqrt{x} = \frac{2}{3}$ or $\sqrt{x} = 2$

$x = \frac{4}{9}$ $x = 4$

30. $(2x - 1) - 2\sqrt{2x - 1} - 15 = 0 \qquad y = \sqrt{2x - 1}$

$$y^2 - 2y - 15 = 0$$
$$(y + 3)(y - 5) = 0$$
$$y + 3 = 0$$
$$y = -3 \quad \textit{or}$$

$$y - 5 = 0$$
$$y = 5$$

*Resubstitute* $\sqrt{2x - 1}$ *for* $y$:

$$\sqrt{2x - 1} = -3$$
$$2x - 1 = 9$$
$$x = 5 \quad \textit{or}$$

$$\sqrt{2x - 1} = 5$$
$$2x - 1 = 25$$
$$x = 13$$

*Possible solutions* 5 *and* 13; *only* 13 *checks.*

31. $kx^2 + 4x - k = 0$

$$x = \frac{-4 \pm \sqrt{4^2 - 4(k)(-k)}}{2k}$$

$$x = \frac{-4 \pm \sqrt{4(4 + k^2)}}{2k}$$

$$x = \frac{-4 \pm 2\sqrt{4 + k^2}}{2k}$$

$$x = -2 \pm \frac{\sqrt{4 + k^2}}{k}$$

32. $4x^2 - 4x + k = 0$

$$x = \frac{-(-4) \pm \sqrt{(-4)^2 - 4(4)k}}{2(4)}$$

$$x = \frac{4 \pm \sqrt{16(1 - k)}}{8}$$

$$x = \frac{4 \pm 4\sqrt{1 - k}}{8}$$

$$x = \frac{1 \pm \sqrt{1 - k}}{4}$$

34. $ax + y = b$
$bx + y = a$

$$D = \begin{vmatrix} a & 1 \\ b & 1 \end{vmatrix} = a(1) - b(1) - a = b$$

$$D_x = \begin{vmatrix} b & 1 \\ a & 1 \end{vmatrix} = b(1) - a(1) = b - a$$

$$D_y = \begin{vmatrix} a & b \\ b & a \end{vmatrix} = a(a) - b(b) = a^2 - b^2$$

$$x = \frac{D_x}{D} = \frac{b - a}{a - b} = -1$$

$$y = \frac{D_y}{D} = \frac{a^2 - b^2}{a - b} = a + b$$

35. $a^2 + by = 1$
$b^2x + ay = 1$

$$D = \begin{vmatrix} a^2 & b \\ b^2 & a \end{vmatrix} = a^2(a) - b^2(b) = a^3 - b^3$$

$$D_x = \begin{vmatrix} 1 & b \\ 1 & a \end{vmatrix} = 1(a) - 1(b) = a - b$$

$$D_y = \begin{vmatrix} a^2 & 1 \\ b^2 & 1 \end{vmatrix} = a^2(1) - b^2(1) = a^2 - b^2$$

$$x = \frac{D_x}{D} = \frac{a - b}{a^3 - b^3} = \frac{a - b}{(a - b)(a^2 + ab + b^2)} = \frac{1}{a^2 + ab + b^2}$$

$$y = \frac{D_y}{D} = \frac{a^2 - b^2}{a^3 - b^3} = \frac{(a + b)(a - b)}{(a - b)(a^2 + ab + b^2)} = \frac{a + b}{a^2 + ab + b^2}$$

36. $ax + by = a$
$bx + ay = a$

$$D = \begin{vmatrix} a & b \\ b & a \end{vmatrix} = a(a) - b(b) - a^2 - b^2$$

$$D_x = \begin{vmatrix} a & b \\ a & a \end{vmatrix} = a(a) - a(b) = a^2 - ab$$

$$D_y = \begin{vmatrix} a & a \\ b & a \end{vmatrix} = a(a) - b(a) = a^2 - ab$$

$$x = \frac{D_x}{D} = \frac{a^2 - ab}{a^2 - b^2} = \frac{a(a - b)}{(a + b)(a - b)} = \frac{a}{a + b}$$

$$y = \frac{D_y}{D} = \frac{a^2 - ab}{a^2 - b^2} = \frac{a}{a + b}$$

37. $x + 2y = 1$
$3x + 4y = 0$

38. $x + 3y + 2z = 1$
$-x + 4z = 3$
$2x + 5x - z = 5$

## Section 8.5

2. $x + y = 32 \quad y = 5x - 4$
$x + 5x - 4 = 32$
$6x = 36$
$x = 6$

$6 + y = 32$
$y = 26$

3. $x - y = 6 \qquad 2y = x + 4$
$2y - x = x$

$2y - 4 - y = 6$
$y = 10$

$2(10) = x + 4$
$16 = x$

4. $x - y = 12 \quad x = 2y + 5$
$2y + 5 - y = 12$
$y = 7$

$x = 2(7) + 5$
$x = 19$

6. $x + y + z = 14$
$x = 4y$
$y + 2x = 18$

$x + y + z = 14 \quad (1)$
$x - 4y = 0 \quad (2)$
$2x + y = 18 \quad (3)$

$-2x + 8y = 0 \quad (2)$
$2x + y = 18$
$9y = 18$
$y = 2$

$2x + 2 = 18$
$2x = 16$
$x = 8$
$8 + 2 + z = 14$
$z = 4$

*The three numbers are* 2,4,6.

7. $x + y = 925$
$2x + 1y = 1150$

$-x - y = -925$
$2x + y = 1150$
$x = 225$ *adult tickets*
$y = 700$ *children's tickets*

8. $x + y = 300$
$2x + 1.5y = 525$

$-2x - 2y = -600$
$2x + 1.5y = 525$
$-.5y = -75$
$y = 150$ *children's tickets*
$x = 150$ *adult tickets*

10. $x + y = 17{,}000$
$.05x + .065y = 970$

$-5x - 5y = -85{,}000$
$5x + 6.5y = 97{,}000$
$1.5y = 12{,}000$
$y = \$8{,}000$ *at* 6.5%
$x = \$9{,}000$ *at* 5 %

11. $x = 2y$
$.075x + .06y = 840$

$.075(2y) + .06y = 840$
$.210y = 840$
$y = \$4{,}000$ *at* 6%
$x = \$8{,}000$ *at* 7.5%

12. $x = 3y$
$.7x + .6y = 1350$
$.7(3y) + .6y = 1350$
$2.7y = 1350$
$y = \$5{,}000$ *at* 6%
$x = \$15{,}000$ *at* 7%

14. $x + y + z = 1600$
$.05x + .07y + .08z = 115$
$z = 3x$

$x + y + 3x = 1600$
$.05x + .07y + .08(3x) = 115$

$-28x - 7y = -11{,}200$
$29x + 7y = 11{,}500$
$x = \$300$ *at* 5%
$y = \$400$ *at* 7%
$z = \$900$ *at* 8%

15. $x + y = 9$
$.2x + .5y = 9(.3)$

$-2x - 2y = -18$
$2x + 5y = 27$
$3y = 9$
$y = 3$ *gals of* 50%
$x = 6$ *gals of* 20%

16. $x + y = 10$
$.3x + .8y = .5(10)$

$-3x - 3y = -30$
$3x + 8y = 50$
$5y = 20$
$y = 4$ *ounces* 80%
$x = 6$ *ounces* 30%

18. $x + y = 40$
$.25x + .50y = 40(.30)$

$-25x - 25y = 1{,}000$
$25x + 50y = 1{,}200$
$25y = 200$
$y = 8$ *gals of* 50%
$x = 32$ *gals of* 25%

19. $3(x - y) = 18$
$2(x + y) = 24$

$3x - 3y = 18$
$2x + 2y = 24$

$6x - 6y = 36$
$-6x - 6y = -72$
$-12y = -36$
$y = 3$ *mph – speed of the current*
$x = 9$ *mph – speed of the boat*

20. $2(x + y) = 20$
$6(x - y) = 12$

$2x + 2y = 20$
$6x - 6y = 12$

$$\begin{array}{r} 6x + 6y = 60 \\ \underline{6x - 6y = 12} \\ 12y = 72 \end{array}$$

$x =$ 6 *mph – speed of the boat*
$y =$ 4 *mph – speed of the current*

22. $3(x + y) = 1500$
$3\frac{1}{3}(x - y) = 1500$

$3x + 3y = 1500$

$3\frac{1}{3}x - 3\frac{1}{3}y = 1500$

$$\begin{array}{r} -10x - 10y = -5{,}000 \\ \underline{10x - 10y = \phantom{-}4{,}500} \\ -20y = -\phantom{0}500 \end{array}$$

$y =$ 25 *mph*
$3(x + 25) = 1{,}500$
$3x + 75 = 1{,}500$
$3x = 1{,}425$
$x =$ 475 *mph*

*Plane in still air*

23. $x + y = 20$
$.10x + .05y = 1.40$

$$\begin{array}{r} -10x - 10y = -200 \\ \underline{10x + 5y = \phantom{-}140} \\ -5y = -\phantom{0}60 \end{array}$$

$y =$ 12 *nickels*
$x =$ 8 *dimes*

24. $x + y = 15$
$.25x + .10y = 2.70$

$$\begin{array}{r} -10x - 10y = -150 \\ \underline{25x + 10y = \phantom{-}270} \\ 15x = \phantom{-}120 \end{array}$$

$x =$ 8 *quarters*
$y =$ 7 *dimes*

26. $x + y + z = 12$
$y = 2x + 2$
$.05x + .10y + .25z = 1.20$

$x + 2x + 2 + z = 12$
$5x + 10(2x + 2) + 25z = 120$

$3x + z = 10$
$25x + 25z = 100$

$$\begin{array}{r} -75x - 25z = -250 \\ \underline{25x + 25z = \phantom{-}100} \\ -50x = -150 \end{array}$$

$x =$ 3 *nickels*
$y =$ 8 *dimes*
$z =$ 1 *quarter*

27. $x = -200p + 700$ *when* $p = \$3$
$x = -200(3) + 700$
$x = 100$ *items*

28. $x = -300p + 900$ *when* $p = 3$
$x = -300(3) + 900$
$x = 0$ *bracelets*

30. $c = 1.1x + 7$ *when* $x = 20$
$c = 1.1(20) + 7$
$c = \$29$

31. $h = at^2 + bt + c$
$h = =16t^2 + 645 + 80$

*Maximum height is* 144 *ft.*
*when* $t = 2$ *seconds*

32. $h = at^2 + bt + c$
$h = -16t^2 + 48t + 64$

*Maximum height is* 100 *feet*
*when* $t = 1.5$ *seconds*

34. $x = -\frac{b}{2a}$

$x = -\frac{-9}{2(3)}$

$x = \frac{3}{2}$

$y = 3\left(\frac{3}{2}\right)^2 - 9\left(\frac{3}{2}\right) - 10$

$y = -\frac{67}{4}$

$\left(\frac{3}{2}, -\frac{67}{4}\right)$ *lowest*

36. $x = -\frac{b}{2a}$

$x = -\frac{18}{2(-6)}$

$x = \frac{3}{2}$

$y = 18\left(\frac{3}{2}\right) - 6\left(\frac{3}{2}\right)^2$

$y = \frac{27}{2}$

$\left(\frac{3}{2}, \frac{27}{2}\right)$ *highest*

37. $t = -\frac{b}{2a}$

$t = -\frac{64}{2(-16)}$

$t = 2$ *seconds*

$h = 64(2) - 16(2)^2$
$y = 64$ *feet*

38. $t = -\frac{b}{2a}$

$t = -\frac{64}{2(-16)}$

$t = 2$ *seconds*

$h = 40 + 64(2) - 16(2)^2$
$h = 104$ *feet*

# Chapter 9

## Section 9.1

2. Domain is {3,5,2}, range is {1,7,3}. This is a function.

3. Domain is {-1,1,2}, range is {3,-5}. This is a function.

4. Domain is {3,-1}, range is {-4,5,2}. This is not a function.

6. Domain is {5,3}, range is {-2,-1}. This is not a function.

7. Domain is {4,3}, range is {3,4,5}. This is not a function.

8. Domain is {4,1,-1}, range is {1,4,-4}. This is a function.

10. Domain is {2,3,4}, range is {4}. This is a function.

11. Yes, a function.

12. Yes, a function.

14. Yes, a function.

15. No, not a function.

16. Yes, a function.

18. No, not a function.

19. Yes, a function.

20. No, not a function.

22. *Given* $x = \sqrt{3x - 2}$

*then* $3x - 2 \geq 0$

$$x \geq \frac{2}{3}$$

*The domain is* $\left\{x \mid x \geq \frac{2}{3}\right\}$.

23. *Given* $x = \sqrt{1 - 4x}$

*then* $1 - 4x \geq 0$

$$x \leq \frac{1}{4}$$

*The domain is* $\left\{x \mid x \leq \frac{1}{4}\right\}$.

24. *Given* $y = \sqrt{2 + 3x}$

*then* $2 + 3x \geq 0$

$$x \geq -\frac{2}{3}$$

*The domain is* $\left\{x \mid x \geq -\frac{2}{3}\right\}$.

26. $$y = \frac{x - 3}{x + 4}$$

$$x + 4 = 0$$
$$x = -4$$

*The domain is* $\{x \mid x \neq -4\}$.

27. $$x = \frac{3}{2x^2 + 5x - 3}$$

$$2x^2 + 5x - 3 = 0$$
$$(x + 3)(2x - 1) = 0$$
$$x = -3 \quad \textit{or}$$

$$x = \frac{1}{2}$$

*The domain is* $\left\{x \mid x \neq -3, x \neq \frac{1}{2}\right\}$.

28. $$y = \frac{-1}{3x^2 - 5x + 2}$$

$$3x^2 - 5x + 2 = 0$$
$$(3x + 2)(x - 1) = 0$$

$$x = \frac{2}{3} \quad \textit{or} \quad x = 1$$

*The domain is* $\left\{x \mid x \neq \frac{2}{3}, x \neq 1\right\}$.

30.

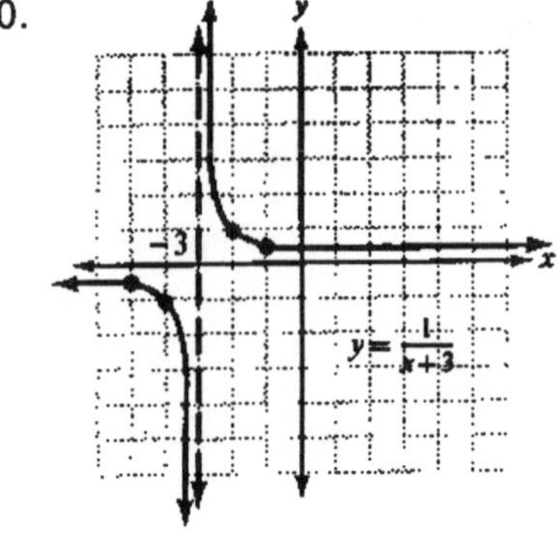

31.

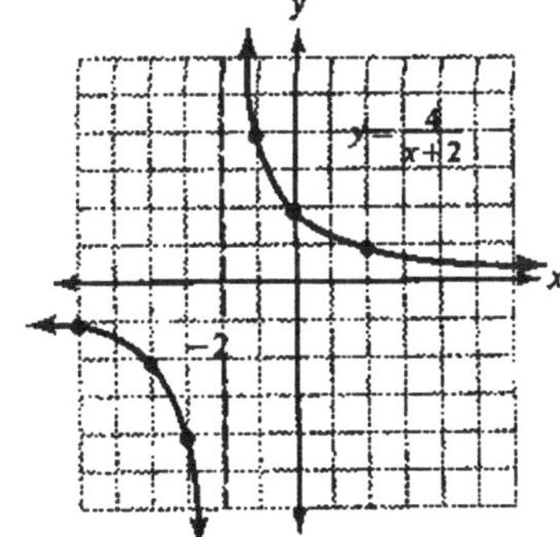


32.

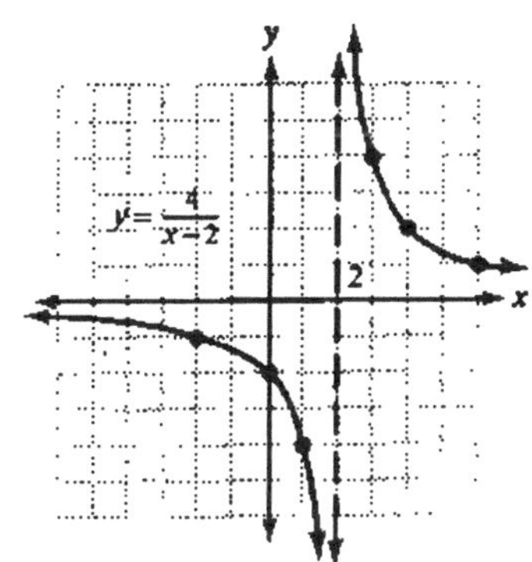


34.

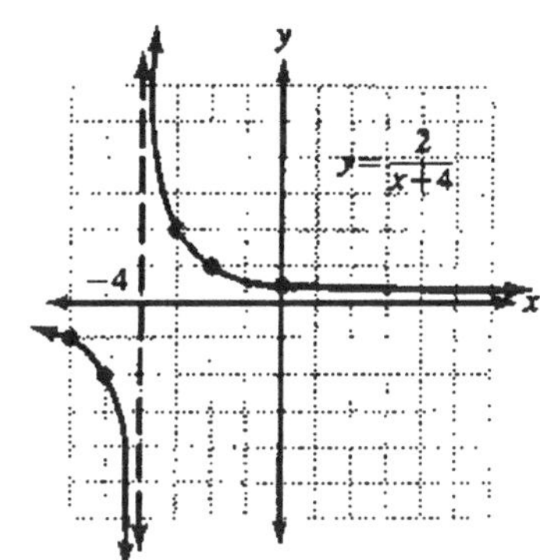


35.

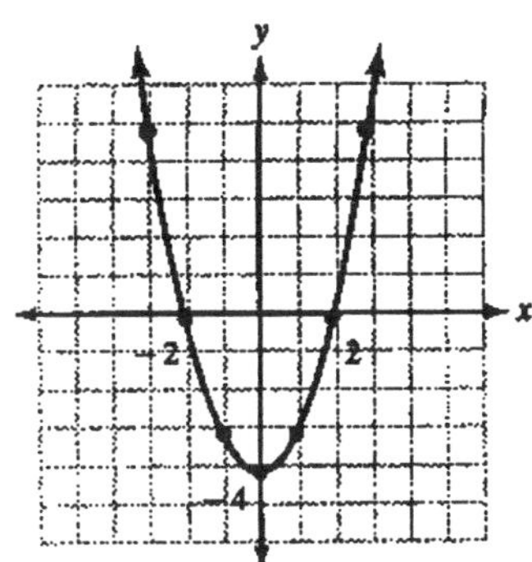


*Domain = all reals*
*Range = $\{y \mid y \geq -4\}$*
*A function*

36.

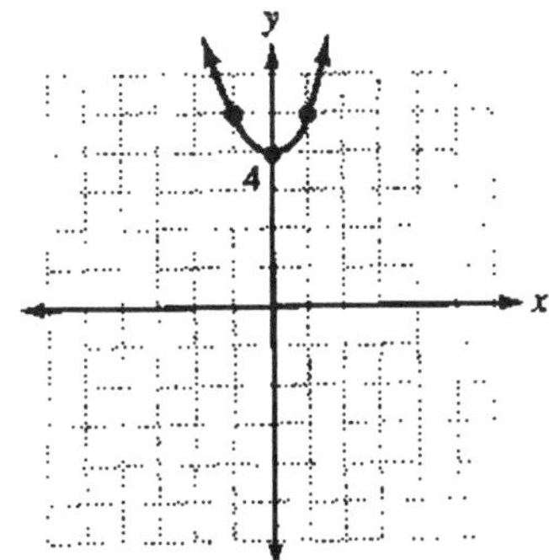


*Domain = all reals*
*Range = $\{y \mid y \geq 4\}$*
*A function*

38.

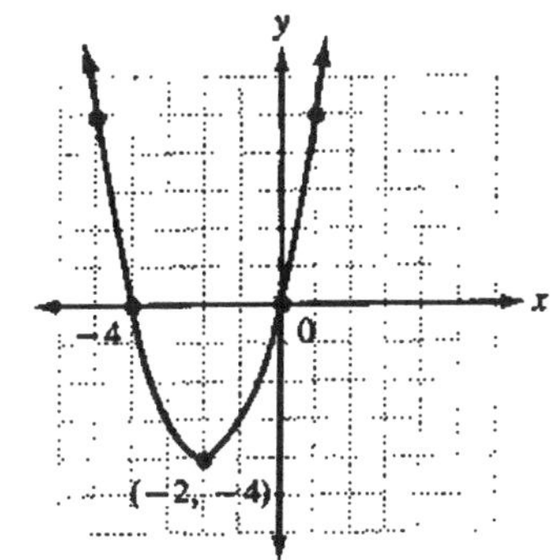


*Domain = all reals*
*Range = $\{y \mid y \geq -4\}$*
*A function*

39.

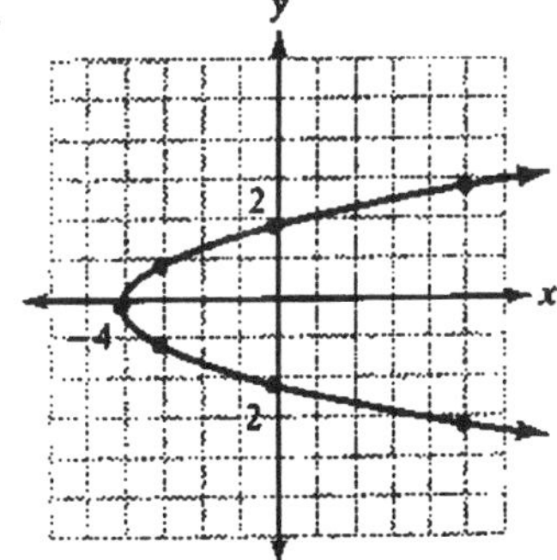


*Domain = $\{x \mid x \geq -4\}$*
*Range = all reals*
*Not a function*

40.

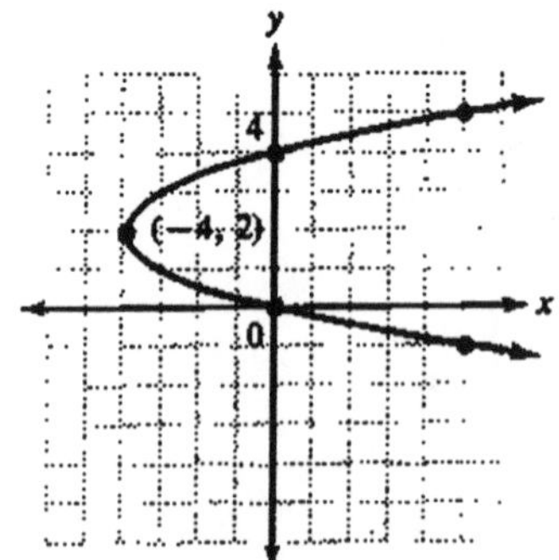


*Domain* = $\{x \mid x \geq -4\}$
*Range* = *all reals*
*Not a function*

42.

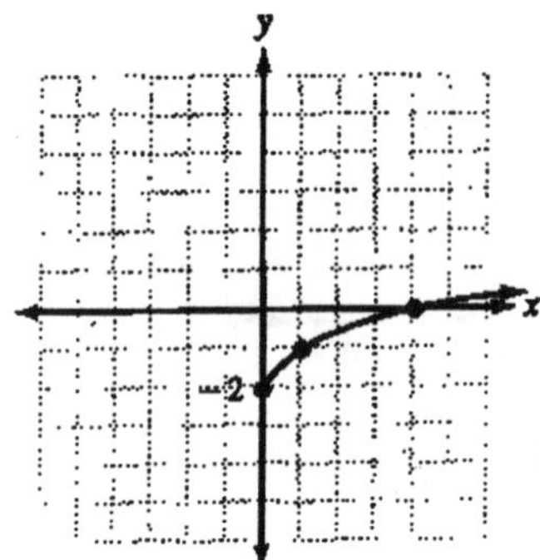


*Domain* = $\{x \mid x \geq 0\}$
*Range* = $\{y \mid y \geq -2\}$
*A function*

43.

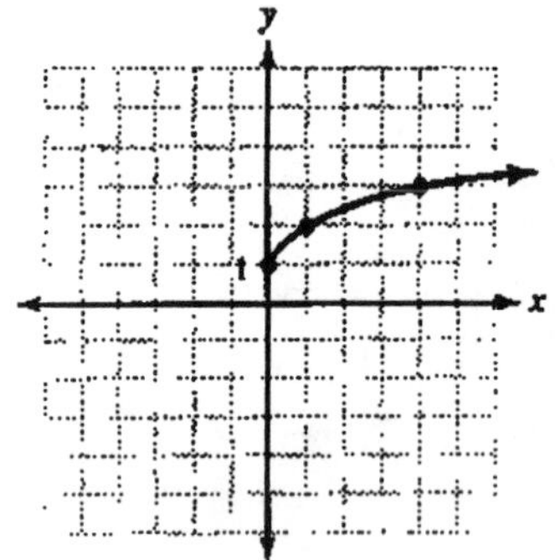


*Domain* = $\{x \mid x \geq 0\}$
*Range* = $\{y \mid y \geq 1\}$
*A function*

44.

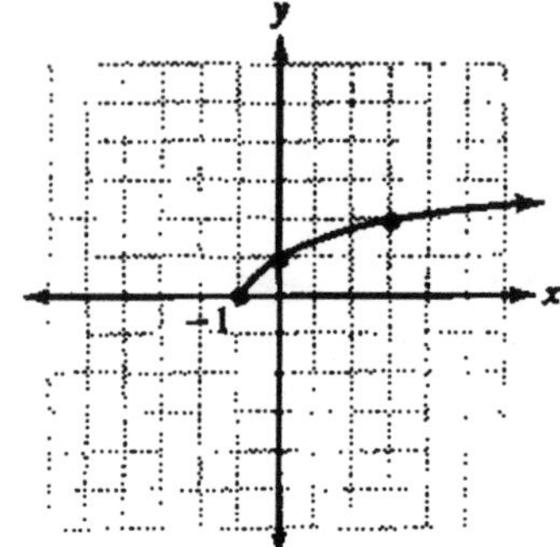


*Domain* = $\{x \mid x \geq -1\}$
*Range* = $\{y \mid y \geq 0\}$
*A function*

46.

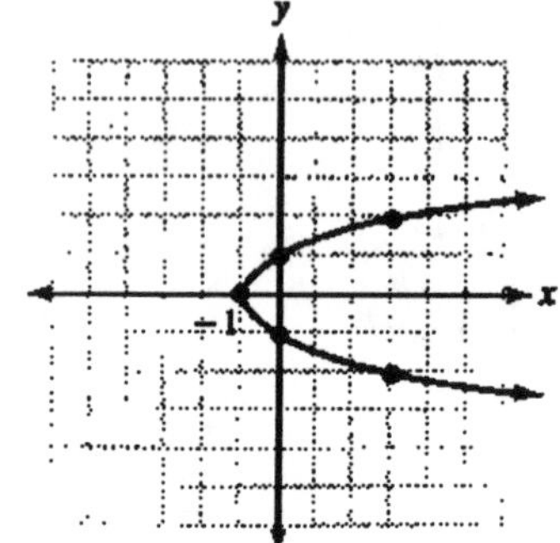


*Domain* = $\{x \mid x \geq -1\}$
*Range* = *all reals*
*Not a function*

47.

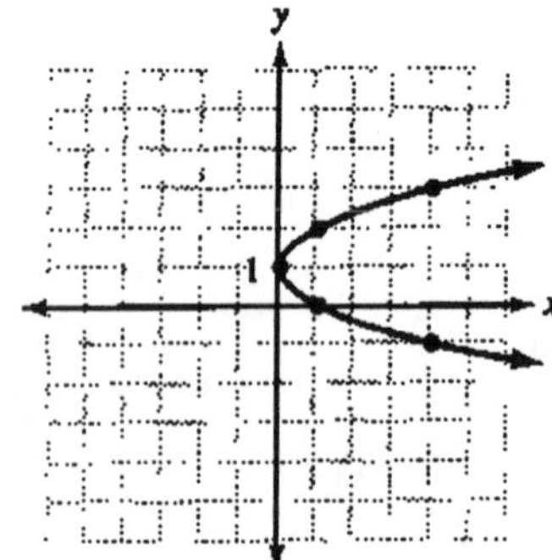


*Domain* = $\{x \mid x \geq 0\}$
*Range* = *all reals*
*Not a function*

48.

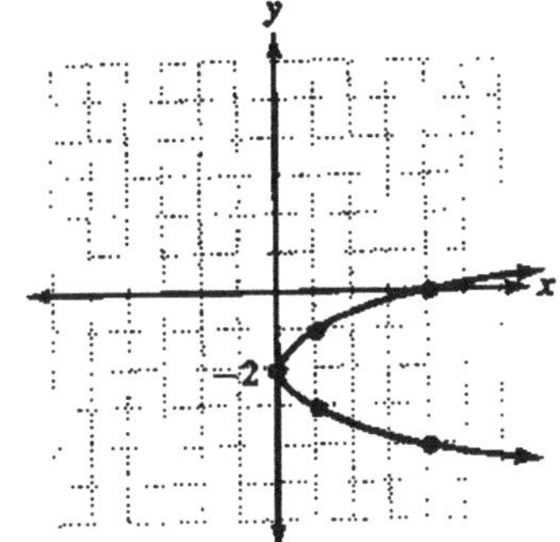


*Domain* = $\{x \mid x \geq 0\}$
*Range* = *all reals*
*Not a function*

50. a. *Yes*

b. *Domain* = $\{x \mid 0 \leq x \leq 80\}$.
*Range* = $\{P \mid 0 \leq P \leq 400\}$.

c. 40

d. $400

51. $4x + 3y = 10$
$2x + y = 4$

$$\begin{array}{r} 4x + 3y = \phantom{-}10 \\ -4x - 2y = -\ 8 \\ \hline y = \phantom{-}2 \end{array}$$

$4x + 3(2) = 10$
$x = 1$

52. $3x - 5y = -2$
$2x - 3y = 1$

$$\begin{array}{r} 6x - 10y = -4 \\ -6x + \phantom{1}9y = -3 \\ \hline -\ \ y = -7 \\ y = \phantom{-}7 \end{array}$$

$6x - 10(7) = -4$
$x = 11$

54. $4x + 2y = -2$

$\frac{2}{3}x + y = 0$

$$\begin{array}{r} 4x + 2y = -2 \\ -4x - 6y = \phantom{-}0 \\ \hline -\ 4y = -2 \\ y = \frac{1}{2} \end{array}$$

$4x + 2\left(\frac{1}{2}\right) = -2$

$4x = -3$

$x = -\frac{3}{4}$

55. $x + y = 3 \quad y = x + 3$
$x + x + 3 = 3$
$x = 0$
$y = 3$

56. $x + y = 6 \quad y = x - 4$
$x + x - 4 = 6$
$x = 5$
$y = 1$

58. $7x - y = 24 \quad x = 2y + 9$
$7(2y + 9) - y = 24$
$y = -3$

$7x - (-3) = 24$
$x = 3$

59. $y = \frac{6}{x - 2}$

| x | y |
|---|---|
| 1.5 | -12 |
| 1.7 | -20 |
| 1.9 | -60 |
| 2.1 | 60 |
| 2.3 | 20 |
| 2.5 | 12 |

60. $y = \dfrac{1}{x - 3}$

| x | y |
|---|---|
| 2.5 | -2 |
| 2.7 | $-\dfrac{10}{3}$ |
| 2.9 | -10 |
| 3.1 | 10 |
| 3.3 | $\dfrac{10}{3}$ |
| 3.5 | 2 |

62. $y = \dfrac{4}{x + 2}$

| x | y |
|---|---|
| -2.1 | -40 |
| -2.01 | -400 |
| -2.001 | -4000 |
| -1.999 | 4000 |
| -1.99 | 400 |
| -1.9 | 40 |

**Section 9.2**

2. $f(3) = 2(3) - 5 = 1$

3. $f(-3) = 2(-3) - 5 = -11$

4. $g(-2) = (-2)^2 + 3(-2) + 4 = 2$

6. $f(-4) = 2(-4) - 5 = -13$

7. $g(-3) = (-3)^2 + 3(-3) + 4 = 4$

8. $g(2) = 2^2 + 3(2) + 4 = 14$

10. $f(2) = 2(2) - 5 = -1$
$g(3) = 3^2 + 3(3) + 4 = 22$
$f(2) - g(3) = -1 - 22 = -23$

11. $f(3) = 2(3) - 5 = 1$
$g(2) = 2^2 + 3(2) + 4 = 14$
$f(3) - g(2) = 1 - 14 = -13$

12. $g(-1) = (-1)^2 + 3(-1) + 4$
$= 2$

$f(-1) = 2(-1) - 5$
$= -7$

$g(-1) + f(-1) = 2 + (-7)$
$= -5$

14. $g(1) = 1$

15. $g\left(\dfrac{1}{2}\right) = 0$

16. $f(3) = \dfrac{1}{2}$

18. $f(\pi) = 0$

19. $f(-2) = 0$
$g(-2) = 2$
$f(-2) + g(-2) = 0 + 2 = 2$

20. $g(1) = 1$
$f(1) = 4$
$g(1) + f(1) = 1 + 4 = 5$

22. $g(0) = 2(0) - 1 = -1$

23. $g(-4) = 2(-4) - 1 = -9$

24. $f(1) = 3(1)^2 - 4(1) + 1 = 0$

26. $g(z) = 2z - 1$

27. $f(a + 3) = 3(a + 3)^2 - 4(a + 3) + 1$
$= 3a^2 + 18a + 27 - 4a - 12 + 1$
$= 3a^2 + 14a + 16$

28. $g(a - 2) = 2(a - 2) - 1$
$= 2a - 5$

30. $f(2) = 3(2)^2 - 4(2) + 1 = 5$

$g[f(2)] = g(5) = 2(5) - 1 = 9$

31. $f(-1) = 3(-1)^2 - 4(-1) + 1 = 8$

$g[f(-1)] = g(8) = 2(8) - 1 = 15$

32. $g(-2) = 2(-2) - 1 = -5$

$f[g(-2)] = f(-5)$

$= 3(-5)^2 - 4(-5) + 1$

$= 96$

34. $g(0) = 2(0) - 1 = -1$

$f[g(0)] = f(-1)$
$= 3(-1)^2 - 4(-1) + 1$
$= 8$

35. $f(x) = 3x$
$f(a) = 3a$

$$\frac{f(x) - f(a)}{x - a} = \frac{3x - 3a}{x - a}$$

$= 3$

36. $f(x) = -2x$
$f(a) = -2a$

$$\frac{f(x) - f(a)}{x - a} = \frac{-2x - (-2a)}{x - a}$$

$$= \frac{-2x + 2a}{x - a}$$

$$= \frac{2(-x + a)}{-1(-x + a)}$$

$= -2$

38. $f(x) = 3x + 1$
$f(a) = 3a + 1$

$$\frac{f(x) - f(a)}{x - a} = \frac{3x + 1 - (3a + 1)}{x - a}$$

$$= \frac{3x - 3a}{x - a}$$

$= 3$

39. $f(x) = x^2$
$f(a) = a^2$

$$\frac{f(x) - f(a)}{x - a} = \frac{x^2 - a^2}{x - a}$$

$$= \frac{(x + a)(x - a)}{x - a}$$

$= x + a$

40. $f(x) = 2x^2$
$f(a) = 2a^2$

$$\frac{f(x) - f(a)}{x - a} = \frac{2x^2 - 2a^2}{x - a}$$

$$= \frac{2(x + a)(x - a)}{x - a}$$

$= 2(x + a)$

42.
$$y = x^2 - 1$$
$$y = a^2 + 1$$

$$\frac{f(x) - f(a)}{x - 1} = \frac{(x^2 - a) - (a^2 - 1)}{x - a}$$

$$= \frac{x^2 - a^2}{x - a}$$

$$= \frac{(x + a)(x - a)}{x - a}$$

$$= x + a$$

43.
$$f(x + h) = 2(x + h) + 3$$
$$= 2x + 2h + 3$$

$$f(x) = 2x + 3$$

$$\frac{f(x + h) - f(x)}{h} = \frac{2x + 2h + 3 - (2x + 3)}{h}$$

$$= \frac{2h}{h}$$

$$= 2$$

44.
$$f(x + h) = 3(x + h) - 2$$
$$= 3x + 3h - 2$$

$$f(x) = 3x - 2$$

$$\frac{f(x + h) - f(x)}{h} = \frac{3x + 3h - 2 - (3x - 2)}{h}$$

$$= \frac{3h}{h}$$

$$= 3$$

46.
$$y = f(x + h)$$
$$= -(x + h) + 4$$
$$= -x - h + 4$$

$$y = f(x)$$
$$= -x + 4$$

$$\frac{f(x + h) - f(x)}{h} = \frac{-x - h + 4 - (-x + 4)}{h}$$

$$= \frac{-h}{h}$$

$$= -1$$

47.
$$y = f(x + h)$$
$$= 3(x + h)^2 - 2$$
$$= 3x^2 + 6xh + 3h^2 - 2$$

$$y = f(x)$$
$$= 3x^2 - x$$

$$\frac{f(x + h) - f(x)}{h} = \frac{3x^2 + 6xh + 3h^2 - 2 - (3x^2 - 2)}{h}$$

$$= \frac{6xh + 3h^2}{h}$$

$$= \frac{3h(2x + h)}{h}$$

$$= 3(2x + h)$$

48.
$$f(x + h) = 4(x + h)^2 + 3$$
$$= 4x^2 + 8xh + 4h^2 + 3$$

$$f(x) = 4x^2 + 3$$

$$\frac{f(x + h) - f(x)}{h} = \frac{4x^2 + 8xh + 4h^2 + 3 - (4x^2 + 3)}{h}$$

$$= \frac{8xh + 4h^2}{h}$$

$$= \frac{4h(2x + h)}{h}$$

$$= 4(2x + h)$$

50. $f + h = f(x) + h(x)$
$= (3x - 5) + (3x^2 - 11x + 10)$
$= 3x^2 - 8x + 5$

51. $g + h = g(x) + h(x)$
$= (x - 2) + (3x^2 - 11x + 10)$
$= 3x^2 - 10x + 8$

52. $f - g = f(x) - g(x)$
$= (3x - 5) - (x - 2)$
$= 2x - 3$

54. $h - g = h(x) - g(x)$
$= (3x^2 - 11x + 10) - (x - 2)$
$= 3x^2 - 12x + 12$

55. $fg = f(x)g(x)$
$= (3x - 5)(x - 2)$
$= 3x^2 - 11x + 10$
$= h(x)$

56. $gf = g(x)f(x)$
$= (x - 2)(3x - 5)$
$= 3x^2 - 11x + 10$
$= h(x)$

58. $gh = g(x)h(x)$
$= (x - 2)(3x^2 - 11x + 10)$
$= 3x^3 - 17x^2 + 32x - 20$

59. $\frac{h}{f} = \frac{h(x)}{f(x)}$

$= \frac{3x^2 - 11x + 10}{3x - 5}$

$= \frac{(3x - 5)(x - 2)}{3x - 5}$

$= x - 2$
$= g(x)$

60. $\frac{h}{g} = \frac{h(x)}{g(x)}$

$= \frac{3x^2 - 11x + 10}{x - 2}$

$= \frac{(x - 2)(3x - 5)}{x - 2}$

$= 3x - 5$
$= f(x)$

62. $\frac{g}{h} = \frac{g(x)}{h(x)}$

$= \frac{x - 2}{3x^2 - 11x + 10}$

$= \frac{x - 2}{(x - 2)(3x - 5)}$

$= \frac{1}{3x - 5}$

$= \frac{1}{f(x)}$

63. $f + g + h = f(x) + g(x) + h(x)$
$= (3x - 5) + (x - 2) + (3x^2 - 11x + 10)$
$= 3x^2 - 7x + 3$

64. $h - g + f = h(x) - g(x) + f(x)$
$= (3x^2 - 11x + 10) - (x - 2) + (3x - 5)$
$= 3x^2 - 9x + 7$

66. $h - fg = h(x) - f(x)g(x)$
$= (3x^2 - 11x + 10) - (3x - 5)(x - 2)$
$= 3x^2 - 11x + 10 - (3x^2 - 11x + 10)$
$= 0$

67. *a.* $f(9) = 24(9) + 33 = \$2.49$

*b.* $f(5) = 24(5) + 33 = \$1.53$ (6 *minutes*)

*c.* $129 = 24x + 33$
$96 = 24x$
$4 = x$
5 *minutes*

68. *a.* $g(x) = 36x + 52$

*b.* $g(5) = 36(5) + 52 = \$2.32$

*c.* $f(9) = 24(9) + 33 = \$2.49$

$g(9) = 36(9) + 52 = \$3.76$

$g(9) - f(9) = \$3.76 - \$2.49 = \$1.27$

70.
$$\begin{aligned} x + y + z &= 6 \quad (1)\\ x - y + 2z &= 7 \quad (2)\\ 2x - y - z &= 0 \quad (3)\end{aligned}$$

$$\begin{array}{rl} x + y + z = 6 & (1)\\ \underline{x - y + 2z = 7} & \underline{(2)}\\ 2x + 3z = 13 & (4)\end{array}$$

$$\begin{array}{r} x + y + z = 6\\ \underline{2x - y - z = 0}\\ 3x = 6\\ x = 2\end{array}$$

$$\begin{array}{rl} 2(2) + 3z = 13 & (4)\\ z = 3 & \end{array}$$

$$\begin{array}{r} 2 + y + 3 = 6\\ y = 1\end{array}$$

71.
$$\begin{aligned} 3x + 4y &= 15 \quad (1)\\ 2x - 5z &= -3 \quad (2)\\ 4y - 3z &= 9 \quad (3)\end{aligned}$$

$$\begin{array}{rl} 6x + 8y = 30 & (1)\\ \underline{-6x + 15z = 9} & (2)\\ 8y + 15z = 39 & (4)\end{array}$$

$$\begin{array}{rl} -8y + 6z = -18 & (3)\\ \underline{8y + 15z = 39} & (4)\\ 21z = 21 & \\ z = 1 & \end{array}$$

$$\begin{array}{r} 4y - 3(1) = 9\\ y = 3\end{array}$$

$$\begin{array}{r} 2x - 5(1) = -3\\ x = 1\end{array}$$

72.
$$\begin{aligned} x + 3y &= 5 \quad (1)\\ 6y + z &= 12 \quad (2)\\ x - 2z &= -10 \quad (3)\end{aligned}$$

$$\begin{array}{rl} x + 3y = 5 & (1)\\ \underline{-x + 2z = 10} & (3)\\ 3y + 2z + 15 & (4)\end{array}$$

$$\begin{array}{rl} 6y + z = 12 & (2)\\ \underline{-6y - 4z = -30} & (4)\\ -3z = -18 & \\ z = 6 & \end{array}$$

$$\begin{array}{r} x - 2(6) = -10\\ x = 2\end{array}$$

$$\begin{array}{r} 6y + 6 = 12\\ y = 1\end{array}$$

74.
$$\begin{aligned} f(-x) &= f(x)\\ (-x)^4 + (-x)^2 &= x^4 + x^2\\ x^4 + x^2 &= x^4 + x^2\end{aligned}$$

75.
$$\begin{aligned} f(-x) &= f(x)\\ (-x)^{-2} &= (x)^{-2}\\ \frac{1}{(-x)^2} &= \frac{1}{x^2}\\ \frac{1}{x^2} &= \frac{1}{x^2}\end{aligned}$$

76.
$$\begin{aligned} f(-x) &= f(x)\\ (-x)^2 - (-x)^{-2} &= x^2 - x^{-2}\\ x^2 - \frac{1}{(-x)^2} &= x^2 - \frac{1}{x^2}\\ x^2 - \frac{1}{x^2} &= x^2 - \frac{1}{x^2}\end{aligned}$$

78.
$$\begin{aligned} f(-x) &= -f(x)\\ (-x)^3 &= -(x)^3\\ -x^3 &= -x^3\end{aligned}$$

79.
$$\begin{aligned} f(-x) &= -f(x)\\ (-x)^3 - (-x) &= -(x^3 - x)\\ -x^3 + x &= -x^3 + x\end{aligned}$$

80. $f(-x) = -f(x)$

$$\frac{5}{-x} = -\left(\frac{5}{x}\right)$$

$$-\frac{5}{x} = -\frac{5}{x}$$

## Section 9.3

2.

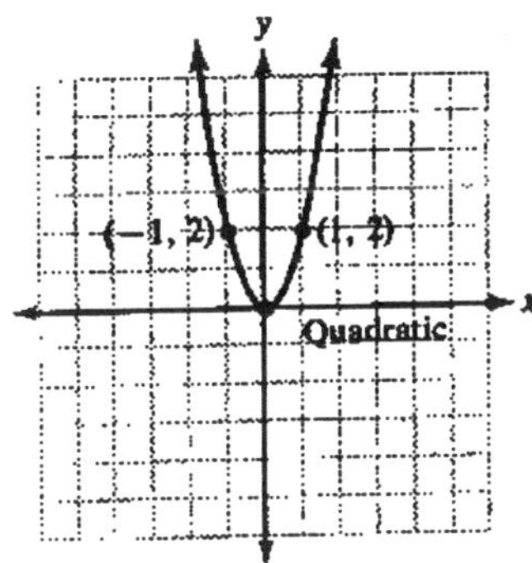


3.

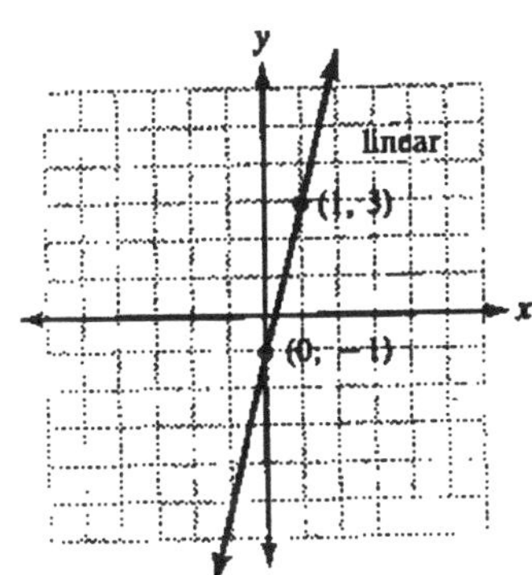


4.

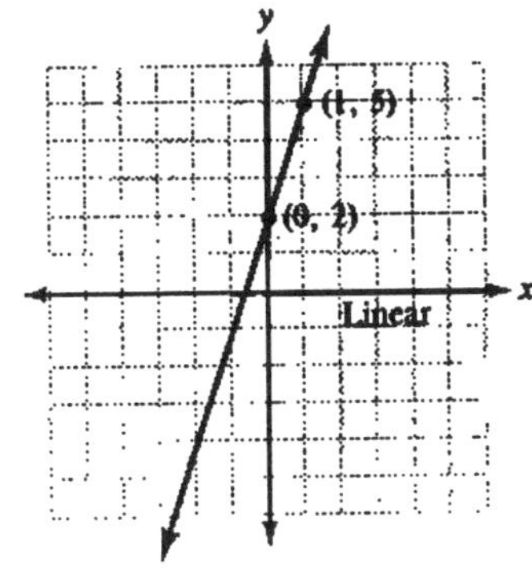


6.

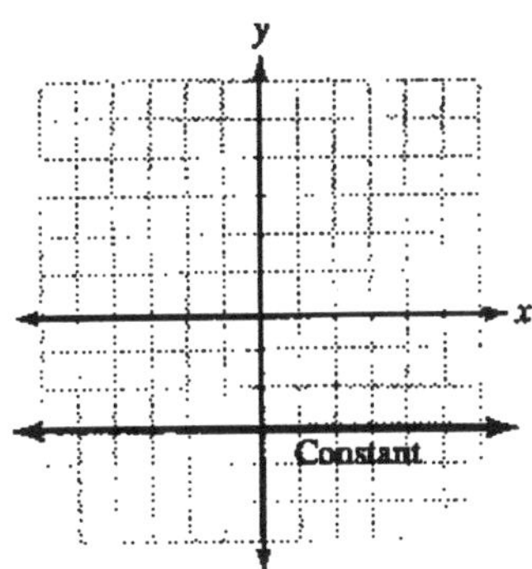


7.

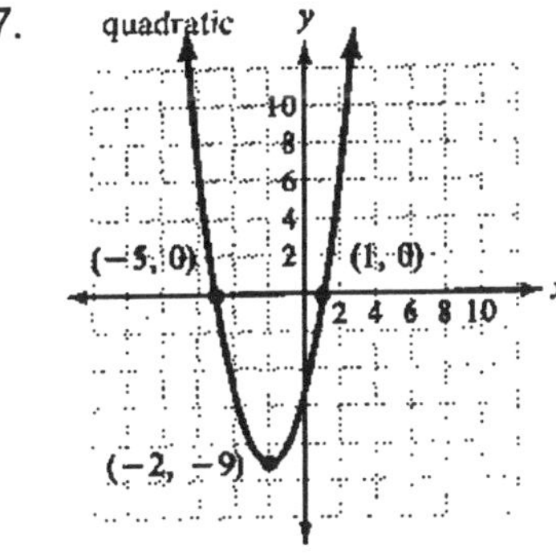


8.

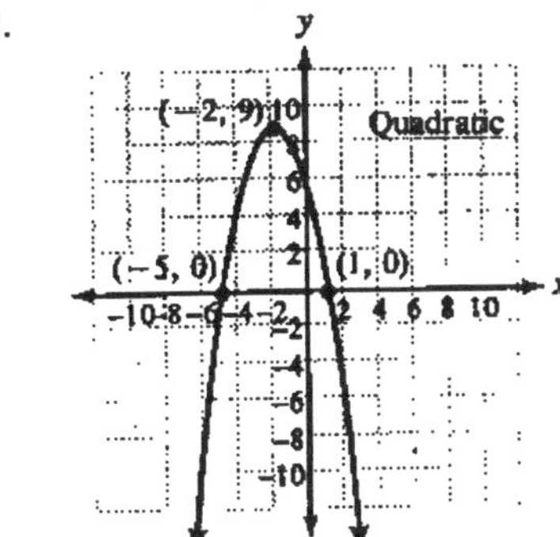


10. $f(x) = -2x + 12 \quad f(x) = 0$

$$-2x + 12 = 0$$
$$x = 6$$

11. $f(x) = -x + 6 \quad f(x) = 0$

$$0 = -x + 6$$
$$-6 = -x$$
$$6 = x$$

12. $f(x) = -x - 8 \quad f(x) = 0$

$$0 = -x - 8$$
$$8 = -x$$
$$-8 = x$$

14. $f(x) = 12x^2 - 5x - 2 \quad f(x) = 0$

$$12x^2 - 5x - 2 = 0$$
$$(4x + 1)(3x - 2) = 0$$
$$x = -\frac{1}{4} \quad or \quad x = \frac{2}{3}$$

15. $f(x) = x^2 + 4x + 1 \quad f(x) = 0$

$$x^2 + 4x + 1 = 0$$
$$x = \frac{-4 \pm \sqrt{4^2 - 4(1)(1)}}{2(1)}$$
$$x = \frac{-4 \pm 2\sqrt{3}}{2}$$
$$x = -2 \pm \sqrt{3}$$

16. $f(x) = x^2 - 4x - 1 \quad f(x) = 0$

$$x^2 - 4x - 1 = 0$$
$$x = \frac{-(-4) \pm \sqrt{(-4)^2 - 4(1)(-1)}}{2(1)}$$
$$x = \frac{4 \pm \sqrt{20}}{2}$$
$$x = \frac{4 \pm 2\sqrt{5}}{2}$$
$$x = 2 \pm \sqrt{5}$$

18. $f(x) = 3x^3 + x^2 - 12x - 4 \quad f(x) = 0$

$$3x^3 + x^2 - 12x - 4 = 0$$
$$x^2(3x + 1) - 4(3x + 1) = 0$$
$$(x + 2)(x - 2)(3x + 1) = 0$$
$$x = -2 \quad or \quad x = 2 \quad or \quad x = -\frac{1}{3}$$

19. $t = -\frac{b}{2a}$

$$t = -\frac{60}{2(-10)}$$
$= 3$ *hours later* (12:00 *noon*)

$$N(3) = 60(3) - 10(3)^2$$
$= 90$ *people*

20. $t = -\frac{b}{2a}$

$$t = -\frac{40}{2(-5)}$$
$t = 4$ *days* (*Friday*)

$$N(4) = 40(4) - 5(4)^2$$
$= 80$ *students*

22. $f(4) = 3^4 = 81$

23. $g(2) = \left(\frac{1}{2}\right)^2 = \frac{1}{4}$

24. $g(-2) = \left(\frac{1}{2}\right)^{-2} = (2)^2 = 4$

26. $f(0) = 3^0 = 1$

27. $g(-1) = \left(\frac{1}{2}\right)^{-1} = (2)^1 = 2$

28. $g(-4) = \left(\frac{1}{2}\right)^{-4} = (2)^4 = 16$

30. $f(-1) = 3^{-1} = \frac{1}{3}$

31. $f(2) = 3^2$
$= 9$

$$g(-2) = \left(\frac{1}{2}\right)^{-2}$$
$= (2)^2$
$= 4$

$$f(2) + g(-2) = 9 + 4$$
$= 13$

32. $f(2) = 3^2 = 9$

$$g(-2) = \left(\frac{1}{2}\right)^{-2} = (2)^2 = 4$$
$$f(2) - g(-2) = 9 - 4 = 5$$

34. $g(2) = \left(\frac{1}{2}\right)^2 = \frac{1}{4}$

$f(-1) = 3^{-1} = \frac{1}{3}$

$g(2) + f(-1) = \frac{1}{4} + \frac{1}{3} = \frac{7}{12}$

35.

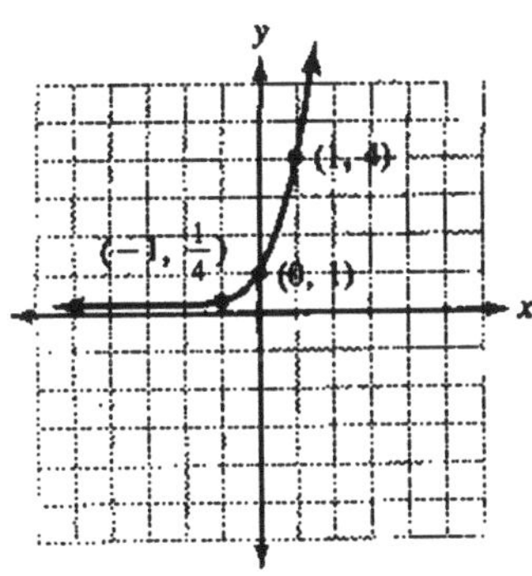


36.

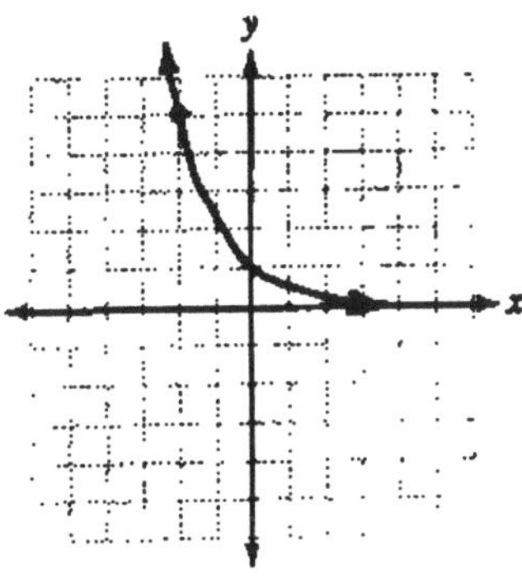


38.

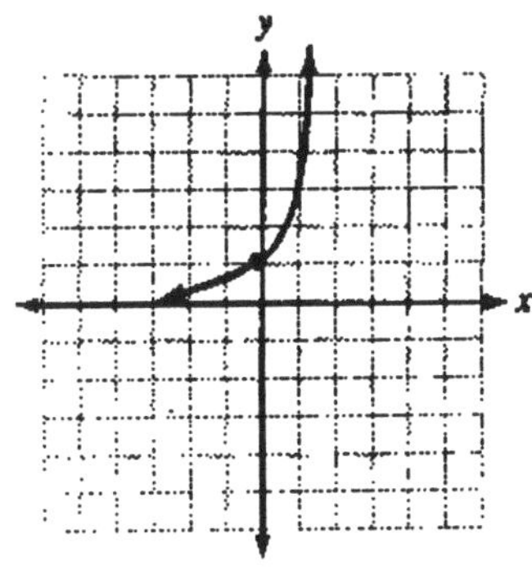


39.

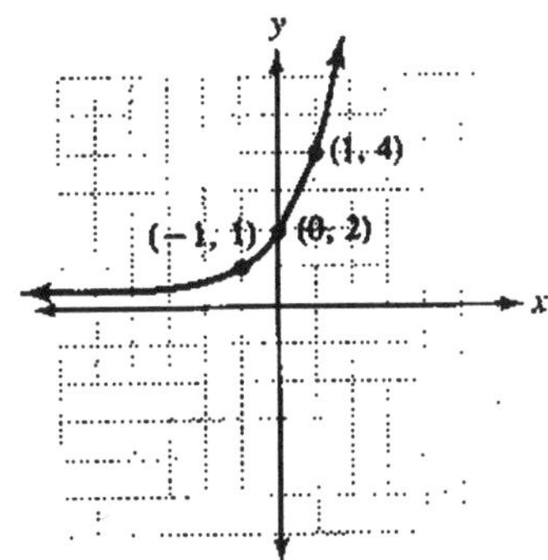


40.

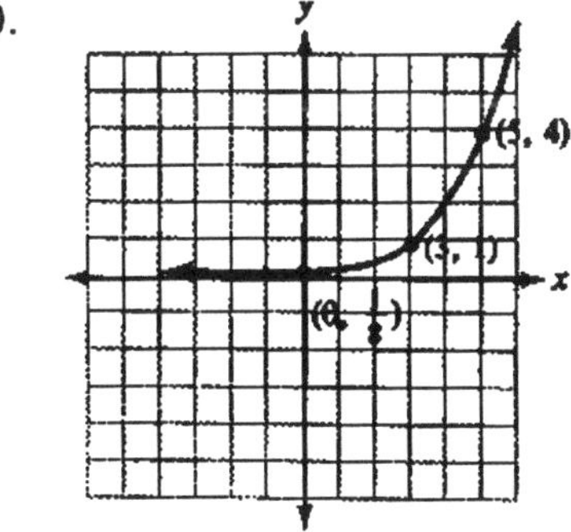


42.

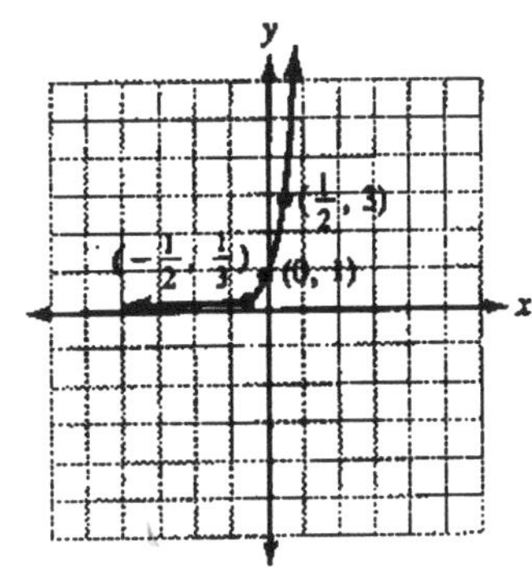


43. See instructor's textbook for graph.

44. See instructor's textbook for graph.

46. See instructor's textbook for graph.

47. $\begin{vmatrix} 3 & 5 \\ -6 & 2 \end{vmatrix} = (3)(2) - (-6)(5) = 36$

48. $\begin{vmatrix} -2 & 0 \\ 0 & -1 \end{vmatrix} = (-2)(-1) - 0(0) = 2$

50. $\begin{vmatrix} 2 & 0 & 0 \\ 0 & -3 & 0 \\ 0 & 0 & 4 \end{vmatrix}$

$= 2\begin{vmatrix} -3 & 0 \\ 0 & 4 \end{vmatrix} - 0\begin{vmatrix} 0 & 0 \\ 0 & 4 \end{vmatrix} + 0\begin{vmatrix} 0 & -3 \\ 0 & 0 \end{vmatrix}$

$= 2(-12 - 0) - 0(0 - 0) + 0(0 - 0)$
$= -24$

## Section 9.4

2. $f(x) = 2x - 5$ *means* $y = 2x - 5$

$x = 2y - 5$ (*inverse*)

$y = \dfrac{x + 5}{2}$

$f^{-1}(x) = \dfrac{x + 5}{2}$

3. $f(x) = x^3$ *means* $y = x^3$

$x = y^3$ (*inverse*)

$y = \sqrt[3]{x}$

$f^{-1}(x) = \sqrt[3]{x}$

4. $f(x) = x^3 - 2$ *means* $y = x^3 - 2$

$x = y^3 - 2$ (*inverse*)

$y = \sqrt[3]{x + 2}$

$f^{-1}(x) = \sqrt[3]{x + 2}$

6. $f(x) = \dfrac{x - 2}{x - 3}$ *means* $y = \dfrac{x - 2}{x - 3}$

$x = \dfrac{y - 2}{y - 3}$ (*inverse*)

$xy - 3x = y - 2$
$xy - y = 3x - 2$
$(x - 1)y = 3x - 2$

$y = \dfrac{3x - 2}{x - 1}$

$f^{-1}(x) = \dfrac{3x - 2}{x - 1}$

7. $f(x) = \dfrac{x - 3}{4}$ *means* $y = \dfrac{x - 3}{4}$

$x = \dfrac{y - 3}{4}$ (*inverse*)

$y = 4x + 3$
$f^{-1}(x) = 4x + 3$

8. $f(x) = \dfrac{x + 7}{2}$ *means* $y = \dfrac{x + 7}{2}$

$x = \dfrac{y + 7}{2}$ (*inverse*)

$y = 2x - 7$
$f^{-1}(x) = 2x - 7$

10. $f(x) = \dfrac{1}{3}x + 1$ *means* $y = \dfrac{1}{3}x + 1$

$x = \dfrac{1}{3}y + 1$ (*inverse*)

$y = 3(x - 1)$
$f^{-1}(x) = 3(x - 1) = 3x - 3$

11. $f(x) = \dfrac{2x + 1}{3x + 1}$ *means* $y = \dfrac{2x + 1}{3x + 1}$

$x = \dfrac{2y + 1}{3y + 1}$

$3xy + x = 2y + 1$
$3xy - 2y = 1 - x$

$y = \dfrac{1 - x}{3x - 2}$

$f^{-1}(x) = \dfrac{1 - x}{3x - 2}$

12. $f(x) = \dfrac{3x + 2}{5x + 1}$ *means* $y = \dfrac{3x + 2}{5x + 1}$

$x = \dfrac{3y + 2}{5y + 1}$

$5xy + x = 3y + 2$
$5xy - 3y = 2 - x$

$y = \dfrac{2 - x}{5x - 3}$

$f^{-1}(x) = \dfrac{2 - x}{5x - 3}$

14.

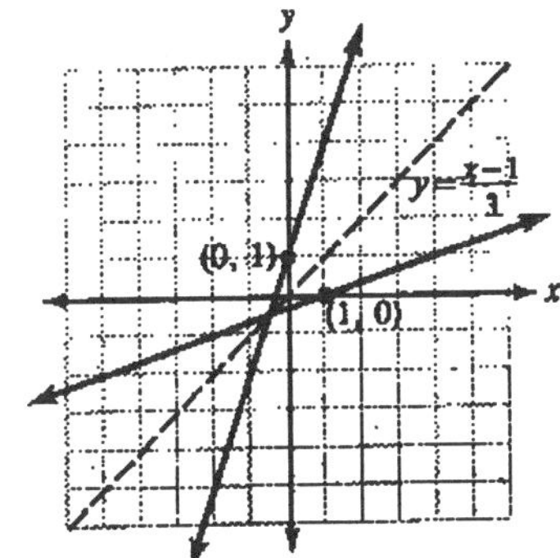

19.

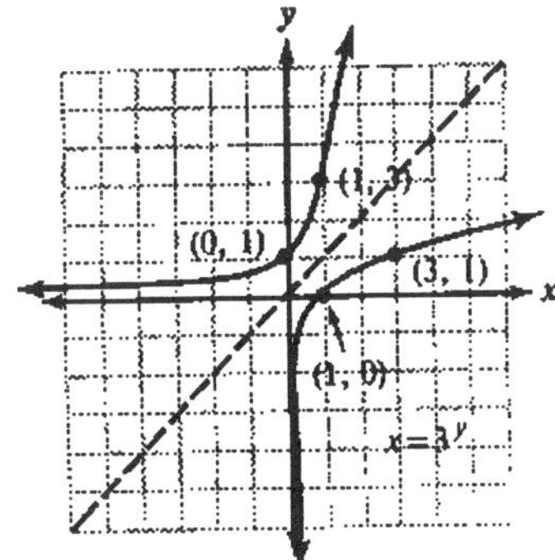

15.

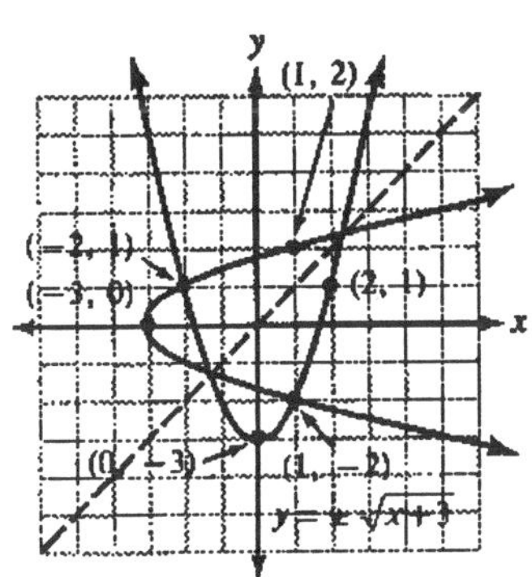

20.

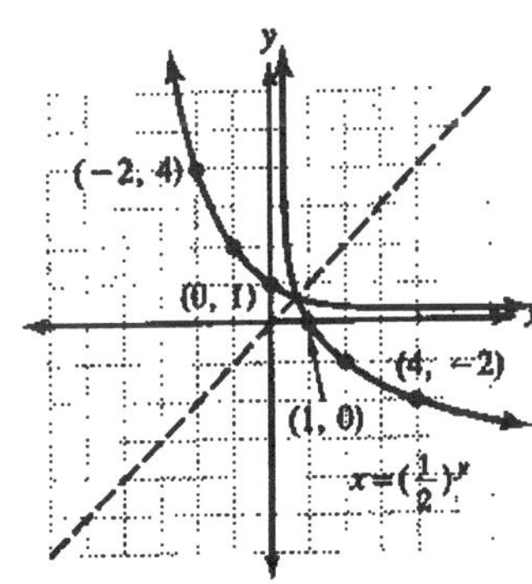

16.

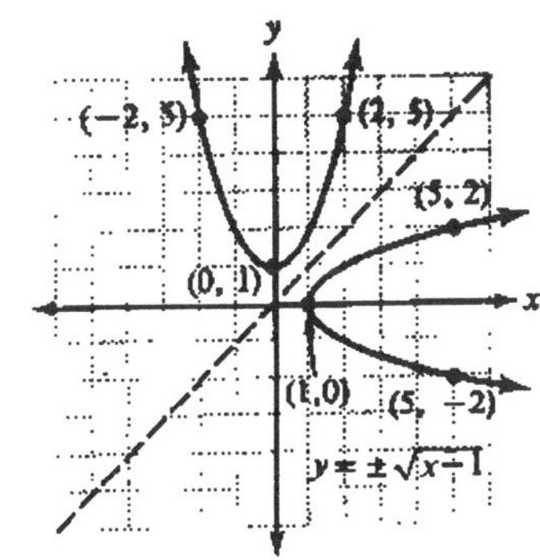

22.

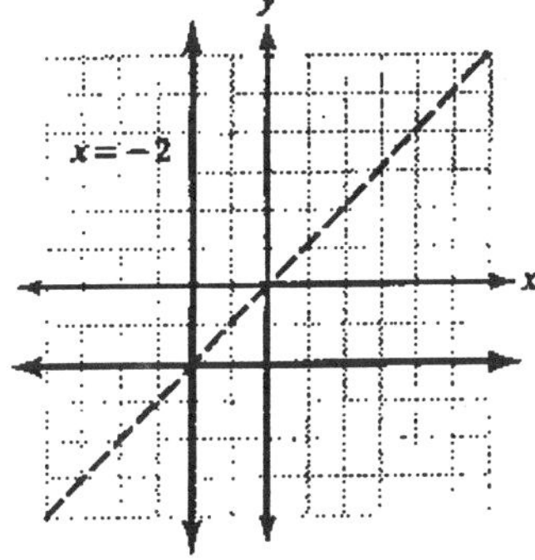

18.

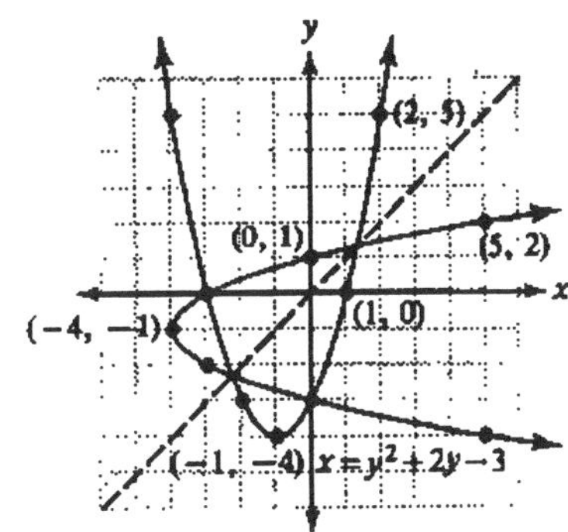

23.

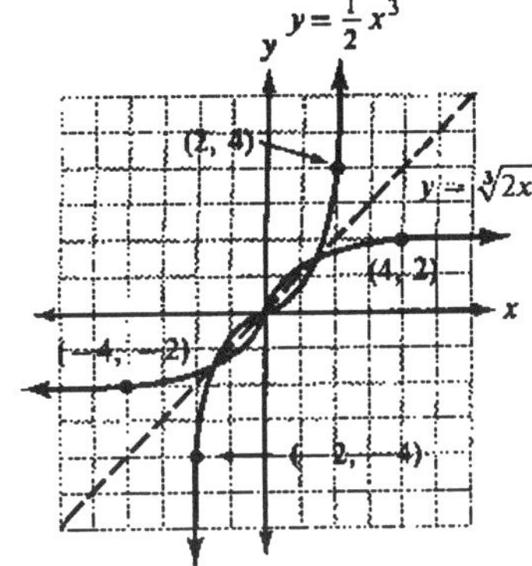

24.

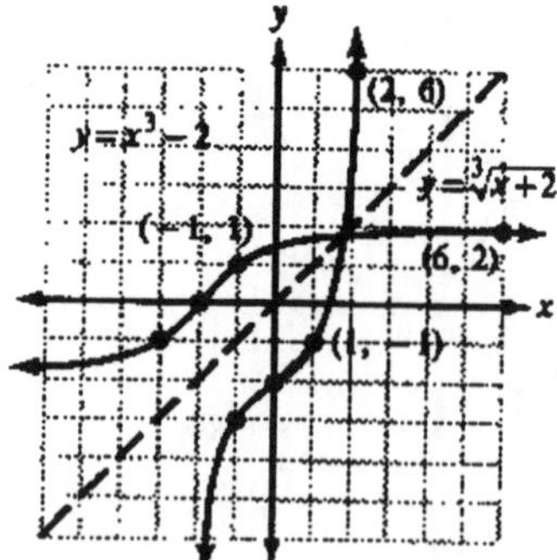


26.

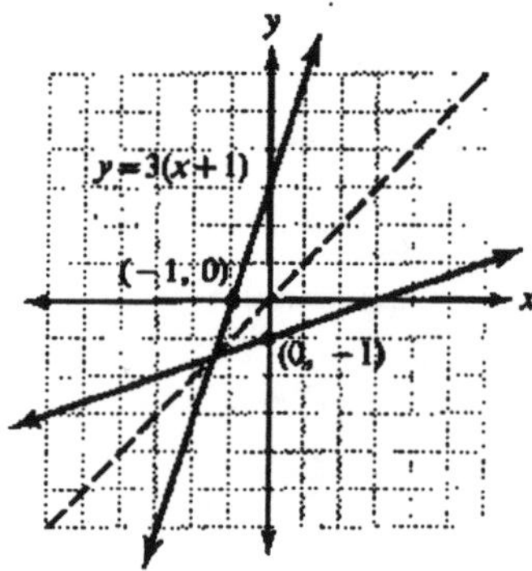


27.

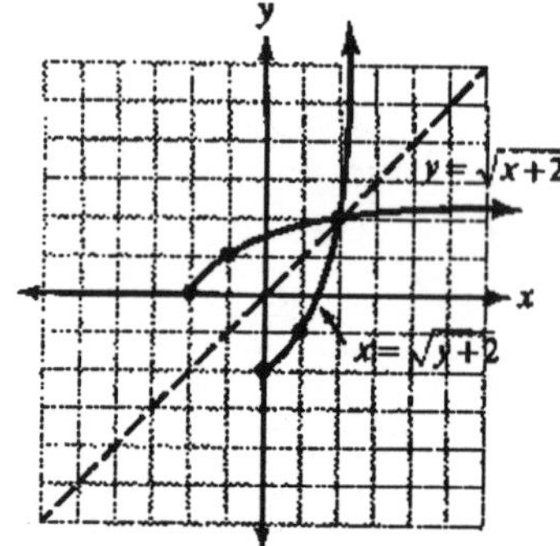


28.

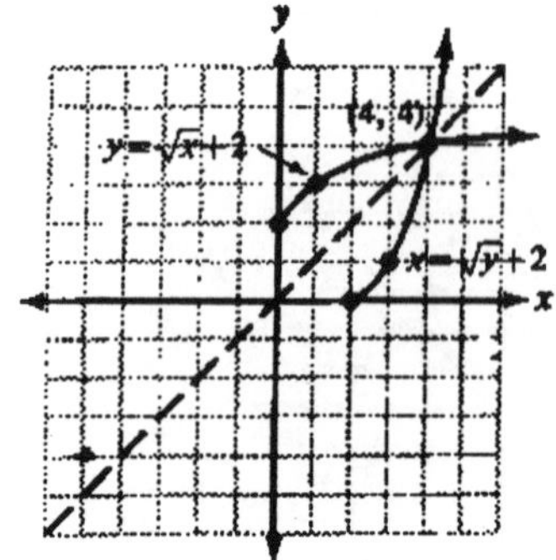


30. *a.* $f(-4) = \frac{1}{2}(-4) + 5$
$= 3$

*b.* $f^{-1}(-4) = 2(-4) - 10$
$= -18$

*c.* $f^{-1}(-4) = -18$

$f(18) = \frac{1}{2}(-18) + 5$
$= -4$

$f[f^{-1}(-4)] = f(18)$
$= -4$

*d.* $f(-4) = 3$
$f^{-1}(3) = 2(3) - 10$
$= -4$

$f^{-1}[f(-4)] = -4$

31. $f(x) = \frac{1}{x}$ *means* $y = \frac{1}{x}$

$x = \frac{1}{y}$ (*inverse*)

$xy = 1$

$y = \frac{1}{x}$

$f^{-1}(x) = \frac{1}{x}$

32. $f(x) = \frac{a}{x}$ *means* $y = \frac{a}{x}$

$x = \frac{a}{y}$ (*inverse*)

$xy = a$

$y = \frac{a}{x}$

$f^{-1}(x) = \frac{a}{x}$

34. *Let x = tea and y = coffee*
$15x + 10y = 15.50$ (1)
$25x + 13y = 24.55$ (2)
$75x + 50y = 77.50$ (1)
$\underline{-75x - 39y = -73.65}$ (2)
$11y = 3.85$
$y = \$.35$/*lb. of coffee*
$x = \$.80$/*lb. of tea*

35. *Let x = oranges and y = apples*

$$10\left(\frac{1}{3}x\right) + 15\left(\frac{1}{12}y\right) = 680 \quad (1)$$

$$5\left[\frac{10x}{3}\right] + \frac{1}{4}\left[\frac{15y}{12}\right] = 2545 \quad (2)$$

$$\begin{array}{rcl} -\ 40x - 15y &=& -\ 8{,}160 \quad (1) \\ 800x + 15y &=& 122{,}160 \quad (2) \\ \hline 760x &=& 114{,}000 \end{array}$$

$x = 150$ *oranges*
$y = 144$ *apples*

36. *If* $B = 2C$ (1)
$A = 3B$ (2)
$A = 9000 + c$ (3)

*Then* $3b = 9000 + C$ (4)

$$3B - C = 9000 \quad (4)$$
$$B - 2C = 0 \quad (1)$$

$$\begin{array}{rcl} 3B - C &=& 9000 \quad (4) \\ -3B + 6C &=& 0 \quad (1) \\ \hline 5C &=& 9000 \end{array}$$

$C = \$1{,}800$
$B = \$3{,}600$
$A = \$10{,}800$

38. $f(x) = 6 - 8x$ *means* $y = 6 - 8x$

$x = 6 - 8y$ (*inverse*)

$$\frac{6 - x}{8} = y$$

$$f^{-1}(x) = \frac{6 - x}{8}$$

$$f(f^{-1}(x)) = 6 - 8\left(\frac{6 - x}{8}\right)$$
$$= 6 - 6 + x$$
$$= x$$

39. $f(x) = x^3 + 1$ *means* $y = x^3 + 1$

$x = y^3 + 1$ (*inverse*)

$$y = \sqrt[3]{x - 1}$$

$$f^{-1}(x) = \sqrt[3]{x - 1}$$

$$f(f^{-1}(x)) = \left(\sqrt[3]{x - 1}\right)^3 + 1$$
$$= x - 1 + 1$$
$$= x$$

40. $f(x) = x^3 - 8$ *means* $y = x^3 - 8$

$$x = y^3 - 8$$

$$y = \sqrt[3]{x + 8}$$

$$f^{-1}(x) = \sqrt[3]{x + 8}$$

$$f(f^{-1}(x)) = \left(\sqrt[3]{x + 8}\right)^3 - 8$$
$$= x + 8 - 8$$
$$= x$$

42. $f(x) = \dfrac{x - 3}{x - 1}$ *means* $y = \dfrac{x - 3}{x - 1}$

$$x = \frac{y - 3}{y - 1}$$

$$xy - x = y - 3$$
$$xy - y = x - 3$$
$$(x - 1)y = x - 3$$

$$y = \frac{x - 3}{x - 1}$$

$$f^{-1}(x) = \frac{x - 3}{x - 1}$$

$$f(f^{-1}(x)) = \frac{\dfrac{x - 3}{x - 1} - 3}{\dfrac{x - 3}{x - 1} - 1}$$

$$= \frac{x - 3 - 3x + 3}{x - 3 - x + 1}$$

$$= \frac{-2x}{-2}$$

$$= x$$

**Section 9.5**

2. *Let* $(4,7) = (x_1,y_1)$

*and* $(8,1) = (x_2,y_2)$

$$d = \sqrt{(8 - 4)^2 + (1 - 7)^2}$$
$$= \sqrt{52}$$
$$= 2\sqrt{13}$$

3. *Let* $(0,9) = (x_1,x_2)$

*and* $(5,0) = (x_2,y_2)$

$$d = \sqrt{(5-0)^2 + (0-9)^2}$$
$$= \sqrt{106}$$

4. *Let* $(-3,0) = (x_1,y_1)$

*and* $(0,4) = (x_2,y_2)$

$$d = \sqrt{(0+3)^2 + (4-0)^2}$$
$$= \sqrt{25}$$
$$= 5$$

6. *Let* $(-8,9) = (x_1,y_1)$

*and* $(-3,-2) = (x_2,y_2)$

$$d = \sqrt{(-3+8)^2 + (-2-9)^2}$$
$$= \sqrt{146}$$

7. *Let* $(-1,-2) = (x_1,y_1)$

*and* $(-10,5) = (x_2,y_2)$

$$d = \sqrt{(-10+1)^2 + (5+2)^2}$$
$$= \sqrt{130}$$

8. *Let* $(-3,-8) = (x_1,y_1)$

*and* $(-1,6) = (x_2,y_2)$

$$d = \sqrt{(-1+3)^2 + (6+8)^2}$$
$$= \sqrt{200}$$
$$= 10\sqrt{2}$$

10. *Let* $(-2,3) = (x_1,y_1)$,

$(x,1) = (x_2,y_2)$

*and* $d = 3$

$$3 = \sqrt{(x+2)^2 + (1-3)^2}$$
$$3 = \sqrt{x^2 + 4x + 4 + 4}$$
$$9 = x^2 + 4x + 8$$
$$x^2 + 4x - 1 = 0$$

$$x = \frac{-4 \pm \sqrt{4^2 - 4(1)(-1)}}{2(1)}$$

$$x = \frac{-4 \pm \sqrt{20}}{2}$$

$$x = \frac{-4 \pm 2\sqrt{5}}{2}$$

$$x = -2 \pm \sqrt{5}$$

11. *Let* $(7,y) = (x_1,y_1)$,

$(8,3) = (x_2,y_2)$

*and* $d = 1$

$$1 = \sqrt{(8-7)^2 + (3-y)^2}$$
$$1 = \sqrt{1 + 9 - 6y + y^2}$$
$$1 = y^2 - 6y + 10$$
$$y^2 - 6y + 9 = 0$$
$$(y-3)(y-3) = 0$$
$$y = 3$$

12. *Let* $(3,-5) = (x_1,y_1)$,

$(3,y) = (x_2,y_2)$

*and* $d = 9$

$$9 = \sqrt{(3-3)^2 + (y+5)^2}$$
$$9 = \sqrt{y^2 + 10y + 25}$$
$$81 = y^2 + 10y + 25$$
$$y^2 + 10y - 56 = 0$$
$$(y+14)(y-4) = 0$$
$$y = -14 \quad \textit{or} \quad y = 4$$

14. *Let* $(a,b) = (3,-1)$; $r = 5$

$$(x-3)^2 + (y+1)^2 = 25$$

15. *Let* $(a,b) = (3,-2);\ r = 3$

$$(x-3)^2 + (y+2)^2 = 9$$

16. *Let* $(a,b) = (-2,4);\ r = 1$

$$(x+2)^2 + (y-4)^2 = 1$$

18. *Let* $(a,b) = (-7,-6);\ r = \sqrt{3}$

$$(x+7)^2 + (y+6)^2 = 3$$

19. *Let* $(a,b) = (0,-5);\ r = 1$

$$(x-0)^2 + (y+5)^2 = 1$$
$$x^2 + (y+5)^2 = 1$$

20. *Let* $(a,b) = (0,-1);\ r = 7$

$$(x-0)^2 + (y+1)^2 = 49$$
$$x^2 + (y+1)^2 = 49$$

22. *Let* $(a,b) = (0,0)$ *and* $r = 5$

$$(x-0)^2 + (y-0) = 25$$
$$x^2 + y^2 = 25$$

23. center = (0,0),
radius = 2

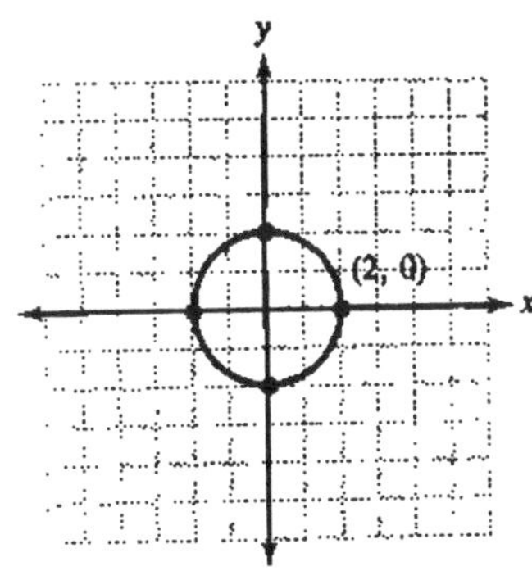


24.
$$x^2 + y^2 = 16$$
$$(x-0)^2 + (y-0)^2 = 4^2$$
*center* = (0,0)
*radius* = 4

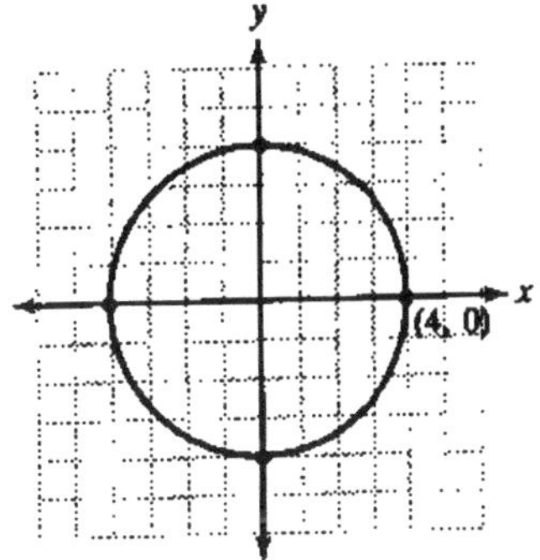


26. $(x-4)^2 + (y-1)^2 = 36$
*center* = (4,1)
*radius* = 6

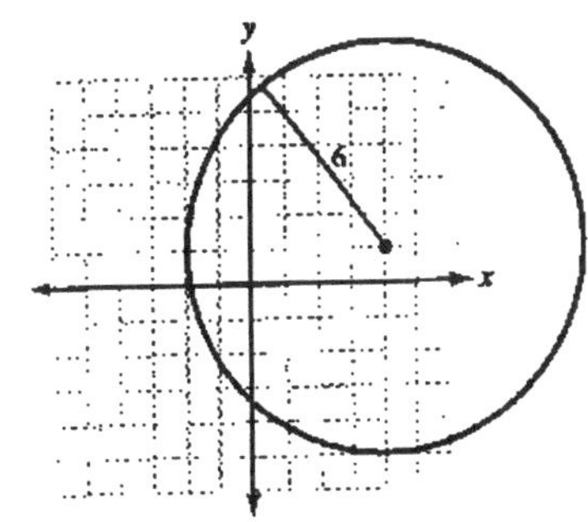


27.
$$(x+2)^2 + (y-4)^2 = 8$$
$$[x-(-2)]^2 + (y-4)^2 = (2\sqrt{2})^2$$
*center* = (−2,4)
*radius* = $2\sqrt{2}$

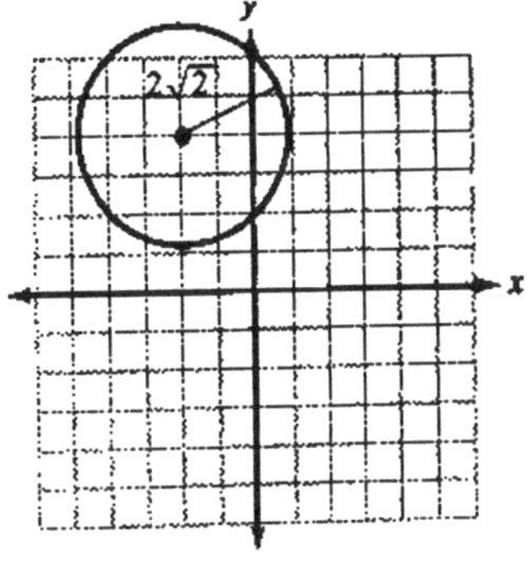

28.
$$(x-3)^2+(y+1)^2=12$$
$$(x-3)^2+[y-(-1)]^2=(2\sqrt{3})^2$$
$$center=(3,-1)$$
$$radius=2\sqrt{3}$$

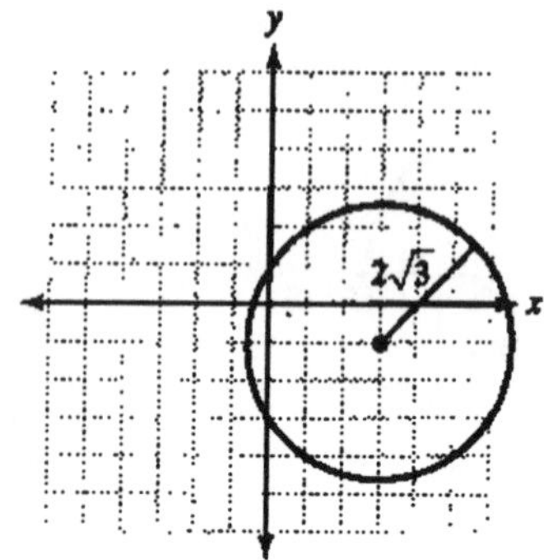


30.
$$(x+3)^2+(y+2)^2=9$$
$$[x-(-3)]^2+[y-(-2)]^2=3^2$$
$$center=(-3,-2)$$
$$radius=3$$

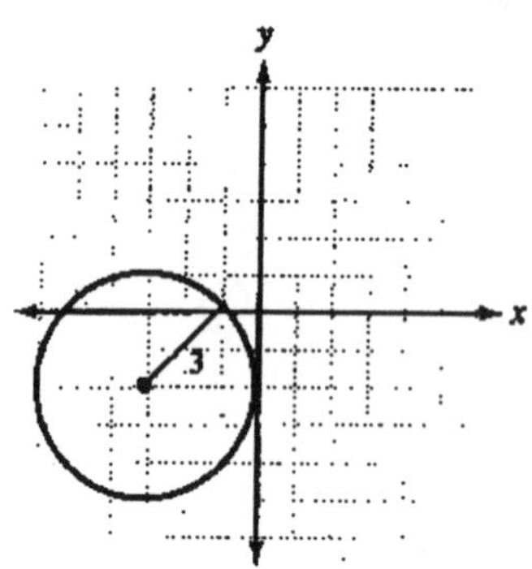


31.
$$x^2+y^2-6y=7$$
$$x^2+y^2-6y+9=7+9$$
$$(x-0)^2+(y-3)^2=42$$
$$center=(0,3)$$
$$radius=4$$

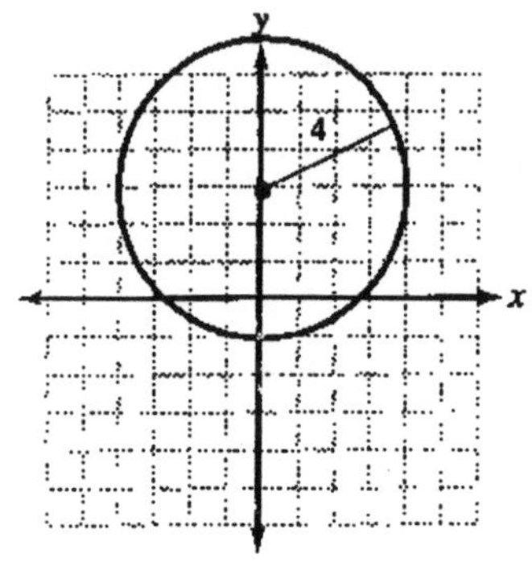


32.
$$x^2+y^2-4y=5$$
$$x^2+y^2-4y+4=5+4$$
$$(x-0)^2+(y-2)^2=3^2$$
$$center=(0,2)$$
$$radius=3$$

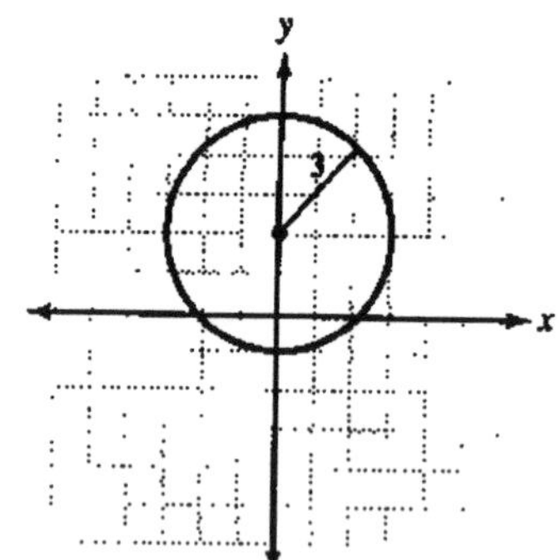


34.
$$x^2+y^2+10x=0$$
$$x^2+10x+25+y^2=0+25$$
$$(x+5)^2+(y-0)^2=5^2$$
$$[x-(-5)]^2+(y-0)^2=5^2$$
$$center=(-5,0)$$
$$radius=5$$

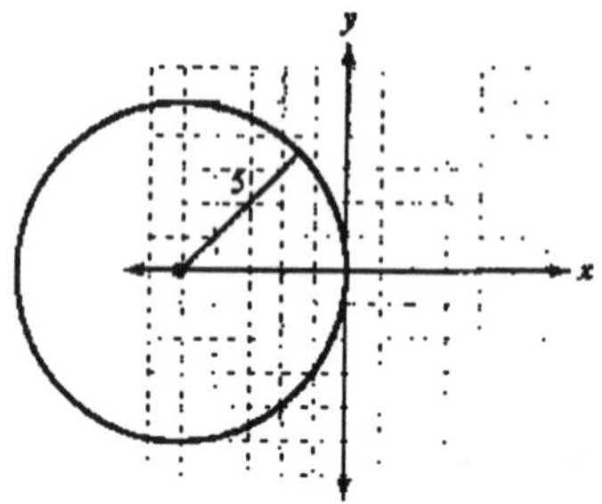


35.
$$x^2+y^2-4x-6y=-4$$
$$x^2-4x+4+y^2-6y+9=-4+4+9$$
$$(x-2)^2+(y-3)^2=3^2$$
$$center=(2,3)$$
$$radius=3$$

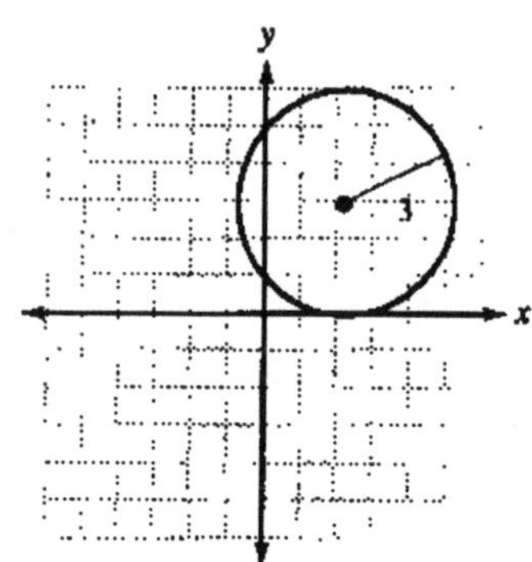

36.
$$x^2 + y^2 - 4x + 2y = 4$$
$$x^2 - 4x + 4 + y^2 + 2y + 1 = 4 + 4 + 1$$
$$(x - 2)^2 + (y + 1)^2 = 3^2$$
$$(x - 2)^2 + [y - (-1)]^2 = 3^2$$
$$\textit{center} = (2, -1)$$
$$\textit{radius} = 3$$

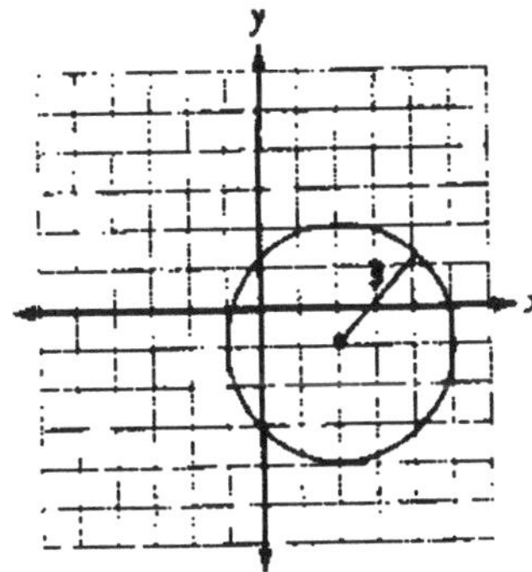

38.
$$x^2 + y^2 - 6x - y = -\frac{1}{4}$$
$$x^2 - 6x + 9 + y^2 - y + \frac{1}{4} = -\frac{1}{4} + 9 + \frac{1}{4}$$
$$(x - 3)^2 + \left(y - \frac{1}{2}\right)^2 = 3^2$$
$$\textit{center} = \left(3, \frac{1}{2}\right)$$
$$\textit{radius} = 3$$

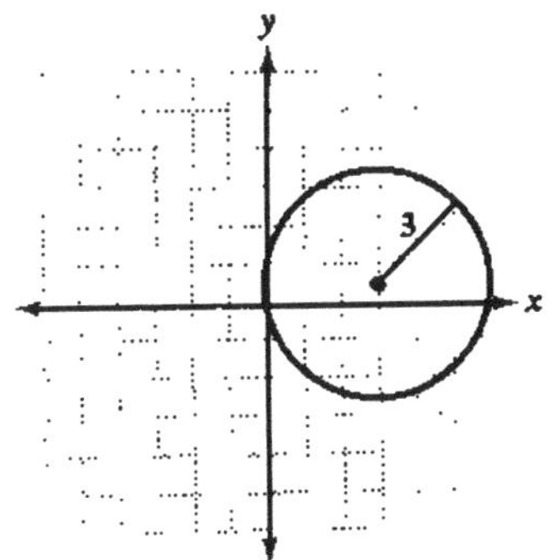

39.
$$\textit{Let } (0,0) = (x_1, y_1)$$
$$\textit{And } (3,4) = (x_2, y_2)$$
$$d = \sqrt{(3 - 0)^2 + (4 - 0)^2}$$
$$d = \sqrt{25}$$
$$d = 5$$
$$(x - 0)^2 + (y - 0)^2 = 5^2$$
$$x^2 + y^2 = 25$$

40.
$$\textit{Let } (0,0) = (x_1, y_1)$$
$$\textit{And } (-5,12) = (x_2, y_2)$$
$$d = \sqrt{(0 + 5)^2 + (0 - 12)^2}$$
$$d = \sqrt{169}$$
$$(x - 0)^2 + (y - 0)^2 = (\sqrt{169})^2$$
$$x^2 + y^2 = 169$$

42.
$$(x - 0)^2 + (y - 0)^2 = 4^2$$
$$x^2 + y^2 + 16$$

43.
$$\textit{Let } (-1,3) = (x_1, y_1)$$
$$\textit{And } (4,3) = (x_2, y_2)$$
$$d = \sqrt{(4 + 1)^2 + (3 - 3)^2}$$
$$d = \sqrt{25}$$
$$d = 5$$
$$(x + 1)^2 + (y - 3)^2 = 25$$

44.
$$\textit{Let } (2,5) = (x_1, y_1)$$
$$\textit{And } (-1,4) = (x_2, y_2)$$
$$d = \sqrt{(-1 - 2)^2 + (4 - 5)^2}$$
$$d = \sqrt{10}$$
$$(x - 2)^2 + (y - 5)^2 = 10$$

46. $x^2 + y^2 = 9$

$$x = \pm\sqrt{9 - y^2}$$

$x = \sqrt{9 - y^2}$ *corresponds to the right half*

$x = -\sqrt{9 - y^2}$ *corresponds to the left half.*

47.
$$C = 2\pi r$$
$$C = 2\pi(5)$$
$$C = 10\pi \textit{ meters}$$

48.
$$A = \pi r^2$$
$$A = \pi(5^2)$$
$$A = 25\pi m^2$$

50. $9x - 8y = 4$
$2x + 3y = 6$

$$D = \begin{vmatrix} 9 & -8 \\ 2 & 3 \end{vmatrix} = 9(3) - 2(-8) = 43$$

$$D_x = \begin{vmatrix} 4 & -8 \\ 6 & 3 \end{vmatrix} = 4(3) - 6(-8) = 60$$

$$D_y = \begin{vmatrix} 9 & 4 \\ 2 & 6 \end{vmatrix} = 9(6) - 2(4) = 46$$

$$x = \frac{D_x}{D} = \frac{60}{43}$$

$$y = \frac{D_y}{D} = \frac{46}{43}$$

51. $3x + 4y = 15$
$2x - 5z = -3$
$4y - 3z = 9$

$$D = \begin{vmatrix} 3 & 4 & 0 \\ 2 & 0 & -5 \\ 0 & 4 & -3 \end{vmatrix}$$

$$= 3\begin{vmatrix} 0 & -5 \\ 4 & -3 \end{vmatrix} - 4\begin{vmatrix} 2 & -5 \\ 0 & -3 \end{vmatrix} + 0\begin{vmatrix} 2 & 0 \\ 0 & 4 \end{vmatrix}$$

$= 3(20) - 4(-6) + 0(0)$
$= 84$

$$D_x = \begin{vmatrix} 15 & 4 & 0 \\ -3 & 0 & -5 \\ 9 & 4 & -3 \end{vmatrix}$$

$$= 15\begin{vmatrix} 0 & -5 \\ 4 & -3 \end{vmatrix} - 4\begin{vmatrix} -3 & -5 \\ 9 & -3 \end{vmatrix} + 0\begin{vmatrix} -3 & 0 \\ 9 & 4 \end{vmatrix}$$

$= 15(20) - 4(54) + 0(-12)$
$= 84$

$$D_y = \begin{vmatrix} 3 & 15 & 0 \\ 2 & -3 & -5 \\ 0 & 9 & -3 \end{vmatrix}$$

$$= 3\begin{vmatrix} -3 & -5 \\ 9 & -3 \end{vmatrix} - 15\begin{vmatrix} 2 & -5 \\ 0 & -3 \end{vmatrix} + 0\begin{vmatrix} 2 & -3 \\ 0 & 9 \end{vmatrix}$$

$= 3(54) - 15(-6) + 0(18)$
$= 252$

$$D_z = \begin{vmatrix} 3 & 4 & 15 \\ 2 & 0 & -3 \\ 0 & 4 & 9 \end{vmatrix}$$

$$= 3\begin{vmatrix} 0 & -3 \\ 4 & 9 \end{vmatrix} - 4\begin{vmatrix} 2 & -3 \\ 0 & 9 \end{vmatrix} + 15\begin{vmatrix} 2 & 0 \\ 0 & 4 \end{vmatrix}$$

$= 3(12) - 4(18) + 15(8)$
$= 84$

$$x = \frac{D_x}{D} = \frac{84}{84} = 1$$

$$y = \frac{D_y}{D} = \frac{252}{84} = 3$$

$$z = \frac{D_z}{D} = \frac{84}{84} = 1$$

52. $x + 3y = 5$
$6y + z = 12$
$x - 2z = -10$

$$D = \begin{vmatrix} 1 & 3 & 0 \\ 0 & 6 & 1 \\ 1 & 0 & -2 \end{vmatrix}$$

$$= 1\begin{vmatrix} 6 & 1 \\ 0 & -2 \end{vmatrix} - 3\begin{vmatrix} 0 & 1 \\ 1 & 0 \end{vmatrix} + 0\begin{vmatrix} 0 & 6 \\ 1 & -2 \end{vmatrix}$$

$= 1(-12) - 3(-1) + 0(-6)$
$= -9$

$$D_x = \begin{vmatrix} 5 & 3 & 0 \\ 12 & 6 & 1 \\ -10 & 0 & -2 \end{vmatrix}$$

$$= 5\begin{vmatrix} 6 & 1 \\ 0 & -2 \end{vmatrix} - 3\begin{vmatrix} 12 & 1 \\ -10 & -2 \end{vmatrix} + 0\begin{vmatrix} 12 & 6 \\ -10 & 0 \end{vmatrix}$$

$= 5(-12) - 3(-14) + 0(60)$
$= -18$

$$D_y = \begin{vmatrix} 1 & 5 & 0 \\ 0 & 12 & 1 \\ 1 & -10 & -2 \end{vmatrix}$$

$$= 1\begin{vmatrix} 12 & 1 \\ -10 & -2 \end{vmatrix} - 5\begin{vmatrix} 0 & 1 \\ 1 & -2 \end{vmatrix} + 0\begin{vmatrix} 0 & 12 \\ 1 & -10 \end{vmatrix}$$

$= 1(-14) - 5(-1) + 0(-12)$
$= -9$

$$D_z = \begin{vmatrix} 1 & 3 & 5 \\ 0 & 6 & 12 \\ 1 & 0 & -10 \end{vmatrix}$$

$$= 1\begin{vmatrix} 6 & 12 \\ 0 & -10 \end{vmatrix} - 3\begin{vmatrix} 0 & 12 \\ 1 & -10 \end{vmatrix} + 5\begin{vmatrix} 0 & 6 \\ 1 & 0 \end{vmatrix}$$

$$= 1(-60) - 3(-12) + 5(-6)$$
$$= -54$$

$$x = \frac{D_x}{D} = \frac{-18}{-9} = 2$$

$$y = \frac{D_y}{D} = \frac{-9}{-9} = 1$$

$$z = \frac{D_z}{D} = \frac{-54}{-9} = 6$$

54. *If the circle is tangent to the x-axis, the radius is* 2.

$$(x - 3)^2 + (y - 2)^2 = 2^2$$
$$(x - 3)^2 + (y - 2)^2 = 4$$

55. *If the circle is tangent to the vertical line x* = 4, *the radius is* 2.

$$(x - 2)^2 + (y - 3)^2 = 2^2$$
$$(x - 2)^2 + (y - 3)^2 = 4$$

56. *If the circle is tangent to the horizontal line y* = 6, *the radius is* 4.

$$(x - 3)^2 + (y - 2)^2 = 4^2$$
$$(x - 3)^2 + (y - 2)^2 = 16$$

58.
$$\begin{aligned} x^2 + y^2 - 8x + 6y &= 144 \\ x^2 - 8x + 16 + y^2 + 6y + 9 &= 144 + 16 + 9 \\ (x - 4)^2 + (y + 3)^2 &= 169 \\ (x - 4)^2 + [y - (-3)]^2 &= 13^2 \\ \textit{center} &= (4, -3) \\ \textit{radius} &= 13 \end{aligned}$$

$$\begin{aligned} 4^2 + (-3)^2 &= c^2 \\ 25 &= c^2 \\ 5 &= c \end{aligned}$$

*The distance from the original is* 5.

59.
$$\begin{aligned} x^2 + y^2 - 6x - 8y &= 144 \\ x^2 - 6x + 9 + y^2 - 8y + 16 &= 144 + 9 + 16 \\ (x - 3)^2 + (y - 4)^2 &= 169 \\ (x - 3)^2 + (y - 4)^2 &= 13^2 \\ \textit{center} &= (3, 4) \\ \textit{radius} &= 13 \end{aligned}$$

$$\begin{aligned} 3^2 + 4^2 &= c^2 \\ 25 &= c^2 \\ 5 &= c \end{aligned}$$

*The distance from the origin is* 5.

60.
$$\begin{aligned} x^2 + y^2 + 8x + 6y &= 144 \\ x^2 + 8x + 16 + y^2 + 6y + 9 &= 144 + 16 + 9 \\ (x + 4)^2 + (y + 3)^2 &= 169 \\ [x - (-4)]^2 + [y - (-3)]^2 &= 13^2 \\ \textit{center} &= (-4, -3) \\ \textit{radius} &= 13 \end{aligned}$$

$$\begin{aligned} (-4)^2 + (-3)^2 &= c^2 \\ 25 &= c^2 \\ 5 &= c \end{aligned}$$

*The distance from the origin is* 5.

## Section 9.6

2.

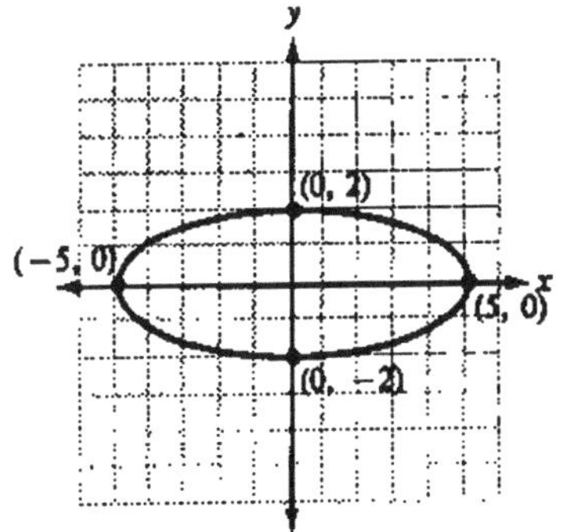


3.

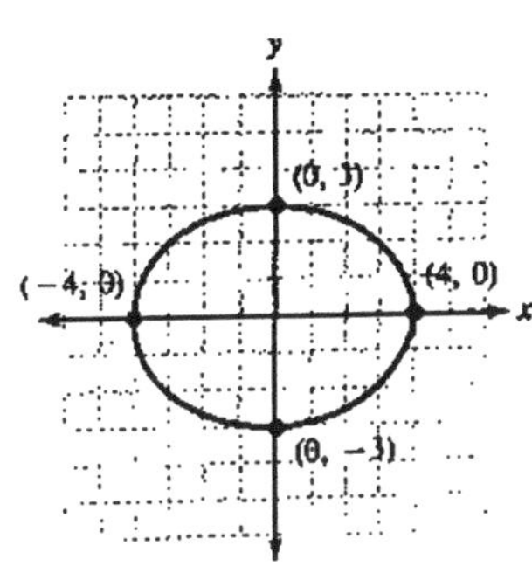

4.

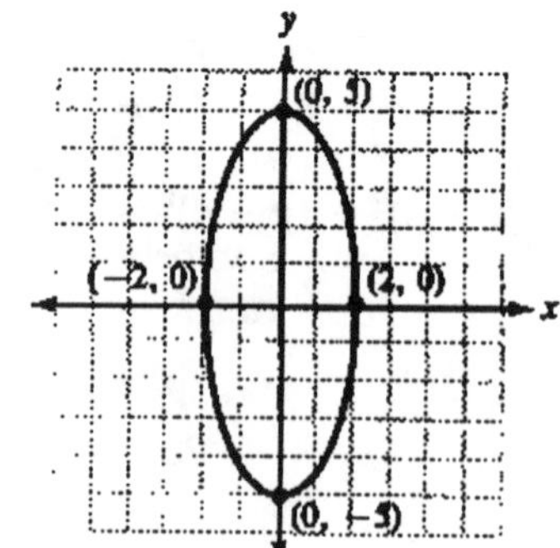


10.

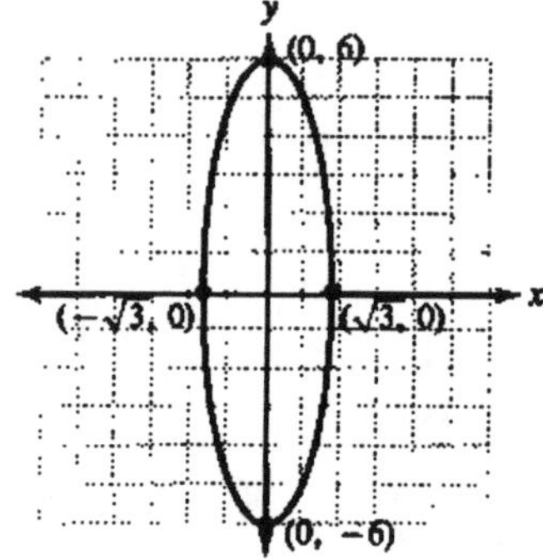


6.

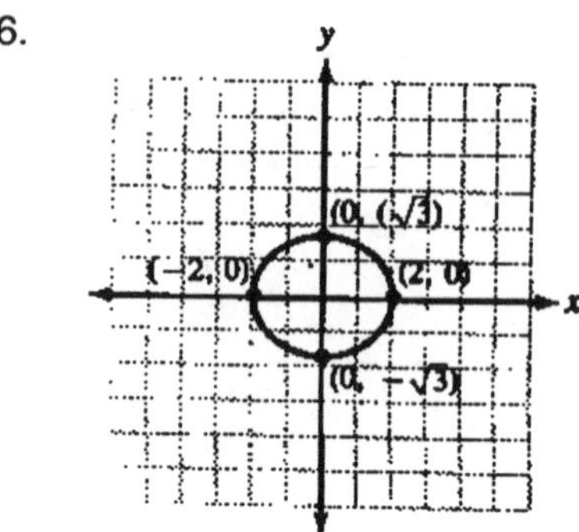


11.

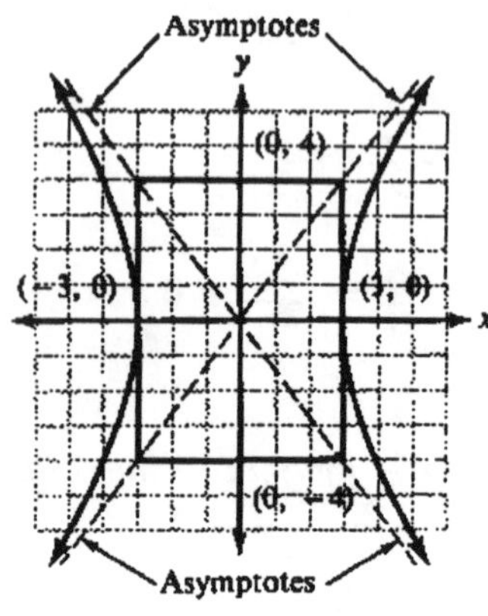


7.

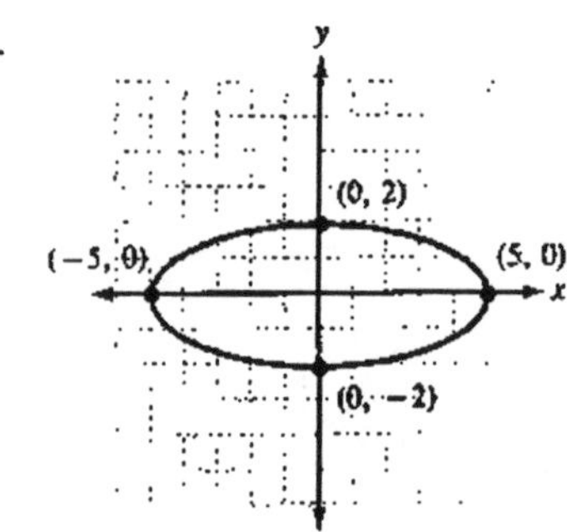


12.

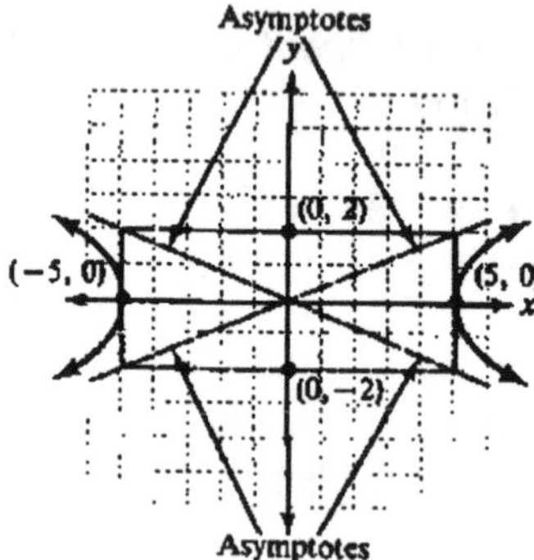


8.

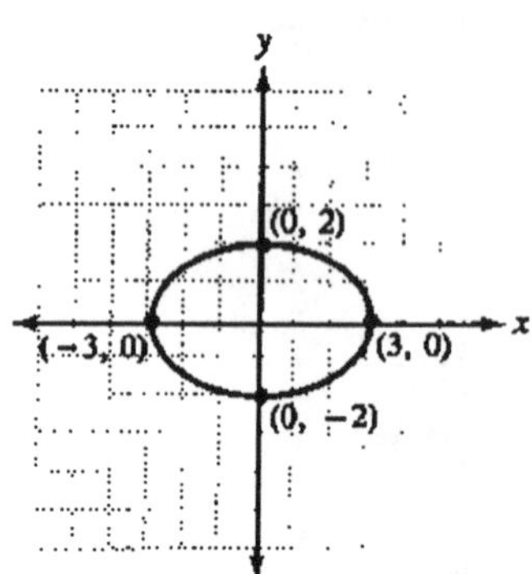


14.

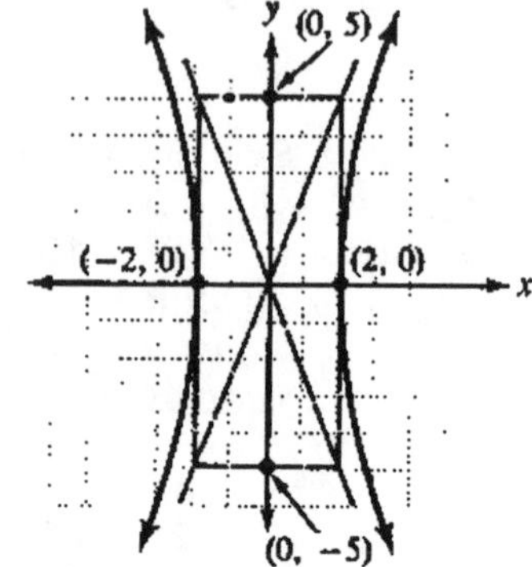

15.

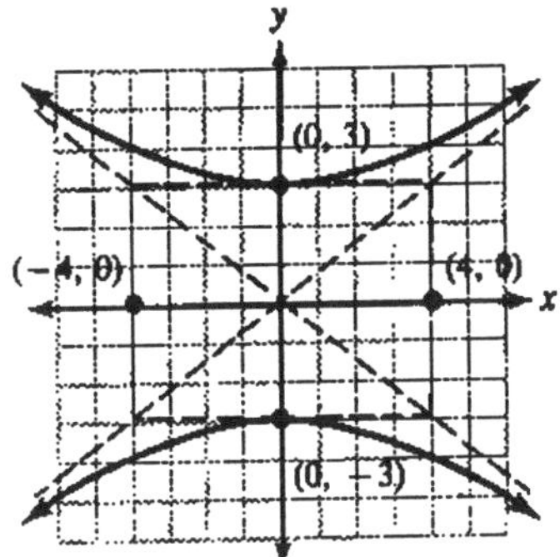


16.

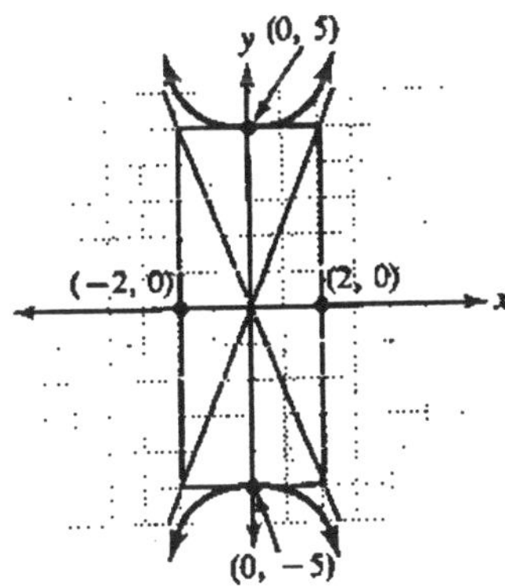


18.

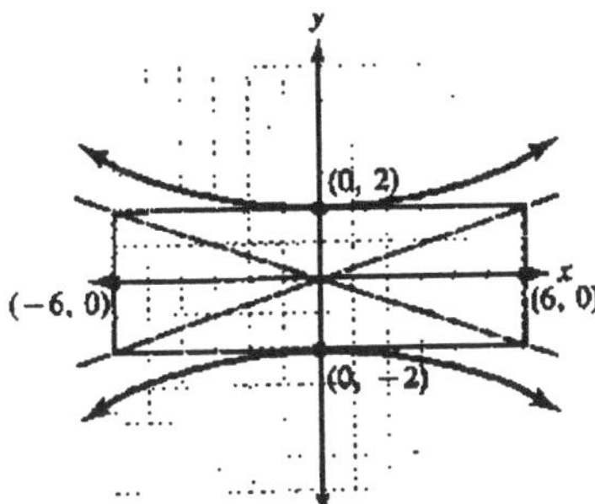


19.

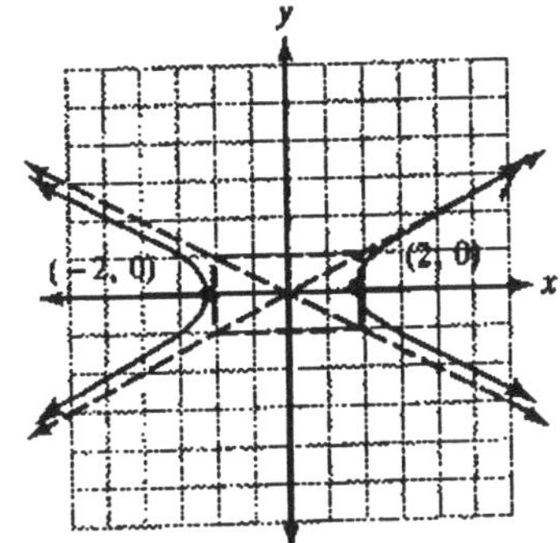


20. See instructor's textbook for graph.

22.

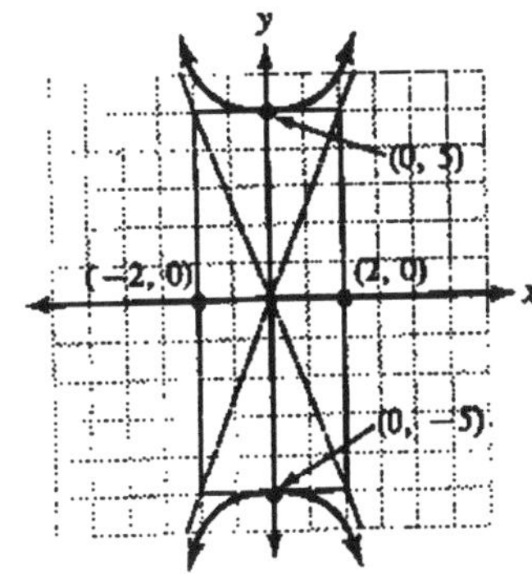


23. $.4x^2 + .9y^2 = 3.6$

$$\frac{x^2}{9} + \frac{y^2}{4} = 1$$

*x–intercepts* $= \pm 3$
*y–intercepts* $= \pm 2$

24. $1.6x^2 + .9y^2 = 14.4$

$$\frac{x^2}{9} + \frac{y^2}{16} = 1$$

*x–intercepts* $= \pm 3$
*y–intercepts* $= \pm 4$

26. $\frac{y^2}{.16} - \frac{x^2}{.25} = 1$

*y–intercepts* $= \pm .4$
*no x–intercepts*

27. $\frac{25x^2}{9} + \frac{25y^2}{4} = 1$

$$\frac{x^2}{\frac{9}{25}} + \frac{y^2}{\frac{4}{25}} = 1$$

*x–intercepts* $= \pm\frac{3}{5}$

*y–intercepts* $= \pm\frac{2}{5}$

28. $\dfrac{16x^2}{9} + \dfrac{16y^2}{25} = 1$

$$\frac{x^2}{\frac{9}{16}} + \frac{y^2}{\frac{25}{16}} = 1$$

$$x\text{-intercepts} = \pm\frac{3}{4}$$

$$y\text{-intercepts} = \pm\frac{5}{4}$$

30. $\dfrac{x^2}{4} + \dfrac{y^2}{25} = 1 \quad y = 3$

$$\frac{x^2}{4} + \frac{3^2}{25} = 1$$

$$\frac{x^2}{4} + \frac{9}{25} = 1$$

$$\frac{x^2}{4} = \frac{16}{25}$$

$$x^2 = \frac{64}{25}$$

$$x = \pm\frac{8}{5}$$

31. $16x^2 + 9y^2 = 144 \quad x = 1.8$

$$\frac{(1.8)^2}{9} + \frac{y^2}{16} = 1$$

$$\frac{y^2}{16} = 1 - .36$$

$$y^2 = (.64)(16)$$
$$y = \pm 3.2$$

32. $49x^2 + 4y^2 = 196$

$$\frac{(1.6)^2}{4} + \frac{y^2}{49} = 1$$

$$\frac{Y^2}{49} = 1 - .64$$

$$y^2 = (.36)(49)$$
$$y = \pm 4.2$$

34. $\dfrac{y^2}{25} - \dfrac{x^2}{4} = 1$

$$4y^2 - 25x^2 = 100$$

$$y^2 = \frac{25x^2}{4} + \frac{100}{4}$$

$$y^2 = \left(\frac{5}{2}x\right)^2 + \left(\frac{10}{2}\right)^2$$

$$y = \pm\frac{5}{2}x$$

35. $|-4| + |4| = 8$

36. $|3| + |-3| = 6$

38.

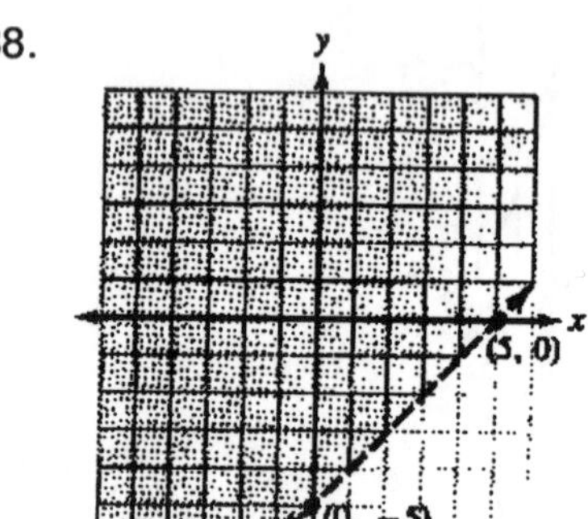


39.

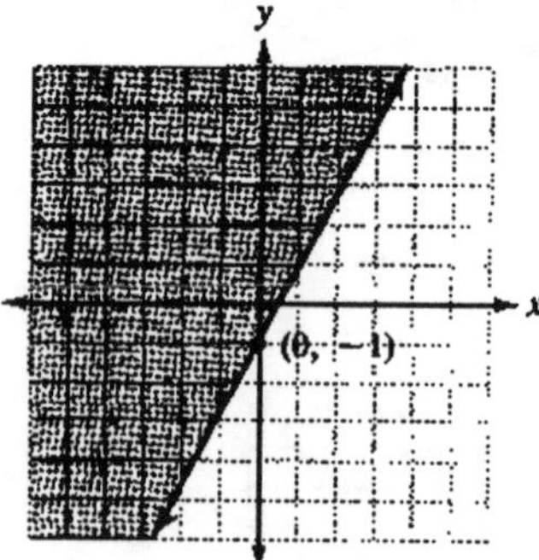

40.

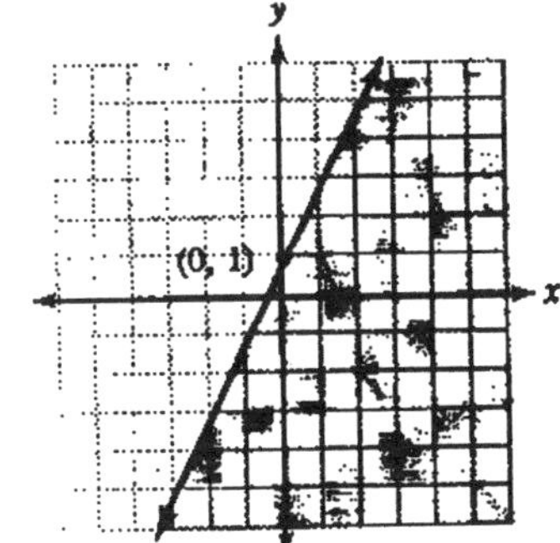


42.

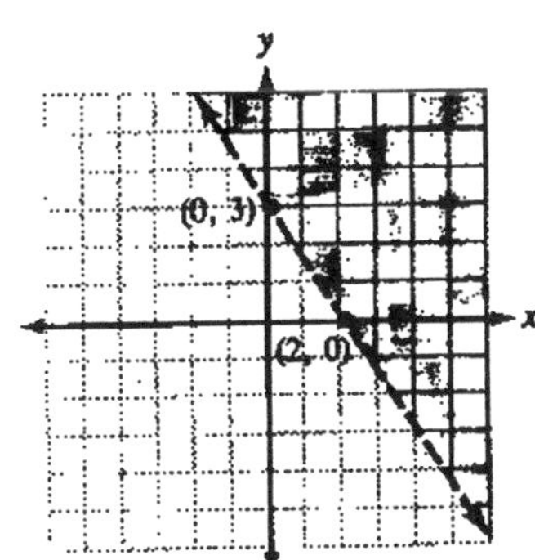


## Section 9.7

2.

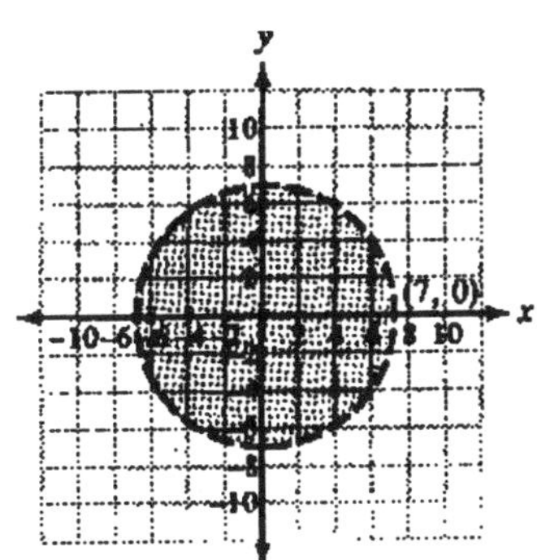


3.

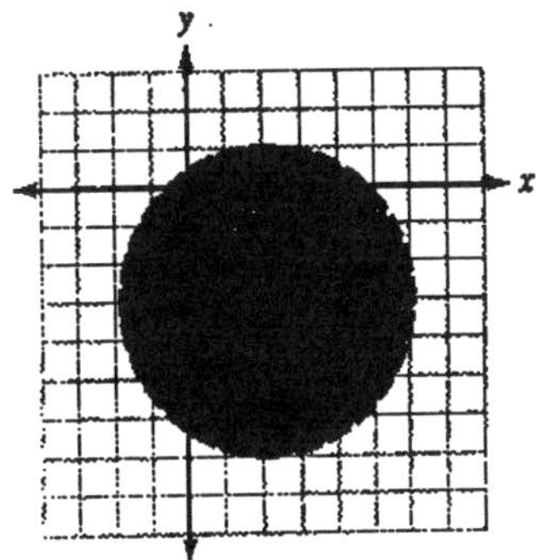


4.

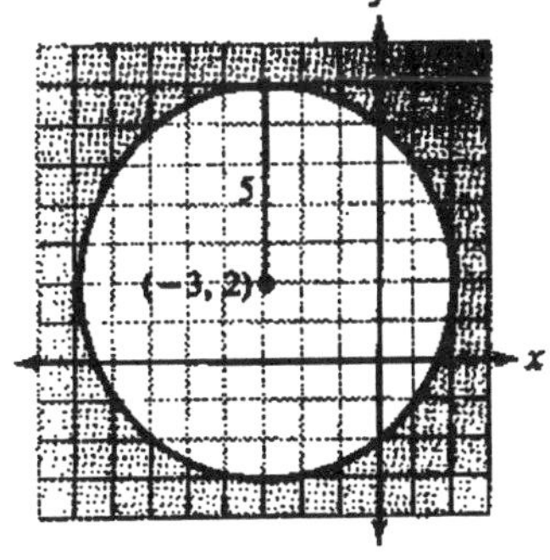


6.

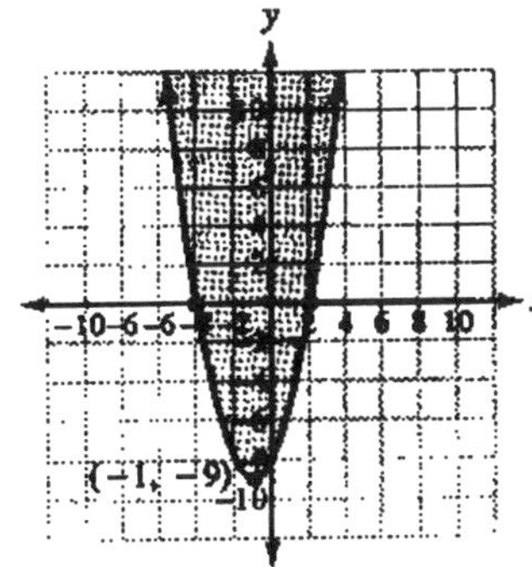


7.

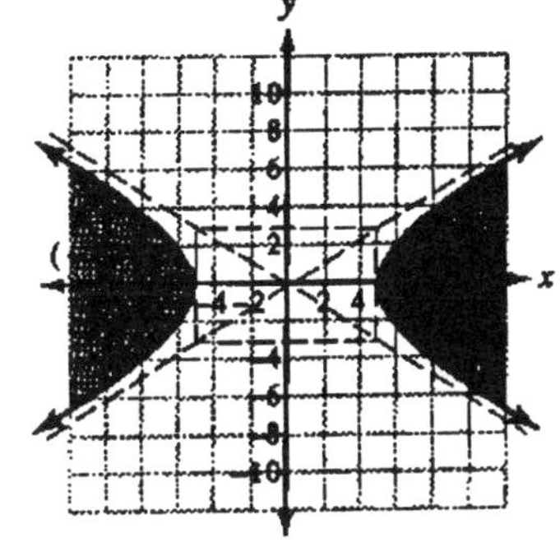

8.

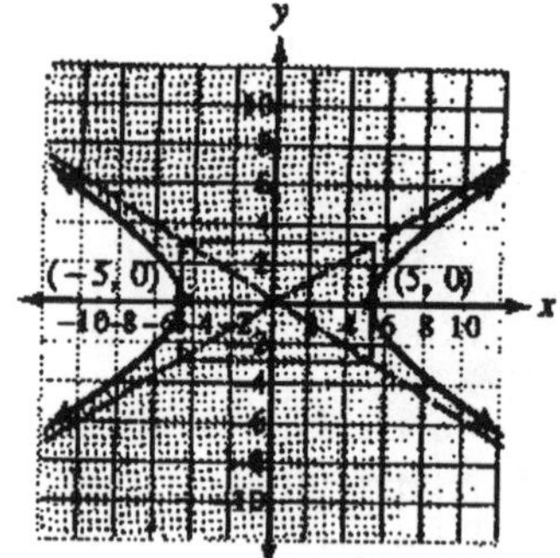


10.

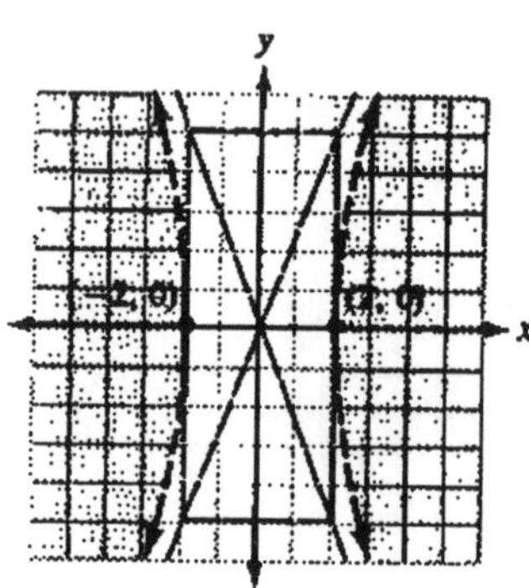


11.

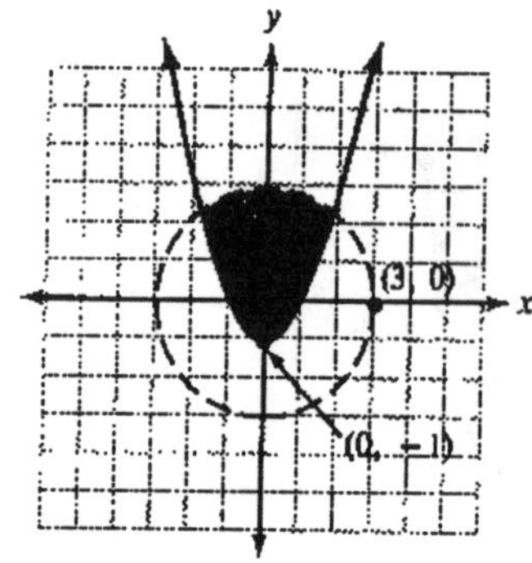


12.

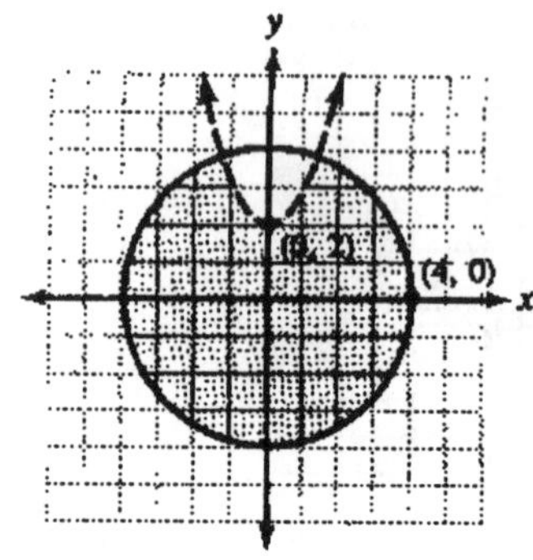


14.

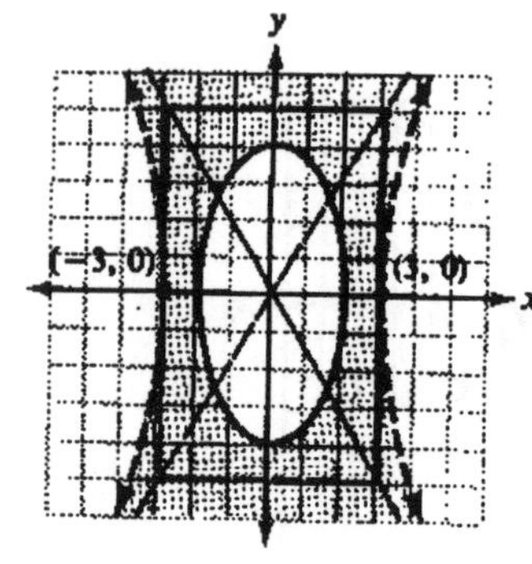


15. No intersection.

16.

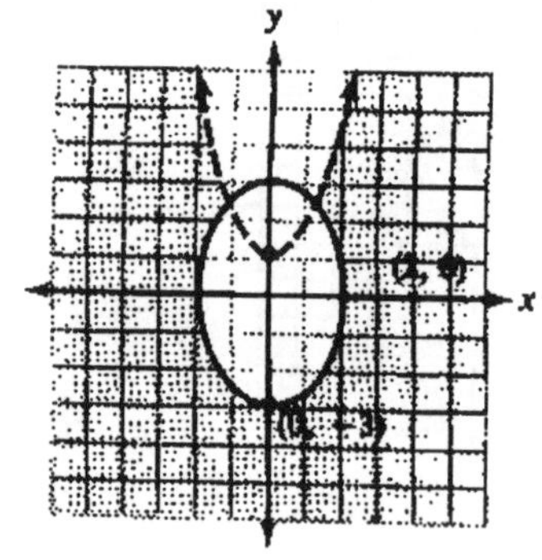


18.

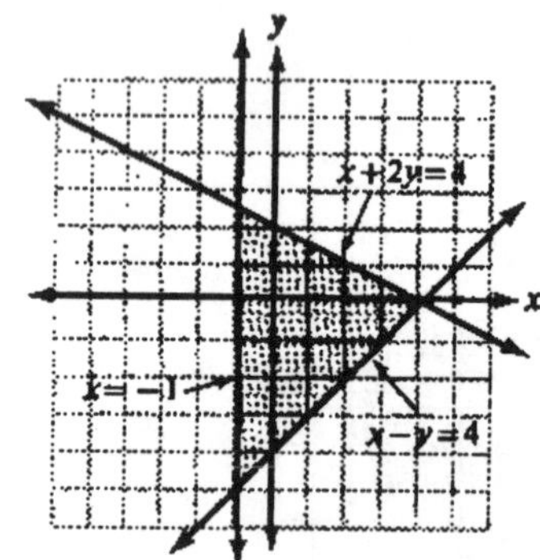


19.

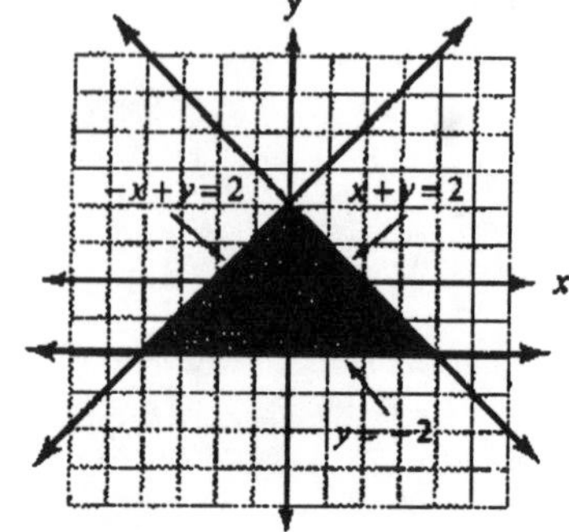

20.

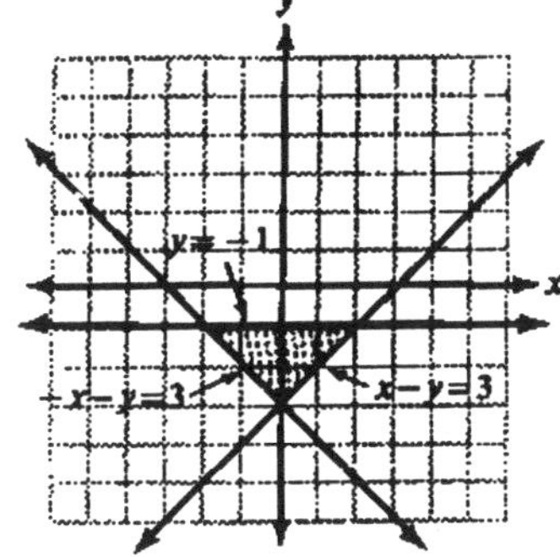


22.

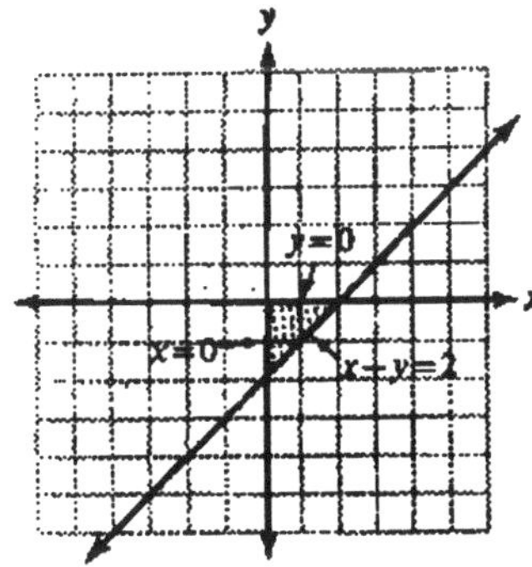


23.

$$x^2 + y^2 = 9$$

$$\begin{aligned} 2x + y &= 3 \\ y &= 3 - 2x \\ x^2 + (3 - 2x)^2 &= 9 \\ x^2 + 9 - 12x + 4x^2 &= 9 \\ 5x^2 - 12x &= 0 \\ x(5x - 12) &= 0 \\ x &= 0 \quad \textit{or} \end{aligned}$$

$$x = \frac{12}{5}$$

$$\begin{aligned} 2x + y &= 3 \\ 2(0) + y &= 3 \\ y &= 3 \quad \textit{or} \end{aligned}$$

$$\begin{aligned} 2x + y &= 3 \\ 2\left(\frac{12}{5}\right) + y &= 3 \end{aligned}$$

$$y = -\frac{9}{5}$$

$$(0,3), \left(\frac{12}{5}, -\frac{9}{5}\right)$$

24.

$$x^2 + y^2 = 9$$

$$\begin{aligned} x + 2y &= 3 \\ x &= 3 - 2y \\ (3 - 2y)^2 + y^2 &= 9 \\ 9 - 12y + 4y^2 + y^2 &= 9 \\ 5y^2 - 12y &= 0 \\ y(5y - 12) &= 0 \\ y &= 0 \quad \textit{or} \end{aligned}$$

$$y = \frac{12}{5}$$

$$\begin{aligned} x + 2y &= 3 \\ x + 2(0) &= 3 \\ x &= 3 \quad \textit{or} \end{aligned}$$

$$\begin{aligned} x + 2y &= 3 \\ x + 2\left(\frac{12}{5}\right) &= 3 \end{aligned}$$

$$x = -\frac{9}{5}$$

$$(3,0), \left(-\frac{9}{5}, \frac{12}{5}\right)$$

26.

$$x^2 + y^2 = 16$$

$$\begin{aligned} x - 2y &= 8 \\ x &= 2y + 8 \end{aligned}$$

$$\begin{aligned} (2y + 8)^2 + y^2 &= 16 \\ 4y^2 + 32y + 64 + y^2 &= 16 \\ 5y^2 + 32y + 48 &= 0 \\ (y + 4)(5y + 12) &= 0 \\ y &= -4 \quad \textit{or} \end{aligned}$$

$$y = -\frac{12}{5}$$

$$\begin{aligned} x - 2(-4) &= 8 \\ x &= 0 \quad \textit{or} \end{aligned}$$

$$x - 2\left(-\frac{12}{5}\right) = 8$$

$$x = \frac{16}{5}$$

$$(0, -4), \left(\frac{16}{5}, -\frac{12}{5}\right)$$

27.

$$\begin{aligned} x^2 + y^2 &= 25 \\ x^2 - y^2 &= 25 \\ \hline 2x^2 &= 50 \\ x^2 &= 25 \\ x &= \pm 5 \end{aligned}$$

$$x^2 + y^2 = 25$$
$$25 + y^2 = 25$$
$$y = 0$$

$(5,0), (-5,0)$

28. $x^2 + y^2 = 4$
$2x^2 - y^2 = 5$
$3x^2 = 9$
$x^2 = 3$
$x = \pm\sqrt{3}$
$(\pm\sqrt{3})^2 + y^2 = 4$
$y^2 = 1$
$y = \pm 1$

$(\sqrt{3}, 1), (\sqrt{3}, -1), (-\sqrt{3}, 1), (-\sqrt{3}, -1)$

30. $x^2 + y^2 = 4$
$x^2 = 4 - y^2$

$y = x^2 - 2$
$x^2 = y + 2$

$4 - y^2 = y + 2$
$y^2 + y - 2 = 0$
$(y + 2)(y - 1) = 0$
$y = -2$ *or*
$y = 1$

$y = -2$
$y = x^2 - 2$
$-2 = x^2 - 2$
$0 = x^2$
$0 = x$ *or*

$y = 1$
$y = x^2 - x$
$1 = x^2 - 2$
$3 = x^2$
$\pm\sqrt{3} = x$

$(0, -2), (\sqrt{3}, 1), (-\sqrt{3}, 1)$

31. $x^2 + y^2 = 16$
$x^2 = 16 - y^2$

$y = x^2 - 4$
$y + 4 = x^2$
$16 - y^2 = y + 4$
$y^2 + y - 12 = 0$
$(y + 4)(y - 3) = 0$
$y = -4$ *or*
$y = 3$

$y = -4$
$y = x^2 - 4$
$-4 = x^2 = 4$
$0 = x^2$
$o = x$ *or*

$y = 3$
$y = x^2 - 4$
$3 = x^2 - 4$
$7 = x^2$
$\pm\sqrt{7} = x$

$(0, -4), (\sqrt{7}, 3), (-\sqrt{7}, 3)$

32. $x^2 + y^2 = 1$
$x^2 = 1 - y^2$

$y = x^2 - 1$
$y + 1 = x^2$

$1 - y^2 = y + 1$
$y^2 + y = 0$
$y(y + 1) = 0$
$y = 0$ *or*
$y = -1$
$y = 0$
$y = x^2 - 1$
$0 = x^2 - 1$
$1 = x^2$
$\pm 1 = x$ *or*

$y = 1$
$y = x^2 - 1$
$-1 = x^2 - 1$
$0 = x^2$
$0 = x$

$(1,0), (-1,0), (0,-1)$

34.
$$4x + 2y = 10$$
$$y = x^2 - 10$$

$$4x + 2(x^2 - 10) = 10$$
$$2x^2 + 4x - 30 = 0$$
$$x^2 + 2x - 15 = 0$$
$$(x + 5)(x - 3) = 0$$
$x = -5$ *or*
$x = 3$

$x = -5$
$y = x^2 - 10$
$y = (-5)^2 - 10$
$y = 15$ *or*

$x = 3$
$y = x^2 - 10$
$y = 3^2 - 10$
$y = -1$

$(-5, 15), (3, -1)$

35.
$$y = x^2 + 2x - 3$$
$$y = -x + 1$$

$$x^2 + 2x - 3 = -x + 1$$
$$x^2 + 2x - 4 = 0$$
$$(x + 4)(x - 1) = 0$$
$x = -4$ *or*
$x = 1$

$x = -4$
$y = -x + 1$
$y = -(-4) + 1$
$y = 5$ *or*

$x = 1$
$y = -1 + 1$
$y = 0$

$(-4, 5), (1, 0)$

36.
$$y = -x^2 - 2x + 3$$
$$y = x - 1$$

$$-x^2 - 2x + 3 = x - 1$$
$$x^2 + 3x - 4 = 0$$
$$(x + 4)(x - 1) = 0$$
$x = -4$ *or*
$x = 1$

$x = -4$
$y = x - 1$
$y = -4 - 1$
$y = -5$ *or*

$x = 1$
$y = 1 - 1$
$y = 0$

$(-4, -5), (1, 0)$

38.
$$y = x^2 - 2x - 4$$
$$y = x - 4$$

$$x^2 - 2x - 4 = x - 4$$
$$x^2 - 3x = 0$$
$$x(x - 3) = 0$$
$x = 0$ *or*
$x = 3$

$x = 0$
$y = x - 4$
$y = 0 - 4$
$y = -4$ *or*

$x = 3$
$y = x - 4$
$y = 3 - 4$
$y = -1$

$(0, -4), (3, -1)$

39.
$$4x^2 - 9y^2 = 36$$
$$\underline{4x^2 + 9y^2 = 36}$$
$$8x^2 = 72$$
$$x^2 = 9$$
$$x = \pm 3$$
$$4(\pm 3)^2 - 9y^2 = 36$$
$$-9y^2 = 0$$
$$y = 0$$

$(3, 0), (-3, 0)$

40.
$$4x^2 + 25y^2 = 100$$
$$\underline{4x^2 - 25y^2 = 100}$$
$$8x^2 = 200$$
$$x^2 = 25$$
$$x = \pm 5$$
$$4(\pm 5)^2 + 25y^2 = 100$$
$$25y^2 = 0$$
$$y = 0$$

$(5, 0), (-5, 0)$

42.
$$x + y = 2$$
$$x = 2 - y$$
$$x^2 - y^2 = 4$$

$$(2 - y)^2 - y^2 = 4$$
$$4 - 4y + y^2 - y^2 = 4$$
$$-4y = 0$$
$$y = 0$$

$$x + y = 2$$
$$x + 0 = 2$$
$$x = 2$$

$(2, 0)$

43.
$$\begin{aligned} x^2 + y^2 &= 89 \\ x^2 - y^2 &= 39 \\ \hline 2x^2 &= 50 \\ x^2 &= 25 \\ x &= \pm 5 \end{aligned}$$

$$\begin{aligned} x^2 + y^2 &= 89 \\ (\pm 5)^2 + y^2 &= 89 \\ y^2 &= 64 \\ y &= \pm 8 \end{aligned}$$

(5,8) *or* (5,-8) *or* (-5,8) *or* (-5,-8)

44.
$$\begin{aligned} x^2 - y^2 &= 35 \\ x^2 + y^2 &= 37 \\ \hline 2x^2 &= 72 \\ x^2 &= 36 \\ x &= \pm 6 \end{aligned}$$

$$\begin{aligned} (\pm 6)^2 - y^2 &= 35 \\ -y^2 &= -1 \\ y^2 &= 1 \\ y &= \pm 1 \end{aligned}$$

(6,1) *or* (6,-1) *or* (-6,1) *or* (-6,-1)

46.
$$\begin{aligned} x^2 &= 2y^2 - 2 \\ x^2 + y^2 &= 25 \\ x^2 &= -y^2 + 25 \end{aligned}$$

$$\begin{aligned} 2y^2 - 2 &= -y^2 + 25 \\ 3y^2 - 27 &= 0 \\ 3(y^2 - 9) &= 0 \\ (y + 3)(y - 3) &= 0 \\ y &= -3 \quad or \\ y &= 3 \end{aligned}$$

$$\begin{aligned} y &= -3 \\ x^2 &= 2(-3)^2 - 2 \\ x^2 &= 16 \\ x &= \pm 4 \quad or \end{aligned}$$

$$\begin{aligned} y &= 3 \\ x^2 &= 2(3)^2 - 2 \\ x^2 &= 16 \\ x &= \pm 4 \end{aligned}$$

(4,-3) *or* (-4,-3) *or* (4,3) *or* (-4,3)

47.
$$\left[\begin{array}{cc|c} 3 & 4 & 7 \\ 1 & 2 & 1 \end{array}\right]$$

$$\left[\begin{array}{cc|c} 1 & \frac{4}{3} & \frac{7}{3} \\ 1 & 2 & 1 \end{array}\right]$$

$$\left[\begin{array}{cc|c} 1 & \frac{4}{3} & \frac{7}{3} \\ 0 & -\frac{2}{3} & \frac{4}{3} \end{array}\right]$$

$$\left[\begin{array}{cc|c} 1 & \frac{4}{3} & \frac{7}{3} \\ 0 & 1 & -2 \end{array}\right]$$

$$\begin{aligned} y &= -2 \\ 3x + 4(-2) &= 7 \\ x &= 5 \end{aligned}$$

(5,-2)

48.
$$\left[\begin{array}{cc|c} 6 & -1 & -25 \\ 2 & 3 & -5 \end{array}\right]$$

$$\left[\begin{array}{cc|c} 6 & -1 & -25 \\ 0 & -10 & -10 \end{array}\right]$$

$$\left[\begin{array}{cc|c} 1 & -\frac{1}{6} & -\frac{25}{6} \\ 0 & 1 & 1 \end{array}\right]$$

$$y = 1$$

$$x - \frac{1}{6}(1) = -\frac{25}{6}$$

$$x = -\frac{24}{6}$$

$$x = -4$$

(-4,1)

50. $\left[\begin{array}{ccc|c} 1 & 1 & 1 & 6 \\ 7 & -1 & 2 & 7 \\ 2 & -1 & -1 & 0 \end{array}\right]$

$\left[\begin{array}{ccc|c} 1 & 1 & 1 & 6 \\ 0 & 2 & -1 & -1 \\ 0 & -3 & -3 & -12 \end{array}\right]$

$\left[\begin{array}{ccc|c} 1 & 1 & 1 & 6 \\ 0 & 1 & -\frac{1}{2} & -\frac{1}{2} \\ 0 & 0 & -\frac{9}{2} & -\frac{27}{2} \end{array}\right]$

$\left[\begin{array}{ccc|c} 1 & 1 & 1 & 6 \\ 0 & 1 & -\frac{1}{2} & -\frac{1}{2} \\ 0 & 0 & 1 & 3 \end{array}\right]$

$y = 3$

$y - \frac{1}{2}(3) = -\frac{1}{2}$

$y = 1$

$x + 1 + 3 = 6$

$x = 2$

$(2, 1, 3)$

51. $\left[\begin{array}{ccc|c} 3 & 4 & 0 & 15 \\ 2 & 0 & -5 & -3 \\ 0 & 4 & -3 & 9 \end{array}\right]$

$\left[\begin{array}{ccc|c} 1 & 4 & 5 & 18 \\ 2 & 0 & -5 & -3 \\ 0 & 4 & -3 & 9 \end{array}\right]$

$\left[\begin{array}{ccc|c} 1 & 4 & 5 & 21 \\ 0 & -8 & -15 & -39 \\ 0 & 4 & -3 & 9 \end{array}\right]$

$\left[\begin{array}{ccc|c} 1 & 4 & 5 & 21 \\ 0 & -8 & -15 & -39 \\ 0 & 0 & -21 & -21 \end{array}\right]$

$\left[\begin{array}{ccc|c} 1 & 4 & 5 & 21 \\ 0 & 1 & \frac{15}{8} & \frac{39}{8} \\ 0 & 0 & 1 & 1 \end{array}\right]$

$z = 1$

$y + \frac{15}{8}(1) = \frac{39}{8}$

$y = 3$

$3x + 4(3) = 15$

$3x = 3$

$x = 1$

$(1, 3, 1)$

52. $\left[\begin{array}{ccc|c} 1 & 3 & 0 & 5 \\ 0 & 6 & 1 & 12 \\ 1 & 0 & -2 & -10 \end{array}\right]$

$\left[\begin{array}{ccc|c} 1 & 3 & 0 & 5 \\ 0 & 6 & 1 & 12 \\ 0 & 3 & 2 & 15 \end{array}\right]$

$\left[\begin{array}{ccc|c} 1 & 3 & 0 & 5 \\ 0 & 6 & 1 & 12 \\ 0 & 0 & -3 & -18 \end{array}\right]$

$\left[\begin{array}{ccc|c} 1 & 3 & 0 & 5 \\ 0 & 1 & \frac{1}{6} & 2 \\ 0 & 0 & 1 & 6 \end{array}\right]$

$z = 6$

$y + \frac{1}{6}(6) = 2$

$y = 1$

$x + 3(1) = 5$

$x = 2$

$(2, 1, 6)$

# CHAPTER 10

## Section 10.1

2. $\log_3 9 = 2$

3. $\log_5 125 = 3$

4. $\log_4 16 = 2$

6. $\log_{10} 0.001 = -3$

7. $\log_2 \frac{1}{32} = -5$

8. $\log_4 \frac{1}{16} = -2$

10. $\log_{1/3} 9 = -2$

11. $\log_3 27 = 3$

12. $\log_3 81 = 4$

14. $2^3 = 8$

15. $2^6 = 64$

16. $2^5 = 32$

18. $9^1 = 9$

19. $10^{-3} = 0.001$

20. $10^{-4} = 0.0001$

22. $7^2 = 49$

23. $5^{-2} = \frac{1}{25}$

24. $3^{-4} = \frac{1}{81}$

26. $4^3 = x$
$64 = x$

27. $5^{-3} = x$
$\frac{1}{125} = x$

28. $2^{-4} = x$
$\frac{1}{16} = x$

30. $3^x = 27$
$3^x = 3^3$
$x = 3$

31. $8^x = 2$
$2^{3x} = 2$
$3x = 1$
$x = \frac{1}{3}$

32. $25^x = 5$
$5^{2x} = 5$
$2x = 1$
$x = \frac{1}{2}$

34. $x^4 = 16$
$x^4 = 2^4$
$x = 2$

35. $x^3 = 5$
$x^3 = \left(5^{1/3}\right)^3$
$x = \sqrt[3]{5}$

36. $x^2 = 8$
$x^2 = \left(\sqrt{8}\right)^2$
$x = \sqrt{8}$ *or* $2\sqrt{2}$ *or* $2^{3/2}$

38.

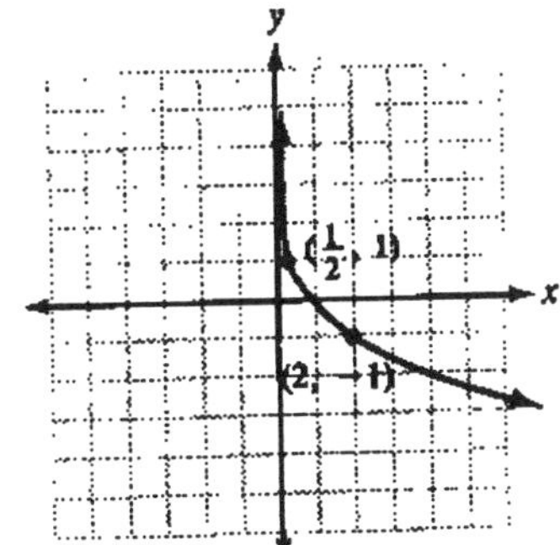


39.

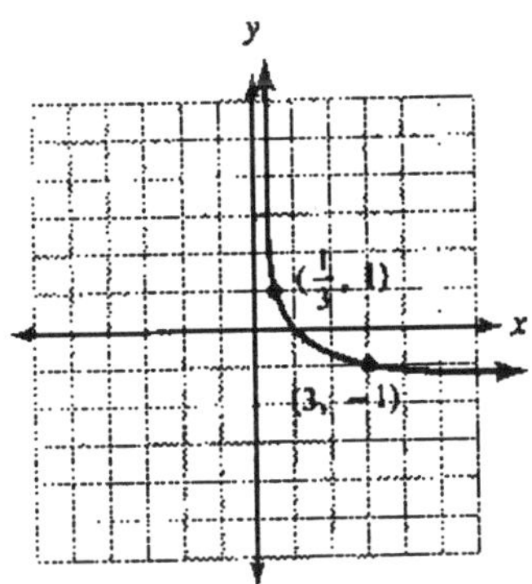


40.

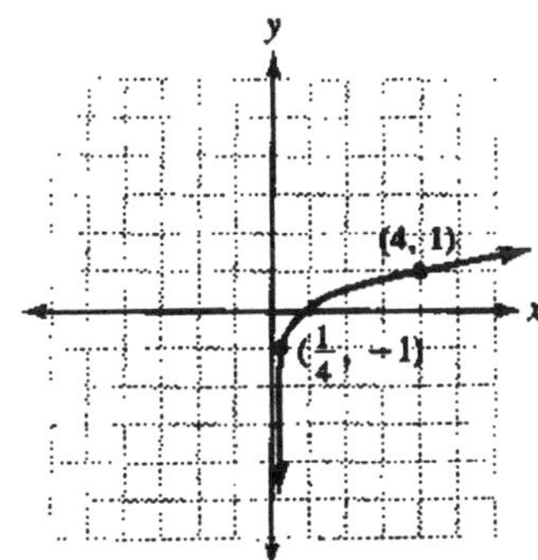


42.

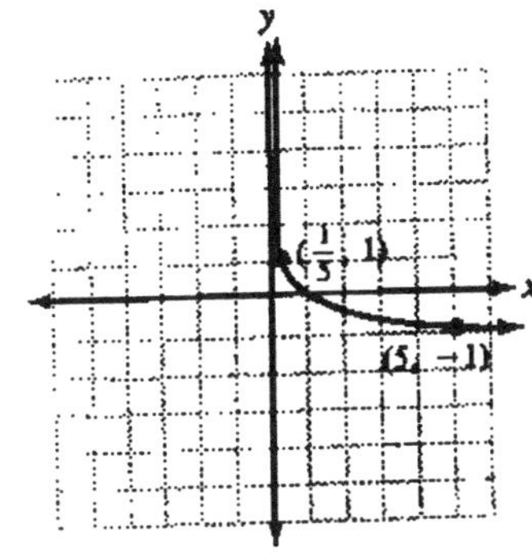


43.

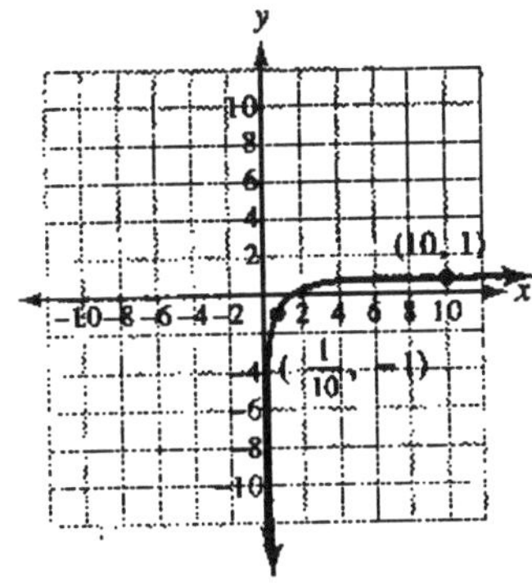


44.

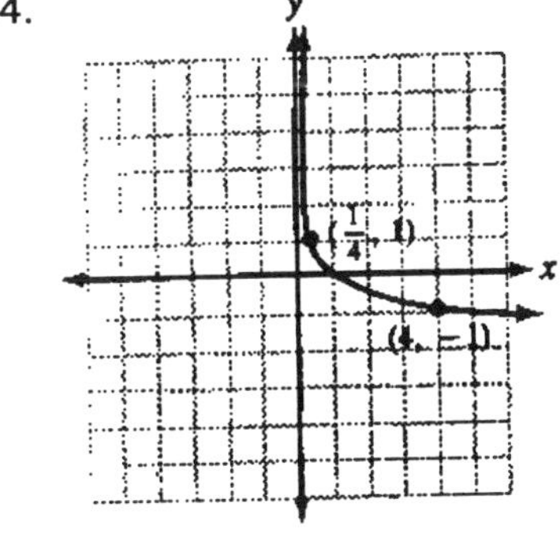


46. $\log_3 9 = \log_3 3^2 = 2$

47. $\log_{25} 125 = \log_{25} 25^{3/2} = \dfrac{3}{2}$

48. $\log_9 27 = \log_9 9^{3/2} = \dfrac{3}{2}$

50. $\log_{10} 10{,}000 = \log_{10} 10^4 = 4$

51. $\log_3 3 = \log_3 3^1 = 1$

52. $\log_4 4 = \log_4 4^1 = 1$

54. $\log_{10} 1 = \log_{10} 10^0 = 0$

55. $\log_3 (\log_6 6) = \log_3 1$
$= \log_3 3^0$
$= 0$

56. $\log_5 (\log_3 3) = \log_5 1$
$= \log_5 5^{\circ}$
$= 0$

58. $\log_4[\log_3(\log_2 8)] = \log_4[\log_3(\log_2 2^3)]$
$= \log_4[\log_3 3]$
$= \log_4 1$
$= \log_4 4^0$
$= 0$

59. $pH = -\log_{10}[H^+]$, $[H^+] = 10^{-7}$
$pH = -\log_{10} 10^{-7}$
$pH = -(-7)$
$pH = 7$

60. $pH = -\log_{10}[H^+]$, $[H^+] = 10^{-3}$
$pH = -\log_{10}[10^{-3}]$
$pH = -(-3)$
$pH = 3$

62. $pH = -\log_{10}[H^+]$, $pH = 4$
$4 = -\log_{10}[H^+]$
$H^+ = 10^{-4}$

63. $m = \log_{10} T$, $T = 100$
$m = \log_{10} 100$
$m = \log_{10} 10^2$
$m = 2$

64. $m = \log_{10} T$, $T = 100{,}000$
$m = \log_{10} 100{,}000$
$m = \log_{10} 10^5$
$m = 5$

66. $m = \log_{10} T$, $m = 6$
$6 = \log_{10} T$
$T = 10^6 = 1{,}000{,}000$
*The earthquake that measures* 6 *on the Richter scale has a shockwave* 1,000,000 *times greater than the smallest shockwave measurable on a seismograph.*

67. *Domain* = {1,3,4}
*Range* = {2,4,1}
*A function*

68. *Domain* = {−2,2}
*Range* = {6,8,3}
*Not a function*

70. $$y = \frac{-4}{x^2 + 2x - 35}$$
$x^2 + 2x - 35 = 0$
$(x + 7)(x - 5) = 0$
$x = -7$ *or*
$x = 5$
*Domain* $= \{x \mid x \neq -7, x \neq 5\}$

71. $f(0) = 2(0)^2 - 18$
$= -18$

72. $f(0) = 2(0)^2 - 18$
$= -18$
$g[-18] = 2(-18) - 6$
$= -42$
$g[f(0)] = -42$

74. $$\frac{g(x)}{f(x)} = \frac{2x - 6}{2x^2 - 18}$$
$$= \frac{2(x - 3)}{2(x + 3)(x - 3)}$$
$$= \frac{1}{x + 3} \qquad x \neq 3$$

75. $$y = \frac{6}{x + 1}$$
$x \neq -1$

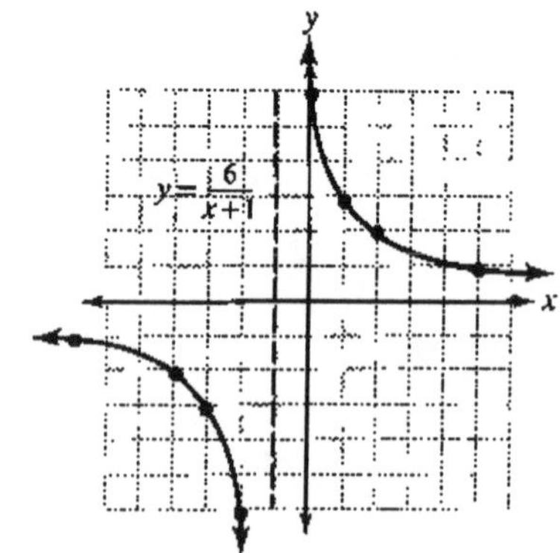

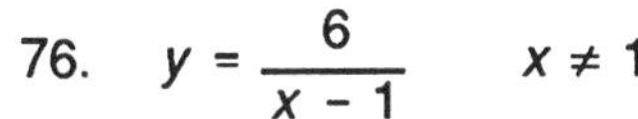

76. $y = \dfrac{6}{x - 1} \qquad x \neq 1$

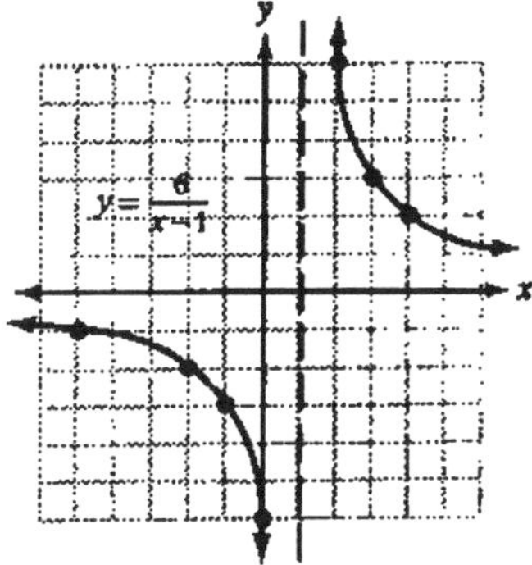


## Section 10.2

2. $\log_2 5x = \log_2 5 + \log_2 x$

3. $\log_6 \dfrac{5}{x} = \log_6 5 - \log_6 x$

4. $\log_3 \dfrac{x}{5} = \log_3 x - \log_3 5$

6. $\log_7 y^3 = 3 \log_7 y$

7. $\log_9 \sqrt[3]{z} = \dfrac{1}{3} \log_9 z$

8. $\log_8 \sqrt{z} = \dfrac{1}{2} \log_8 z$

10. $\log_{10} x^2 y^4$
$= 2 \log_{10} x + 4 \log_{10} y$

11. $\log_5 \sqrt{x} \cdot y^4$
$= \dfrac{1}{2} \log_5 x + 4 \log_5 y$

12. $\log_8 \sqrt[3]{xy^6} = \dfrac{1}{3} \log_8 xy^6$
$= \dfrac{1}{3}(\log_8 x + 6 \log_8 y)$
$= \dfrac{1}{3} \log_8 x + 2 \log_8 y$

14. $\log_b \dfrac{3x}{y} = \log_b 3 + \log_b x - \log_b y$

15. $\log_{10} \dfrac{4}{xy}$
$= \log_{10} 4 - \log_{10} x - \log_{10} y$

16. $\log_{10} \dfrac{5}{4y}$
$= \log_{10} 5 - \log_{10} 4 - \log_{10} y$

18. $\log_{10} \dfrac{\sqrt{x} \cdot y}{z^3}$
$= \dfrac{1}{2} \log_{10} x + \log_{10} y - 3 \log_{10} z$

19. $\log_{10} \dfrac{x^3 \cdot \sqrt{y}}{z^4}$
$= 3 \log_{10} x + \dfrac{1}{2} \log_{10} y - 4 \log_{10} z$

20. $\log_{10} \dfrac{x^4 \cdot \sqrt[3]{y}}{\sqrt{z}}$
$= 4 \log_{10} x + \dfrac{1}{3} \log_{10} y - \dfrac{1}{2} \log_{10} z$

22. $\log_b \sqrt[4]{\dfrac{x^4 y^3}{z^5}} = \log_b \left(\dfrac{x^4 y^3}{z^5}\right)^{1/4}$
$= \dfrac{1}{4}(4 \log_b x + 3 \log_b y - 5 \log_b z)$
$= \log_b x + \dfrac{3}{4} \log_b y - \dfrac{5}{4} \log_b z$

23. $\log_b x + \log_b z = \log_b xz$

24. $\log_b x - \log_b z = \log_b \dfrac{x}{z}$

26. $4 \log_2 x + 5 \log_2 y$
$= \log_2 x^4 + \log_2 y^5$
$= \log_2 x^4 y^5$

27. $\dfrac{1}{2} \log_{10} x + \dfrac{1}{3} \log_{10} y$
$= \log_{10} \sqrt{x} + \log_{10} \sqrt[3]{y}$
$= \log_{10} \sqrt{x}\, \sqrt[3]{y}$

28. $\frac{1}{3}\log_{10} x - \frac{1}{4}\log_{10} y$

$= \log_{10} \sqrt[3]{x} - \log_{10} \sqrt[4]{y}$

$= \log_{10} \frac{\sqrt[3]{x}}{\sqrt[4]{y}}$

30. $2 \log_3 x + 3 \log_3 y - \log_3 z$

$= \log_3 x^2 + \log_3 y^3 - \log_3 z$

$= \log_3 \frac{x^2y^3}{z}$

31. $\frac{1}{2}\log_2 x - 3 \log_2 y - 4 \log_2 z$

$= \log_2 \sqrt{x} - \log_2 y^3 + \log_2 z^4$

$= \log_2 \frac{\sqrt{x}}{y^3 z^4}$

32. $3 \log_{10} x - \log_{10} y - \log_{10} z$

$= \log_{10} x^3 - \log_{10} y - \log_{10} z$

$= \log_{10} \frac{x^3}{yz}$

34. $3 \log_{10} x - \frac{4}{3}\log_{10} y - 5 \log_{10} z$

$= \log_{10} x^3 - \log_{10} y^{4/3} - \log_{10} z^5$

$= \log_{10} \frac{x^3}{y^{4/3} z^5}$

35. $\log_2 x + \log_2 3 = 1$

$\log_2 x(3) = 1$

$2^1 = 3x$

$\frac{2}{3} = x$

36. $\log_3 x + \log_3 3 = 1$

$\log_3 x(3) = 1$

$3^1 = 3x$

$1 = x$

38. $\log_3 x + \log_3 2 = 2$

$\log_3 x(2) = 2$

$3^2 = 2x$

$9 = 2x$

$\frac{9}{2} = x$

39. $\log_3 x + \log_3(x - 2) = 1$

$\log_3 x(x - 2) = 1$

$3^1 = x(x - 2)$

$x^2 - 2x - 3 = 0$

$(x - 3)(x + 1) = 0$

$x = 3$ *or*

$x = -1$

*Possible solutions:* $-1$ *and* 3; *only* 3 *checks.*

40. $\log_6 x + \log_6 (x - 1) = 1$

$\log_6 x(x - 1) = 1$

$6^1 = x(x - 1)$

$x^2 - x - 6 = 0$

$(x + 2)(x - 3) = 0$

$x = -2$ *or*

$x = 3$

*Possible solutions* $-2$ *and* 3; *only* 3 *checks.*

42. $\log_4(x - 2) - \log_4(x + 1) = 1$

$\log_4 \frac{x - 2}{x + 1} = 1$

$4^1 = \frac{x - 2}{x + 1}$

$4x + 4 = x - 2$

$x = -2$

*Possible solution* $-2$, *which does not check;* $\varnothing$

43. $\log_2 x + \log_2(x - 2) = 3$

$\log_2 x(x - 2) = 3$

$2^3 = x(x - 2)$

$x^2 - 2x - 8 = 0$

$(x + 2)(x - 4) = 0$

$x = -2$ *or*

$x = 4$

*Possible solutions* $-2$ *and* 4; *only* 4 *checks.*

44. $\log_4 x + \log_4(x + 6) = 2$
$\log_4 x(x + 6) = 2$
$4^2 = x(x + 6)$
$x^2 + 6x - 16 = 0$
$(x + 8)(x - 2) = 0$
$x = -8$ *or*

$x = 2$
*Possible solutions* $-8$ *and* $2$;
*only* $2$ *checks.*

46. $\log_{27} x + \log_{27}(x + 8) = \frac{2}{3}$

$\log_{27}[x(x + 8)] = \frac{2}{3}$
$27^{2/3} = x(x + 8)$

$x^2 + 8x - 9 = 0$
$(x + 9)(x - 1) = 0$
$x = -9$ *or*

$x = 1$
*Possible solutions* $-9$ *and* $1$;
*only* $1$ *checks.*

47. $\log_5 \sqrt{x} + \log_5\sqrt{6x + 5} = 1$
$\log_5 \sqrt{x}\ \sqrt{6x + 5} = 1$
$5^1 = \sqrt{x}\ \sqrt{6x + 5}$
$25 = x(6x + 5)$
$6x^2 + 5x - 25 = 0$
$(2x + 5)(3x - 5) = 0$

$x = -\frac{5}{2}$ *or*

$x = \frac{5}{3}$

*Possible solutions* $-\frac{5}{2}$ *and* $\frac{5}{3}$;

*only* $\frac{5}{3}$ *checks.*

48. $\log_2 \sqrt{x} + \log_2 \sqrt{6x + 5} = 1$
$\log_2 \sqrt{x}\ \sqrt{6x + 5} = 1$
$2^1 = \sqrt{x}\ \sqrt{6x + 5}$
$4 = x(6x + 5)$
$6x^2 + 5x - 4 = 0$
$(3x + 4)(2x - 1) = 0$
$= -\frac{4}{3}$ *or*

$x = \frac{1}{2}$

*Possible solutions* $-\frac{4}{3}$ *and* $\frac{1}{2}$;

*only* $\frac{1}{2}$ *checks.*

50. $N = \log_{10} \frac{P_1}{P_2},\ P_1 = 100,\ P_2 = 1$

$N = \log_{10} \frac{100}{1}$

$N = \log_{10} 10^2$
$10^N = 10^2$
$N = 2$

$N = 10(\log_{10}P_1 - \log_{10}P_2),\ P_1 = 100,\ P_2 = 1$

$N = \log_{10}(\log_{10}100 - \log_{10}1)$

$N = \log_{10}\left(\frac{100}{1}\right)$

$N = \log_{10}10^2$
$10^N = 10^2$
$N = 2$

51. $\log_{10}(8.43 \times 10^2)$
$= \log_{108}8.43 + 2 \log_{10} 10$
$= \log_{10} 8.43 + 2(1)$
$= 2 + \log_{10} 8.43$

52. $\log_{10}(2.76 \times 10^3)$
$= \log_{10} 2.76 + 3 \log_{10} 10$
$= \log_{10} 2.76 + 3(1)$
$= 3 + \log_{10} 2.76$

54. $\log_{10} A = \log_{10} 3(2)^{t/5600}$
$\log_{10} A = \log_{10} 3 + t/5600 \log_{10} 2$

55. $f(x) = 2x - 3$

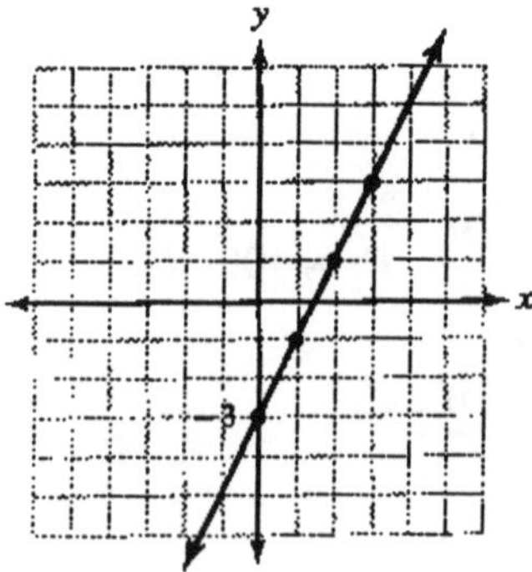


56. $f(x) = 3$

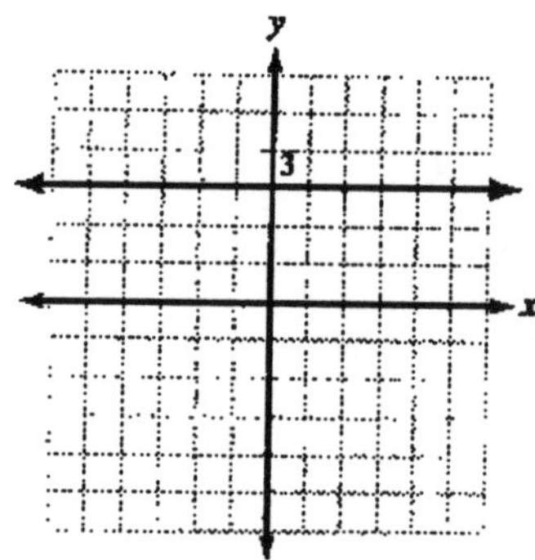


58. $f(x) = 3^x$

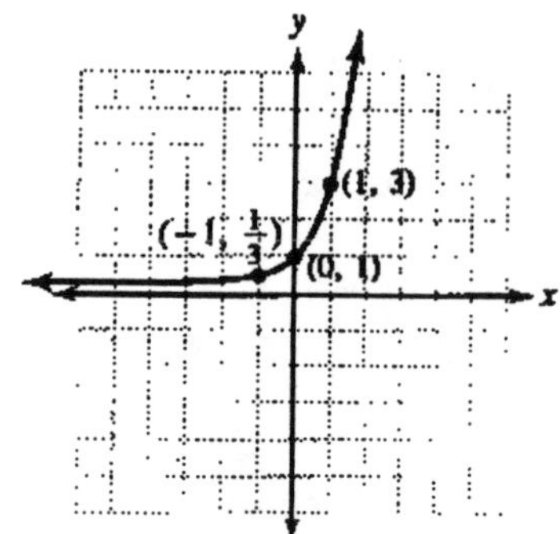


59. $0 = 4x - 3$

$\frac{3}{4} = x$

60. $0 = -3x + 1$

$\frac{1}{3} = x$

62. $0 = x^2 - 8x - 1$

$$x = \frac{-(-8) \pm \sqrt{(-8)^2 - 4(1)(-1)}}{2(1)}$$

$$= \frac{8 \pm \sqrt{68}}{2}$$

$$= \frac{8 \pm 2\sqrt{17}}{2}$$

$$= 4 \pm \sqrt{17}$$

63. $f(x) = 2x + 3$
$y = 2x + 3$
$x = 2y + 3$

$\frac{x - 3}{2} = y$

$f^{-1}(x) = \frac{x - 3}{2}$

64. $f(x) = 3x - 2$
$y = 3x - 2$
$x = 3y - 2$

$\frac{x + 2}{3} = y$

$f^{-1}(x) = \frac{x + 2}{3}$

66. $f(x) = x^2 + 2$
$y = x^2 + 2$
$x = y^2 + 2$
$\pm\sqrt{x - 2} = y$

67. $f(x) = \frac{x - 3}{5}$
$y = \frac{x - 3}{5}$
$x = \frac{y - 3}{5}$
$5x + 3 = y$
$f^{-1}(x) = 5x + 3$

68. $f(x) = \frac{x + 2}{3}$
$y = \frac{x + 2}{3}$
$x = \frac{y + 2}{3}$
$3x - 2 = y$
$f^{-1}(x) = 3x - 2$

## Section 10.3

2. $\log 426 = \log(4.26 \cdot 10^2)$
$= 0.6294 + 2$
$= 2.6294$

3. $\log 37.8 = \log(3.78 \cdot 10^1)$
$= 0.5775 + 1$
$= 1.5775$

4. $\log 42{,}600 = \log(4.26 \cdot 10^4)$
$= 0.6294 + 4$
$= 4.6294$

6. $\log 0.4261 = \log(4.261 \cdot 10^{-1})$
$= .6294 - 1$
$= -0.3706$

7. $\log 0.0378 = \log(3.78 \cdot 10^{-2})$
$= 0.5775 - 2$
$= -1.4225$

8. $\log 0.0426 = \log(4.26 \cdot 10^{-2})$
$= 0.6294 - 2$
$= -1.3706$

10. $\log 4{,}900 = \log(4.9 \cdot 10^3)$
$= 0.6902 + 3$
$= 3.6902$

11. $\log 600 = \log(6.00 \cdot 10^2)$
$= 0.7782 + 2$
$= 2.7782$

12. $\log 900 = \log(9 \cdot 10^2)$
$= 0.9542 + 2$
$= 2.9542$

14. $\log 10{,}200 = \log(1.02 \cdot 10^4)$
$= 0.0086 + 4$
$= 4.0086$

15. $\log 0.00971 = \log(9.71 \cdot 10^{-3})$
$= 0.9872 - 3$
$= -2.0128$

16. $\log 0.0312 = \log(3.12 \cdot 10^{-2})$
$= 0.4942 - 2$
$= -1.5058$

18. $\log 0.00052 = \log(5.2 \cdot 10^{-4})$
$= 0.7160 - 4$
$= -3.2840$

19. $\log 0.399 = \log(3.99 \cdot 10^{-1})$
$= 0.6010 - 1$
$= -0.3990$

20. $\log 0.111 = \log(1.11 \cdot 10^{-1})$
$= 0.0453 - 1$
$= -0.9547$

22. $\log x = 4.8802$
$\log x = 0.8802 + 4$
$x = 7.59 \cdot 10^4$
$x = 75{,}900$

23. $\log x = -2.1198$
$\log x = 0.8802 - 3$
$x = 7.59 \cdot 10^{-3}$
$x = 0.00759$

24. $\log x = -3.1198$
$\log x = 0.8802 - 4$
$x = 7.59 \cdot 10^{-4}$
$x = 0.000759$

26. $\log x = 5.5911$
$\log x = 0.5911 + 5$
$x = 3.90 \cdot 10^5$
$x = 390{,}000$

27. $\log x = -5.3497$
$\log x = 0.6503 - 6$
$x = 4.47 \cdot 10^{-6}$
$x = 0.00000447$

28. $\log x = -1.5670$
$\log x = 0.4320 - 2$
$x = 2.71 \cdot 10^{-2}$
$x = 0.0271$

30. $\log x = -4.2000$
$\log x = 0.8000 - 5$
$x = 6.31 \cdot 10^{-5}$
$x = 0.0000631$

31. $\log x = 10$
$\log x = 0 + 10$
$x = 1 \cdot 10^{10}$
$x = 10^{10}$

32. $\log x = -1$
$\log x = 0 - 1$
$x = 1 \cdot 10^{-1}$
$x = 0.1$ *or* $\frac{1}{10}$

34. $\log x = 1$
$\log x = 0 + 1$
$x = 1 \cdot 10^1$
$x = 10$

35. $\log x = 20$
$\log x = 0 + 20$
$x = 1 \cdot 10^{20}$
$x = 10^{20}$

36. $\log x = -20$
$\log x = 0 - 20$
$x = 1 \cdot 10^{-20}$
$x = 10^{-20}$

38. $\log x = 4$
$\log x = 0 + 4$
$x = 1 \cdot 10^4$
$x = 10{,}000$

39. $\log x = \log_2 8$
$\log x = \log_2 2^3$
$\log x = 3^2$
$x = 10^3$
$x = 1{,}000$

40. $\log x = \log_3 9$
$\log x = \log_3 3^2$
$\log x = 2^3$
$x = 10^2$
$x = 100$

42. $\log x = \log 10$
$x = 10$

43. $pH = -\log [H^+]1, \quad [H^+] = 6.5 \times 10^{-4}$
$pH = -\log 6.5 \times 10^{-4}$
$pH \approx 3.19$

44. $pH = -\log[H^+], \quad [H^+] = 1.88 \times 10^{-6}$
$pH = -\log 1.88 \times 10^{-6}$
$pH \approx 5.73$

46. $pH = -\log[H^+], \quad pH = 5.75$
$5.75 = -\log[H^+]$
$H^+ = 10^{-5.75}$
$\log H^+ = \log 10^{-5.75}$
$= -5.75 \log 10$
$= -5.75 + 6 - 6$
$= .25 - 6$
$H^+ = 1.78 \cdot 10^{-6}$

47. $M = \log T, \quad M = 5.5$
$5.5 = \log T$
$T = 10^{5.5}$
$\log T = \log 10^{5.5}$
$\log T = 5.5 \log 10$
$\log T = 5.5$
$T = 3.16 \times 10^5$

48. $M = \log T, \quad M = 6.6$
$6.6 = \log T$
$T = 10^{6.6}$
$\log T = \log 10^{6.6}$
$\log T = 6.6 \log 10$
$\log T = 6.6$
$T = 3.98 \times 10^6$

50. $M = \log T, \quad M = 8.7$
$8.7 = \log T$
$T = 10^{8.7}$
$\log T = \log 10^{8.7}$
$\log T = 8.7 \log 10$
$\log T = 8.7$
$T = 5.01 \times 10^8$

51. $6.5 - 5.5 = 1$
$M = \log T, \quad M = 1$
$1 = \log T$
$T = 10^1$
$T = 10$ *times as large*

52. $8.5 - 5.5 = 3$
$M = \log T, \quad M = 3$
$3 = \log T$
$T = 10^3$
$T = 1{,}000$ *times as large*

54. *If* $P = \$9000, \quad t = 4,$ *and* $w = \$3000$

$$\log(1 - r) = \frac{1}{t} \log \frac{w}{p}$$

$$\log(1 - r) = \frac{1}{4} \log \frac{3000}{9000}$$

$$\log(1 - r) = .25 \log \frac{1}{3}$$

$= .25(-.4771)$
$= -.1192$
$= -.1192 + 1 - 1$
$= .8808 - 1$
$1 - r = 7.60 \times 10^{-1}$
$1 - r = .760$
$-r = -.24$
$r = .24$ *or* 24%

55. *If* $P = \$7550$, $t = 5$, *and* $w = \$5750$

$$\log(1 - r) = \frac{1}{t} \log \frac{w}{p}$$

$$\log(1 - r) = \frac{1}{5} \log \frac{5750}{7550}$$

$$\begin{aligned} \log(1 - r) &= .2 \log .7616 \\ &= .2(-.1183) \\ &= -.0236 \\ &= -.0236 + 1 - 1 \\ &= .9763 - 1 \\ 1 - r &= 9.47 \times 10^{-1} \\ 1 - r &= .947 \\ -r &= -.053 \\ r &= .053 \quad \textit{or} \quad 5.3\% \end{aligned}$$

56. *If* $P = \$7550$, $t = 3$, *and* $w = \$5750$

$$\log(1 - r) = \frac{1}{t} \log \frac{w}{p}$$

$$\log(1 - r) = \frac{1}{3} \log \frac{5750}{7550}$$

$$\begin{aligned} \log(1 - r) &= .333 \log .7616 \\ &= .333(-.1183) \\ &= -.0394 \\ &= -.0394 + 1 - 1 \\ &= .9606 - 1 \\ 1 - r &= 9.13 \times 10^{-1} \\ 1 - r &= .913 \\ -r &= -.087 \\ r &= .087 \quad \textit{or} \quad 8.7\% \end{aligned}$$

58. $\ln 1 = 0$

59. $\log e^5 = 5$

60. $\log e^{-3} = -3$

62. $$\begin{aligned} \ln e^y &= y \ln e \\ &= y(1) \\ &= y \end{aligned}$$

63. $$\begin{aligned} \ln 10e^{3t} &= \ln 10 + \ln e^{3t} \\ &= \ln 10 + 3t \ln e \\ &= \ln 10 + 3t \end{aligned}$$

64. $$\begin{aligned} \ln 10e^{4t} &= \ln 10 + \ln e^{4t} \\ &= \ln 10 + 4t \ln e \\ &= \ln 10 + 4t \end{aligned}$$

66. $$\begin{aligned} \ln Ae^{-3t} &= \ln A + \ln e^{-3t} \\ &= \ln A - 3t \ln e \\ &= \ln A - 3t \end{aligned}$$

67. $$\begin{aligned} \ln 15 &= \ln (3)(5) \\ &= \ln 3 + \ln 5 \\ &= 1.0986 + 1.6094 \\ &= 2.7080 \end{aligned}$$

68. $$\begin{aligned} \ln 10 &= \ln (2)(5) \\ &= \ln 2 + \ln 5 \\ &= .6931 + 1.6094 \\ &= 2.3025 \end{aligned}$$

70. $$\begin{aligned} \ln \frac{1}{5} &= \ln 1 - \ln 5 \\ &= 0 - 1.6094 \\ &= -1.6094 \end{aligned}$$

71. $$\begin{aligned} \ln 9 &= \ln (3)(3) \\ &= \ln 3 + \ln 3 \\ &= 1.0986 + 1.0986 \\ &= 2.1972 \end{aligned}$$

72. $\ln 25 = \ln 5^2$
$= 2 \ln 5$
$= 2(1.6094)$
$= 3.2188$

74. $\ln 81 = \ln 3^4$
$= 4 \ln 3$
$= 4(1.0986)$
$= 4.3944$

75. $d = \sqrt{(x_2 - x_1)^2 + (y_2 - y_1)^2}$
$\sqrt{13} = \sqrt{(1 - x)^2 + (6 - 3)^2}$
$13 = 1 - 2x + x^2 + 9$
$0 = x^2 - 2x - 3$
$0 = (x - 3)(x + 1)$
$x = 3$ *or* $x = -1$

76. $d = \sqrt{(x_2 - x_1)^2 + (y_2 - y_1)^2}$
$\sqrt{2} = \sqrt{(1 - 2)^2 + (2 - y)^2}$
$2 = 1 + 4 - 4y + y^2$
$0 = y^2 - 4y + 3$
$0 = (y - 1)(y - 3)$
$y = 1$ *or* $y = 3$

78. $x^2 + y^2 - 8x + 2y = 8$
$x^2 - 8x + y^2 + 2y = 8$
$x^2 - 8x + 16 + y^2 + 2y + 1 = 8 + 16 + 1$
$(x - 4)^2 + (y + 1)^2 = 25$
$(x - 4)^2 + [y - (-1)]^2 = 5^2$

The center is (4,-1) and the radius is 5.

79.

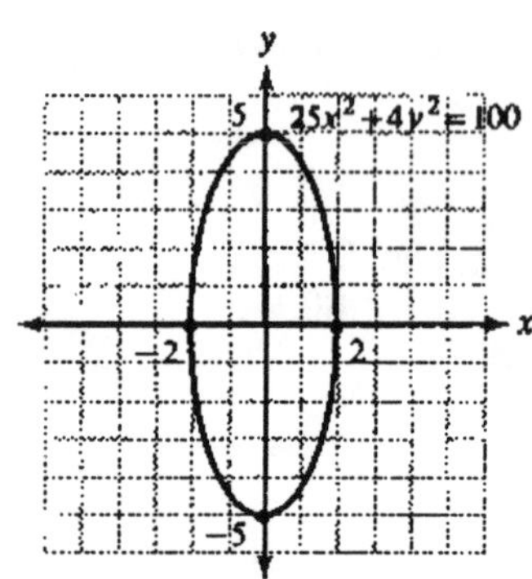


80.

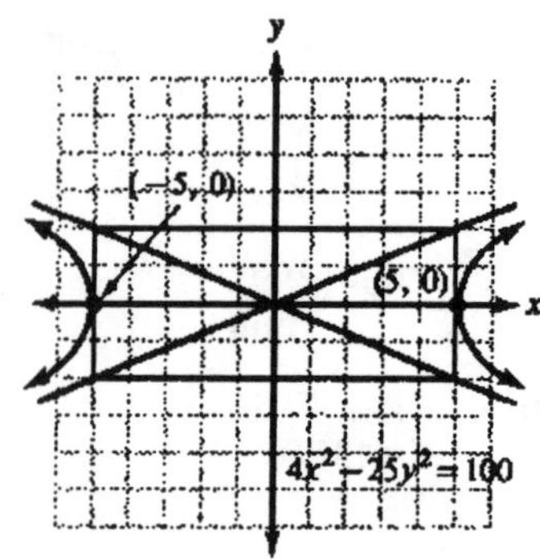


## Section 10.4

2. $4^x = 3$
$x = \dfrac{\log 3}{\log 4}$
$x = 0.7925$

3. $5^x = 3$
$x = \dfrac{\log 3}{\log 5}$
$x = 0.6826$

4. $3^x = 4$
$x = \dfrac{\log 4}{\log 3}$
$x = 1.2619$

6. $7^{-x} = 8$

$-x = \dfrac{\log 8}{\log 7}$

$x = -1.0686$

7. $12^{-x} = 5$

$-x = \dfrac{\log 5}{\log 12}$

$x = -0.6477$

8. $8^{-x} = 7$
$-x = \dfrac{\log 7}{\log 8}$
$x = -0.9358$

10. $9^{x+1} = 3$
$(x + 1)\log 9 = \log 3$

$$x = \frac{\log 3}{\log 9} - 1$$

$$x = \frac{.4771}{.9542} - 1$$

$$x = -0.5000$$

11. $4^{x-1} = 4$
$(x - 1)\log 4 = \log 4$

$$x = \frac{\log 4}{\log 4} + 1$$

$$x = 2.0000$$

12. $3^{x-1} = 9$
$(x - 1)\log 3 = \log 9$

$$x = \frac{\log 9}{\log 3} + 1$$

$$x = \frac{.9542}{.4771} + 1$$

$$x = 3.0000$$

14. $2^{2x+1} = 3$
$(2x + 1)\log 2 = \log 3$

$$x = \frac{1}{2}\left(\frac{\log 3}{\log 2} - 1\right)$$

$$x = \frac{1}{2}\left(\frac{.4771}{.3010} - 1\right)$$

$$x = 0.2925$$

15. $3^{1-2x} = 2$
$(1 - 2x)\log 3 = \log 2$

$$x = -\frac{1}{2}\left(\frac{\log 2}{\log 3} - 1\right)$$

$$x = -\frac{1}{2}\left(\frac{.3010}{.4771} - 1\right)$$

$$x = 0.1845$$

16. $2^{1-2x} = 3$
$(1 - 2x)\log 2 = \log 3$

$$x = -\frac{1}{2}\left(\frac{\log 3}{\log 2} - 1\right)$$

$$x = -\frac{1}{2}\left(\frac{.4771}{.3010} - 1\right)$$

$$x = -0.2925$$

18. $10^{3x-4} = 15$
$(3x - 4)\log 10 = \log 15$

$$x = \frac{1}{3}\left(\frac{\log 15}{\log 10} + 4\right)$$

$$x = \frac{1}{3}\left(\frac{1.1760}{1} + 4\right)$$

$$x = 1.7254$$

19. $6^{5-2x} = 4$
$(5 - 2x)\log 6 = \log 4$

$$x = -\frac{1}{2}\left(\frac{\log 4}{\log 6} - 5\right)$$

$$x = -\frac{1}{2}\left(\frac{.6020}{.7782} - 5\right)$$

$$x = 2.1131$$

20. $9^{7-3x} = 5$
$(7 - 3x)\log 9 = \log 5$

$$x = -\frac{1}{3}\left(\frac{\log 5}{\log 9} - 7\right)$$

$$x = -\frac{1}{3}\left(\frac{.6990}{.9542} - 7\right)$$

$$x = 2.0892$$

22. $A = 5000\left(1 + \frac{.12}{4}\right)^{4(10)}$

$\log A = 4.212459$
$A = \$16,310.19$

23. $P = 200,\ r = .08,$
$n = 2,\ t = 10$

$$A = 200\left(1 + \frac{.08}{2}\right)^{2(10)}$$

$$A = \$438.22$$

24. $P = 200,\ r = .08,$
$n = 1,\ t = 10$

$$A = 200\left(1 + \frac{.08}{1}\right)^{1(10)}$$

$A = \$431.79$

26. $A = \$1000$ (\$500 *doubled*),
$r = .06,\ n = 12$ *and* $p = \$500$

$$1000 = 500\left(1 + \frac{.06}{2}\right)^{2t}$$

$t = 11.6$ *years*

27. $A = \$3000$ (1000 *tripled*),
$r = .12,\ n = 6,\ p = \$1000$

$$3000 = 1000\left(1 + \frac{.12}{6}\right)^{6t}$$

$t = 9.25$ *years*

28. $A = \$4000,\ r = .12,$
$n = 6,$ *and* $p = \$1000$

$$4000 = 1000\left(1 + \frac{.12}{6}\right)^{6t}$$

$t = 11.7$ *years*

30. $\log_9 27 = \dfrac{\log 27}{\log 9}$

$\log_9 27 = 1.5000$

31. $\log_{16} 8 = \dfrac{\log 8}{\log 16}$

$\log_{16} 8 = 0.7500$

32. $\log_{27} 9 = \dfrac{\log 9}{\log 27}$

$\log_{27} 9 = 0.6667$

34. $\log_3 12 = \dfrac{\log 12}{\log 3}$

$\log_3 12 = 2.2619$

35. $\log_{15} 7 = \dfrac{\log 7}{\log 15}$

$\log_{15} 7 = 0.7186$

36. $\log_{12} 3 = \dfrac{\log 3}{\log 12}$

$\log_{12} 3 = 0.4421$

38. $\log_6 180 = \dfrac{\log 180}{\log 6}$

$\log_6 180 = 2.8982$

39. $\log_4 321 = \dfrac{\log 321}{\log 4}$

$\log_4 321 = 4.1632$

40. $\log_5 462 = \dfrac{\log 462}{\log 5}$

$\log_5 462 = 3.8122$

42. $\ln 3450 = 8.1461$

43. $\ln .345 = -1.0642$

44. $\ln .0345 = -3.3668$

46. $\ln 100 = 4.6052$

47. $\ln 45{,}000 = 10.7144$

48. $\ln 450{,}000 = 13.0170$

50. $p = 100{,}000e^{.05t}$
$\ln P = \ln 100{,}000 + .05(0) \ln e$
$P = 100{,}000$

51. $45{,}000 = 15{,}000e^{.04t}$
$\ln 3 = .04t \ln e$

$$t = \frac{\ln 3}{.04}$$

$t = 27.5$ *years*

52. $45{,}000 = 15{,}000e^{.08t}$
$\ln 3 = .08t \ln e$

$$t = \frac{\ln 3}{.08}$$

$t = 13.7$ *years*